Ernest F. Haeussler, Jr. • Richard S. Paul • Richard J. Wood

Second Custom Edition for The Ohio State University

# *Introductory*
# MATHEMATICAL ANALYSIS

Taken from:

*Introductory Mathematical Analysis for Business, Economics,
and the Life and Social Sciences,* Twelfth Edition
by Ernest F. Haeussler. Jr., Richard S. Paul and Richard J. Wood

Taken from:

*Introductory Mathematical Analysis for Business, Economics, and the Life and Social Sciences,* Twelfth Edition
by Ernest F. Haeussler, Jr., Richard S. Paul, and Richard J. Wood
Copyright © 2008 by Prentice-Hall, Inc.
A Pearson Education Company
Upper Saddle River, New Jersey 07458

This special edition published in cooperation with Pearson Custom Publishing.

Printed in the United States of America

10  9  8  7  6  5  4  3  2  1

ISBN 0-536-46107-4

2007360910

JP

Please visit our web site at *www.pearsoncustom.com*

PEARSON CUSTOM PUBLISHING
501 Boylston Street, Suite 900, Boston, MA 02116
A Pearson Education Company

# CONTENTS

# PREFACE

The twelfth edition of *Introductory Mathematical Analysis* continues to provide a mathematical foundation for students in business, economics, and the life and social sciences. It begins with noncalculus topics such as functions, equations, mathematics of finance, matrix algebra, linear programming, and probability. Then it progresses through both single-variable and multivariable calculus, including continuous random variables. Technical proofs, conditions, and the like are sufficiently described but are not overdone. Our guiding philosophy led us to include those proofs and general calculations that shed light on how the corresponding calculations are done in applied problems. Informal intuitive arguments are often given too.

## Organization Changes to the Twelfth Edition

The few organization changes for this edition reflect comments of adoptees and reviewers. The material in the former Appendix A (as it appeared in Editions 9 through 11) has been folded into the body of the text. In particular, Summation Notation now appears as Section 5 in Chapter 1. The former Summation section from Chapter 14 has also been included in the new Section 5 of Chapter 1. Many instructors found the introduction of summation notation at the same time as a major concept, namely the integral, to be distracting. Our intention is that locating summation in Chapter 1 should accord the topic a more appropriate status. Summation notation is simple but to the extent that it will be new for many students it should brighten a chapter that is otherwise review work for most students. Having summation notation at hand so early in the text allows us to practice with it several times, notably in the work on combinatorics and probability (Chapter 8), before it becomes indispensible in conjunction with the integral (Chapter 14).

The topic of Interest Compounded Continuously has been moved from Chapter 10 to become Section 3 in Chapter 5 on the Mathematics of Finance. Since exponential functions, and the number *e*, are introduced in Chapter 4 this is quite a natural move and allows a more unified treatment of interest rates. A number of instructors thought it important to be able to compare continuously compounded interest with ordinary compound interest while the latter is fresh in the minds of students. However, continuous annuities are still in Chapter 15 as an application of integration.

Finally, Differentiability and Continuity, formerly a separate section, is now included as part of Section 1 of Chapter 11 and we have removed A Comment on Homogeneous Functions from Chapter 17.

## Applications

An abundance and variety of applications for the intended audience appear throughout the book; students continually see how the mathematics they are learning can be used. These applications cover such diverse areas as business, economics, biology, medicine, sociology, psychology, ecology, statistics, earth science, and archaeology. Many of these real-world situations are drawn from literature and are documented by references, sometimes from the Web. In some, the background and context are given in order to stimulate interest. However, the text is self-contained, in the sense that it assumes no prior exposure to the concepts on which the applications are based. The **Principles in Practice** element provides students with further applications. Located in the margins of Chapters 1 through 17, these additional exercises give students real-world applications and more opportunities to see the chapter material put into practice. An icon indicates Principles in Practice problems that can be solved using a graphing calculator. Answers to Principles in Practice problems appear at the end of the text and complete solutions to these problems are found in the Solutions Manuals.

## Simplified Language and Terminology

In this edition a special effort has been made to choose good terminology without introducing simultaneously an alternative word or phrase connected by the word *or*. For example, when introducing terminology for a point $(a, b)$ in the plane, "We call $a$ the *abscissa* or *x-coordinate* ..." has been replaced by "We call $a$ the *x-coordinate* ...". In a similar vein, we now speak of a *Simplex Table* rather than of a *Simplex Tableau*. In general, we have tried to be more colloquial when doing so can be done without sacrificing mathematical precision.

## Improved Pedagogy

We noticed in reviewing Section 9.3, on Markov Chains, that considerable simplification to the problem of finding steady state vectors is obtained by writing state vectors as columns rather than rows. This does necessitate that a transition matrix $\mathbf{T} = [t_{ij}]$ have

$$t_{ij} = \text{probability that next state is } i \text{ given that current state is } j$$

but avoids artificial transpositions later.

In Chapter 13 on Curve Sketching we have greatly expanded the use of *sign charts*. In particular, a sign chart for a first derivative is always accompanied by a further line interpreting the results for the function which is to be graphed. Thus, on an interval where we record '+' for $f'$ we also record '/' for $f$ and on an interval where we record '−' for $f'$ we also record '\' for $f$. The resulting strings of such elements, say /\/, with further embellishments that we describe in the text, provide a very preliminary sketch of the curve in question. We freely acknowledge that this is a blackboard technique used by many instructors, but it appears too rarely in textbooks.

Throughout the text we have retained the popular "Now work Problem $n$" feature of other Prentice Hall books. The idea is that after a worked example, students are directed to an end of section problem that reinforces the ideas of the worked example. For the most part, problems led to this way are odd-numbered so that students can check their answers in the back of the book or find complete solutions in the Student Solutions Manual.

In the same vein, we have expanded the use of cautionary warnings to the student. These are represented by *CAUTION* icons that point out commonly made errors. As before, **Definitions** are clearly stated and displayed. Key concepts, as well as important rules and formulas, are boxed to emphasize their importance.

Each chapter (except Chapter 0) has a review section that contains a list of important terms and symbols, a chapter summary, and numerous review problems. In the twelfth edition we have referenced key examples with each group of important terms and symbols.

Answers to odd-numbered problems appear at the end of the book. For many of the differentiation problems, the answers appear in both 'unsimplified' and 'simplified' forms. (Of course 'simplified' is in any event a subjective term when applied to mathematical expressions, that tends to presuppose the nature of subsequent calculations with such expressions.) This allows students to readily check their work.

## Examples and Exercises

More than 850 examples are worked out in detail. Some include a *strategy* that is specifically designed to guide the student through the logistics of the solution before the solution is obtained. An abundant number of diagrams (almost 500) and exercises (more than 5000) are included. Of the exercises, more than 900 are new for the twelfth edition. In each exercise set, grouped problems are given in increasing order of difficulty. In many exercise sets the problems progress from the basic mechanical drill-type to more interesting thought-provoking problems. Many real-world type problems with real data are included. Considerable effort has been made to produce a proper balance between the drill-type exercises and the problems requiring the integration of the concepts learned.

## Technology

In order that students appreciate the value of current *technology,* optional graphing calculator material appears throughout the text both in the exposition and exercises. It appears for a variety of reasons: as a mathematical tool, to visualize a concept, as a computing aid, and to reinforce concepts. Although calculator displays for a TI-83 Plus accompany the corresponding technology discussion, our approach is general enough so that it can be applied to other graphing calculators.

In the exercise sets, graphing calculator problems are indicated by an icon. To provide flexibility for an instructor in planning assignments, these problems are usually placed at the end of an exercise set.

## Course Planning

Because instructors plan a course outline to serve the individual needs of a particular class and curriculum, we will not attempt to provide detailed sample outlines. However, depending on the background of the students, some instructors will choose to omit Chapter 0 (Algebra Refresher). A considerable number of courses can be served by the book.

A program that allows three quarters of Mathematics for well-prepared Business students can start a first course with Chapter 1 and choose such topics as are of interest, up to and including Chapter 9. For example, if the students are concurrently taking a Finance course then it may be desirable to exclude Chapter 5 on the Mathematics of Finance (to avoid duplication of material for distinct credits). Others will find that Chapter 7 on Linear Programming includes more material than their students need. In this case, specific sections such as 7.3, 7.5, and 7.8 can be excluded without loss of continuity. On the other hand, Section 1.1 introduces some business terms, such as total revenue, fixed cost, variable cost and profit that recur throughout the book. Similarly, Section 3.2 introduces the notion of supply and demand equations, and Section 3.6 discusses the equilibrium point and the break-even point, all of fundamental importance for business applications.

A second, single quarter, course on Differential Calculus will use Chapter 10 on Limits and Continuity, followed by the three 'differentiation chapters', 11 through 13 inclusive. Here, Section 12.6 on Newton's Method can be omitted without loss of continuity while some instructors may prefer to review Chapter 4 on Exponential and Logarithmic Functions prior to their study as differentiable functions.

Finally, Chapters 14 through 17 inclusive could define a third, single quarter, course on Integral Calculus with an introduction to Multivariable Calculus. In an applied course it is well to stress the use of tables to find integrals and thus the techniques of 'parts' and 'partial fractions', in 15.1 and 15.2 respectively, should be considered optional. Chapter 16 is certainly not needed for Chapter 17 and Section 15.7 on Improper Integrals can be safely omitted if Chapter 16 is not covered.

Schools which have two academic terms per year tend to give business students a term devoted to Finite Mathematics and a term devoted to Calculus. For these schools we recommend Chapters 1 through 9 for the first course, starting wherever the preparation of the students allows, and Chapters 10 through 17 for the second—deleting most optional material.

## Supplements

The *Instructor's Solution Manual* has worked solutions to all problems, including those in the Principles in Practice elements and in the Mathematical Snapshots.

The *Test Item File*, used by some instructors, provides over 1700 test questions, keyed to chapter and section. It includes an editing feature that allows questions to be added or changed. Also for instructors is *TestGen*, an algorithmic test generator that allows for multiple tests to be created. It is fully editable.

The *Student Solutions Manual* includes worked solutions for all odd-numbered problems and all Principles in Practice problems.

## Acknowledgments

We express our appreciation to the following colleagues who contributed comments and suggestions that were valuable to us in the evolution of this text:

E. Adibi (*Chapman University*); R. M. Alliston (*Pennsylvania State University*); R. A. Alo (*University of Houston*); K. T. Andrews (*Oakland University*); M. N. de Arce (*University of Puerto Rico*); E. Barbut (*University of Idaho*); G. R. Bates (*Western Illinois University*); D. E. Bennett (*Murray State University*); C. Bernett (*Harper College*); A. Bishop (*Western Illinois University*); P. Blau (*Shawnee State University*); R. Blute (*University of Ottawa*); S. A. Book (*California State University*); A. Brink (*St. Cloud State University*); R. Brown (*York University*); R. W. Brown (*University of Alaska*); S. D. Bulman-Fleming (*Wilfrid Laurier University*); D. Calvetti (*National College*); D. Cameron (*University of Akron*); K. S. Chung (*Kapiolani Community College*); D. N. Clark (*University of Georgia*); E. L. Cohen (*University of Ottawa*); J. Dawson (*Pennsylvania State University*); A. Dollins (*Pennsylvania State University*); G. A. Earles (*St. Cloud State University*); B. H. Edwards (*University of Florida*); J. R. Elliott (*Wilfrid Laurier University*); J. Fitzpatrick (*University of Texas at El Paso*); M. J. Flynn (*Rhode Island Junior College*); G. J. Fuentes (*University of Maine*); L. Gerber (*St. John's University*); T. G. Goedde (*The University of Findlay*); S. K. Goel (*Valdosta State University*); G. Goff (*Oklahoma State University*); J. Goldman (*DePaul University*); J. T. Gresser (*Bowling Green State University*); L. Griff (*Pennsylvania State University*); F. H. Hall (*Pennsylvania State University*); V. E. Hanks (*Western Kentucky University*); R. C. Heitmann (*The University of Texas at Austin*); J. N. Henry (*California State University*); W. U. Hodgson (*West Chester State College*); B. C. Horne, Jr. (*Virginia Polytechnic Institute and State University*); J. Hradnansky (*Pennsylvania State University*); P. Huneke (*The Ohio State University*); C. Hurd (*Pennsylvania State University*); J. A. Jiminez (*Pennsylvania State University*); W. C. Jones (*Western Kentucky University*); R. M. King (*Gettysburg College*); M. M. Kostreva (*University of Maine*); G. A. Kraus (*Gannon University*); J. Kucera (*Washington State University*); M. R. Latina (*Rhode Island Junior College*); P. Lockwood-Cooke (*West Texas A&M University*); J. F. Longman (*Villanova University*); I. Marshak (*Loyola University of Chicago*); D. Mason (*Elmhurst College*); F. B. Mayer (*Mt. San Antonio College*); P. McDougle (*University of Miami*); F. Miles (*California State University*); E. Mohnike (*Mt. San Antonio College*); C. Monk (*University of Richmond*); R. A. Moreland (*Texas Tech University*); J. G. Morris (*University of Wisconsin-Madison*); J. C. Moss (*Paducah Community College*); D. Mullin (*Pennsylvania State University*); E. Nelson (*Pennsylvania State University*); S. A. Nett (*Western Illinois University*); R. H. Oehmke (*University of Iowa*); Y. Y. Oh (*Pennsylvania State University*); J. U. Overall (*University of La Verne*); A. Panayides (*William Patterson University*); D. Parker (*University of Pacific*); N. B. Patterson (*Pennsylvania State University*); V. Pedwaydon (*Lawrence Technical University*); E. Pemberton (*Wilfrid Laurier University*); M. Perkel (*Wright State University*); D. B. Priest (*Harding College*); J. R. Provencio (*University of Texas*); L. R. Pulsinelli (*Western Kentucky University*); M. Racine (*University of Ottawa*); N. M. Rice (*Queen's University*); A. Santiago (*University of Puerto Rico*);

J. R. Schaefer (*University of Wisconsin–Milwaukee*); S. Sehgal (*The Ohio State University*); W. H. Seybold, Jr. (*West Chester State College*); G. Shilling (*The University of Texas at Arlington*); S. Singh (*Pennsylvania State University*); L. Small (*Los Angeles Pierce College*); E. Smet (*Huron College*); J. Stein (*California State University, Long Beach*); M. Stoll (*University of South Carolina*); T. S. Sullivan (*Southern Illinois University Edwardsville*); E. A. Terry (*St. Joseph's University*); A. Tierman (*Saginaw Valley State University*); B. Toole (*University of Maine*); J. W. Toole (*University of Maine*); D. H. Trahan (*Naval Postgraduate School*); J. P. Tull (*The Ohio State University*); L. O. Vaughan, Jr. (*University of Alabama in Birmingham*); L. A. Vercoe (*Pennsylvania State University*); M. Vuilleumier (*The Ohio State University*); B. K. Waits (*The Ohio State University*); A. Walton (*Virginia Polytechnic Institute and State University*); H. Walum (*The Ohio State University*); E. T. H. Wang (*Wilfrid Laurier University*); A. J. Weidner (*Pennsylvania State University*); L. Weiss (*Pennsylvania State University*); N. A. Weigmann (*California State University*); S. K. Wong (*Ohio State University*); G. Woods (*The Ohio State University*); C. R. B. Wright (*University of Oregon*); C. Wu (*University of Wisconsin–Milwaukee*); B. F. Wyman (*Ohio State University*).

Some exercises are taken from problem supplements used by students at Wilfrid Laurier University. We wish to extend special thanks to the Department of Mathematics of Wilfrid Laurier University for granting Prentice Hall permission to use and publish this material, and also to Prentice Hall, who in turn allowed us to make use of this material.

We again express our sincere gratitude to the faculty and course coordinators of The Ohio State University and Columbus State University who took a keen interest in this and other editions, offering a number of invaluable suggestions.

Special thanks are due to Cindy Trimble of C Trimble & Associates for her careful checking of the manuscript solutions manuals, and answer pages. Her work was extraordinarily detailed and helpful to the authors.

*Ernest F. Haeussler, Jr.*
*Richard S. Paul*
*Richard J. Wood*

# LIMITS AND CONTINUITY

 National Debt

The philosopher Zeno of Elea was fond of paradoxes about motion. His most famous one goes something like this. The warrior Achilles agrees to run a race against a tortoise. Achilles can run 10 meters per second and the tortoise only 1 meter per second, so the tortoise gets a 10-meter head start. Since Achilles is so much faster, he should still win. But by the time he has covered his first 10 meters and reached the place where the tortoise started, the tortoise has advanced 1 meter and is still ahead. And after Achilles has covered that 1 meter, the tortoise has advanced another 0.1 meter and is still ahead. And after Achilles has covered that 0.1 meter, the tortoise has advanced another 0.01 meter and is still ahead. And so on. Therefore, Achilles gets closer and closer to the tortoise but can never catch up.

Zeno's audience knew, of course, that the argument was fishy. The position of Achilles at time $t$ after the race has begun is $(10 \text{ m/s})t$. The position of the tortoise at the same time $t$ is $(1 \text{ m/s})t + 10 \text{ m}$. When these are equal, Achilles and the tortoise are side by side. To solve the resulting equation

$$(10 \text{ m/s})t = (1 \text{ m/s})t + 10 \text{ m}$$

for $t$ is to find the time at which Achilles pulls even with the tortoise.

The solution is $t = 1\frac{1}{9}$ seconds, at which time Achilles will have run $(1\frac{1}{9}\text{s})(10 \text{ m/s}) = 11\frac{1}{9}$ meters.

What puzzled Zeno and his listeners is how it could be that

$$10 + 1 + \frac{1}{10} + \frac{1}{100} + \cdots = 11\frac{1}{9}$$

where the left side represents an *infinite sum* and the right side is a finite result. The modern solution to this problem is the concept of a limit, which is the key topic of this chapter. The left side of the equation is an infinite geometric series. Using limit notation, summation notation, and the formula from Section 5.4 for the sum of a geometric series, we write

$$\lim_{k \to \infty} \sum_{n=0}^{k} 10^{1-n} = \lim_{k \to \infty} \frac{10 \left(1 - \left(\frac{1}{10}\right)^{k+1}\right)}{1 - \frac{1}{10}} = \frac{100}{9} = 11\frac{1}{9}$$

OBJECTIVE

To study limits and their basic properties.

# 10.1  Limits

• • •

Perhaps you have been in a parking-lot situation in which you must "inch up" to the car in front, but yet you do not want to bump or touch it. This notion of getting closer and closer to something, but yet not touching it, is very important in mathematics and is involved in the concept of *limits*, which lies at the foundation of calculus. Basically, we will let a variable "inch up" to a particular value and examine the effect it has on the values of a function.

For example, consider the function

$$f(x) = \frac{x^3 - 1}{x - 1}$$

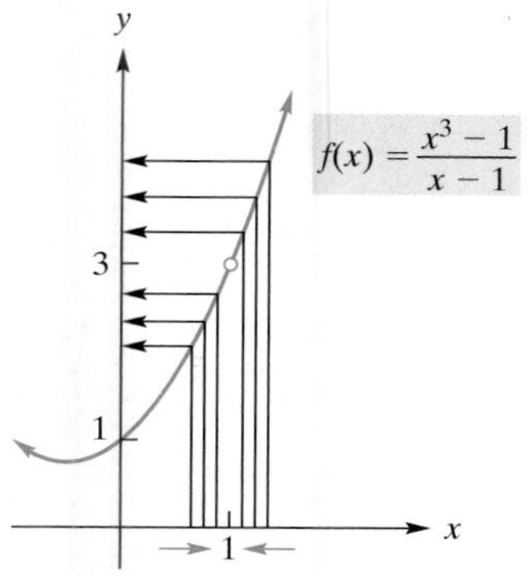

Although this function is not defined at $x = 1$, we may be curious about the behavior of the function values as $x$ gets very close to 1. Table 10.1 gives some values of $x$ that are slightly less than 1 and some that are slightly greater, as well as their corresponding function values. Notice that as $x$ takes on values closer and closer to 1, regardless of whether $x$ approaches it *from the left* ($x < 1$) or *from the right* ($x > 1$), the corresponding values of $f(x)$ get closer and closer to one and only one number, namely 3. This is also clear from the graph of $f$ in Figure 10.1. Notice there that even though the function is not defined at $x = 1$ (as indicated by the hollow dot), the function values get closer and closer to 3 as $x$ gets closer and closer to 1. To express this, we say that the **limit** of $f(x)$ as $x$ approaches 1 is 3 and write

$$\lim_{x \to 1} \frac{x^3 - 1}{x - 1} = 3$$

FIGURE 10.1  $\displaystyle\lim_{x \to 1} \frac{x^3 - 1}{x - 1} = 3.$

We can make $f(x)$ as close to 3 as we wish, and keep it that close, by taking $x$ sufficiently close to, but not equal to, 1. The limit exists at 1, even though 1 is not in the domain of $f$.

**TABLE 10.1**

|  | $x < 1$ |  | $x > 1$ |
| --- | --- | --- | --- |
| $x$ | $f(x)$ | $x$ | $f(x)$ |
| 0.8 | 2.44 | 1.2 | 3.64 |
| 0.9 | 2.71 | 1.1 | 3.31 |
| 0.95 | 2.8525 | 1.05 | 3.1525 |
| 0.99 | 2.9701 | 1.01 | 3.0301 |
| 0.995 | 2.985025 | 1.005 | 3.015025 |
| 0.999 | 2.997001 | 1.001 | 3.003001 |

We can also consider the limit of a function as $x$ approaches a number that is in the domain. Let us examine the limit of $f(x) = x + 3$ as $x$ approaches 2:

$$\lim_{x \to 2}(x + 3)$$

Obviously, if $x$ is close to 2 (but not equal to 2), then $x + 3$ is close to 5. This is also apparent from the table and graph in Figure 10.2. Thus,

$$\lim_{x \to 2}(x + 3) = 5$$

Given a function $f$ and a number $a$, there *may* be two ways of associating a number to the pair $(f, a)$. One such number is the *evaluation of $f$ at $a$*, namely $f(a)$. It *exists* precisely when $a$ is in the domain of $f$. For example, if $f(x) = \dfrac{x^3 - 1}{x - 1}$, our first example, then $f(1)$ does not *exist*. Another way of associating a number to the pair

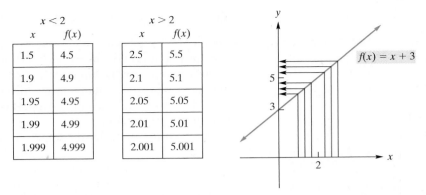

| x < 2 | | | x > 2 | |
| --- | --- | --- | --- | --- |
| $x$ | $f(x)$ | | $x$ | $f(x)$ |
| 1.5 | 4.5 | | 2.5 | 5.5 |
| 1.9 | 4.9 | | 2.1 | 5.1 |
| 1.95 | 4.95 | | 2.05 | 5.05 |
| 1.99 | 4.99 | | 2.01 | 5.01 |
| 1.999 | 4.999 | | 2.001 | 5.001 |

**FIGURE 10.2** $\lim_{x \to 2}(x+3) = 5$.

$(f, a)$ is *the limit of* $f(x)$ *as x approaches a,* which is denoted $\lim_{x \to a} f(x)$. We have given two examples. Here is the general case.

> **DEFINITION**
>
> *The limit of* $f(x)$ *as x approaches a* is the number $L$, written
>
> $$\lim_{x \to a} f(x) = L$$
>
> provided that $f(x)$ is arbitrarily close to $L$ for all $x$ sufficiently close to, but not equal to, $a$. If there is no such number, we say that the limit *does not exist.*

We emphasize that, when finding a limit, we are concerned not with what happens to $f(x)$ when $x$ equals $a$, but only with what happens to $f(x)$ when $x$ is close to $a$. In fact, even if $f(a)$ *exists,* the preceding definition explicitly rules out consideration of it. In our second example, $f(x) = x+3$, we have $f(2) = 5$ and also $\lim_{x \to 2}(x+3) = 5$, but it is quite possible to have a function $f$ and a number $a$ for which both $f(a)$ and $\lim_{x \to a} f(x)$ exist and are different, Moreover, a limit must be independent of the way in which $x$ *approaches a,* meaning the way in which $x$ gets close to $a$. That is, the limit must be the same whether $x$ approaches $a$ from the left or from the right (for $x < a$ or $x > a$, respectively).

### ● EXAMPLE 1   Estimating a Limit from a Graph

**a.** *Estimate* $\lim_{x \to 1} f(x)$, *where the graph of f is given in Figure* 10.3(a).

**Solution:** If we look at the graph for values of $x$ near 1, we see that $f(x)$ is near 2. Moreover, as $x$ gets closer and closer to 1, $f(x)$ appears to get closer and closer to 2. Thus, we estimate that

$$\lim_{x \to 1} f(x) \text{ is } 2$$

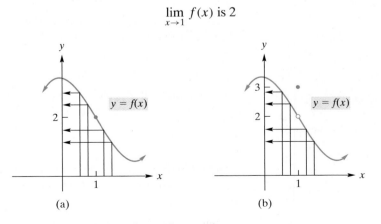

**FIGURE 10.3**   Investigation of $\lim_{x \to 1} f(x)$.

**b.** *Estimate* $\lim_{x \to 1} f(x)$, *where the graph of f is given in Figure* 10.3(b).

Solution: Although $f(1) = 3$, this fact has no bearing whatsoever on the limit of $f(x)$ as $x$ approaches 1. We see that as $x$ gets closer and closer to 1, $f(x)$ appears to get closer and closer to 2. Thus, we estimate that

$$\lim_{x \to 1} f(x) \text{ is } 2$$

NOW WORK PROBLEM 1 ●●

Up to now, all of the limits that we have considered did indeed exist. Next we look at some situations in which a limit does not exist.

● **EXAMPLE 2   Limits That Do Not Exist**

**a.** *Estimate* $\lim_{x \to -2} f(x)$ *if it exists, where the graph of f is given in Figure* 10.4.

Solution: As $x$ approaches $-2$ from the left ($x < -2$), the values of $f(x)$ appear to get closer to 1. But as $x$ approaches $-2$ from the right ($x > -2$), $f(x)$ appears to get closer to 3. Hence, as $x$ approaches $-2$, the function values do not settle down to one and only one number. We conclude that

$$\lim_{x \to -2} f(x) \text{ does not exist}$$

Note that the limit does not exist even though the function is defined at $x = -2$.

**b.** *Estimate* $\lim_{x \to 0} \dfrac{1}{x^2}$ *if it exists.*

Solution: Let $f(x) = 1/x^2$. The table in Figure 10.5 gives values of $f(x)$ for some values of $x$ near 0. As $x$ gets closer and closer to 0, the values of $f(x)$ get larger and larger without bound. This is also clear from the graph. Since the values of $f(x)$ do not approach a *number* as $x$ approaches 0,

$$\lim_{x \to 0} \frac{1}{x^2} \text{ does not exist}$$

NOW WORK PROBLEM 3 ●●

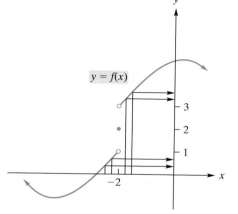

FIGURE 10.4   $\lim_{x \to -2} f(x)$ does not exist.

| $x$ | $f(x)$ |
|-----|--------|
| $\pm 1$ | 1 |
| $\pm 0.5$ | 4 |
| $\pm 0.1$ | 100 |
| $\pm 0.01$ | 10,000 |
| $\pm 0.001$ | 1,000,000 |

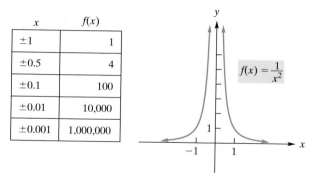

FIGURE 10.5   $\lim_{x \to 0} \dfrac{1}{x^2}$ does not exist.

# TECHNOLOGY

**Problem:** Estimate $\lim_{x\to 2} f(x)$ if

$$f(x) = \frac{x^3 + 2.1x^2 - 10.2x + 4}{x^2 + 2.5x - 9}$$

**Solution:** One method of finding the limit is by constructing a table of function values $f(x)$ when $x$ is close to 2. From Figure 10.6, we estimate the limit to be 1.57. Alternatively, we can estimate the limit from the graph of $f$. Figure 10.7 shows the graph of $f$ in the standard window of $[-10, 10] \times [-10, 10]$. First we zoom in several times around $x = 2$ and obtain Figure 10.8. After tracing around $x = 2$, we estimate the limit to be 1.57.

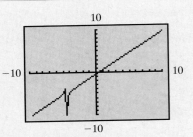

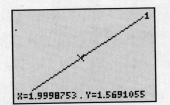

FIGURE 10.7   Graph of $f(x)$ in standard window.

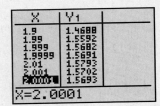

FIGURE 10.6   $\lim_{x\to 2} f(x) \approx 1.57$.

FIGURE 10.8   Zooming and tracing around $x = 2$ gives $\lim_{x\to 2} f(x) \approx 1.57$.

## Properties of Limits

To determine limits, we do not always want to compute function values or sketch a graph. Alternatively, there are several properties of limits that we may be able to employ. The following properties may seem reasonable to you:

1. If $f(x) = c$ is a constant function, then

$$\lim_{x\to a} f(x) = \lim_{x\to a} c = c$$

2. $\lim_{x\to a} x^n = a^n$, for any positive integer $n$

### EXAMPLE 3   Applying Limit Properties 1 and 2

a. $\lim_{x\to 2} 7 = 7$; $\lim_{x\to -5} 7 = 7$

b. $\lim_{x\to 6} x^2 = 6^2 = 36$

c. $\lim_{t\to -2} t^4 = (-2)^4 = 16$

NOW WORK PROBLEM 9

Some other properties of limits are as follows:

If $\lim_{x\to a} f(x)$ and $\lim_{x\to a} g(x)$ exist, then

3.
$$\lim_{x\to a}[f(x) \pm g(x)] = \lim_{x\to a} f(x) \pm \lim_{x\to a} g(x)$$

*That is, the limit of a sum or difference is the sum or difference, respectively, of the limits.*

4.
$$\lim_{x\to a}[f(x) \cdot g(x)] = \lim_{x\to a} f(x) \cdot \lim_{x\to a} g(x)$$

*That is, the limit of a product is the product of the limits.*

**5.**  $\lim_{x \to a}[cf(x)] = c \cdot \lim_{x \to a} f(x)$, where $c$ is a constant

   *That is, the limit of a constant times a function is the constant times the limit of the function.*

**APPLYING LIMIT PROPERTIES**

The volume of helium in a spherical balloon (in cubic centimeters), as a function of the radius $r$ in centimeters, is given by $V(r) = \frac{4}{3}\pi r^3$. Find $\lim_{r \to 1} V(r)$.

● **EXAMPLE 4   Applying Limit Properties**

**a.** $\lim_{x \to 2}(x^2 + x) = \lim_{x \to 2} x^2 + \lim_{x \to 2} x$      (Property 3)

$\qquad\qquad = 2^2 + 2 = 6$      (Property 2)

**b.** Property 3 can be extended to the limit of a finite number of sums and differences. For example,

$$\lim_{q \to -1}(q^3 - q + 1) = \lim_{q \to -1} q^3 - \lim_{q \to -1} q + \lim_{q \to -1} 1$$

$$= (-1)^3 - (-1) + 1 = 1$$

**c.** $\lim_{x \to 2}[(x + 1)(x - 3)] = \lim_{x \to 2}(x + 1) \cdot \lim_{x \to 2}(x - 3)$      (Property 4)

$$= \left[\lim_{x \to 2} x + \lim_{x \to 2} 1\right] \cdot \left[\lim_{x \to 2} x - \lim_{x \to 2} 3\right]$$

$$= (2 + 1) \cdot (2 - 3) = 3(-1) = -3$$

**d.** $\lim_{x \to -2} 3x^3 = 3 \cdot \lim_{x \to -2} x^3$      (Property 5)

$$= 3(-2)^3 = -24$$

NOW WORK PROBLEM 11 ●●

**LIMIT OF A POLYNOMIAL**

The revenue function for a certain product is given by $R(x) = 500x - 6x^2$. Find $\lim_{x \to 8} R(x)$.

● **EXAMPLE 5   Limit of a Polynomial Function**

Let $f(x) = c_n x^n + c_{n-1} x^{n-1} + \cdots + c_1 x + c_0$ define a polynomial function. Then

$$\lim_{x \to a} f(x) = \lim_{x \to a}(c_n x^n + c_{n-1} x^{n-1} + \cdots + c_1 x + c_0)$$

$$= c_n \cdot \lim_{x \to a} x^n + c_{n-1} \cdot \lim_{x \to a} x^{n-1} + \cdots + c_1 \cdot \lim_{x \to a} x + \lim_{x \to a} c_0$$

$$= c_n a^n + c_{n-1} a^{n-1} + \cdots + c_1 a + c_0 = f(a)$$

Thus, we have the following property:

If $f$ is a polynomial function, then

$$\lim_{x \to a} f(x) = f(a)$$

In other words, if $f$ is a polynomial and $a$ is any number, then both ways of associating a number to the pair $(f, a)$, namely evaluation and forming the limit, exist and are equal.

NOW WORK PROBLEM 13 ●●

The result of Example 5 allows us to find many limits simply by evaluation. For example, we can find

$$\lim_{x \to -3}(x^3 + 4x^2 - 7)$$

by substituting $-3$ for $x$ because $x^3 + 4x^2 - 7$ is a polynomial function:

$$\lim_{x \to -3}(x^3 + 4x^2 - 7) = (-3)^3 + 4(-3)^2 - 7 = 2$$

Similarly,

$$\lim_{h \to 3}[2(h - 1)] = 2(3 - 1) = 4$$

We want to stress that one does not find limits simply by evaluating, "plugging in" as some say, unless there is a rule that covers the situation. We were able to find the previous two limits by evaluation because we have a rule that applies to limits of polynomial functions. However, indiscriminate use of evaluation can lead to errors. To illustrate, in Example 1(b) we have $f(1) = 3$, which is not $\lim_{x \to 1} f(x)$; in Example 2(a), $f(-2) = 2$, which is not $\lim_{x \to -2} f(x)$.

The next two limit properties concern quotients and roots.

If $\lim_{x \to a} f(x)$ and $\lim_{x \to a} g(x)$ exist, then

6.
$$\lim_{x \to a} \frac{f(x)}{g(x)} = \frac{\lim_{x \to a} f(x)}{\lim_{x \to a} g(x)} \quad \text{if} \quad \lim_{x \to a} g(x) \neq 0$$

*That is, the limit of a quotient is the quotient of limits, provided that the denominator does not have a limit of* 0.

7.
$$\lim_{x \to a} \sqrt[n]{f(x)} = \sqrt[n]{\lim_{x \to a} f(x)} \qquad \text{(See Footnote 1)}$$

**CAUTION**

Note that in Example 6(a) the numerator and denominator of the function are polynomials. In general, we can determine a limit of a rational function by evaluation, provided that the denominator is not 0 at $a$.

● **EXAMPLE 6    Applying Limit Properties 6 and 7**

**a.** $\lim\limits_{x \to 1} \dfrac{2x^2 + x - 3}{x^3 + 4} = \dfrac{\lim_{x \to 1}(2x^2 + x - 3)}{\lim_{x \to 1}(x^3 + 4)} = \dfrac{2 + 1 - 3}{1 + 4} = \dfrac{0}{5} = 0$

**b.** $\lim\limits_{t \to 4} \sqrt{t^2 + 1} = \sqrt{\lim\limits_{t \to 4}(t^2 + 1)} = \sqrt{17}$

**c.** $\lim\limits_{x \to 3} \sqrt[3]{x^2 + 7} = \sqrt[3]{\lim\limits_{x \to 3}(x^2 + 7)} = \sqrt[3]{16} = \sqrt[3]{8 \cdot 2} = 2\sqrt[3]{2}$

NOW WORK PROBLEM 15    ●●●

### Limits and Algebraic Manipulation

We now consider limits to which our limit properties do not apply and which cannot be determined by evaluation. A fundamental result is the following:

If $f$ and $g$ are two functions for which $f(x) = g(x)$, for all $x \neq a$, then

$$\lim_{x \to a} f(x) = \lim_{x \to a} g(x)$$

(meaning that if either limit exists, then the other exists and they are equal).

**CAUTION**

The condition for equality of the limits does not preclude the possibility that $f(a) = g(a)$. The condition only concerns $x \neq a$.

The result follows directly from the definition of limit since the value of $\lim_{x \to a} f(x)$ depends only on those values $f(x)$ for $x$ that are close to $a$. We repeat: The evaluation of $f$ at $a$, $f(a)$, or lack of its existence, is irrelevant in the

---

[1] If $n$ is even, we require that $\lim_{x \to a} f(x)$ be positive.

determination of $\lim_{x \to a} f(x)$ unless we have a specific rule that applies, such as in the case when $f$ is a polynomial.

---

**PRINCIPLES IN PRACTICE 4**

**APPLYING LIMIT PROPERTY**

The rate of change of productivity $p$ (in number of units produced per hour) increases with time on the job by the function

$$p(t) = \frac{50(t^2 + 4t)}{t^2 + 3t + 20}$$

Find $\lim_{t \to 2} p(t)$.

---

### EXAMPLE 7  Finding a Limit

*Find* $\lim\limits_{x \to -1} \dfrac{x^2 - 1}{x + 1}$.

**Solution:** As $x \to -1$, both numerator and denominator approach zero. Because the limit of the denominator is 0, we *cannot* use Property 6. However, since what happens to the quotient when $x$ equals $-1$ is of no concern, we can assume that $x \neq -1$ and simplify the fraction:

$$\frac{x^2 - 1}{x + 1} = \frac{(x + 1)(x - 1)}{x + 1} = x - 1 \quad \text{for } x \neq -1$$

This algebraic manipulation (factoring and cancellation) of the original function $\dfrac{x^2 - 1}{x + 1}$ yields a new function $x - 1$, which is the same as the original function for $x \neq -1$. Thus the fundamental result displayed on the previous page applies and we have

$$\lim_{x \to -1} \frac{x^2 - 1}{x + 1} = \lim_{x \to -1} (x - 1) = -1 - 1 = -2$$

Notice that, although the original function is not defined at $-1$, it *does* have a limit as $x \to -1$.

NOW WORK PROBLEM 21

---

When both $f(x)$ and $g(x)$ approach 0 as $x \to a$, then the limit

$$\lim_{x \to a} \frac{f(x)}{g(x)}$$

is said to have the *form* 0/0. Similarly, we speak of *form* $k/0$, for $k \neq 0$ if $f(x)$ approaches $k \neq 0$ as $x \to a$ but $g(x)$ approaches 0 as $x \to a$.

In Example 7, the method of finding a limit by evaluation does not work. Replacing $x$ by $-1$ gives 0/0, which has no meaning. When the meaningless form 0/0 arises, algebraic manipulation (as in Example 7) may result in a function that agrees with the original function, except possibly at the limiting value. In Example 7 the new function, $x - 1$, is a polynomial and its limit *can* be found by evaluation.

In the beginning of this section, we found

$$\lim_{x \to 1} \frac{x^3 - 1}{x - 1}$$

by examining a table of function values of $f(x) = (x^3 - 1)/(x - 1)$ and also by considering the graph of $f$. This limit has the form 0/0. Now we will determine the limit by using the technique used in Example 7.

---

**CAUTION**

There is frequently confusion about which principle is being used in this example and in Example 7. It is this:

If $f(x) = g(x)$ for $x \neq a$

then $\lim\limits_{x \to a} f(x) = \lim\limits_{x \to a} g(x)$

### EXAMPLE 8  Form 0/0

*Find* $\lim\limits_{x \to 1} \dfrac{x^3 - 1}{x - 1}$.

**Solution:** As $x \to 1$, both the numerator and denominator approach 0. Thus, we will try to express the quotient in a different form for $x \neq 1$. By factoring, we have

$$\frac{x^3 - 1}{x - 1} = \frac{(x - 1)(x^2 + x + 1)}{(x - 1)} = x^2 + x + 1 \quad \text{for } x \neq 1$$

(Alternatively, long division would give the same result.) Therefore,

$$\lim_{x \to 1} \frac{x^3 - 1}{x - 1} = \lim_{x \to 1} (x^2 + x + 1) = 1^2 + 1 + 1 = 3$$

as we showed before.

NOW WORK PROBLEM 23

**PRINCIPLES IN PRACTICE 5**

**FORM 0/0**

The length of a material increases as it is heated up according to the equation $l = 125 + 2x$. The rate at which the length is increasing is given by

$$\lim_{h\to 0} \frac{125 + 2(x+h) - (125 + 2x)}{h}$$

Calculate this limit.

## EXAMPLE 9 Form 0/0

*If* $f(x) = x^2 + 1$, *find* $\lim_{h\to 0} \frac{f(x+h) - f(x)}{h}$.

**Solution:**

$$\lim_{h\to 0} \frac{f(x+h) - f(x)}{h} = \lim_{h\to 0} \frac{[(x+h)^2 + 1] - (x^2 + 1)}{h}$$

Here we treat $x$ as a constant because $h$, not $x$, is changing. As $h \to 0$, both the numerator and denominator approach 0. Therefore, we will try to express the quotient in a different form, for $h \neq 0$. We have

$$\begin{aligned}\lim_{h\to 0} \frac{[(x+h)^2 + 1] - (x^2 + 1)}{h} &= \lim_{h\to 0} \frac{[x^2 + 2xh + h^2 + 1] - x^2 - 1}{h} \\ &= \lim_{h\to 0} \frac{2xh + h^2}{h} \\ &= \lim_{h\to 0} \frac{h(2x+h)}{h} \\ &= \lim_{h\to 0}(2x + h) \\ &= 2x\end{aligned}$$

The expression

$$\frac{f(x+h) - f(x)}{h}$$

is called a *difference quotient*. The limit of the difference quotient lies at the heart of differential calculus. You will encounter such limits in Chapter 11.

Note: It is the fourth equality above, $\lim_{h\to 0} \frac{h(2x+h)}{h} = \lim_{h\to 0}(2x+h)$, that uses the fundamental result. When $\frac{h(2x+h)}{h}$ and $2x + h$ are considered as *functions of h*, they are seen to be equal, for all $h \neq 0$. It follows that their limits as $h$ approaches 0 are equal.

NOW WORK PROBLEM 35

## A Special Limit

We conclude this section with a note concerning a most important limit, namely,

$$\lim_{x\to 0}(1 + x)^{1/x}$$

Figure 10.9 shows the graph of $f(x) = (1 + x)^{1/x}$. Although $f(0)$ does not exist, as $x \to 0$ it is clear that the limit of $(1 + x)^{1/x}$ exists. It is approximately 2.71828 and is denoted by the letter $e$. This, you may recall, is the base of the system of natural logarithms. The limit

This limit will be used in Chapter 12.

$$\lim_{x\to 0}(1 + x)^{1/x} = e$$

can actually be considered the definition of $e$. It can be shown that this agrees with the definition of $e$ that we gave in Section 4.1.

| $x$ | $(1+x)^{1/x}$ |
|---|---|
| 0.5 | 2.2500 |
| 0.1 | 2.5937 |
| 0.01 | 2.7048 |
| 0.001 | 2.7169 |

| $x$ | $(1+x)^{1/x}$ |
|---|---|
| −0.5 | 4.0000 |
| −0.1 | 2.8680 |
| −0.01 | 2.7320 |
| −0.001 | 2.7196 |

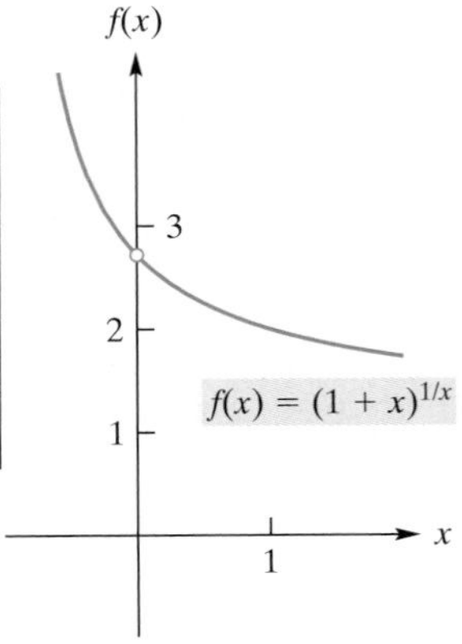


FIGURE 10.9 $\lim_{x\to 0}(1 + x)^{1/x} = e$.

# Problems 10.1

*In Problems 1–4, use the graph of f to estimate each limit if it exists.*

*1. Graph of $f$ appears in Figure 10.10.

   **(a)** $\lim_{x \to 0} f(x)$    **(b)** $\lim_{x \to 1} f(x)$    **(c)** $\lim_{x \to 2} f(x)$

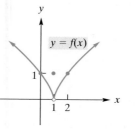

**FIGURE 10.10**   Diagram for Problem 1.

**2.** Graph of $f$ appears in Figure 10.11.

   **(a)** $\lim_{x \to -1} f(x)$    **(b)** $\lim_{x \to 0} f(x)$    **(c)** $\lim_{x \to 1} f(x)$

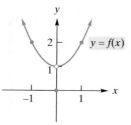

**FIGURE 10.11**   Diagram for Problem 2.

*3. Graph of $f$ appears in Figure 10.12.

   **(a)** $\lim_{x \to -1} f(x)$    **(b)** $\lim_{x \to 1} f(x)$    **(c)** $\lim_{x \to 2} f(x)$

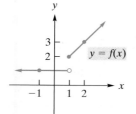

**FIGURE 10.12**   Diagram for Problem 3.

**4.** Graph of $f$ appears in Figure 10.13.

   **(a)** $\lim_{x \to -1} f(x)$    **(b)** $\lim_{x \to 0} f(x)$    **(c)** $\lim_{x \to 1} f(x)$

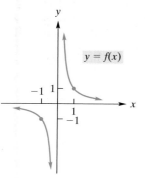

**FIGURE 10.13**   Diagram for Problem 4.

*In Problems 5–8, use your calculator to complete the table, and use your results to estimate the given limit.*

**5.** $\lim\limits_{x \to -1} \dfrac{3x^2 + 2x - 1}{x + 1}$

| $x$ | $-0.9$ | $-0.99$ | $-0.999$ | $-1.001$ | $-1.01$ | $-1.1$ |
|-----|--------|---------|----------|----------|---------|--------|
| $f(x)$ | | | | | | |

**6.** $\lim\limits_{x \to -3} \dfrac{x^2 - 9}{x + 3}$

| $x$ | $-3.1$ | $-3.01$ | $-3.001$ | $-2.999$ | $-2.99$ | $-2.9$ |
|-----|--------|---------|----------|----------|---------|--------|
| $f(x)$ | | | | | | |

**7.** $\lim\limits_{x \to 0} \dfrac{e^x - 1}{x}$

| $x$ | $-0.1$ | $-0.01$ | $-0.001$ | $0.001$ | $0.01$ | $0.1$ |
|-----|--------|---------|----------|---------|--------|-------|
| $f(x)$ | | | | | | |

**8.** $\lim\limits_{h \to 0} \dfrac{\sqrt{1 + h} - 1}{h}$

| $h$ | $-0.1$ | $-0.01$ | $-0.001$ | $0.001$ | $0.01$ | $0.1$ |
|-----|--------|---------|----------|---------|--------|-------|
| $f(x)$ | | | | | | |

*In Problems 9–34, find the limits.*

*9. $\lim\limits_{x \to 2} 16$

**10.** $\lim\limits_{x \to 3} 2x$

*11. $\lim\limits_{t \to -5} (t^2 - 5)$

**12.** $\lim\limits_{t \to 1/3} (5t - 7)$

*13. $\lim\limits_{x \to -2} (3x^3 - 4x^2 + 2x - 3)$

**14.** $\lim\limits_{r \to 9} \dfrac{4r - 3}{11}$

*15. $\lim\limits_{t \to -3} \dfrac{t - 2}{t + 5}$

**16.** $\lim\limits_{x \to -6} \dfrac{x^2 + 6}{x - 6}$

**17.** $\lim\limits_{h \to 0} \dfrac{h}{h^2 - 7h + 1}$

**18.** $\lim\limits_{z \to 0} \dfrac{z^2 - 5z - 4}{z^2 + 1}$

**19.** $\lim\limits_{p \to 4} \sqrt{p^2 + p + 5}$

**20.** $\lim\limits_{y \to 15} \sqrt{y + 3}$

*21. $\lim\limits_{x \to -2} \dfrac{x^2 + 2x}{x + 2}$

**22.** $\lim\limits_{x \to -1} \dfrac{x + 1}{x + 1}$

*23. $\lim\limits_{x \to 2} \dfrac{x^2 - x - 2}{x - 2}$

**24.** $\lim\limits_{t \to 0} \dfrac{t^3 + 3t^2}{t^3 - 4t^2}$

**25.** $\lim\limits_{x \to 3} \dfrac{x^2 - x - 6}{x - 3}$

**26.** $\lim\limits_{t \to 2} \dfrac{t^2 - 4}{t - 2}$

**27.** $\lim\limits_{x \to 3} \dfrac{x - 3}{x^2 - 9}$

**28.** $\lim\limits_{x \to 0} \dfrac{x^2 - 2x}{x}$

**29.** $\lim\limits_{x \to 4} \dfrac{x^2 - 9x + 20}{x^2 - 3x - 4}$

**30.** $\lim\limits_{x \to -3} \dfrac{x^4 - 81}{x^2 + 8x + 15}$

**31.** $\lim\limits_{x \to 2} \dfrac{3x^2 - x - 10}{x^2 + 5x - 14}$

**32.** $\lim\limits_{x \to -4} \dfrac{x^2 + 2x - 8}{x^2 + 5x + 4}$

**33.** $\lim\limits_{h \to 0} \dfrac{(2 + h)^2 - 2^2}{h}$

**34.** $\lim\limits_{x \to 0} \dfrac{(x + 2)^2 - 4}{x}$

*35. Find $\lim\limits_{h \to 0} \dfrac{(x + h)^2 - x^2}{h}$ by treating $x$ as a constant.

**36.** Find $\lim\limits_{h \to 0} \dfrac{3(x + h)^2 + 7(x + h) - 3x^2 - 7x}{h}$ by treating $x$ as a constant.

*In Problems 37–42, find $\lim\limits_{h \to 0} \dfrac{f(x + h) - f(x)}{h}$.*

**37.** $f(x) = 7 - 3x$         **38.** $f(x) = 2x + 3$

**39.** $f(x) = x^2 - 3$

**40.** $f(x) = x^2 + x + 1$

**41.** $f(x) = x^3 - 4x^2$

**42.** $f(x) = 3 - x + 4x^2$

**43.** Find $\lim\limits_{x \to 6} \dfrac{\sqrt{x-2} - 2}{x - 6}$ (*Hint:* First rationalize the numerator by multiplying both the numerator and denominator by $\sqrt{x-2} + 2$.)

**44.** Find the constant $c$ so that $\lim\limits_{x \to 3} \dfrac{x^2 + x + c}{x^2 - 5x + 6}$ exists. For that value of $c$, determine the limit. (*Hint:* Find the value of $c$ for which $x - 3$ is a factor of the numerator.)

**45. Power Plant** The maximum theoretical efficiency of a power plant is given by

$$E = \frac{T_h - T_c}{T_h}$$

where $T_h$ and $T_c$ are the respective absolute temperatures of the hotter and colder reservoirs. Find (a) $\lim\limits_{T_c \to 0} E$ and (b) $\lim\limits_{T_c \to T_h} E$.

**46. Satellite** When a 3200-lb satellite revolves about the earth in a circular orbit of radius $r$ ft, the total mechanical energy

$E$ of the earth–satellite system is given by

$$E = -\frac{7.0 \times 10^{17}}{r} \text{ ft-lb}$$

Find the limit of $E$ as $r \to 7.5 \times 10^7$ ft.

*In Problems 47–50, use a graphing calculator to graph the functions, and then estimate the limits. Round your answers to two decimal places.*

**47.** $\lim\limits_{x \to 2} \dfrac{x^4 + x^3 - 24}{x^2 - 4}$

**48.** $\lim\limits_{x \to 0} x^x$

**49.** $\lim\limits_{x \to 9} \dfrac{x - 10\sqrt{x} + 21}{3 - \sqrt{x}}$

**50.** $\lim\limits_{x \to 1} \dfrac{x^3 + x^2 - 5x + 3}{x^3 + 2x^2 - 7x + 4}$

**51. Water Purification** The cost of purifying water is given by $C = \dfrac{50{,}000}{p} - 6500$, where $p$ is the percent of impurities remaining after purification. Graph this function on your graphing calculator, and determine $\lim\limits_{p \to 0} C$. Discuss what this means.

**52. Profit Function** The profit function for a certain business is given by $P(x) = 224x - 3.1x^2 - 800$. Graph this function on your graphing calculator, and use the evaluation function to determine $\lim\limits_{x \to 53.2} P(x)$, utilizing the rule about the limit of a polynomial function.

## 10.2 Limits (Continued)

OBJECTIVE

To study one-sided limits, infinite limits, and limits at infinity.

### One-Sided Limits

Figure 10.14 shows the graph of a function $f$. Notice that $f(x)$ is not defined when $x = 0$. As $x$ approaches 0 *from the right,* $f(x)$ approaches 1. We write this as

$$\lim_{x \to 0^+} f(x) = 1$$

On the other hand, as $x$ approaches 0 *from the left,* $f(x)$ approaches $-1$, and we write

$$\lim_{x \to 0^-} f(x) = -1$$

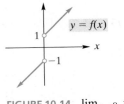

**FIGURE 10.14** $\lim_{x\to 0} f(x)$ does not exist.

Limits like these are called **one-sided limits.** From the preceding section, we know that the limit of a function as $x \to a$ is independent of the way $x$ approaches $a$. Thus, the limit will exist if and only if both one-sided limits exist and are equal. We therefore conclude that

$$\lim_{x \to 0} f(x) \text{ does not exist}$$

As another example of a one-sided limit, consider $f(x) = \sqrt{x - 3}$ as $x$ approaches 3. Since $f$ is defined only when $x \geq 3$, we may speak of the limit as $x$ approaches 3 from the right. If $x$ is slightly greater than 3, then $x - 3$ is a positive number that is close to 0, so $\sqrt{x - 3}$ is close to 0. We conclude that

$$\lim_{x \to 3^+} \sqrt{x - 3} = 0$$

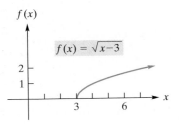

**FIGURE 10.15**
$\lim_{x \to 3^+} \sqrt{x - 3} = 0.$

This limit is also evident from Figure 10.15.

### Infinite Limits

In the previous section, we considered limits of the form 0/0—that is, limits where both the numerator and denominator approach 0. Now we will examine limits where the denominator approaches 0, but the numerator approaches a number different from 0. For example, consider

$$\lim_{x \to 0} \frac{1}{x^2}$$

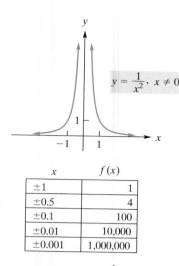

| $x$ | $f(x)$ |
|---|---|
| ±1 | 1 |
| ±0.5 | 4 |
| ±0.1 | 100 |
| ±0.01 | 10,000 |
| ±0.001 | 1,000,000 |

**FIGURE 10.16** $\lim_{x\to 0}\dfrac{1}{x^2}=\infty$.

**CAUTION**

The use of the "equality" sign in this situation does not mean that the limit exists. On the contrary, the symbolism here ($\infty$) is a way of saying specifically that there is no limit, and it indicates why there is no limit.

**FIGURE 10.18** $x\to -1^+$.

Here, as $x$ approaches 0, the denominator approaches 0 and the numerator approaches 1. Let us investigate the behavior of $f(x)=1/x^2$ when $x$ is close to 0. The number $x^2$ is positive and also close to 0. Thus, dividing 1 by such a number results in a very large number. In fact, the closer $x$ is to 0, the larger the value of $f(x)$. For example, see the table of values in Figure 10.16, which also shows the graph of $f$. Clearly, as $x\to 0$ both from the left and from the right, $f(x)$ increases without bound. Hence, no limit exists at 0. We say that as $x\to 0$, $f(x)$ becomes positively infinite, and symbolically we express this "infinite limit" by writing

$$\lim_{x\to 0}\frac{1}{x^2}=\infty$$

If $\lim_{x\to a} f(x)$ does not exist, it may be for a reason other than that the values $f(x)$ become arbitrarily large as $x$ gets close to $a$. For example, look again at the situation in Example 2 of Section 10.1. Here we have

$$\lim_{x\to -2} f(x)\text{ does not exist, but }\lim_{x\to -2} f(x)\neq\infty$$

Consider now the graph of $y=f(x)=1/x$ for $x\neq 0$. (See Figure 10.17.) As $x$ approaches 0 from the right, $1/x$ becomes positively infinite; as $x$ approaches 0 from the left, $1/x$ becomes negatively infinite. Symbolically, these infinite limits are written

$$\lim_{x\to 0^+}\frac{1}{x}=\infty\quad\text{and}\quad\lim_{x\to 0^-}\frac{1}{x}=-\infty$$

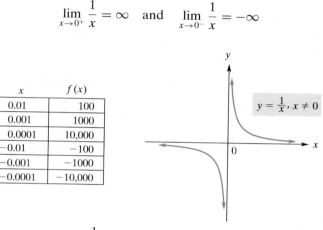

| $x$ | $f(x)$ |
|---|---|
| 0.01 | 100 |
| 0.001 | 1000 |
| 0.0001 | 10,000 |
| −0.01 | −100 |
| −0.001 | −1000 |
| −0.0001 | −10,000 |

**FIGURE 10.17** $\lim_{x\to 0}\dfrac{1}{x}$ does not exist.

Either one of these facts implies that

$$\lim_{x\to 0}\frac{1}{x}\text{ does not exist}$$

**EXAMPLE 1  Infinite Limits**

*Find the limit (if it exists).*

**a.** $\lim_{x\to -1^+}\dfrac{2}{x+1}$

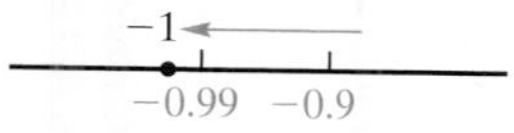

**Solution:** As $x$ approaches $-1$ from the right (think of values of $x$ such as $-0.9, -0.99$, and so on, as shown in Figure 10.18), $x+1$ approaches 0, but is always positive. Since we are dividing 2 by positive numbers approaching 0, the results, $2/(x+1)$, are positive numbers that are becoming arbitrarily large. Thus,

$$\lim_{x\to -1^+}\frac{2}{x+1}=\infty$$

and the limit does not exist. By a similar analysis, you should be able to show that

$$\lim_{x\to -1^-}\frac{2}{x+1}=-\infty$$

**b.** $\lim\limits_{x \to 2} \dfrac{x+2}{x^2-4}$

**Solution:** As $x \to 2$, the numerator approaches 4 and the denominator approaches 0. Hence, we are dividing numbers near 4 by numbers near 0. The results are numbers that become arbitrarily large in magnitude. At this stage, we can write

$$\lim_{x \to 2} \frac{x+2}{x^2-4} \text{ does not exist}$$

However, let us see if we can use the symbol $\infty$ or $-\infty$ to be more specific about "does not exist." Notice that

$$\lim_{x \to 2} \frac{x+2}{x^2-4} = \lim_{x \to 2} \frac{x+2}{(x+2)(x-2)} = \lim_{x \to 2} \frac{1}{x-2}$$

Since

$$\lim_{x \to 2^+} \frac{1}{x-2} = \infty \quad \text{and} \quad \lim_{x \to 2^-} \frac{1}{x-2} = -\infty$$

$\lim\limits_{x \to 2} \dfrac{x+2}{x^2-4}$ is neither $\infty$ nor $-\infty$.

NOW WORK PROBLEM 31 ◖◗●

Example 1 considered limits of the form $k/0$, where $k \neq 0$. It is important that you distinguish the form $k/0$ from the form $0/0$, which was discussed in Section 10.1. These two forms are handled quite differently.

◖● **EXAMPLE 2** **Finding a Limit**

*Find* $\lim\limits_{t \to 2} \dfrac{t-2}{t^2-4}$.

**Solution:** As $t \to 2$, *both* numerator and denominator approach 0 (form $0/0$). Thus, we first simplify the fraction, for $t \neq 2$, as we did in Section 10.1, and then take the limit:

$$\lim_{t \to 2} \frac{t-2}{t^2-4} = \lim_{t \to 2} \frac{t-2}{(t+2)(t-2)} = \lim_{t \to 2} \frac{1}{t+2} = \frac{1}{4}$$

NOW WORK PROBLEM 37 ◖◗●

**Limits at Infinity**

Now let us examine the function

$$f(x) = \frac{1}{x}$$

You should be able to obtain

$$\lim_{x \to \infty} \frac{1}{x} \quad \text{and} \quad \lim_{x \to -\infty} \frac{1}{x}$$

without the benefit of a graph or a table. Dividing 1 by a large positive number results in a small positive number, and as the divisors get arbitrarily large, the quotients get arbitrarily small. A similar argument can be made for the limit as $x \to -\infty$.

as $x$ becomes infinite, first in a positive sense and then in a negative sense. From Table 10.2, you can see that as $x$ increases without bound through positive values, the values of $f(x)$ approach 0. Likewise, as $x$ decreases without bound through negative values, the values of $f(x)$ also approach 0. These observations are also apparent from the graph in Figure 10.17. There, as you move to the right along the curve through positive $x$-values, the corresponding $y$-values approach 0. Similarly, as you move

**TABLE 10.2** Behavior of $f(x)$ as $x \to \pm\infty$

| $x$ | $f(x)$ | $x$ | $f(x)$ |
|---|---|---|---|
| 1000 | 0.001 | $-1000$ | $-0.001$ |
| 10,000 | 0.0001 | $-10,000$ | $-0.0001$ |
| 100,000 | 0.00001 | $-100,000$ | $-0.00001$ |
| 1,000,000 | 0.000001 | $-1,000,000$ | $-0.000001$ |

to the left along the curve through negative $x$-values, the corresponding $y$-values approach 0. Symbolically, we write

$$\lim_{x \to \infty} \frac{1}{x} = 0 \quad \text{and} \quad \lim_{x \to -\infty} \frac{1}{x} = 0$$

Both of these limits are called *limits at infinity*.

PRINCIPLES IN PRACTICE 1

LIMITS AT INFINITY

The demand function for a certain product is given by $p(x) = \dfrac{10{,}000}{(x+1)^2}$, where $p$ is the price in dollars and $x$ is the quantity sold. Graph this function on your graphing calculator in the window $[0, 10] \times [0, 10{,}000]$. Use the TRACE function to find $\lim_{x \to \infty} p(x)$. Determine what is happening to the graph and what this means about the demand function.

● EXAMPLE 3    **Limits at Infinity**

*Find the limit (if it exists).*

**a.** $\displaystyle \lim_{x \to \infty} \frac{4}{(x-5)^3}$

Solution: As $x$ becomes very large, so does $x - 5$. Since the cube of a large number is also large, $(x-5)^3 \to \infty$. Dividing 4 by very large numbers results in numbers near 0. Thus,

$$\lim_{x \to \infty} \frac{4}{(x-5)^3} = 0$$

**b.** $\displaystyle \lim_{x \to -\infty} \sqrt{4-x}$

Solution: As $x$ gets negatively infinite, $4-x$ becomes positively infinite. Because square roots of large numbers are large numbers, we conclude that

$$\lim_{x \to -\infty} \sqrt{4-x} = \infty$$

In our next discussion we will need a certain limit, namely, $\lim_{x \to \infty} 1/x^p$, where $p > 0$. As $x$ becomes very large, so does $x^p$. Dividing 1 by very large numbers results in numbers near 0. Thus, $\lim_{x \to \infty} 1/x^p = 0$. In general,

$$\lim_{x \to \infty} \frac{1}{x^p} = 0 \quad \text{and} \quad \lim_{x \to -\infty} \frac{1}{x^p} = 0$$

where $p > 0$.[2] For example,

$$\lim_{x \to \infty} \frac{1}{\sqrt[3]{x}} = \lim_{x \to \infty} \frac{1}{x^{1/3}} = 0$$

Let us now find the limit of the rational function

$$f(x) = \frac{4x^2 + 5}{2x^2 + 1}$$

as $x \to \infty$. (Recall from Section 2.2 that a rational function is a quotient of polynomials.) As $x$ gets larger and larger, *both* the numerator and denominator of $f(x)$ become infinite. However, the form of the quotient can be changed, so that we can draw a conclusion as to whether or not it has a limit. To do this, we divide both the numerator and denominator by the greatest power of $x$ that occurs in the denominator. Here it is $x^2$. This gives

$$\lim_{x \to \infty} \frac{4x^2 + 5}{2x^2 + 1} = \lim_{x \to \infty} \frac{\dfrac{4x^2 + 5}{x^2}}{\dfrac{2x^2 + 1}{x^2}} = \lim_{x \to \infty} \frac{\dfrac{4x^2}{x^2} + \dfrac{5}{x^2}}{\dfrac{2x^2}{x^2} + \dfrac{1}{x^2}}$$

$$= \lim_{x \to \infty} \frac{4 + \dfrac{5}{x^2}}{2 + \dfrac{1}{x^2}} = \frac{\displaystyle\lim_{x \to \infty} 4 + 5 \cdot \lim_{x \to \infty} \dfrac{1}{x^2}}{\displaystyle\lim_{x \to \infty} 2 + \lim_{x \to \infty} \dfrac{1}{x^2}}$$

---

[2] For $\lim_{x \to -\infty} 1/x^p$, we assume that $p$ is such that $1/x^p$ is defined for $x < 0$.

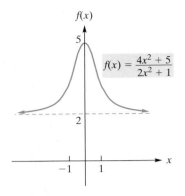

**FIGURE 10.19**
$\lim_{x \to \infty} f(x) = 2$ and
$\lim_{x \to -\infty} f(x) = 2$.

Since $\lim_{x\to\infty} 1/x^p = 0$ for $p > 0$,

$$\lim_{x\to\infty} \frac{4x^2 + 5}{2x^2 + 1} = \frac{4 + 5(0)}{2 + 0} = \frac{4}{2} = 2$$

Similarly, the limit as $x \to -\infty$ is 2. These limits are clear from the graph of $f$ in Figure 10.19.

For the preceding function, there is an easier way to find $\lim_{x\to\infty} f(x)$. For *large* values of $x$, in the numerator the term involving the greatest power of $x$, namely, $4x^2$, dominates the sum $4x^2 + 5$, and the dominant term in the denominator, $2x^2 + 1$, is $2x^2$. Thus, as $x \to \infty$, $f(x)$ can be approximated by $(4x^2)/(2x^2)$. As a result, to determine the limit of $f(x)$, it suffices to determine the limit of $(4x^2)/(2x^2)$. That is,

$$\lim_{x\to\infty} \frac{4x^2 + 5}{2x^2 + 1} = \lim_{x\to\infty} \frac{4x^2}{2x^2} = \lim_{x\to\infty} 2 = 2$$

as we saw before. In general, we have the following rule:

---

**Limits at Infinity for Rational Functions**

If $f(x)$ is a *rational function* and $a_n x^n$ and $b_m x^m$ are the terms in the numerator and denominator, respectively, with the greatest powers of $x$, then

$$\lim_{x\to\infty} f(x) = \lim_{x\to\infty} \frac{a_n x^n}{b_m x^m}$$

and

$$\lim_{x\to-\infty} f(x) = \lim_{x\to-\infty} \frac{a_n x^n}{b_m x^m}$$

---

Let us apply this rule to the situation where the degree of the numerator is greater than the degree of the denominator. For example,

$$\lim_{x\to-\infty} \frac{x^4 - 3x}{5 - 2x} = \lim_{x\to-\infty} \frac{x^4}{-2x} = \lim_{x\to-\infty} \left(-\frac{1}{2}x^3\right) = \infty$$

(Note that in the next-to-last step, as $x$ becomes very negative, so does $x^3$; moreover, $-\frac{1}{2}$ times a very negative number is very positive.) Similarly,

$$\lim_{x\to\infty} \frac{x^4 - 3x}{5 - 2x} = \lim_{x\to\infty} \left(-\frac{1}{2}x^3\right) = -\infty$$

From this illustration, we make the following conclusion:

---

If the degree of the numerator of a *rational function* is greater than the degree of the denominator, then the function has no limit as $x \to \infty$ and no limit as $x \to -\infty$.

---

●**EXAMPLE 4   Limits at Infinity for Rational Functions**

*Find the limit (if it exists).*

**a.** $\lim\limits_{x\to\infty} \dfrac{x^2 - 1}{7 - 2x + 8x^2}$

Solution:
$$\lim_{x\to\infty} \frac{x^2 - 1}{7 - 2x + 8x^2} = \lim_{x\to\infty} \frac{x^2}{8x^2} = \lim_{x\to\infty} \frac{1}{8} = \frac{1}{8}$$

**b.** $\lim\limits_{x\to-\infty} \dfrac{x}{(3x - 1)^2}$

Solution:
$$\lim_{x\to-\infty} \frac{x}{(3x - 1)^2} = \lim_{x\to-\infty} \frac{x}{9x^2 - 6x + 1} = \lim_{x\to-\infty} \frac{x}{9x^2}$$
$$= \lim_{x\to-\infty} \frac{1}{9x} = \frac{1}{9} \cdot \lim_{x\to-\infty} \frac{1}{x} = \frac{1}{9}(0) = 0$$

**c.** $\lim\limits_{x \to \infty} \dfrac{x^5 - x^4}{x^4 - x^3 + 2}$

**Solution:** Since the degree of the numerator is greater than that of the denominator, there is no limit. More precisely,

$$\lim_{x \to \infty} \frac{x^5 - x^4}{x^4 - x^3 + 2} = \lim_{x \to \infty} \frac{x^5}{x^4} = \lim_{x \to \infty} x = \infty$$

NOW WORK PROBLEM 21 ●●●

To find $\lim\limits_{x \to 0} \dfrac{x^2 - 1}{7 - 2x + 8x^2}$, we cannot simply determine the limit of $\dfrac{x^2}{8x^2}$. That simplification applies only in case $x \to \infty$ or $x \to -\infty$. Instead, we have

$$\lim_{x \to 0} \frac{x^2 - 1}{7 - 2x + 8x^2} = \frac{0 - 1}{7 - 0 + 0} = -\frac{1}{7}$$

Let us now consider the limit of the polynomial function $f(x) = 8x^2 - 2x$ as $x \to \infty$:

$$\lim_{x \to \infty} (8x^2 - 2x)$$

Because a polynomial is a rational function with denominator 1, we have

$$\lim_{x \to \infty} (8x^2 - 2x) = \lim_{x \to \infty} \frac{8x^2 - 2x}{1} = \lim_{x \to \infty} \frac{8x^2}{1} = \lim_{x \to \infty} 8x^2$$

That is, the limit of $8x^2 - 2x$ as $x \to \infty$ is the same as the limit of the term involving the greatest power of $x$, namely, $8x^2$. As $x$ becomes very large, so does $8x^2$. Thus,

$$\lim_{x \to \infty} (8x^2 - 2x) = \lim_{x \to \infty} 8x^2 = \infty$$

In general, we have the following:

> As $x \to \infty$ (or $x \to -\infty$), the limit of a *polynomial function* is the same as the limit of its term that involves the greatest power of $x$.

**CAUTION**

The preceding technique applies only to limits of rational functions at *infinity*.

**PRINCIPLES IN PRACTICE 3**

**LIMITS AT INFINITY FOR POLYNOMIAL FUNCTIONS**

The cost $C$ of producing $x$ units of a certain product is given by $C(x) = 50{,}000 + 200x + 0.3x^2$. Use your graphing calculator to explore $\lim\limits_{x \to \infty} C(x)$ and determine what this means.

Do not use dominant terms when a function is not rational.

● **EXAMPLE 5  Limits at Infinity for Polynomial Functions**

**a.** $\lim_{x \to -\infty}(x^3 - x^2 + x - 2) = \lim_{x \to -\infty} x^3$. As $x$ becomes very negative, so does $x^3$. Thus,

$$\lim_{x \to -\infty} (x^3 - x^2 + x - 2) = \lim_{x \to -\infty} x^3 = -\infty$$

**b.** $\lim_{x \to -\infty}(-2x^3 + 9x) = \lim_{x \to -\infty} -2x^3 = \infty$, because $-2$ times a very negative number is very positive.

NOW WORK PROBLEM 9 ●●●

The technique of focusing on dominant terms to find limits as $x \to \infty$ or $x \to -\infty$ is valid for *rational functions,* but it is not necessarily valid for other types of functions. For example, consider

$$\lim_{x \to \infty} \left( \sqrt{x^2 + x} - x \right) \tag{1}$$

Notice that $\sqrt{x^2 + x} - x$ is not a rational function. It is *incorrect* to infer that because $x^2$ dominates in $x^2 + x$, the limit in (1) is the same as

$$\lim_{x \to \infty} \left( \sqrt{x^2} - x \right) = \lim_{x \to \infty} (x - x) = \lim_{x \to \infty} 0 = 0$$

It can be shown (see Problem 62) that the limit in (1) is not 0, but is $\frac{1}{2}$.

The ideas discussed in this section will now be applied to a case-defined function.

PRINCIPLES IN PRACTICE 4

**LIMITS FOR A CASE-DEFINED FUNCTION**

A plumber charges $100 for the first hour of work at your house and $75 for every hour (or fraction thereof) afterward. The function for what an $x$-hour visit will cost you is

$$f(x) = \begin{cases} \$100 & \text{if } 0 < x \leq 1 \\ \$175 & \text{if } 1 < x \leq 2 \\ \$250 & \text{if } 2 < x \leq 3 \\ \$325 & \text{if } 3 < x \leq 4 \end{cases}$$

Find $\lim_{x \to 1} f(x)$ and $\lim_{x \to 2.5} f(x)$.

● **EXAMPLE 6    Limits for a Case-Defined Function**

If $f(x) = \begin{cases} x^2 + 1 & \text{if } x \geq 1 \\ 3 & \text{if } x < 1 \end{cases}$, *find the limit (if it exists).*

**a.** $\lim_{x \to 1^+} f(x)$

**Solution:** Here $x$ gets close to 1 from the right. For $x > 1$, we have $f(x) = x^2 + 1$. Thus,

$$\lim_{x \to 1^+} f(x) = \lim_{x \to 1^+} (x^2 + 1)$$

If $x$ is greater than 1, but close to 1, then $x^2 + 1$ is close to 2. Therefore,

$$\lim_{x \to 1^+} f(x) = \lim_{x \to 1^+} (x^2 + 1) = 2$$

**b.** $\lim_{x \to 1^-} f(x)$

**Solution:** Here $x$ gets close to 1 from the left. For $x < 1$, $f(x) = 3$. Hence,

$$\lim_{x \to 1^-} f(x) = \lim_{x \to 1^-} 3 = 3$$

**c.** $\lim_{x \to 1} f(x)$

**Solution:** We want the limit as $x$ approaches 1. However, the rule of the function depends on whether $x \geq 1$ or $x < 1$. Thus, we must consider one-sided limits. The limit as $x$ approaches 1 will exist if and only if both one-sided limits exist and are the same. From parts (a) and (b),

$$\lim_{x \to 1^+} f(x) \neq \lim_{x \to 1^-} f(x) \qquad \text{since } 2 \neq 3$$

Therefore,

$$\lim_{x \to 1} f(x) \qquad \text{does not exist}$$

**d.** $\lim_{x \to \infty} f(x)$

**Solution:** For very large values of $x$, we have $x \geq 1$, so $f(x) = x^2 + 1$. Thus,

$$\lim_{x \to \infty} f(x) = \lim_{x \to \infty} (x^2 + 1) = \lim_{x \to \infty} x^2 = \infty$$

**e.** $\lim_{x \to -\infty} f(x)$

**Solution:** For very negative values of $x$, we have $x < 1$, so $f(x) = 3$. Hence,

$$\lim_{x \to -\infty} f(x) = \lim_{x \to -\infty} 3 = 3$$

All the limits in parts (a) through (c) should be obvious from the graph of $f$ in Figure 10.20.

NOW WORK PROBLEM 57 ●●●

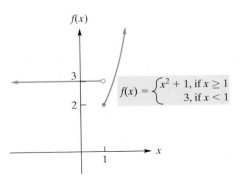

FIGURE 10.20    Graph of case-defined function.

# Problems 10.2

**1.** For the function $f$ given in Figure 10.21, find the following limits. If the limit does not exist, so state that, or use the symbol $\infty$ or $-\infty$ where appropriate.

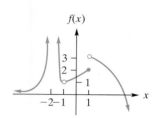

**FIGURE 10.21** Diagram for Problem 1.

(a) $\lim_{x \to 1^-} f(x)$  (b) $\lim_{x \to 1^+} f(x)$

(c) $\lim_{x \to 1} f(x)$  (d) $\lim_{x \to \infty} f(x)$

(e) $\lim_{x \to -2^-} f(x)$  (f) $\lim_{x \to -2^+} f(x)$

(g) $\lim_{x \to -2} f(x)$  (h) $\lim_{x \to -\infty} f(x)$

(i) $\lim_{x \to -1^-} f(x)$  (j) $\lim_{x \to -1^+} f(x)$

(k) $\lim_{x \to -1} f(x)$

**2.** For the function $f$ given in Figure 10.22, find the following limits. If the limit does not exist, so state that, or use the symbol $\infty$ or $-\infty$ where appropriate.

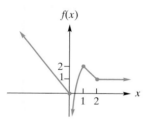

**FIGURE 10.22** Diagram for Problem 2.

(a) $\lim_{x \to 0^-} f(x)$  (b) $\lim_{x \to 0^+} f(x)$

(c) $\lim_{x \to 0} f(x)$  (d) $\lim_{x \to -\infty} f(x)$

(e) $\lim_{x \to 1} f(x)$  (f) $\lim_{x \to \infty} f(x)$

(g) $\lim_{x \to 2^+} f(x)$

*In each of Problems 3–54, find the limit. If the limit does not exist, so state that, or use the symbol $\infty$ or $-\infty$ where appropriate.*

**3.** $\lim_{x \to 3^+} (x - 2)$

**4.** $\lim_{x \to -1^+} (1 - x^2)$

**5.** $\lim_{x \to -\infty} 5x$

**6.** $\lim_{x \to -\infty} 19$

**7.** $\lim_{x \to 0^-} \dfrac{6x}{x^4}$

**8.** $\lim_{x \to 2} \dfrac{7}{x - 1}$

**\*9.** $\lim_{x \to -\infty} x^2$

**10.** $\lim_{t \to \infty} (t - 1)^3$

**11.** $\lim_{h \to 0^+} \sqrt{h}$

**12.** $\lim_{h \to 5^-} \sqrt{5 - h}$

**13.** $\lim_{x \to -2^-} \dfrac{-3}{x + 2}$

**14.** $\lim_{x \to 0^-} 2^{1/2}$

**15.** $\lim_{x \to 1^+} \left(4\sqrt{x - 1}\right)$

**16.** $\lim_{x \to 2^+} \left(x\sqrt{x^2 - 4}\right)$

**17.** $\lim_{x \to \infty} \sqrt{x + 10}$

**18.** $\lim_{x \to -\infty} -\sqrt{1 - 10x}$

**19.** $\lim_{x \to \infty} \dfrac{3}{\sqrt{x}}$

**20.** $\lim_{x \to \infty} \dfrac{-6}{5x\sqrt[3]{x}}$

**\*21.** $\lim_{x \to \infty} \dfrac{x + 8}{x - 3}$

**22.** $\lim_{x \to \infty} \dfrac{2x - 4}{3 - 2x}$

**23.** $\lim_{x \to -\infty} \dfrac{x^2 - 1}{x^3 + 4x - 3}$

**24.** $\lim_{r \to \infty} \dfrac{r^3}{r^2 + 1}$

**25.** $\lim_{t \to \infty} \dfrac{3t^3 + 2t^2 + 9t - 1}{5t^2 - 5}$

**26.** $\lim_{x \to \infty} \dfrac{5x}{3x^7 - x^3 + 4}$

**27.** $\lim_{x \to \infty} \dfrac{7}{2x + 1}$

**28.** $\lim_{x \to -\infty} \dfrac{2}{(4x - 1)^3}$

**29.** $\lim_{x \to \infty} \dfrac{3 - 4x - 2x^3}{5x^3 - 8x + 1}$

**30.** $\lim_{x \to -\infty} \dfrac{3 - 2x - 2x^3}{7 - 5x^3 + 2x^2}$

**\*31.** $\lim_{x \to 3^-} \dfrac{x + 3}{x^2 - 9}$

**32.** $\lim_{x \to -3^-} \dfrac{3x}{9 - x^2}$

**33.** $\lim_{w \to \infty} \dfrac{2w^2 - 3w + 4}{5w^2 + 7w - 1}$

**34.** $\lim_{x \to \infty} \dfrac{4 - 3x^3}{x^3 - 1}$

**35.** $\lim_{x \to \infty} \dfrac{6 - 4x^2 + x^3}{4 + 5x - 7x^2}$

**36.** $\lim_{x \to -\infty} \dfrac{3x - x^3}{x^3 + x + 1}$

**\*37.** $\lim_{x \to -3^-} \dfrac{5x^2 + 14x - 3}{x^2 + 3x}$

**38.** $\lim_{t \to 3} \dfrac{t^2 - 4t + 3}{t^2 - 2t - 3}$

**39.** $\lim_{x \to 1} \dfrac{x^2 - 3x + 1}{x^2 + 1}$

**40.** $\lim_{x \to -1} \dfrac{3x^3 - x^2}{2x + 1}$

**41.** $\lim_{x \to 1^+} \left(1 + \dfrac{1}{x - 1}\right)$

**42.** $\lim_{x \to -\infty} -\dfrac{x^5 + 2x^3 - 1}{x^5 - 4x^2}$

**43.** $\lim_{x \to -7^-} \dfrac{x^2 + 1}{\sqrt{x^2 - 49}}$

**44.** $\lim_{x \to -2^+} \dfrac{x}{\sqrt{16 - x^4}}$

**45.** $\lim_{x \to 0^+} \dfrac{5}{x + x^2}$

**46.** $\lim_{x \to \infty} \left(x + \dfrac{1}{x}\right)$

**47.** $\lim_{x \to 1} x(x - 1)^{-1}$

**48.** $\lim_{x \to 1/2} \dfrac{1}{2x - 1}$

**49.** $\lim_{x \to 1^+} \left(\dfrac{-5}{1 - x}\right)$

**50.** $\lim_{x \to 3} \left(-\dfrac{7}{x - 3}\right)$

**51.** $\lim_{x \to 0} |x|$

**52.** $\lim_{x \to 0} \left|\dfrac{1}{x}\right|$

**53.** $\lim_{x \to -\infty} \dfrac{x + 1}{x}$

**54.** $\lim_{x \to \infty} \left(\dfrac{3}{x} - \dfrac{2x^2}{x^2 + 1}\right)$

*In Problems 55–58, find the indicated limits. If the limit does not exist, so state that, or use the symbol $\infty$ or $-\infty$ where appropriate.*

**55.** $f(x) = \begin{cases} 2 & \text{if } x \le 2 \\ 1 & \text{if } x > 2 \end{cases}$

(a) $\lim_{x \to 2^+} f(x)$  (b) $\lim_{x \to 2^-} f(x)$

(c) $\lim_{x \to 2} f(x)$  (d) $\lim_{x \to \infty} f(x)$

(e) $\lim_{x \to -\infty} f(x)$

**56.** $f(x) = \begin{cases} x & \text{if } x \le 2 \\ -2 + 4x - x^2 & \text{if } x > 2 \end{cases}$

(a) $\lim_{x \to 2^+} f(x)$  (b) $\lim_{x \to 2^-} f(x)$

(c) $\lim_{x \to 2} f(x)$  (d) $\lim_{x \to \infty} f(x)$

(e) $\lim_{x \to -\infty} f(x)$

*57. $g(x) = \begin{cases} x & \text{if } x < 0 \\ -x & \text{if } x > 0 \end{cases}$

(a) $\lim_{x \to 0^+} g(x)$    (b) $\lim_{x \to 0^-} g(x)$

(c) $\lim_{x \to 0} g(x)$    (d) $\lim_{x \to \infty} g(x)$

(e) $\lim_{x \to -\infty} g(x)$

58. $g(x) = \begin{cases} x^2 & \text{if } x < 0 \\ -x & \text{if } x > 0 \end{cases}$

(a) $\lim_{x \to 0^+} g(x)$    (b) $\lim_{x \to 0^-} g(x)$

(c) $\lim_{x \to 0} g(x)$    (d) $\lim_{x \to \infty} g(x)$

(e) $\lim_{x \to -\infty} g(x)$

59. **Average Cost**   If $c$ is the total cost in dollars to produce $q$ units of a product, then the average cost per unit for an output of $q$ units is given by $\bar{c} = c/q$. Thus, if the total cost equation is $c = 5000 + 6q$, then

$$\bar{c} = \frac{5000}{q} + 6$$

For example, the total cost of an output of 5 units is $5030, and the average cost per unit at this level of production is $1006. By finding $\lim_{q \to \infty} \bar{c}$, show that the average cost approaches a level of stability if the producer continually increases output. What is the limiting value of the average cost? Sketch the graph of the average-cost function.

60. **Average Cost**   Repeat Problem 59, given that the fixed cost is $12,000 and the variable cost is given by the function $c_v = 7q$.

61. **Population**   The population of a certain small city $t$ years from now is predicted to be

$$N = 50,000 - \frac{2000}{t + 1}$$

Find the population in the long run; that is, find $\lim_{t \to \infty} N$.

62. Show that

$$\lim_{x \to \infty} \left( \sqrt{x^2 + x} - x \right) = \frac{1}{2}$$

(*Hint:* Rationalize the numerator by multiplying the expression $\sqrt{x^2 + x} - x$ by

$$\frac{\sqrt{x^2 + x} + x}{\sqrt{x^2 + x} + x}$$

Then express the denominator in a form such that $x$ is a factor.)

63. **Host–Parasite Relationship**   For a particular host–parasite relationship, it was determined that when the host density (number of hosts per unit of area) is $x$, the number of hosts parasitized over a period of time is

$$y = \frac{900x}{10 + 45x}$$

If the host density were to increase without bound, what value would $y$ approach?

64. If $f(x) = \begin{cases} \sqrt{2 - x} & \text{if } x < 2 \\ x^3 + k(x + 1) & \text{if } x \geq 2 \end{cases}$, determine the value of the constant $k$ for which $\lim_{x \to 2} f(x)$ exists.

*In Problems 65 and 66, use a calculator to evaluate the given function when $x = 1, 0.5, 0.2, 0.1, 0.01, 0.001,$ and $0.0001$. From your results, speculate about $\lim_{x \to 0^+} f(x)$.*

65. $f(x) = x^{2x}$    66. $f(x) = e^{-1/x}$

67. Graph $f(x) = \sqrt{4x^2 - 1}$. Use the graph to estimate $\lim_{x \to 1/2^+} f(x)$.

68. Graph $f(x) = \dfrac{\sqrt{x^2 - 9}}{x + 3}$. Use the graph to estimate $\lim_{x \to -3^-} f(x)$ if it exists. Use the symbol $\infty$ or $-\infty$ if appropriate.

69. Graph $f(x) = \begin{cases} 2x^2 + 3 & \text{if } x < 2 \\ 2x + 5 & \text{if } x \geq 2 \end{cases}$. Use the graph to estimate each of the following limits if it exists:

(a) $\lim_{x \to 2^-} f(x)$    (b) $\lim_{x \to 2^+} f(x)$    (c) $\lim_{x \to 2} f(x)$

---

OBJECTIVE

To study continuity and to find points of discontinuity for a function.

## 10.3 Continuity

Many functions have the property that there is no "break" in their graphs. For example, compare the functions

$$f(x) = x \quad \text{and} \quad g(x) = \begin{cases} x & \text{if } x \neq 1 \\ 2 & \text{if } x = 1 \end{cases}$$

whose graphs appear in Figures 10.23 and 10.24, respectively. The graph of $f$ is unbroken, but the graph of $g$ has a break at $x = 1$. Stated another way, if you were to trace both graphs with a pencil, you would have to lift the pencil off the graph of $g$ when $x = 1$, but you would not have to lift it off the graph of $f$. These situations can be expressed by limits. As $x$ approaches 1, compare the limit of each function with the value of the function at $x = 1$:

$$\lim_{x \to 1} f(x) = 1 = f(1)$$

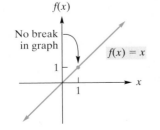

FIGURE 10.23
Continuous at 1.

whereas

$$\lim_{x \to 1} g(x) = 1 \neq 2 = g(1)$$

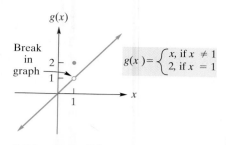

Break in graph

$$g(x) = \begin{cases} x, & \text{if } x \neq 1 \\ 2, & \text{if } x = 1 \end{cases}$$

**FIGURE 10.24**  Discontinuous at 1.

In Section 10.1 we stressed that given a function $f$ and a number $a$, there are two important ways to associate a number to the pair $(f, a)$. One is simple evaluation, $f(a)$, which *exists* precisely if $a$ is in the domain of $f$. The other is $\lim_{x \to a} f(x)$, whose existence and determination can be more challenging. For the functions $f$ and $g$ above, the limit of $f$ as $x \to 1$ is the same as $f(1)$, but the limit of $g$ as $x \to 1$ is *not* the same as $g(1)$. For these reasons, we say that $f$ is *continuous* at 1 and $g$ is *discontinuous* at 1.

### DEFINITION

A function $f$ is ***continuous*** at $a$ if and only if the following three conditions are met:

1. $f(a)$ exists
2. $\lim_{x \to a} f(x)$ exists
3. $\lim_{x \to a} f(x) = f(a)$

If $f$ is not continuous at $a$, then $f$ is said to be ***discontinuous*** at $a$, and $a$ is called a ***point of discontinuity*** of $f$.

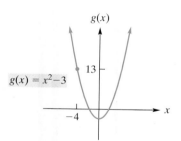

**FIGURE 10.25**  $f$ is continuous at 7.

### ● EXAMPLE 1  Applying the Definition of Continuity

**a.** *Show that $f(x) = 5$ is continuous at 7.*

**Solution:** We must verify that the preceding three conditions are met. First, $f(7) = 5$, so $f$ is defined at $x = 7$. Second,

$$\lim_{x \to 7} f(x) = \lim_{x \to 7} 5 = 5$$

Thus, $f$ has a limit as $x \to 7$. Third,

$$\lim_{x \to 7} f(x) = 5 = f(7)$$

Therefore, $f$ is continuous at 7. (See Figure 10.25.)

**b.** *Show that $g(x) = x^2 - 3$ is continuous at $-4$.*

**Solution:** The function $g$ is defined at $x = -4$: $g(-4) = 13$. Also,

$$\lim_{x \to -4} g(x) = \lim_{x \to -4} (x^2 - 3) = 13 = g(-4)$$

Therefore, $g$ is continuous at $-4$. (See Figure 10.26.)

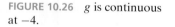

$g(x) = x^2 - 3$

**FIGURE 10.26**  $g$ is continuous at $-4$.

NOW WORK PROBLEM 1 ●●●

We say that a function is *continuous on an interval* if it is continuous at each point there. In this situation, the graph of the function is connected over the interval. For example, $f(x) = x^2$ is continuous on the interval $[2, 5]$. In fact, in Example 5 of Section 10.1, we showed that, for *any* polynomial function $f$, for any number $a$, $\lim_{x \to a} f(x) = f(a)$. This means that

A polynomial function is continuous at every point.

It follows that such a function is continuous on every interval. We say that a function is **continuous on its domain** if it is continuous at each point in its domain. If the domain of such a function is the set of all real numbers, we may simply say that the function is continuous.

● **EXAMPLE 2** **Continuity of Polynomial Functions**

The functions $f(x) = 7$ and $g(x) = x^2 - 9x + 3$ are polynomial functions. Therefore, they are continuous on their domains. For example, they are continuous at 3.

NOW WORK PROBLEM 13 ●●●

When is a function discontinuous? We can say that a function $f$ defined on an open interval containing $a$ is discontinuous at $a$ if

1. $f$ has no limit as $x \to a$

    or

2. as $x \to a$, $f$ has a limit that is different from $f(a)$

If $f$ is not defined at $a$, we will say also, in that case, that $f$ is discontinuous at $a$. In Figure 10.27, we can find points of discontinuity by inspection.

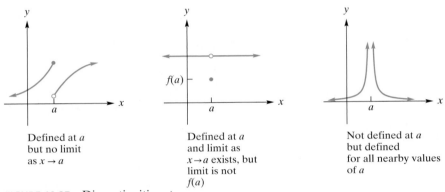

Defined at $a$
but no limit
as $x \to a$

Defined at $a$
and limit as
$x \to a$ exists, but
limit is not
$f(a)$

Not defined at $a$
but defined
for all nearby values
of $a$

**FIGURE 10.27** Discontinuities at $a$.

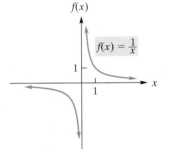

**FIGURE 10.28** Infinite discontinuity at 0.

● **EXAMPLE 3** **Discontinuities**

**a.** Let $f(x) = 1/x$. (See Figure 10.28.) Note that $f$ is not defined at $x = 0$, but it is defined for all other $x$ nearby. Thus, $f$ is discontinuous at 0. Moreover, $\lim_{x \to 0^+} f(x) = \infty$ and $\lim_{x \to 0^-} f(x) = -\infty$. A function is said to have an **infinite discontinuity** at $a$ when at least one of the one-sided limits is either $\infty$ or $-\infty$ as $x \to a$. Hence, $f$ has an *infinite discontinuity* at $x = 0$.

**b.** Let $f(x) = \begin{cases} 1 & \text{if } x > 0 \\ 0 & \text{if } x = 0 \\ -1 & \text{if } x < 0 \end{cases}$.

(See Figure 10.29.) Although $f$ is defined at $x = 0$, $\lim_{x \to 0} f(x)$ does not exist. Thus, $f$ is discontinuous at 0.

NOW WORK PROBLEM 29 ●●●

The following property indicates where the discontinuities of a rational function occur:

### Discontinuities of a Rational Function

A rational function is discontinuous at points where the denominator is 0 and is continuous otherwise. Thus, a rational function is continuous on its domain.

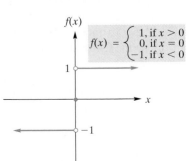

**FIGURE 10.29** Discontinuous case-defined function.

The rational function $f(x) = \frac{x+1}{x+1}$ is continuous on its domain but it is not defined at $-1$. It is discontinuous at $-1$. The graph of $f$ is a horizontal straight line with a "hole" in it at $-1$.

● EXAMPLE 4   **Locating Discontinuities in Rational Functions**

*For each of the following functions, find all points of discontinuity.*

**a.** $f(x) = \dfrac{x^2 - 3}{x^2 + 2x - 8}$

Solution:  This rational function has denominator

$$x^2 + 2x - 8 = (x+4)(x-2)$$

which is 0 when $x = -4$ or $x = 2$. Thus, $f$ is discontinuous only at $-4$ and 2.

**b.** $h(x) = \dfrac{x+4}{x^2+4}$

Solution:  For this rational function, the denominator is never 0. (It is always positive.) Therefore, $h$ has no discontinuity.

NOW WORK PROBLEM 19 ●●

● EXAMPLE 5   **Locating Discontinuities in Case-Defined Functions**

*For each of the following functions, find all points of discontinuity.*

**a.** $f(x) = \begin{cases} x + 6 & \text{if } x \geq 3 \\ x^2 & \text{if } x < 3 \end{cases}$

Solution:  The cases defining the function are given by polynomials, which are continuous, so the only possible place for a discontinuity is at $x = 3$, where the separation of cases occurs. We know that $f(3) = 3 + 6 = 9$. So because

$$\lim_{x \to 3^+} f(x) = \lim_{x \to 3^+} (x+6) = 9$$

and

$$\lim_{x \to 3^-} f(x) = \lim_{x \to 3^-} x^2 = 9$$

we can conclude that $\lim_{x \to 3} f(x) = 9 = f(3)$ and the function has no points of discontinuity. We can reach the same conclusion by inspecting the graph of $f$ in Figure 10.30.

**b.** $f(x) = \begin{cases} x + 2 & \text{if } x > 2 \\ x^2 & \text{if } x < 2 \end{cases}$

Solution:  Since $f$ is not defined at $x = 2$, it is discontinuous at 2. Note, however, that

$$\lim_{x \to 2^-} f(x) = \lim_{x \to 2^-} x^2 = 4 = \lim_{x \to 2^+} x + 2 = \lim_{x \to 2^+} f(x)$$

shows that $\lim_{x \to 2} f(x)$ exists. (See Figure 10.31.)

NOW WORK PROBLEM 31 ●●

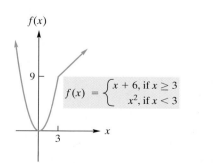

FIGURE 10.30   Continuous case-defined function.

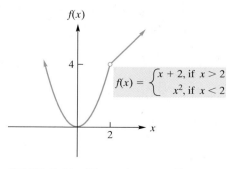

FIGURE 10.31   Discontinuous at 2.

●EXAMPLE 6   "Post-Office" Function

The post-office function

$$c = f(x) = \begin{cases} 39 & \text{if } 0 < x \le 1 \\ 63 & \text{if } 1 < x \le 2 \\ 87 & \text{if } 2 < x \le 3 \\ 111 & \text{if } 3 < x \le 4 \end{cases}$$

gives the cost $c$ (in cents) of mailing, first-class, an item of weight $x$ (ounces), for $0 < x \le 4$, in July 2006. It is clear from its graph in Figure 10.32 that $f$ has discontinuities at 1, 2, and 3 and is constant for values of $x$ between successive discontinuities. Such a function is called a *step function* because of the appearance of its graph.

NOW WORK PROBLEM 35 ●●●

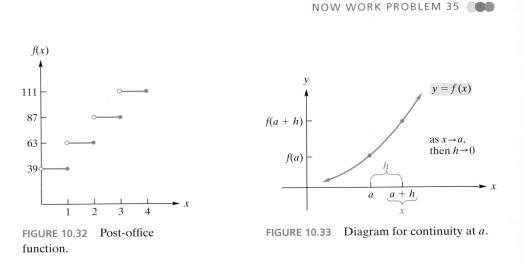

FIGURE 10.32   Post-office function.

FIGURE 10.33   Diagram for continuity at $a$.

There is another way to express continuity besides that given in the definition. If we take the statement

$$\lim_{x \to a} f(x) = f(a)$$

and replace $x$ by $a+h$, then as $x \to a$, we have $h \to 0$; and as $h \to 0$ we have $x \to a$. It follows that $\lim_{x \to a} f(x) = \lim_{h \to 0} f(a+h)$, provided the limits exist (Figure 10.33). Thus, the statement

$$\lim_{h \to 0} f(a+h) = f(a)$$

assuming both sides exist, also defines continuity at $a$.

This method of expressing continuity at $a$ is used frequently in mathematical proofs.

**T E C H N O L O G Y**

By observing the graph of a function, we may be able to determine where a discontinuity occurs. However, we can be fooled. For example, the function

$$f(x) = \frac{x-1}{x^2-1}$$

is discontinuous at $\pm 1$, but the discontinuity at 1 is not obvious from the graph of $f$ in Figure 10.34. On the other hand, the discontinuity at $-1$ is obvious. Note that $f$ is defined neither at $-1$ nor at 1.

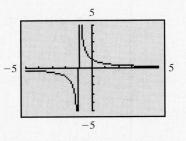

FIGURE 10.34   Discontinuity at 1 is not apparent from graph of $f(x) = \dfrac{x-1}{x^2-1}$.

TABLE 10.3  Demand Schedule

| Price/Unit, $p$ | Quantity/Week, $q$ |
|---|---|
| $20 | 0 |
| 10 | 5 |
| 5 | 15 |
| 4 | 20 |
| 2 | 45 |
| 1 | 95 |

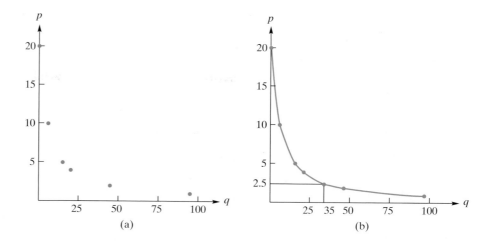

FIGURE 10.35  Viewing data via a continuous function.

Often, it is helpful to describe a situation by a continuous function. For example, the demand schedule in Table 10.3 indicates the number of units of a particular product that consumers will demand per week at various prices. This information can be given graphically, as in Figure 10.35(a), by plotting each quantity–price pair as a point. Clearly, the graph does not represent a continuous function. Furthermore, it gives us no information as to the price at which, say, 35 units would be demanded. However, if we connect the points in Figure 10.35(a) by a smooth curve [see Figure 10.35(b)], we get a so-called demand curve. From it, we could guess that at about $2.50 per unit, 35 units would be demanded.

Frequently, it is possible and useful to describe a graph, as in Figure 10.35(b), by means of an equation that defines a continuous function $f$. Such a function not only gives us a demand equation, $p = f(q)$, which allows us to anticipate corresponding prices and quantities demanded, but also permits a convenient mathematical analysis of the nature and basic properties of demand. Of course, some care must be used in working with equations such as $p = f(q)$. Mathematically, $f$ may be defined when $q = \sqrt{37}$, but from a practical standpoint, a demand of $\sqrt{37}$ units could be meaningless to our particular situation. For example, if a unit is an egg, then a demand of $\sqrt{37}$ eggs make no sense.

We remark that exponential functions and logarithmic functions are continuous on their domains. Thus, exponential functions have no discontinuities while a logarithmic function has only a discontinuity at 0 (which is an infinite discontinuity).

# Problems 10.3

*In Problems 1–6, use the definition of continuity to show that the given function is continuous at the indicated point.*

**\*1.** $f(x) = x^3 - 5x; x = 2$

**2.** $f(x) = \dfrac{x-3}{5x}; x = -3$

**3.** $g(x) = \sqrt{2 - 3x}; x = 0$

**4.** $f(x) = \dfrac{x}{8}; x = 2$

**5.** $h(x) = \dfrac{x-4}{x+4}; x = 4$

**6.** $f(x) = \sqrt[3]{x}; x = -1$

*In Problems 7–12, determine whether the function is continuous at the given points.*

**7.** $f(x) = \dfrac{x+4}{x-2}; -2, 0$

**8.** $f(x) = \dfrac{x^2 - 4x + 4}{6}; 2, -2$

**9.** $g(x) = \dfrac{x-3}{x^2-9}; 3, -3$

**10.** $h(x) = \dfrac{3}{x^2+4}; 2, -2$

**11.** $f(x) = \begin{cases} x+2 & \text{if } x \geq 2 \\ x^2 & \text{if } x < 2 \end{cases}; 2, 0$

**12.** $f(x) = \begin{cases} \dfrac{1}{x} & \text{if } x \neq 0 \\ 0 & \text{if } x = 0 \end{cases}; 0, -1$

*In Problems 13–16, give a reason why the function is continuous on its domain.*

**\*13.** $f(x) = 2x^2 - 3$

**14.** $f(x) = \dfrac{2 + 3x - x^2}{5}$

**15.** $f(x) = \dfrac{x-1}{x^2+4}$

**16.** $f(x) = x(1-x)$

*In Problems 17–34, find all points of discontinuity.*

**17.** $f(x) = 3x^2 - 3$

**18.** $h(x) = x - 2$

**\*19.** $f(x) = \dfrac{3}{x+4}$

**20.** $f(x) = \dfrac{x^2 + 3x - 4}{x^2 - 4}$

**21.** $g(x) = \dfrac{(2x^2 - 3)^3}{15}$

**22.** $f(x) = -1$

**23.** $f(x) = \dfrac{x^2 + 6x + 9}{x^2 + 2x - 15}$  **24.** $g(x) = \dfrac{x - 3}{x^2 + x}$

**25.** $h(x) = \dfrac{x - 7}{x^3 - x}$  **26.** $f(x) = \dfrac{2x - 3}{3 - 2x}$

**27.** $p(x) = \dfrac{x}{x^2 + 1}$  **28.** $f(x) = \dfrac{x^4}{x^4 - 1}$

**\*29.** $f(x) = \begin{cases} 1 & \text{if } x \geq 0 \\ -1 & \text{if } x < 0 \end{cases}$  **30.** $f(x) = \begin{cases} 2x + 1 & \text{if } x \geq -1 \\ 1 & \text{if } x < -1 \end{cases}$

**\*31.** $f(x) = \begin{cases} 0 & \text{if } x \leq 1 \\ x - 1 & \text{if } x > 1 \end{cases}$  **32.** $f(x) = \begin{cases} x - 3 & \text{if } x > 2 \\ 3 - 2x & \text{if } x < 2 \end{cases}$

**33.** $f(x) = \begin{cases} x^2 + 1 & \text{if } x > 2 \\ 8x & \text{if } x < 2 \end{cases}$  **34.** $f(x) = \begin{cases} \dfrac{16}{x^2} & \text{if } x \geq 2 \\ 3x - 2 & \text{if } x < 2 \end{cases}$

**\*35. Telephone Rates** Suppose the long-distance rate for a telephone call from Hazleton, Pennsylvania, to Los Angeles, California, is \$0.10 for the first minute and \$0.06 for each additional minute or fraction thereof. If $y = f(t)$ is a function that indicates the total charge $y$ for a call of $t$ minutes' duration, sketch the graph of $f$ for $0 < t \leq 4\frac{1}{2}$. Use your graph to determine the values of $t$, where $0 < t \leq 4\frac{1}{2}$, at which discontinuities occur.

**36.** The *greatest integer function*, $f(x) = \lfloor x \rfloor$, is defined to be the greatest integer less than or equal to $x$, where $x$ is any real number. For example, $\lfloor 3 \rfloor = 3$, $\lfloor 1.999 \rfloor = 1$, $\lfloor \frac{1}{4} \rfloor = 0$, and $\lfloor -4.5 \rfloor = -5$. Sketch the graph of this function for $-3.5 \leq x \leq 3.5$. Use your sketch to determine the values of $x$ at which discontinuities occur.

**37. Inventory** Sketch the graph of

$$y = f(x) = \begin{cases} -100x + 600 & \text{if } 0 \leq x < 5 \\ -100x + 1100 & \text{if } 5 \leq x < 10 \\ -100x + 1600 & \text{if } 10 \leq x < 15 \end{cases}$$

A function such as this might describe the inventory $y$ of a company at time $x$. Is $f$ continuous at 2? At 5? At 10?

**38.** Graph $g(x) = e^{-1/x^2}$. Because $g$ is not defined at $x = 0$, $g$ is discontinuous at 0. Based on the graph of $g$, is

$$f(x) = \begin{cases} e^{-1/x^2} & \text{if } x \neq 0 \\ 0 & \text{if } x = 0 \end{cases}$$

continuous at 0?

## 10.4 Continuity Applied to Inequalities

In Section 1.2, we solved linear inequalities. We now turn our attention to showing how the notion of continuity can be applied to solving a nonlinear inequality such as $x^2 + 3x - 4 < 0$. The ability to do this will be important in our study of calculus.

Recall (from Section 2.5) that the $x$-intercepts of the graph of a function $g$ (that is, the points where the graph meets the $x$-axis) have $x$-coordinates that are the roots of the equation $g(x) = 0$, and these are called zeros of $g$. Conversely, any zero of $g$ gives rise to an $x$-intercept of the graph of the function. Hence, from the graph of $y = g(x)$ in Figure 10.36, we conclude that $r_1$, $r_2$, and $r_3$ are zeros of $g$ and any other zeros of $g$ will give rise to $x$-intercepts (beyond what is actually shown of the graph). Assume that in fact all the zeros of $g$, and hence all the $x$-intercepts, are shown. Note further from Figure 10.36 that the three zeros determine four open intervals on the $x$-axis:

$$(-\infty, r_1) \quad (r_1, r_2) \quad (r_2, r_3) \quad (r_3, \infty)$$

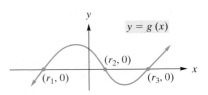

**FIGURE 10.36** $r_1, r_2$, and $r_3$ are zeros of $g$.

To solve $x^2 + 3x - 4 > 0$, we let

$$f(x) = x^2 + 3x - 4 = (x + 4)(x - 1)$$

Because $f$ is a polynomial function, it is continuous. The zeros of $f$ are $-4$ and 1; hence, the graph of $f$ has $x$-intercepts $(-4, 0)$ and $(1, 0)$. (See Figure 10.37.) The zeros determine three intervals on the $x$-axis:

$$(-\infty, -4) \quad (-4, 1) \quad (1, \infty)$$

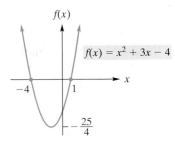

**FIGURE 10.37** $-4$ and 1 are zeros of $f$.

Consider the interval $(-\infty, -4)$. Since $f$ is continuous on this interval, we claim that either $f(x) > 0$ or $f(x) < 0$ *throughout* the interval. If this were not the case, then $f(x)$ would indeed change sign on the interval. By the continuity of $f$, there would be a point where the graph intersects the $x$-axis—for example, at $(x_0, 0)$. (See Figure 10.38.) But then $x_0$ would be a zero of $f$. However, this cannot be, because there is no zero of $f$ that is less than $-4$. Hence, $f(x)$ must be strictly positive or strictly negative on $(-\infty, -4)$. A similar argument can be made for each of the other intervals.

To determine the sign of $f(x)$ on any one of the three intervals, it suffices to determine its sign at any point in the interval. For instance, $-5$ is in $(-\infty, -4)$ and

$$f(-5) = 6 > 0 \qquad \text{Thus, } f(x) > 0 \text{ on } (-\infty, -4)$$

Similarly, 0 is in $(-4, 1)$, and

$$f(0) = -4 < 0 \qquad \text{Thus, } f(x) < 0 \text{ on } (-4, 1)$$

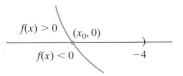

**FIGURE 10.38** Change of sign for a continuous function.

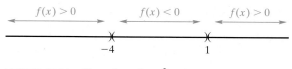

FIGURE 10.39   Sign chart for $x^2 + 3x - 4$.

Finally, 3 is in $(1, \infty)$, and

$$f(3) = 14 > 0 \qquad \text{Thus, } f(x) > 0 \text{ on } (1, \infty)$$

(See the "sign chart" in Figure 10.39.) Therefore,

$$x^2 + 3x - 4 > 0 \quad \text{on} \quad (-\infty, -4) \text{ and } (1, \infty)$$

so we have solved the inequality. These results are obvious from the graph in Figure 10.37. The graph lies above the $x$-axis (that is, $f(x) > 0$) on $(-\infty, -4)$ and on $(1, \infty)$.

### ● EXAMPLE 1   Solving a Quadratic Inequality

*Solve $x^2 - 3x - 10 > 0$.*

**Solution:** If $f(x) = x^2 - 3x - 10$, then $f$ is a polynomial (quadratic) function and thus is continuous everywhere. To find the real zeros of $f$, we have

$$x^2 - 3x - 10 = 0$$
$$(x + 2)(x - 5) = 0$$
$$x = -2, 5$$

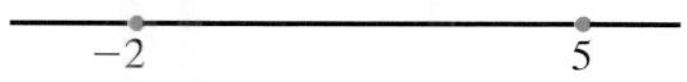

FIGURE 10.40   Zeros of $x^2 - 3x - 10$.

The zeros $-2$ and $5$ are shown in Figure 10.40. These zeros determine three intervals:

$$(-\infty, -2) \quad (-2, 5) \quad (5, \infty)$$

To determine the sign of $f(x)$ on $(-\infty, -2)$, we choose a point in that interval, say, $-3$. The sign of $f(x)$ throughout $(-\infty, -2)$ is the same as that of $f(-3)$. Because

$$f(x) = (x + 2)(x - 5) \qquad \text{[factored form of } f(x)\text{]}$$

we have

$$f(-3) = (-3 + 2)(-3 - 5)$$

and hence

$$\text{sign}(f(-3)) = \text{sign}(-3 + 2)(-3 - 5) = \text{sign}(-3 + 2)\text{sign}(-3 - 5) = (-)(-) = +$$

We found the sign of $f(-3)$ by using the signs of the factors of $f(x)$ evaluated at $-3$. Thus, $f(x) > 0$ on $(-\infty, -2)$. To test the other two intervals, we will choose the points 0 and 6. We find that

$$\text{sign}(f(0)) = \text{sign}(0 + 2)\text{sign}(0 - 5) = (+)(-) = -$$

so $f(x) < 0$ on $(-2, 5)$, and

$$\text{sign}(f(6)) = \text{sign}(6 + 2)\text{sign}(6 - 5) = (+)(+) = +$$

so $f(x) > 0$ on $(5, \infty)$. A summary of our results is in the sign chart in Figure 10.41. Therefore, $x^2 - 3x - 10 > 0$ on $(-\infty, -2) \cup (5, \infty)$.

NOW WORK PROBLEM 1 ●●

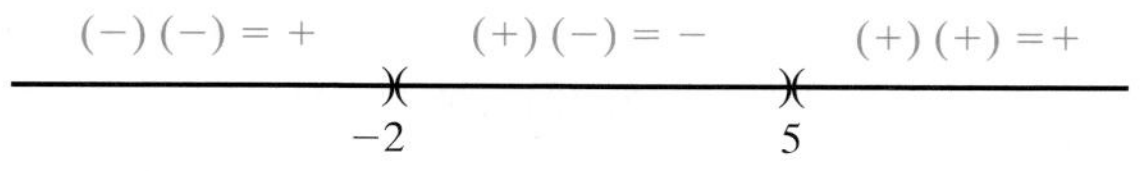

FIGURE 10.41   Sign chart for $(x + 2)(x - 5)$.

SOLVING A POLYNOMIAL INEQUALITY

An open box is formed by cutting a square piece out of each corner of an 8-inch-by-10-inch piece of metal. If each side of the cutout squares is $x$ inches long, the volume of the box is given by $V(x) = x(8 - 2x)(10 - 2x)$. This problem makes sense only when this volume is positive. Find the values of $x$ for which the volume is positive.

● **EXAMPLE 2    Solving a Polynomial Inequality**

*Solve $x(x - 1)(x + 4) \le 0$.*

**Solution:** If $f(x) = x(x-1)(x+4)$, then $f$ is a polynomial function and is continuous everywhere. The zeros of $f$ are 0, 1, and $-4$, which are shown in Figure 10.42. These zeros determine four intervals:

$$(-\infty, -4) \quad (-4, 0) \quad (0, 1) \quad (1, \infty)$$

Now, at a test point in each interval, we find the sign of $f(x)$:

$$\text{sign}(f(-5)) = (-)(-)(-) = - \qquad \text{so } f(x) < 0 \text{ on } (-\infty, -4)$$
$$\text{sign}(f(-2)) = (-)(-)(+) = + \qquad \text{so } f(x) > 0 \text{ on } (-4, 0)$$
$$\text{sign}\left(f\left(\frac{1}{2}\right)\right) = (+)(-)(+) = - \qquad \text{so } f(x) < 0 \text{ on } (0, 1)$$
$$\text{sign}(f(2)) = (+)(+)(+) = + \qquad \text{so } f(x) > 0 \text{ on } (1, \infty)$$

Figure 10.43 shows the sign chart for $f(x)$. Thus, $x(x - 1)(x + 4) \le 0$ on $(-\infty, -4]$ and $[0, 1]$. Note that $-4, 0,$ and 1 are included in the solution because these values satisfy the equality ($=$) part of the inequality ($\le$).

NOW WORK PROBLEM 11 ●●●

**FIGURE 10.42**   Zeros of $x(x - 1)(x + 4)$.

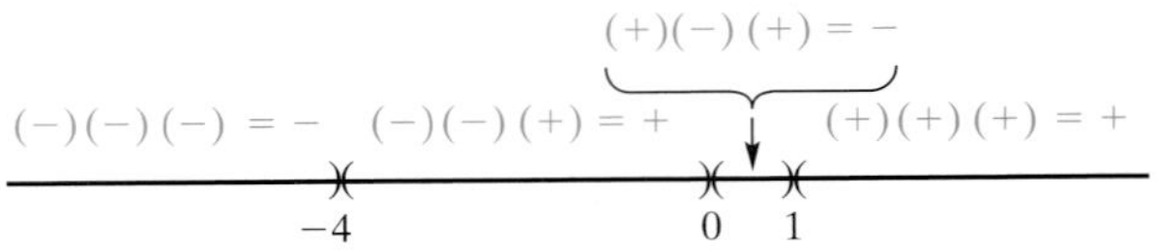

**FIGURE 10.43**   Sign chart for $x(x - 1)(x + 4)$.

● **EXAMPLE 3    Solving a Rational Function Inequality**

*Solve $\dfrac{x^2 - 6x + 5}{x} \ge 0$.*

**Solution:** Let $f(x) = \dfrac{x^2 - 6x + 5}{x} = \dfrac{(x - 1)(x - 5)}{x}$. For a rational function $f$, we solve the inequality by considering the intervals determined by the zeros of $f$ and the points where $f$ is discontinuous, for it is around such points that the sign of $f(x)$ may change. Here the zeros are 1 and 5. The function is discontinuous at 0 and continuous otherwise. In Figure 10.44, we have placed a hollow dot at 0 to indicate that $f$ is not defined there. We thus consider the intervals

$$(-\infty, 0) \quad (0, 1) \quad (1, 5) \quad (5, \infty)$$

Determining the sign of $f(x)$ at a test point in each interval, we find that

$$\text{sign}(f(-1)) = \frac{(-)(-)}{(-)} = - \qquad \text{so } f(x) < 0 \text{ on } (-\infty, 0)$$
$$\text{sign}\left(f\left(\frac{1}{2}\right)\right) = \frac{(-)(-)}{(+)} = + \qquad \text{so } f(x) > 0 \text{ on } (0, 1)$$
$$\text{sign}(f(2)) = \frac{(+)(-)}{(+)} = - \qquad \text{so } f(x) < 0 \text{ on } (1, 5)$$
$$\text{sign}(f(6)) = \frac{(+)(+)}{(+)} = + \qquad \text{so } f(x) > 0 \text{ on } (5, \infty)$$

The sign chart for $f(x)$ is shown in Figure 10.45. Therefore, $f(x) \ge 0$ on $(0, 1]$ and $[5, \infty)$. (Why are 1 and 5 included, but 0 is excluded?) Figure 10.46 shows the graph of $f$. Notice that the solution of $f(x) \ge 0$ consists of all $x$-values for which the graph lies on or above the $x$-axis.

**FIGURE 10.44**   Zeros and points of discontinuity for $\dfrac{(x - 1)(x - 5)}{x}$.

NOW WORK PROBLEM 17 ●●●

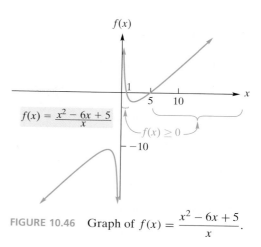

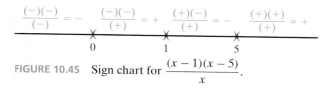

FIGURE 10.45   Sign chart for $\dfrac{(x-1)(x-5)}{x}$.

FIGURE 10.46   Graph of $f(x) = \dfrac{x^2 - 6x + 5}{x}$.

● EXAMPLE 4   **Solving Nonlinear Inequalities**

**a.** *Solve* $x^2 + 1 > 0$.

Solution: The equation $x^2 + 1 = 0$ has no real roots. Thus, $f(x) = x^2 + 1$ has no real zero. Also, $f$ is continuous. Therefore, $f(x)$ is always positive or is always negative. But $x^2$ is always positive or zero, so $x^2 + 1$ is always positive. Hence, the solution of $x^2 + 1 > 0$ is $(-\infty, \infty)$.

**b.** *Solve* $x^2 + 1 < 0$.

Solution: From part (a), $x^2 + 1$ is always positive, so $x^2 + 1 < 0$ has no solution.

NOW WORK PROBLEM 7 ●●●

## Problems 10.4

*In Problems 1–26, solve the inequalities by the technique discussed in this section.*

*1. $x^2 - 3x - 4 > 0$

2. $x^2 - 8x + 15 > 0$

3. $x^2 - 3x - 10 \le 0$

4. $14 - 5x - x^2 \le 0$

5. $2x^2 + 11x + 14 < 0$

6. $x^2 - 4 < 0$

*7. $x^2 + 4 < 0$

8. $2x^2 - x - 2 \le 0$

9. $(x+2)(x-3)(x+6) \le 0$

10. $(x+5)(x+2)(x-7) \le 0$

*11. $-x(x-5)(x+4) > 0$

12. $(x+2)^2 > 0$

13. $x^3 + 4x \ge 0$

14. $(x+2)^2(x^2-1) < 0$

15. $x^3 + 8x^2 + 15x \le 0$

16. $x^3 + 6x^2 + 9x < 0$

*17. $\dfrac{x}{x^2 - 9} < 0$

18. $\dfrac{x^2 - 1}{x} < 0$

19. $\dfrac{4}{x-1} \ge 0$

20. $\dfrac{3}{x^2 - 5x + 6} > 0$

21. $\dfrac{x^2 - x - 6}{x^2 + 4x - 5} \ge 0$

22. $\dfrac{x^2 + 4x - 5}{x^2 + 3x + 2} \le 0$

23. $\dfrac{3}{x^2 + 6x + 5} \le 0$

24. $\dfrac{2x + 1}{x^2} \le 0$

25. $x^2 + 2x \ge 2$

26. $x^4 - 16 \ge 0$

27. **Revenue**   Suppose that consumers will purchase $q$ units of a product when the price of *each* unit is $28 - 0.2q$ dollars. How many units must be sold in order that sales revenue will at least $750?

28. **Forest Management**   A lumber company owns a forest that is of rectangular shape, 1 mi × 2 mi. The company wants to cut a uniform strip of trees along the outer edges of the forest. At most, how wide can the strip be if the company wants at least $1\frac{5}{16}$ mi² of forest to remain?

29. **Container Design**   A container manufacturer wishes to make an open box by cutting a 4-in. square from each corner of a square sheet of aluminum and then turning up the sides. The box is to contain at least 324 in.³. Find the dimensions of the smallest sheet of aluminum that can be used.

30. **Workshop Participation**   Imperial Education Services (I.E.S.) is offering a workshop in data processing to key personnel at Zeta Corporation. The price per person is $50, and Zeta Corporation guarantees that at least 50 people will attend. Suppose I.E.S. offers to reduce the charge for *everybody* by $0.50 for each person over the 50 who attends. How should I.E.S. limit the size of the group so that the total revenue it receives will never be less than that received for 50 persons?

31. Graph $f(x) = x^3 + 7x^2 - 5x + 4$. Use the graph to determine the solution of

$$x^3 + 7x^2 - 5x + 4 \le 0$$

32. Graph $f(x) = \dfrac{3x^2 - 0.5x + 2}{6.2 - 4.1x}$. Use the graph to determine the solution of

$$\dfrac{3x^2 - 0.5x + 2}{6.2 - 4.1x} > 0$$

*A novel way of solving a nonlinear inequality like $f(x) > 0$ is by examining the graph of $g(x) = f(x)/|f(x)|$, whose range consists only of 1 and $-1$:*

$$g(x) = \dfrac{f(x)}{|f(x)|} = \begin{cases} 1 & \text{if } f(x) > 0 \\ -1 & \text{if } f(x) < 0 \end{cases}$$

*The solution of $f(x) > 0$ consists of all intervals for which $g(x) = 1$. Using this technique, solve the inequalities in Problems 33 and 34.*

33. $6x^2 - x - 2 > 0$

34. $\dfrac{x^2 + x - 1}{x^2 + x - 2} < 0$

---

# 10.5 Review

## Important Terms and Symbols

**Examples**

**Section 10.1** **Limits**
$\lim_{x \to a} f(x) = L$

Ex. 8, p. 455

**Section 10.2** **Limits (Continued)**
$\lim_{x \to a^-} f(x) = L$ $\lim_{x \to a^+} f(x) = L$ $\lim_{x \to a} f(x) = \infty$
$\lim_{x \to \infty} f(x) = L$ $\lim_{x \to -\infty} f(x) = L$

Ex. 1, p. 459
Ex. 3, p. 461

**Section 10.3** **Continuity**
continuous at $a$ discontinuous at $a$
continuous on an interval continuous on its domain

Ex. 3, p. 468
Ex. 4, p. 469

**Section 10.4** **Continuity Applied to Inequalities**
sign chart

Ex. 1, p. 473

## Summary

The notion of a limit lies at the foundation of calculus. To say that $\lim_{x \to a} f(x) = L$ means that the values of $f(x)$ can be made as close to the number $L$ as we like by taking $x$ sufficiently close to, but different from, $a$. If $\lim_{x \to a} f(x)$ and $\lim_{x \to a} g(x)$ exist and $c$ is a constant, then

1. $\lim_{x \to a} c = c$
2. $\lim_{x \to a} x^n = a^n$
3. $\lim_{x \to a}[f(x) \pm g(x)] = \lim_{x \to a} f(x) \pm \lim_{x \to a} g(x)$
4. $\lim_{x \to a}[f(x) \cdot g(x)] = \lim_{x \to a} f(x) \cdot \lim_{x \to a} g(x)$
5. $\lim_{x \to a}[cf(x)] = c \cdot \lim_{x \to a} f(x)$
6. $\lim_{x \to a} \dfrac{f(x)}{g(x)} = \dfrac{\lim_{x \to a} f(x)}{\lim_{x \to a} g(x)}$ if $\lim_{x \to a} g(x) \neq 0$,
7. $\lim_{x \to a} \sqrt[n]{f(x)} = \sqrt[n]{\lim_{x \to a} f(x)}$
8. If $f$ is a polynomial function, then $\lim_{x \to a} f(x) = f(a)$

Property 8 implies that the limit of a polynomial function as $x \to a$ can be found by simply evaluating the polynomial at $a$. However, with other functions, $f$, evaluation at $a$ may lead to the meaningless form $0/0$. In such cases, algebraic manipulation such as factoring and cancellation may yield a function $g$ that agrees with $f$, for $x \neq a$, and for which the limit can be determined.

If $f(x)$ approaches $L$ as $x$ approaches $a$ from the right, then we write $\lim_{x \to a^+} f(x) = L$. If $f(x)$ approaches $L$ as $x$ approaches $a$ from the left, we write $\lim_{x \to a^-} f(x) = L$. These limits are called one-sided limits.

The infinity symbol $\infty$, which does not represent a number, is used in describing limits. The statement

$$\lim_{x \to \infty} f(x) = L$$

means that as $x$ increases without bound, the values of $f(x)$ approach the number $L$. A similar statement applies for the situation when $x \to -\infty$, which means that $x$ is decreasing without bound. In general, if $p > 0$, then

$$\lim_{x \to \infty} \frac{1}{x^p} = 0 \quad \text{and} \quad \lim_{x \to -\infty} \frac{1}{x^p} = 0$$

If $f(x)$ increases without bound as $x \to a$, then we write $\lim_{x \to a} f(x) = \infty$. Similarly, if $f(x)$ decreases without bound, we have $\lim_{x \to a} f(x) = -\infty$. To say that the limit of a function is $\infty$ (or $-\infty$) does not mean that the limit exists. Rather, it is a way of saying that the limit does not exist and tells *why* there is no limit.

There is a rule for evaluating the limit of a rational function (quotient of polynomials) as $x \to \infty$ or $-\infty$. If $f(x)$ is a rational function and $a_n x^n$ and $b_m x^m$ are the terms in the numerator and denominator, respectively, with the greatest powers of $x$, then

$$\lim_{x \to \infty} f(x) = \lim_{x \to \infty} \frac{a_n x^n}{b_m x^m}$$

and

$$\lim_{x \to -\infty} f(x) = \lim_{x \to -\infty} \frac{a_n x^n}{b_m x^m}$$

In particular, as $x \to \infty$ or $-\infty$, the limit of a polynomial is the same as the limit of the term that involves the greatest power of $x$. This means that, for a nonconstant polynomial, the limit as $x \to \infty$ or $-\infty$ is either $\infty$ or $-\infty$.

A function $f$ is continuous at $a$ if and only if

1. $f(a)$ exists
2. $\lim_{x \to a} f(x)$ exists
3. $\lim_{x \to a} f(x) = f(a)$

Geometrically this means that the graph of $f$ has no break when $x = a$. If a function is not continuous at $a$, then the function is said to be discontinuous at $a$. Polynomial functions and rational functions are continuous on their domains. Thus polynomial functions have no discontinuities and a rational function is discontinuous only at points where its denominator is zero.

To solve the inequality $f(x) > 0$ (or $f(x) < 0$), we first find the real zeros of $f$ and the values of $x$ for which $f$ is discontinuous. These values determine intervals, and on each interval, $f(x)$ is either always positive or always negative. To find the sign on any one of these intervals, it suffices to find the sign of $f(x)$ at any point there. After the signs are determined for all intervals and assembled on a sign chart, it is easy to give the solution of $f(x) > 0$ (or $f(x) < 0$).

# Review Problems

*Problem numbers shown in color indicate problems suggested for use as a practice chapter test.*

*In Problems 1–28, find the limits if they exist. If the limit does not exist, so state that, or use the symbol $\infty$ or $-\infty$ where appropriate.*

1. $\lim\limits_{x\to-1}(2x^2+6x-1)$

2. $\lim\limits_{x\to 0}\dfrac{2x^2-3x+1}{2x^2-2}$

3. $\lim\limits_{x\to 3}\dfrac{x^2-9}{x^2-3x}$

4. $\lim\limits_{x\to-4}\dfrac{2x+3}{x^2-4}$

5. $\lim\limits_{h\to 0}(x+h)$

6. $\lim\limits_{x\to 2}\dfrac{x^2-4}{x^2-3x+2}$

7. $\lim\limits_{x\to-4}\dfrac{x^3+4x^2}{x^2+2x-8}$

8. $\lim\limits_{x\to 1}\dfrac{x^2+x-2}{x^2+4x-5}$

9. $\lim\limits_{x\to\infty}\dfrac{2}{x+1}$

10. $\lim\limits_{x\to\infty}\dfrac{x^2+1}{2x^2}$

11. $\lim\limits_{x\to\infty}\dfrac{2x+5}{7x-4}$

12. $\lim\limits_{x\to-\infty}\dfrac{1}{x^4}$

13. $\lim\limits_{t\to 3}\dfrac{2t-3}{t-3}$

14. $\lim\limits_{x\to-\infty}\dfrac{x^6}{x^5}$

15. $\lim\limits_{x\to-\infty}\dfrac{x+3}{1-x}$

16. $\lim\limits_{x\to 4}\sqrt[3]{64}$

17. $\lim\limits_{x\to\infty}\dfrac{x^2-1}{(3x+2)^2}$

18. $\lim\limits_{x\to 1}\dfrac{x^2+x-2}{x-1}$

19. $\lim\limits_{x\to 3^-}\dfrac{x+3}{x^2-9}$

20. $\lim\limits_{x\to 2}\dfrac{2-x}{x-2}$

21. $\lim\limits_{x\to\infty}\sqrt{3x}$

22. $\lim\limits_{y\to 5^+}\sqrt{y-5}$

23. $\lim\limits_{x\to\infty}\dfrac{x^{100}+(1/x^3)}{\pi-x^{97}}$

24. $\lim\limits_{x\to-\infty}\dfrac{ex^2-x^4}{31x-2x^3}$

25. $\lim\limits_{x\to 1} f(x)$ if $f(x)=\begin{cases}x^2 & \text{if } 0\le x<1\\ x & \text{if } x>1\end{cases}$

26. $\lim\limits_{x\to 3} f(x)$ if $f(x)=\begin{cases}x+5 & \text{if } x<3\\ 6 & \text{if } x\ge 3\end{cases}$

27. $\lim\limits_{x\to 4^+}\dfrac{\sqrt{x^2-16}}{4-x}$ (*Hint:* For $x>4$, $\sqrt{x^2-16}=\sqrt{x-4}\sqrt{x+4}$.)

28. $\lim\limits_{x\to 5^+}\dfrac{x^2-3x-10}{\sqrt{x-5}}$ (*Hint:* For $x>5$, $\dfrac{x-5}{\sqrt{x-5}}=\sqrt{x-5}$.)

29. If $f(x)=8x-2$, find $\lim\limits_{h\to 0}\dfrac{f(x+h)-f(x)}{h}$.

30. If $f(x)=2x^2-3$, find $\lim\limits_{h\to 0}\dfrac{f(x+h)-f(x)}{h}$.

31. **Host–Parasite Relationship** For a particular host–parasite relationship, it was determined that when the host density (number of hosts per unit of area) is $x$, then the number of hosts parasitized over a certain period of time is

$$y=23\left(1-\dfrac{1}{1+2x}\right)$$

If the host density were to increase without bound, what value would $y$ approach?

32. **Predator–Prey Relationship** For a particular predator–prey relationship, it was determined that the number $y$ of prey consumed by an individual predator over a period of time was a function of the prey density $x$ (the number of prey per unit of area). Suppose

$$y=f(x)=\dfrac{10x}{1+0.1x}$$

If the prey density were to increase without bound, what value would $y$ approach?

33. Using the definition of continuity, show that the function $f(x)=x+5$ is continuous at $x=7$.

34. Using the definition of continuity, show that the function $f(x)=\dfrac{x-5}{x^2+2}$ is continuous at $x=5$.

35. State whether $f(x)=x^2/5$ is continuous at each real number. Give a reason for your answer.

36. State whether $f(x)=x^2-2$ is continuous everywhere. Give a reason for your answer.

*In Problems 37–44, find the points of discontinuity (if any) for each function.*

37. $f(x)=\dfrac{x^2}{x+3}$

38. $f(x)=\dfrac{0}{x^3}$

39. $f(x)=\dfrac{x-1}{2x^2+3}$

40. $f(x)=(2-3x)^3$

41. $f(x)=\dfrac{4-x^2}{x^2+3x-4}$

42. $f(x)=\dfrac{2x+6}{x^3+x}$

43. $f(x)=\begin{cases}x+4 & \text{if } x>-2\\ 3x+6 & \text{if } x\le-2\end{cases}$

44. $f(x)=\begin{cases}1/x & \text{if } x<1\\ 1 & \text{if } x\ge 1\end{cases}$

*In Problems 45–52, solve the given inequalities.*

45. $x^2+4x-12>0$

46. $3x^2-3x-6\le 0$

47. $x^5\le 7x^4$

48. $x^3+8x^2+15x\ge 0$

49. $\dfrac{x+5}{x^2-1}<0$

50. $\dfrac{x(x+5)(x+8)}{3}<0$

51. $\dfrac{x^2+3x}{x^2+2x-8}\ge 0$

52. $\dfrac{x^2-9}{x^2-16}\le 0$

53. Graph $f(x)=\dfrac{x^3+3x^2-19x+18}{x^3-2x^2+x-2}$. Use the graph to estimate $\lim_{x\to 2} f(x)$.

54. Graph $f(x)=\dfrac{\sqrt{x+3}-2}{x-1}$. From the graph, estimate $\lim_{x\to 1} f(x)$.

55. Graph $f(x)=x\ln x$. From the graph, estimate the one-sided limit $\lim_{x\to 0^+} f(x)$.

56. Graph $f(x)=\dfrac{e^x-1}{(e^x+1)(e^{2x}-e^x)}$. Use the graph to estimate $\lim_{x\to 0} f(x)$.

57. Graph $f(x)=x^3-x^2+x-6$. Use the graph to determine the solution of

$$x^3-x^2+x-6\ge 0$$

58. Graph $f(x)=\dfrac{x^5-4}{x^3+1}$. Use the graph to determine the solution of

$$\dfrac{x^5-4}{x^3+1}\le 0$$

# Mathematical Snapshot

## National Debt

The size of the U.S. national debt is of great concern to many people and is frequently a topic in the news. The magnitude of the debt affects the confidence in the U.S. economy of both domestic and foreign investors, corporate officials, and political leaders. There are those who believe that to reduce the debt there must be cuts in government spending, which could affect government programs, or there must be an increase in revenues, possibly through tax increases.

Suppose that it is possible for the debt to be reduced continuously at an annual fixed rate. This is similar to compounding interest continuously, as studied in Chapter 5, except that instead of adding interest to an amount at each instant of time, you would be subtracting from the debt at each instant. Let us see how you could model this situation.

Suppose the debt $D_0$ at time $t = 0$ is reduced at an annual rate $r$. Furthermore, assume that there are $k$ time periods of equal length in a year. At the end of the first period, the original debt is reduced by $D_0\left(\frac{r}{k}\right)$, so the new debt is

$$D_0 - D_0\left(\frac{r}{k}\right) = D_0\left(1 - \frac{r}{k}\right)$$

At the end of the second period, this debt is reduced by $D_0\left(1 - \frac{r}{k}\right)\frac{r}{k}$, so the new debt is

$$D_0\left(1 - \frac{r}{k}\right) - D_0\left(1 - \frac{r}{k}\right)\frac{r}{k}$$
$$= D_0\left(1 - \frac{r}{k}\right)\left(1 - \frac{r}{k}\right)$$
$$= D_0\left(1 - \frac{r}{k}\right)^2$$

The pattern continues. At the end of the third period the debt is $D_0\left(1 - \frac{r}{k}\right)^3$, and so on. At the end of $t$ years the number of periods is $kt$ and the debt is $D_0\left(1 - \frac{r}{k}\right)^{kt}$. If the debt is to be reduced at each instant of time, then $k \to \infty$. Thus you want to find

$$\lim_{k\to\infty} D_0\left(1 - \frac{r}{k}\right)^{kt}$$

which can be rewritten as

$$D_0\left[\lim_{k\to\infty}\left(1 - \frac{r}{k}\right)^{-k/r}\right]^{-rt}$$

If you let $x = -r/k$, then the condition $k \to \infty$ implies that $x \to 0$. Hence the limit inside the brackets has the form $\lim_{x\to 0}(1+x)^{1/x}$, which we pointed out in Section 10.1 is $e$. Therefore, if the debt $D_0$ at time $t = 0$ is reduced

continuously at an annual rate $r$, then $t$ years later the debt $D$ is given by

$$D = D_0 e^{-rt}$$

For example, assume the U.S. national debt of \$8432 billion (rounded to the nearest billion) in July 2006 and a continuous reduction rate of 6% annually. Then the debt $t$ years from now is given by

$$D = 8432e^{-0.06t}$$

where $D$ is in billions of dollars. This means that in 10 years, the debt will be $8432e^{-0.6} \approx \$4628$ billion. Figure 10.47 shows the graph of $D = 8432e^{-rt}$ for various rates $r$. Of course, the greater the value of $r$, the faster the debt

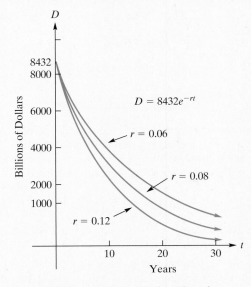

**FIGURE 10.47** Budget debt is reduced continuously.

reduction. Notice that for $r = 0.06$, the debt at the end of 30 years is still considerable (approximately $1394 billion).

It is interesting to note that decaying radioactive elements also follow the model of continuous debt reduction,
$$D = D_0 e^{-rt}.$$

To find out where the U.S. national debt currently stands, visit one of the national debt clocks on the Internet. You can find them by looking for "national debt clock" using any search engine.

## Problems

*In the following problems, assume a current national debt of $8432 billion.*

1. If the debt were reduced to $8000 billion a year from now, what annual rate of continuous debt reduction would be involved? Give your answer to the nearest percent.

2. For a continuous debt reduction at an annual rate of 6%, determine the number of years from now required for the debt to be reduced by one-half. Give your answer to the nearest year.

3. What assumptions underlie a model of debt reduction that uses an exponential function? What are the limitations of this approach?

# 11

# DIFFERENTIATION

Marginal Propensity to Consume

Government regulations generally limit the number of fish taken from a given fishing ground by commercial fishing boats in a season. This prevents over-fishing, which depletes the fish population and leaves, in the long run, fewer fish to catch.

From a strictly commercial perspective, the ideal regulations would maximize the number of fish available for the year-to-year fish harvest. The key to finding those ideal regulations is a mathematical function called the reproduction curve. For a given fish habitat, this function estimates the a fish population a year from now, $P(n+1)$, based on the population now, $P(n)$, assuming no external intervention (i.e., no fishing, no influx of predators, and so on).

The figure to the bottom left shows a typical reproduction curve. Also graphed is the line $P(n+1) = P(n)$, the line along which the populations $P(n+1)$ and $P(n)$ would be equal. Notice the intersection of the curve and the straight line at point $A$. This is where, because of habitat crowding, the population has reached its maximum sustainable size. A population that is this size one year will be the same size the next year.

For any point on the horizontal axis, the distance between the reproduction curve and the line $P(n+1) = P(n)$ represents the sustainable harvest: the number of fish that could be caught, after the spawn have grown to maturity, so that in the end the population is back at the same size it was a year ago.

Commercially speaking, the optimal population size is the one where the distance between the reproduction curve and the line $P(n+1) = P(n)$ is the greatest. This condition is met where the slopes of the reproduction curve and the line $P(n+1) = P(n)$ are equal. (The slope of $P(n+1) = P(n)$ is of course 1.) Thus, for a maximum fish harvest year after year, regulations should aim to keep the fish population fairly close to $P_0$.

A central idea here is that of the slope of a curve at a given point. That idea is the cornerstone concept of this chapter.

Now we begin our study of calculus. The ideas involved in calculus are completely different from those of algebra and geometry. The power and importance of these ideas and their applications will be clear to you later in the book. In this chapter we introduce the *derivative* of a function, and you will learn important rules for finding derivatives. You will also see how the derivative is used to analyze the rate of change of a quantity, such as the rate at which the position of a body is changing.

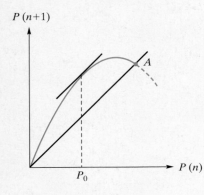

# 11.1 The Derivative

To develop the idea of a tangent line to a curve, to define the slope of a curve, and to define a derivative and give it a geometric interpretation. To compute derivatives by using the limit definition.

One of the main problems with which calculus deals is finding the slope of the *tangent line* at a point on a curve. In geometry you probably thought of a tangent line, or *tangent,* to a circle as a line that meets the circle at exactly one point (Figure 11.1). However, this idea of a tangent is not very useful for other kinds of curves. For example, in Figure 11.2(a), the lines $L_1$ and $L_2$ intersect the curve at exactly one point $P$. Although we would not think of $L_2$ as the tangent at this point, it seems natural that $L_1$ is. In Figure 11.2(b) we intuitively would consider $L_3$ to be the tangent at point $P$, even though $L_3$ intersects the curve at other points.

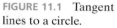

**FIGURE 11.1** Tangent lines to a circle.

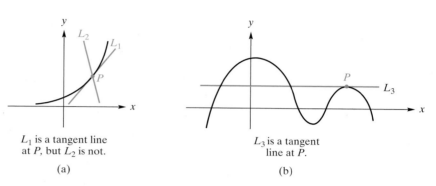

$L_1$ is a tangent line at $P$, but $L_2$ is not.

(a)

$L_3$ is a tangent line at $P$.

(b)

**FIGURE 11.2** Tangent line at a point.

From the previous examples, you can see that we must drop the idea that a tangent is simply a line that intersects a curve at only one point. To obtain a suitable definition of tangent line, we use the limit concept and the geometric notion of a *secant line*. A **secant line** is a line that intersects a curve at two or more points.

Look at the graph of the function $y = f(x)$ in Figure 11.3. We wish to define the tangent line at point $P$. If $Q$ is a different point on the curve, the line $PQ$ is a secant line. If $Q$ moves along the curve and approaches $P$ from the right (see Figure 11.4), typical secant lines are $PQ'$, $PQ''$, and so on. As $Q$ approaches $P$ from the left, they are $PQ_1$, $PQ_2$, and so on. *In both cases, the secant lines approach the same limiting position.* This common limiting position of the secant lines is defined to be the **tangent line** to the curve at $P$. This definition seems reasonable and applies to curves in general, not just circles.

A curve does not necessarily have a tangent line at each of its points. For example, the curve $y = |x|$ does not have a tangent at $(0, 0)$. As you can see in Figure 11.5, a secant line through $(0, 0)$ and a nearby point to its right on the curve must always be

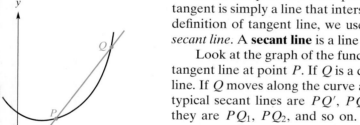

**FIGURE 11.3** Secant line $PQ$.

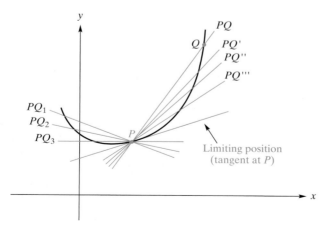

**FIGURE 11.4** The tangent line is a limiting position of secant lines.

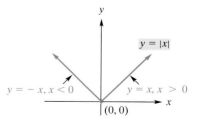

**FIGURE 11.5** No tangent line to graph of $y = |x|$ at $(0, 0)$.

the line $y = x$. Thus the limiting position of such secant lines is also the line $y = x$. However, a secant line through $(0, 0)$ and a nearby point to its left on the curve must always be the line $y = -x$. Hence, the limiting position of such secant lines is also the line $y = -x$. Since there is no common limiting position, there is no tangent line at $(0, 0)$.

Now that we have a suitable definition of a tangent to a curve at a point, we can define the *slope of a curve* at a point.

### DEFINITION
The **slope of a curve** at a point $P$ is the slope, if it exists, of the tangent line at $P$.

Since the tangent at $P$ is a limiting position of secant lines $PQ$, we consider the slope of the tangent to be the limiting value of the slopes of the secant lines as $Q$ approaches $P$. For example, let us consider the curve $f(x) = x^2$ and the slopes of some secant lines $PQ$, where $P = (1, 1)$. For the point $Q = (2.5, 6.25)$, the slope of $PQ$ (see Figure 11.6) is

$$m_{PQ} = \frac{\text{rise}}{\text{run}} = \frac{6.25 - 1}{2.5 - 1} = 3.5$$

Table 11.1 includes other points $Q$ on the curve, as well as the corresponding slopes of $PQ$. Notice that as $Q$ approaches $P$, the slopes of the secant lines seem to approach 2. Thus, we expect the slope of the indicated tangent line at $(1, 1)$ to be 2. This will be confirmed later, in Example 1. But first, we wish to generalize our procedure.

For the curve $y = f(x)$ in Figure 11.7, we will find an expression for the slope at the point $P = (a, f(a))$. If $Q = (z, f(z))$, the slope of the secant line $PQ$ is

$$m_{PQ} = \frac{f(z) - f(a)}{z - a}$$

If the difference $z - a$ is called $h$, then we can write $z$ as $a + h$. Here we must have $h \neq 0$, for if $h = 0$, then $z = a$, and no secant line exists. Accordingly,

$$m_{PQ} = \frac{f(z) - f(a)}{z - a} = \frac{f(a + h) - f(a)}{h}$$

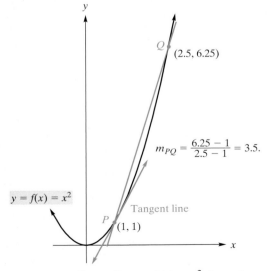

**FIGURE 11.6**   Secant line to $f(x) = x^2$ through $(1, 1)$ and $(2.5, 6.25)$.

**TABLE 11.1** Slopes of Secant Lines to the Curve $f(x) = x^2$ at $P = (1, 1)$

| $Q$ | Slope of $PQ$ |
|---|---|
| $(2.5, 6.25)$ | $(6.25 - 1)/(2.5 - 1) = 3.5$ |
| $(2, 4)$ | $(4 - 1)/(2 - 1) = 3$ |
| $(1.5, 2.25)$ | $(2.25 - 1)/(1.5 - 1) = 2.5$ |
| $(1.25, 1.5625)$ | $(1.5625 - 1)/(1.25 - 1) = 2.25$ |
| $(1.1, 1.21)$ | $(1.21 - 1)/(1.1 - 1) = 2.1$ |
| $(1.01, 1.0201)$ | $(1.021 - 1)/(1.01 - 1) = 2.01$ |

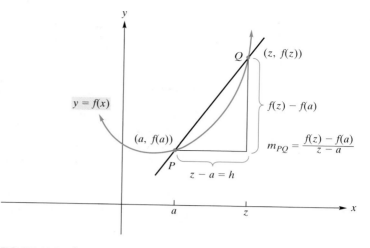

**FIGURE 11.7**  Secant line through $P$ and $Q$.

Which of these two forms for $m_{PQ}$ is most convenient depends on the nature of the function $f$. As $Q$ moves along the curve toward $P$, $z$ approaches $a$. This means that $h$ approaches zero. The limiting value of the slopes of the secant lines—which is the slope of the tangent line at $(a, f(a))$—is

$$m_{\tan} = \lim_{z \to a} \frac{f(z) - f(a)}{z - a} = \lim_{h \to 0} \frac{f(a + h) - f(a)}{h} \qquad (1)$$

Again, which of these two forms is most convenient—which limit is easiest to determine—depends on the nature of the function $f$. In Example 1, we will use this limit to confirm our previous expectation that the slope of the tangent line to the curve $f(x) = x^2$ at $(1, 1)$ is 2.

### ● EXAMPLE 1    Finding the Slope of a Tangent Line

*Find the slope of the tangent line to the curve* $y = f(x) = x^2$ *at the point* $(1, 1)$.

**Solution:** The slope is the limit in Equation (1) with $f(x) = x^2$ and $a = 1$:

$$\lim_{h \to 0} \frac{f(1 + h) - f(1)}{h} = \lim_{h \to 0} \frac{(1 + h)^2 - (1)^2}{h}$$

$$= \lim_{h \to 0} \frac{1 + 2h + h^2 - 1}{h} = \lim_{h \to 0} \frac{2h + h^2}{h}$$

$$= \lim_{h \to 0} \frac{h(2 + h)}{h} = \lim_{h \to 0} (2 + h) = 2$$

Therefore, the tangent line to $y = x^2$ at $(1, 1)$ has slope 2. (Refer to Figure 11.6.)

NOW WORK PROBLEM 1 ●●

We can generalize Equation (1) so that it applies to any point $(x, f(x))$ on a curve. Replacing $a$ by $x$ gives a function, called the *derivative* of $f$, whose input is $x$ and whose output is the slope of the tangent line to the curve at $(x, f(x))$, provided that the tangent line *exists* and *has* a slope. (If the tangent line exists but is *vertical* then it has no slope.) We thus have the following definition, which forms the basis of differential calculus:

**DEFINITION**
The *derivative* of a function $f$ is the function denoted $f'$ (read "$f$ prime") and defined by

$$f'(x) = \lim_{z \to x} \frac{f(z) - f(x)}{z - x} = \lim_{h \to 0} \frac{f(x + h) - f(x)}{h} \qquad (2)$$

provided that this limit exists. If $f'(a)$ can be found (while perhaps not all $f'(x)$ can be found) $f$ is said to be *differentiable* at $a$, and $f'(a)$ is called the derivative of $f$ at $a$ or the derivative of $f$ with respect to $x$ at $a$. The process of finding the derivative is called *differentiation.*

In the definition of the derivative, the expression

$$\frac{f(z) - f(x)}{z - x} = \frac{f(x + h) - f(x)}{h}$$

where $z = x + h$, is called a **difference quotient.** Thus $f'(x)$ is the limit of a difference quotient.

**● EXAMPLE 2 Using the Definition to Find the Derivative**

*If $f(x) = x^2$, find the derivative of $f$.*

**Solution:** Applying the definition of a derivative gives

$$f'(x) = \lim_{h \to 0} \frac{f(x + h) - f(x)}{h}$$

$$= \lim_{h \to 0} \frac{(x + h)^2 - x^2}{h} = \lim_{h \to 0} \frac{x^2 + 2xh + h^2 - x^2}{h}$$

$$= \lim_{h \to 0} \frac{2xh + h^2}{h} = \lim_{h \to 0} \frac{h(2x + h)}{h} = \lim_{h \to 0}(2x + h) = 2x$$

Observe that, in taking the limit, we treated $x$ as a constant, because it was $h$, not $x$, that was changing. Also, note that $f'(x) = 2x$ defines a function of $x$, which we can interpret as giving the slope of the tangent line to the graph of $f$ at $(x, f(x))$. For example, if $x = 1$, then the slope is $f'(1) = 2(1) = 2$, which confirms the result in Example 1.

NOW WORK PROBLEM 3 ●●●

Don't be sloppy when applying the limit definition of a derivative. Write $\lim_{h \to 0}$ at each step before the limit is actually taken. Unfortunately, some students neglect to take the final limit, and $h$ appears in their answer. This is a quick way to lose points on an examination.

Besides the notation $f'(x)$, other common ways to denote the derivative of $y = f(x)$ at $x$ are

$$\frac{dy}{dx} \qquad \text{(pronounced "dee } y\text{, dee } x\text{" or "dee } y \text{ by dee } x\text{")}$$

$$\frac{d}{dx}(f(x)) \qquad \text{("dee } f(x)\text{, dee } x\text{" or "dee by dee } x \text{ of } f(x)\text{")}$$

$$y' \qquad \text{("}y\text{ prime")}$$

$$D_x y \qquad \text{("dee } x \text{ of } y\text{")}$$

$$D_x(f(x)) \qquad \text{("dee } x \text{ of } f(x)\text{")}$$

 **CAUTION**

The notation $\dfrac{dy}{dx}$, which is called *Leibniz notation*, should **not** be thought of as a fraction, although it looks like one. It is a single symbol for a derivative. We have not yet attached any meaning to individual symbols such as $dy$ and $dx$.

Because the derivative gives the slope of the tangent line, $f'(a)$ is the slope of the line tangent to the graph of $y = f(x)$ at $(a, f(a))$.

Two other notations for the derivative of $f$ at $a$ are

$$\left.\frac{dy}{dx}\right|_{x=a} \qquad \text{and} \qquad y'(a)$$

● EXAMPLE 3   **Finding an Equation of a Tangent Line**

*If* $f(x) = 2x^2 + 2x + 3$, *find an equation of the tangent line to the graph of f at* $(1, 7)$.

Solution:

> **Strategy**   We will first determine the slope of the tangent line by computing the derivative and evaluating it at $x = 1$. Using this result and the point $(1, 7)$ in a point–slope form gives an equation of the tangent line.

We have

$$f'(x) = \lim_{h \to 0} \frac{f(x+h) - f(x)}{h}$$

$$= \lim_{h \to 0} \frac{(2(x+h)^2 + 2(x+h) + 3) - (2x^2 + 2x + 3)}{h}$$

$$= \lim_{h \to 0} \frac{2x^2 + 4xh + 2h^2 + 2x + 2h + 3 - 2x^2 - 2x - 3}{h}$$

$$= \lim_{h \to 0} \frac{4xh + 2h^2 + 2h}{h} = \lim_{h \to 0} (4x + 2h + 2)$$

So

$$f'(x) = 4x + 2$$

and

$$f'(1) = 4(1) + 2 = 6$$

In Example 3 it is *not* correct to say that, since the derivative is $4x + 2$, the tangent line at $(1, 7)$ is $y - 7 = (4x + 2)(x - 1)$. The derivative must be **evaluated** at the point of tangency to determine the slope of the tangent line.

Thus, the tangent line to the graph at $(1, 7)$ has slope 6. A point–slope form of this tangent is

$$y - 7 = 6(x - 1)$$

which in slope–intercept form is

$$y = 6x + 1$$

NOW WORK PROBLEM 25   ◖●●

● EXAMPLE 4   **Finding the Slope of a Curve at a Point**

*Find the slope of the curve* $y = 2x + 3$ *at the point where* $x = 6$.

Solution: The slope of the curve is the slope of the tangent line. Letting $y = f(x) = 2x + 3$, we have

$$\frac{dy}{dx} = \lim_{h \to 0} \frac{f(x+h) - f(x)}{h} = \lim_{h \to 0} \frac{(2(x+h) + 3) - (2x + 3)}{h}$$

$$= \lim_{h \to 0} \frac{2h}{h} = \lim_{h \to 0} 2 = 2$$

Since $dy/dx = 2$, the slope when $x = 6$, or in fact at any point, is 2. Note that the curve is a straight line and thus has the same slope at each point.

NOW WORK PROBLEM 19   ◖●●

● EXAMPLE 5   **A Function with a Vertical Tangent Line**

*Find* $\dfrac{d}{dx}(\sqrt{x})$.

Solution:  Letting $f(x) = \sqrt{x}$, we have

$$\frac{d}{dx}(\sqrt{x}) = \lim_{h \to 0} \frac{f(x+h) - f(x)}{h} = \lim_{h \to 0} \frac{\sqrt{x+h} - \sqrt{x}}{h}$$

You should become familiar with the procedure of rationalizing the *numerator*.

As $h \to 0$, both the numerator and denominator approach zero. This can be avoided by rationalizing the *numerator*:

$$\frac{\sqrt{x+h} - \sqrt{x}}{h} = \frac{\sqrt{x+h} - \sqrt{x}}{h} \cdot \frac{\sqrt{x+h} + \sqrt{x}}{\sqrt{x+h} + \sqrt{x}}$$

$$= \frac{(x+h) - x}{h(\sqrt{x+h} + \sqrt{x})} = \frac{h}{h(\sqrt{x+h} + \sqrt{x})}$$

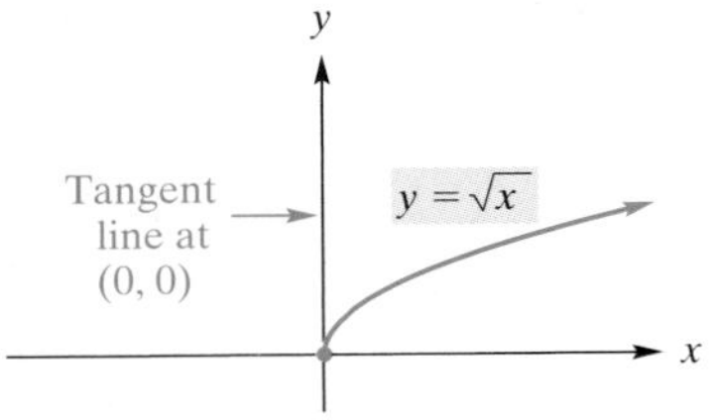

Therefore,

$$\frac{d}{dx}(\sqrt{x}) = \lim_{h \to 0} \frac{h}{h(\sqrt{x+h} + \sqrt{x})} = \lim \frac{1}{\sqrt{x+h} + \sqrt{x}} = \frac{1}{\sqrt{x} + \sqrt{x}} = \frac{1}{2\sqrt{x}}$$

**FIGURE 11.8** Vertical tangent line at $(0, 0)$.

Note that the original function, $\sqrt{x}$, is defined for $x \geq 0$, but its derivative, $1/(2\sqrt{x})$, is defined only when $x > 0$. The reason for this is clear from the graph of $y = \sqrt{x}$ in Figure 11.8. When $x = 0$, the tangent is a vertical line, so its slope is not defined.

NOW WORK PROBLEM 17 ◖●●

In Example 5 we saw that the function $y = \sqrt{x}$ is not differentiable when $x = 0$, because the tangent line is vertical at that point. It is worthwhile mentioning that $y = |x|$ also is not differentiable when $x = 0$, but for a different reason: There is *no* tangent line at all at that point. (Refer back to Figure 11.5.) Both examples show that the domain of $f'$ may be strictly contained in the domain of $f$.

It is wise for you to see variables other than $x$ and $y$ involved in a problem. Example 6 illustrates the use of other variables.

To indicate a derivative, Leibniz notation is often useful because it makes it convenient to emphasize the independent and dependent variables involved. For example, if the variable $p$ is a function of the variable $q$, we speak of the derivative of $p$ with respect to $q$, written $dp/dq$.

**PRINCIPLES IN PRACTICE 1**

**FINDING THE DERIVATIVE OF $H$ WITH RESPECT TO $t$**

If a ball is thrown upward at a speed of 40 ft/s from a height of 6 feet, its height $H$ in feet after $t$ seconds is given by $H = 6 + 40t - 16t^2$. Find $\dfrac{dH}{dt}$.

◖● **EXAMPLE 6** **Finding the Derivative of $p$ with Respect to $q$**

If $p = f(q) = \dfrac{1}{2q}$, find $\dfrac{dp}{dq}$.

**Solution:** We will do this problem first using the $h \to 0$ limit (the only one we have used so far) and then using $r \to q$ to illustrate the other variant of the limit.

$$\frac{dp}{dq} = \frac{d}{dq}\left(\frac{1}{2q}\right) = \lim_{h \to 0} \frac{f(q+h) - f(q)}{h}$$

$$= \lim_{h \to 0} \frac{\dfrac{1}{2(q+h)} - \dfrac{1}{2q}}{h} = \lim_{h \to 0} \frac{\dfrac{q - (q+h)}{2q(q+h)}}{h}$$

$$= \lim_{h \to 0} \frac{q - (q+h)}{h(2q(q+h))} = \lim_{h \to 0} \frac{-h}{h(2q(q+h))}$$

$$= \lim_{h \to 0} \frac{-1}{2q(q+h)} = -\frac{1}{2q^2}$$

We also have

$$\frac{dp}{dq} = \lim_{r \to q} \frac{f(r) - f(q)}{r - q}$$

$$= \lim_{r \to q} \frac{\dfrac{1}{2r} - \dfrac{1}{2q}}{r - q} = \lim_{r \to q} \frac{\dfrac{q - r}{2rq}}{r - q}$$

$$= \lim_{r \to q} \frac{-1}{2rq} = \frac{-1}{2q^2}$$

We leave it you to decide which form leads to the simpler limit calculation in this case.

Note that when $q = 0$, neither the function nor its derivative exists.

NOW WORK PROBLEM 15

Keep in mind that the derivative of $y = f(x)$ at $x$ is nothing more than a limit, namely

$$\lim_{h \to 0} \frac{f(x+h) - f(x)}{h}$$

equivalently

$$\lim_{z \to x} \frac{f(z) - f(x)}{z - x}$$

whose use we have just illustrated. Although we can interpret the derivative as a function that gives the slope of the tangent line to the curve $y = f(x)$ at the point $(x, f(x))$, this interpretation is simply a geometric convenience that assists our understanding. The preceding limit may exist, aside from any geometric considerations at all. As you will see later, there are other useful interpretations of the derivative.

In Section 11.4, we will make technical use of the following relationship between differentiability and continuity. However, it is of fundamental importnace and needs to be understood from the outset.

If $f$ is differentiable at $a$, then $f$ is continuous at $a$.

To establish this result, we will assume that $f$ is differentiable at $a$. Then $f'(a)$ exists, and

$$\lim_{h \to 0} \frac{f(a+h) - f(a)}{h} = f'(a).$$

Consider the numerator $f(a+h) - f(a)$ as $h \to 0$. We have

$$\lim_{h \to 0} (f(a+h) - f(a)) = \lim_{h \to 0} \left( \frac{f(a+h) - f(a)}{h} \cdot h \right)$$

$$= \lim_{h \to 0} \frac{f(a+h) - f(a)}{h} \cdot \lim_{h \to 0} h$$

$$= f'(a) \cdot 0 = 0$$

Thus, $\lim_{h \to 0}(f(a+h) - f(a)) = 0$. This means that $f(a+h) - f(a)$ approaches 0 as $h \to 0$. Consequently,

$$\lim_{h \to 0} f(a+h) = f(a)$$

As stated in Section 10.3, this condition means that $f$ is continuous at $a$. The foregoing, then, proves that $f$ is continuous at $a$ when $f$ is differentiable there. More simply, we say that **differentiability at a point implies continuity at that point.**

If a function is not continuous at a point, then it cannot have a derivative there. For example, the function in Figure 11.9 is discontinuous at $a$. The curve has no tangent at that point, so the function is not differentiable there.

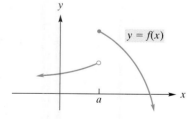

FIGURE 11.9   $f$ is not continuous at $a$, so $f$ is not differentiable at $a$.

### ● EXAMPLE 7   Continuity and Differentiability

**a.** Let $f(x) = x^2$. The derivative, $2x$, is defined for all values of $x$, so $f(x) = x^2$ must be continuous for all values of $x$.

**b.** The function $f(p) = \dfrac{1}{2p}$ is not continuous at $p = 0$ because $f$ is not defined there. Thus, the derivative does not exist at $p = 0$.

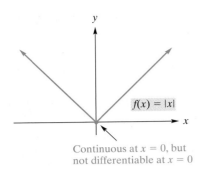

**FIGURE 11.10** Continuity does not imply differentiability.

The converse of the statement that differentiability implies continuity is *false*. That is, it is false that continuity implies differentiability. In Example 8, you will see a function that is continuous at a point, but not differentiable there.

⬤**EXAMPLE 8** **Continuity Does Not Imply Differentiability**

The function $y = f(x) = |x|$ is continuous at $x = 0$. (See Figure 11.10.) As we mentioned earlier, there is no tangent line at $x = 0$. Thus, the derivative does not exist there. This shows that continuity does *not* imply differentiability.

## TECHNOLOGY

Many graphing calculators have a numerical derivative feature that estimates the derivative of a function at a point. With the TI-83 Plus we would use the "nDeriv" command, in which we must enter the function, the variable, and the value of the variable (separated by commas) in the format

nDeriv(function, variable, value of variable)

For example, the derivative of $f(x) = \sqrt{x^3 + 2}$ at $x = 1$ is estimated in Figure 11.11. Thus, $f'(1) \approx 0.866$.

On the other hand, we can take the "limit of a difference quotient" approach to estimate this derivative. To make use of the table feature of a graphing calculator, we can enter $f(x)$ as $Y_1$. Then, for $Y_2$, we enter the following form of the difference quotient:

$$(Y_1(1 + X) - Y_1(1))/X$$

(Here, $x$ plays the role of $h$.) Figure 11.12 shows a table for $Y_2$ as $x$ approaches 0 from both the left and right. This table strongly suggests that $f'(1) \approx 0.866$.

```
nDeriv(√(X^3+2),
X,1)
          .8660253677
■
```

**FIGURE 11.11** Numerical derivative.

```
  X   │ Y₂
 .01  │ .87252
 .001 │ .86667
 1E⁻⁴ │ .86609
 1E⁻⁵ │ .86603
 -.01 │ .85953
 -.001│ .86538
▓▓▓▓  │ .86596
X=-1E⁻⁴
```

**FIGURE 11.12** Limit of a difference quotient as $x \to 0$.

# Problems 11.1

*In Problems 1 and 2, a function f and a point P on its graph are given.*

(a) *Find the slope of the secant line PQ for each point $Q = (x, f(x))$ whose x-value is given in the table. Round your answers to four decimal places.*

(b) *Use your results from part (a) to estimate the slope of the tangent line at P.*

*1. $f(x) = x^3 + 3$, $P = (-2, -5)$

| x-value of Q | -3 | -2.5 | -2.2 | -2.1 | -2.01 | -2.001 |
|---|---|---|---|---|---|---|
| $m_{PQ}$ | | | | | | |

2. $f(x) = e^{2x}$, $P = (0, 1)$

| x-value of Q | 1 | 0.5 | 0.2 | 0.1 | 0.01 | 0.001 |
|---|---|---|---|---|---|---|
| $m_{PQ}$ | | | | | | |

*In Problems 3–18, use the definition of the derivative to find each of the following.*

*3. $f'(x)$ if $f(x) = x$

4. $f'(x)$ if $f(x) = 4x - 1$

5. $\dfrac{dy}{dx}$ if $y = 3x + 5$

6. $\dfrac{dy}{dx}$ if $y = -5x$

7. $\dfrac{d}{dx}(5 - 4x)$

8. $\dfrac{d}{dx}\left(1 - \dfrac{x}{2}\right)$

9. $f'(x)$ if $f(x) = 3$

10. $f'(x)$ if $f(x) = 7.01$

11. $\dfrac{d}{dx}(x^2 + 4x - 8)$

12. $y'$ if $y = x^2 + 5x + 1$

13. $\dfrac{dp}{dq}$ if $p = 3q^2 + 2q + 1$

14. $\dfrac{d}{dx}(x^2 - x - 3)$

*15. $y'$ if $y = \dfrac{6}{x}$

16. $\dfrac{dC}{dq}$ if $C = 7 + 2q - 3q^2$

*17. $f'(x)$ if $f(x) = \sqrt{x + 2}$

18. $H'(x)$ if $H(x) = \dfrac{3}{x - 2}$

*19. Find the slope of the curve $y = x^2 + 4$ at the point $(-2, 8)$.

20. Find the slope of the curve $y = 1 - x^2$ at the point $(1, 0)$.

21. Find the slope of the curve $y = 4x^2 - 5$ when $x = 0$.

22. Find the slope of the curve $y = \sqrt{x}$ when $x = 1$.

In Problems 23–28, find an equation of the tangent line to the curve at the given point.

**23.** $y = x + 4$; $(3, 7)$

**24.** $y = 3x^2 - 4$; $(1, -1)$

*25. $y = x^2 + 2x + 3$; $(1, 6)$

**26.** $y = (x - 7)^2$; $(6, 1)$

**27.** $y = \dfrac{3}{x - 1}$; $(2, 3)$

**28.** $y = \dfrac{5}{1 - 3x}$; $(2, -1)$

**29. Banking**   Equations may involve derivatives of functions. In an article on interest rate deregulation, Christofi and Agapos[1] solve the equation

$$r = \left(\frac{\eta}{1 + \eta}\right)\left(r_L - \frac{dC}{dD}\right)$$

for $\eta$ (the Greek letter "eta"). Here $r$ is the deposit rate paid by commercial banks, $r_L$ is the rate earned by commercial banks, $C$ is the administrative cost of transforming deposits into return-earning assets, $D$ is the savings deposits level, and $\eta$ is the deposit elasticity with respect to the deposit rate. Find $\eta$.

In Problems 30 and 31, use the numerical derivative feature of your graphing calculator to estimate the derivatives of the functions at the indicated values. Round your answers to three decimal places.

**30.** $f(x) = \sqrt{2x^2 + 3x}$; $x = 1, x = 2$

**31.** $f(x) = e^x(4x - 7)$; $x = 0, x = 1.5$

In Problems 32 and 33, use the "limit of a difference quotient" approach to estimate $f'(x)$ at the indicated values of $x$. Round your answers to three decimal places.

**32.** $f(x) = \dfrac{e^x}{x + 1}$; $x = 1, x = 10$

**33.** $f(x) = \dfrac{x^2 + 4x + 2}{x^3 - 3}$; $x = 2, x = -4$

**34.** Find an equation of the tangent line to the curve $f(x) = x^2 + x$ at the point $(-2, 2)$. Graph both the curve and the tangent line. Notice that the tangent line is a good approximation to the curve near the point of tangency.

**35.** The derivative of $f(x) = x^3 - x + 2$ is $f'(x) = 3x^2 - 1$. Graph both the function $f$ and its derivative $f'$. Observe that there are two points on the graph of $f$ where the tangent line is horizontal. For the $x$-values of these points, what are the corresponding values of $f'(x)$? Why are these results expected? Observe the intervals where $f'(x)$ is positive. Notice that tangent lines to the graph of $f$ have positive slopes over these intervals. Observe the interval where $f'(x)$ is negative. Notice that tangent lines to the graph of $f$ have negative slopes over this interval.

In Problems 36 and 37, verify the identity $(z - x)\left(\sum_{i=0}^{n-1} x^i z^{n-1-i}\right) = z^n - x^n$ for the indicated values of $n$ and calculate the derivative using the $z \to x$ form of the definition of the derivative in Equation (2).

**36.** $n = 4, n = 3, n = 2$;   $f'(x)$ if $f(x) = 2x^4 + x^3 - 3x^2$

**37.** $n = 5, n = 3$;   $f'(x)$ if $f(x) = 4x^5 - 3x^3$

OBJECTIVE

To develop basic differentiation rules, namely, formulas for the derivative of a constant, of $x^n$, of a constant times a function, and of sums and differences of functions.

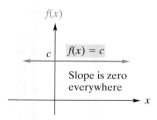

**FIGURE 11.13**   The slope of a constant function is 0.

# 11.2  Rules for Differentiation

You would probably agree that differentiating a function by direct use of the definition of a derivative can be tedious. Fortunately, there are rules that give us completely mechanical and efficient procedures for differentiation. They also avoid the direct use of limits. We will look at some of these rules in this section.

We begin by showing that the derivative of a constant function is zero. Recall that the graph of the constant function $f(x) = c$ is a horizontal line (see Figure 11.13), which has a slope of zero at each point. This means that $f'(x) = 0$ regardless of $x$. As a formal proof of this result, we apply the definition of the derivative to $f(x) = c$:

$$f'(x) = \lim_{h \to 0}\frac{f(x + h) - f(x)}{h} = \lim_{h \to 0}\frac{c - c}{h}$$

$$= \lim_{h \to 0}\frac{0}{h} = \lim_{h \to 0} 0 = 0$$

Thus, we have our first rule:

**RULE 1   Derivative of a Constant**

If $c$ is a constant, then

$$\frac{d}{dx}(c) = 0$$

That is, the derivative of a constant function is zero.

---

[1] A. Christofi and A. Agapos, "Interest Rate Deregulation: An Empirical Justification," *Review of Business and Economic Research*, XX, no. 1 (1984), 39–49.

● EXAMPLE 1    **Derivatives of Constant Functions**

**a.** $\dfrac{d}{dx}(3) = 0$ because 3 is a constant function.

**b.** If $g(x) = \sqrt{5}$, then $g'(x) = 0$ because $g$ is a constant function. For example, the derivative of $g$ when $x = 4$ is $g'(4) = 0$.

**c.** If $s(t) = (1{,}938{,}623)^{807.4}$, then $ds/dt = 0$.

NOW WORK PROBLEM 1  ●○●

The next rule gives a formula for the derivative of "$x$ raised to a constant power"—that is, the derivative of $f(x) = x^n$, where $n$ is an arbitrary real number. A function of this form is called a **power function.** For example, $f(x) = x^2$ is a power function. While the rule we record is valid for all real $n$, we will establish it only in the case where $n$ is a positive integer. The rule is so central to differential calculus that it warrants a detailed calculation—if only in the case where $n$ is a positive integer. Whether we use the $h \to 0$ form of the definition of derivative or the $z \to x$ form, the calculation of $\dfrac{dx^n}{dx}$ is instructive and provides good practice with summation notation, whose use is more essential in later chapters. We provide a calculation for each possibility. As you will see, we must either expand $(x + h)^n$, to use the $h \to 0$ form of Equation (2) from Section 11.1, or factor $z^n - x^n$, to use the $z \to x$ form.

For the first of these we recall the *binomial theorem* of Section 9.2:

$$(x + h)^n = \sum_{i=0}^{n} {}_nC_i x^{n-i} h^i$$

where the ${}_nC_i$ are the binomial coefficients, whose precise descriptions, except for ${}_nC_0 = 1$ and ${}_nC_1 = n$, are not necessary here (but are given in Section 8.2). For the second we have

$$(z - x)\left(\sum_{i=0}^{n-1} x^i z^{n-1-i}\right) = z^n - x^n$$

which is easily verified by carrying out the multiplication using the rules for manipulating summations given in Section 1.5. In fact we have

$$(z - x)\left(\sum_{i=0}^{n-1} x^i z^{n-1-i}\right) = z\sum_{i=0}^{n-1} x^i z^{n-1-i} - x\sum_{i=0}^{n-1} x^i z^{n-1-i}$$

$$= \sum_{i=0}^{n-1} x^i z^{n-i} - \sum_{i=0}^{n-1} x^{i+1} z^{n-1-i}$$

$$= \left(z^n + \sum_{i=1}^{n-1} x^i z^{n-i}\right) - \left(\sum_{i=0}^{n-2} x^{i+1} z^{n-1-i} + x^n\right)$$

$$= z^n - x^n$$

where you should check that the two summations in the second to last line really do cancel as shown.

---

**RULE 2    Derivative of $x^n$**

If $n$ is any real number, then

$$\frac{d}{dx}(x^n) = nx^{n-1}$$

That is, the derivative of a constant power of $x$ is the exponent times $x$ raised to a power one less than the given power.

For $n$ a positive integer, if $f(x) = x^n$, the definition of the derivative gives

$$f'(x) = \lim_{h \to 0} \frac{f(x+h) - f(x)}{h} = \lim_{h \to 0} \frac{(x+h)^n - x^n}{h}$$

By our previous discussion on expanding $(x+h)^n$,

$$f'(x) = \lim_{h \to 0} \frac{\sum_{i=0}^{n} {}_nC_i x^{n-i} h^i - x^n}{h}$$

$$\overset{(1)}{=} \lim_{h \to 0} \frac{\sum_{i=1}^{n} {}_nC_i x^{n-i} h^i}{h}$$

$$\overset{(2)}{=} \lim_{h \to 0} \frac{h \sum_{i=1}^{n} {}_nC_i x^{n-i} h^{i-1}}{h}$$

$$\overset{(3)}{=} \lim_{h \to 0} \sum_{i=1}^{n} {}_nC_i x^{n-i} h^{i-1}$$

$$\overset{(4)}{=} \lim_{h \to 0} \left( nx^{n-1} + \sum_{i=2}^{n} {}_nC_i x^{n-i} h^{i-1} \right)$$

$$\overset{(5)}{=} nx^{n-1}$$

where we justify the further steps as follows:

**(1)** The $i = 0$ term in the summation is ${}_nC_0 x^n h^0 = x^n$ so it cancels with the separate, last, term: $-x^n$.

**(2)** We are able to extract a common factor of $h$ from each term in the sum.

**(3)** This is the crucial step. The expressions separated by the equal sign are limits as $h \to 0$ of functions of $h$ that are equal for $h \neq 0$.

**(4)** The $i = 1$ term in the summation is ${}_nC_1 x^{n-1} h^0 = nx^{n-1}$. It is the only one that does not contain a factor of $h$, and we separated it from the other terms.

**(5)** Finally, in determining the limit we made use of the fact that the isolated term is independent of $h$; while all the others contain $h$ as a factor and so have limit 0 as $h \to 0$.

Now, using the $z \to x$ limit for the definition of the derivative and $f(x) = x^n$, we have

$$f'(x) = \lim_{z \to x} \frac{f(z) - f(x)}{z - x} = \lim_{h \to 0} \frac{z^n - x^n}{z - x}$$

By our previous discussion on factoring $z^n - x^n$ we have

$$f'(x) = \lim_{z \to x} \frac{(z - x) \left( \sum_{i=0}^{n-1} x^i z^{n-1-i} \right)}{z - x}$$

$$\overset{(1)}{=} \lim_{z \to x} \sum_{i=0}^{n-1} x^i z^{n-1-i}$$

$$\overset{(2)}{=} \sum_{i=0}^{n-1} x^i x^{n-1-i}$$

$$\overset{(3)}{=} \sum_{i=0}^{n-1} x^{n-1}$$

$$\overset{(4)}{=} nx^{n-1}$$

where this time we justify the further steps as follows:

**(1)** Here the crucial step comes first. The expressions separated by the equal sign are limits as $z \to x$ of functions of $z$ that are equal for $z \neq x$.

**(2)** The limit is given by evaluation because the expression is a polynomial in the variable $z$.

**(3)** An obvious rule for exponents is used.

**(4)** Each term in the sum is $x^{n-1}$, independent of $i$, and there are $n$ such terms.

### ● EXAMPLE 2   Derivatives of Powers of $x$

**a.** By Rule 2, $\dfrac{d}{dx}(x^2) = 2x^{2-1} = 2x$.

**b.** If $F(x) = x = x^1$, then $F'(x) = 1 \cdot x^{1-1} = 1 \cdot x^0 = 1$. Thus, the derivative of $x$ with respect to $x$ is 1.

**c.** If $f(x) = x^{-10}$, then $f'(x) = -10x^{-10-1} = -10x^{-11}$.

NOW WORK PROBLEM 3 ●●●

When we apply a differentiation rule to a function, sometimes the function must first be rewritten so that it has the proper form for that rule. For example, to differentiate $f(x) = \dfrac{1}{x^{10}}$ we would first rewrite $f$ as $f(x) = x^{-10}$ and then proceed as in Example 2(c).

### ● EXAMPLE 3   Rewriting Functions in the Form $x^n$

**a.** To differentiate $y = \sqrt{x}$, we rewrite $\sqrt{x}$ as $x^{1/2}$ so that it has the form $x^n$. Thus,

$$\frac{dy}{dx} = \frac{1}{2}x^{(1/2)-1} = \frac{1}{2}x^{-1/2} = \frac{1}{2\sqrt{x}}$$

which agrees with our limit calculation in Example 5 of Section 11.1.

**b.** Let $h(x) = \dfrac{1}{x\sqrt{x}}$. To apply Rule 2, we must rewrite $h(x)$ as $h(x) = x^{-3/2}$ so that it has the form $x^n$. We have

$$h'(x) = \frac{d}{dx}(x^{-3/2}) = -\frac{3}{2}x^{(-3/2)-1} = -\frac{3}{2}x^{-5/2}$$

NOW WORK PROBLEM 39 ●●●

**CAUTION**

In Example 3(b), do not rewrite $\dfrac{1}{x\sqrt{x}}$ as $\dfrac{1}{x^{3/2}}$ and then merely differentiate the denominator.

Now that we can say immediately that the derivative of $x^3$ is $3x^2$, the question arises as to what we could say about the derivative of a *multiple* of $x^3$, such as $5x^3$. Our next rule will handle this situation of differentiating a constant times a function.

**RULE 3   Constant Factor Rule**

If $f$ is a differentiable function and $c$ is a constant, then $cf(x)$ is differentiable, and

$$\frac{d}{dx}(cf(x)) = cf'(x)$$

That is, the derivative of a constant times a function is the constant times the derivative of the function.

*Proof.* If $g(x) = cf(x)$, applying the definition of the derivative of $g$ gives

$$g'(x) = \lim_{h \to 0} \frac{g(x+h) - g(x)}{h} = \lim_{h \to 0} \frac{cf(x+h) - cf(x)}{h}$$

$$= \lim_{h \to 0} \left( c \cdot \frac{f(x+h) - f(x)}{h} \right) = c \cdot \lim_{h \to 0} \frac{f(x+h) - f(x)}{h}$$

But $\lim\limits_{h \to 0} \dfrac{f(x+h) - f(x)}{h}$ is $f'(x)$; so $g'(x) = cf'(x)$.

● EXAMPLE 4    **Differentiating a Constant Times a Function**

*Differentiate the following functions.*

**a.** $g(x) = 5x^3$

Solution:  Here $g$ is a constant (5) times a function ($x^3$). So

$$\frac{d}{dx}(5x^3) = 5\frac{d}{dx}(x^3) \qquad \text{(Rule 3)}$$

$$= 5(3x^{3-1}) = 15x^2 \qquad \text{(Rule 2)}$$

**b.** $f(q) = \dfrac{13q}{5}$

Solution:

**Strategy**  We first rewrite $f$ as a constant times a function and then apply Rule 2.

Because $\dfrac{13q}{5} = \dfrac{13}{5}q$, $f$ is the constant $\dfrac{13}{5}$ times the function $q$. Thus,

$$f'(q) = \frac{13}{5}\frac{d}{dq}(q) \qquad \text{(Rule 3)}$$

$$= \frac{13}{5} \cdot 1 = \frac{13}{5} \qquad \text{(Rule 2)}$$

**c.** $y = \dfrac{0.25}{\sqrt[5]{x^2}}$

Solution:  We can express $y$ as a constant times a function:

$$y = 0.25 \cdot \frac{1}{\sqrt[5]{x^2}} = 0.25x^{-2/5}$$

Hence,

$$y' = 0.25\frac{d}{dx}(x^{-2/5}) \qquad \text{(Rule 3)}$$

$$= 0.25\left(-\frac{2}{5}x^{-7/5}\right) = -0.1x^{-7/5} \qquad \text{(Rule 2)}$$

NOW WORK PROBLEM 7  ◖◗●

The next rule involves derivatives of sums and differences of functions.

**CAUTION**

To differentiate $f(x) = (4x)^3$, you may be tempted to write $f'(x) = 3(4x)^2$. **This is incorrect!** Do you see why? The reason is that Rule 2 applies to a power of the variable $x$, **not** a power of an expression involving $x$, such as $4x$. To apply our rules, we must get a suitable form for $f(x)$. We can rewrite $(4x)^3$ as $4^3x^3 = 64x^3$. Thus,

$$f'(x) = 64\frac{d}{dx}(x^3) = 64(3x^2) = 192x^2$$

**RULE 4    Sum or Difference Rule**

If $f$ and $g$ are differentiable functions, then $f + g$ and $f - g$ are differentiable, and

$$\frac{d}{dx}(f(x) + g(x)) = f'(x) + g'(x)$$

and

$$\frac{d}{dx}(f(x) - g(x)) = f'(x) - g'(x)$$

That is, the derivative of the sum (difference) of two functions is the sum (difference) of their derivatives.

*Proof.* For the case of a sum, if $F(x) = f(x) + g(x)$, applying the definition of the derivative of $F$ gives

$$F'(x) = \lim_{h \to 0} \frac{F(x+h) - F(x)}{h}$$

$$= \lim_{h \to 0} \frac{(f(x+h) + g(x+h)) - (f(x) + g(x))}{h}$$

$$= \lim_{h \to 0} \frac{(f(x+h) - f(x)) + (g(x+h) - g(x))}{h} \qquad \text{(regrouping)}$$

$$= \lim_{h \to 0} \left( \frac{f(x+h) - f(x)}{h} + \frac{g(x+h) - g(x)}{h} \right)$$

Because the limit of a sum is the sum of the limits,

$$F'(x) = \lim_{h \to 0} \frac{f(x+h) - f(x)}{h} + \lim_{h \to 0} \frac{g(x+h) - g(x)}{h}$$

But these two limits are $f'(x)$ and $g'(x)$. Thus,

$$F'(x) = f'(x) + g'(x)$$

The proof for the derivative of a difference of two functions is similar.

Rule 4 can be extended to the derivative of any number of sums and differences of functions. For example,

$$\frac{d}{dx}[f(x) - g(x) + h(x) + k(x)] = f'(x) - g'(x) + h'(x) + k'(x)$$

### ● EXAMPLE 5   Differentiating Sums and Differences of Functions

*Differentiate the following functions.*

**a.** $F(x) = 3x^5 + \sqrt{x}$

   **Solution:** Here $F$ is the sum of two functions, $3x^5$ and $\sqrt{x}$. Therefore,

$$F'(x) = \frac{d}{dx}(3x^5) + \frac{d}{dx}(x^{1/2}) \qquad \text{(Rule 4)}$$

$$= 3\frac{d}{dx}(x^5) + \frac{d}{dx}(x^{1/2}) \qquad \text{(Rule 3)}$$

$$= 3(5x^4) + \frac{1}{2}x^{-1/2} = 15x^4 + \frac{1}{2\sqrt{x}} \qquad \text{(Rule 2)}$$

**b.** $f(z) = \dfrac{z^4}{4} - \dfrac{5}{z^{1/3}}$

   **Solution:** To apply our rules, we will rewrite $f(z)$ in the form $f(z) = \frac{1}{4}z^4 - 5z^{-1/3}$. Since $f$ is the difference of two functions,

$$f'(z) = \frac{d}{dz}\left(\frac{1}{4}z^4\right) - \frac{d}{dz}(5z^{-1/3}) \qquad \text{(Rule 4)}$$

$$= \frac{1}{4}\frac{d}{dz}(z^4) - 5\frac{d}{dz}(z^{-1/3}) \qquad \text{(Rule 3)}$$

$$= \frac{1}{4}(4z^3) - 5\left(-\frac{1}{3}z^{-4/3}\right) \qquad \text{(Rule 2)}$$

$$= z^3 + \frac{5}{3}z^{-4/3}$$

**c.** $y = 6x^3 - 2x^2 + 7x - 8$

   **Solution:**

$$\frac{dy}{dx} = \frac{d}{dx}(6x^3) - \frac{d}{dx}(2x^2) + \frac{d}{dx}(7x) - \frac{d}{dx}(8)$$

$$= 6\frac{d}{dx}(x^3) - 2\frac{d}{dx}(x^2) + 7\frac{d}{dx}(x) - \frac{d}{dx}(8)$$

$$= 6(3x^2) - 2(2x) + 7(1) - 0$$
$$= 18x^2 - 4x + 7$$

NOW WORK PROBLEM 47

In Examples 6 and 7, we need to rewrite the given function in a form to which our rules apply.

### ● EXAMPLE 6   Finding a Derivative

*Find the derivative of* $f(x) = 2x(x^2 - 5x + 2)$ *when* $x = 2$.

**Solution:**  We multiply and then differentiate each term:

$$f(x) = 2x^3 - 10x^2 + 4x$$
$$f'(x) = 2(3x^2) - 10(2x) + 4(1)$$
$$= 6x^2 - 20x + 4$$
$$f'(2) = 6(2)^2 - 20(2) + 4 = -12$$

NOW WORK PROBLEM 75

### ● EXAMPLE 7   Finding an Equation of a Tangent Line

*Find an equation of the tangent line to the curve*

$$y = \frac{3x^2 - 2}{x}$$

*when* $x = 1$.

**Solution:**

> **Strategy**   First we find $\dfrac{dy}{dx}$, which gives the slope of the tangent line at any point. Evaluating $\dfrac{dy}{dx}$ when $x = 1$ gives the slope of the required tangent line. We then determine the $y$-coordinate of the point on the curve when $x = 1$. Finally, we substitute the slope and both of the coordinates of the point in point–slope form to obtain an equation of the tangent line.

Rewriting $y$ as a difference of two functions, we have

$$y = \frac{3x^2}{x} - \frac{2}{x} = 3x - 2x^{-1}$$

Thus,

$$\frac{dy}{dx} = 3(1) - 2((-1)x^{-2}) = 3 + \frac{2}{x^2}$$

The slope of the tangent line to the curve when $x = 1$ is

$$\left.\frac{dy}{dx}\right|_{x=1} = 3 + \frac{2}{1^2} = 5$$

To find the $y$-coordinate of the point on the curve where $x = 1$, we evaluate $y = \dfrac{3x^2 - 2}{x}$ at $x = 1$. This gives

$$y = \frac{3(1)^2 - 2}{1} = 1$$

**CAUTION**

To obtain the $y$-value of the point on the curve when $x = 1$, evaluate the original function, not the derived function.

Hence, the point $(1, 1)$ lies on both the curve and the tangent line. Therefore, an equation of the tangent line is

$$y - 1 = 5(x - 1)$$

In slope–intercept form, we have

$$y = 5x - 4$$

## Problems 11.2

*In Problems 1–74, differentiate the functions.*

*1. $f(x) = 5$

2. $f(x) = \left(\frac{6}{7}\right)^{2/3}$

*3. $y = x^6$

4. $f(x) = x^{21}$

5. $y = x^{80}$

6. $y = x^{5.3}$

*7. $f(x) = 9x^2$

8. $y = 4x^3$

9. $g(w) = 8w^7$

10. $v(x) = x^e$

11. $y = \frac{2}{3}x^4$

12. $f(p) = \sqrt{3}p^4$

13. $f(t) = \frac{t^7}{25}$

14. $y = \frac{x^7}{7}$

15. $f(x) = x + 3$

16. $f(x) = 3x - 2$

17. $f(x) = 4x^2 - 2x + 3$

18. $F(x) = 5x^2 - 9x$

19. $g(p) = p^4 - 3p^3 - 1$

20. $f(t) = -13t^2 + 14t + 1$

21. $y = x^3 - \sqrt{x}$

22. $y = -8x^4 + \ln 2$

23. $y = -13x^3 + 14x^2 - 2x + 3$

24. $V(r) = r^8 - 7r^6 + 3r^2 + 1$

25. $f(x) = 2(13 - x^4)$

26. $\phi(t) = 5(t^3 - 3^2)$

27. $g(x) = \frac{13 - x^4}{3}$

28. $f(x) = \frac{5(x^4 - 6)}{2}$

29. $h(x) = 4x^4 + x^3 - \frac{9x^2}{2} + 8x$

30. $k(x) = -2x^2 + \frac{5}{3}x + 11$

31. $f(x) = \frac{3x^4}{10} + \frac{7}{3}x^3$

32. $p(x) = \frac{x^7}{7} + \frac{2x}{3}$

33. $f(x) = x^{3/5}$

34. $f(x) = 2x^{-14/5}$

35. $y = x^{3/4} + 2x^{5/3}$

36. $y = 5x^3 - x^{-2/5}$

37. $y = 11\sqrt{x}$

38. $y = \sqrt{x^7}$

*39. $f(r) = 6\sqrt[3]{r}$

40. $y = 4\sqrt[8]{x^2}$

41. $f(x) = x^{-4}$

42. $f(s) = 2s^{-3}$

43. $f(x) = x^{-3} + x^{-5} - 2x^{-6}$

44. $f(x) = 100x^{-3} + 10x^{1/2}$

45. $y = \frac{1}{x}$

46. $f(x) = \frac{2}{x^3}$

*47. $y = \frac{8}{x^5}$

48. $y = \frac{1}{4x^5}$

49. $g(x) = \frac{4}{3x^3}$

50. $y = \frac{1}{x^2}$

51. $f(t) = \frac{1}{2t}$

52. $g(x) = \frac{7}{9x}$

53. $f(x) = \frac{x}{7} + \frac{7}{x}$

54. $\Phi(x) = \frac{x^3}{3} - \frac{3}{x^3}$

55. $f(x) = -9x^{1/3} + 5x^{-2/5}$

56. $f(z) = 3z^{1/4} - 12^2 - 8z^{-3/4}$

57. $q(x) = \frac{1}{\sqrt[3]{8x^2}}$

58. $f(x) = \frac{3}{\sqrt[4]{x^3}}$

59. $y = \frac{2}{\sqrt{x}}$

60. $y = \frac{1}{2\sqrt{x}}$

61. $y = x^2\sqrt{x}$

62. $f(x) = (2x^3)(4x^2)$

63. $f(x) = x(3x^2 - 10x + 7)$

64. $f(x) = x^3(3x^6 - 5x^2 + 4)$

65. $f(x) = x^3(3x)^2$

66. $s(x) = \sqrt[3]{x}(\sqrt[4]{x} - 6x + 3)$

67. $v(x) = x^{-2/3}(x + 5)$

68. $f(x) = x^{3/5}(x^2 + 7x + 11)$

69. $f(q) = \frac{3q^2 + 4q - 2}{q}$

70. $f(w) = \frac{w - 5}{w^5}$

71. $f(x) = (x + 1)(x + 3)$

72. $f(x) = x^2(x - 2)(x + 4)$

73. $w(x) = \frac{x^2 + x^3}{x^2}$

74. $f(x) = \frac{7x^3 + x}{6\sqrt{x}}$

*For each curve in Problems 75–78, find the slopes at the indicated points.*

*75. $y = 3x^2 + 4x - 8$; $(0, -8)$, $(2, 12)$, $(-3, 7)$

76. $y = 5 - 6x - 2x^3$; $(0, 5)$, $(\frac{3}{2}, -\frac{43}{4})$, $(-3, 77)$

77. $y = 4$; when $x = -4$, $x = 7$, $x = 22$

78. $y = 3x - 4\sqrt{x}$; when $x = 4$, $x = 9$, $x = 25$

*In Problems 79–82, find an equation of the tangent line to the curve at the indicated point.*

79. $y = 4x^2 + 5x + 6$; $(1, 15)$

80. $y = \frac{1 - x^2}{5}$; $(4, -3)$

81. $y = \frac{1}{x^3}$; $\left(2, \frac{1}{8}\right)$

82. $y = -\sqrt[3]{x}$; $(8, -2)$

83. Find an equation of the tangent line to the curve
$$y = 3 + x - 5x^2 + x^4$$
when $x = 0$.

84. Repeat Problem 83 for the curve
$$y = \frac{\sqrt{x}(2 - x^2)}{x}$$
when $x = 4$.

85. Find all points on the curve
$$y = \frac{5}{2}x^2 - x^3$$
where the tangent line is horizontal.

86. Repeat Problem 85 for the curve
$$y = \frac{x^5}{5} - x + 1$$

87. Find all points on the curve
$$y = x^2 - 5x + 3$$
where the slope is 1.

88. Repeat Problem 87 for the curve
$$y = x^4 - 31x + 11$$

89. If $f(x) = \sqrt{x} + \frac{1}{\sqrt{x}}$, evaluate the expression
$$\frac{x - 1}{2x\sqrt{x}} - f'(x)$$

90. **Economics** Eswaran and Kotwal[2] consider agrarian economies in which there are two types of workers, permanent and casual. Permanent workers are employed on long-term contracts and may receive benefits such as holiday gifts and emergency aid. Casual workers are hired on a daily basis and perform routine and menial tasks such as weeding, harvesting, and threshing. The difference $z$ in the present-value cost of hiring a permanent worker over

[2]M. Eswaran and A. Kotwal, "A Theory of Two-Tier Labor Markets in Agrarian Economies," *The American Economic Review*, 75, no. 1 (1985), 162–77.

that of hiring a casual worker is given by

$$z = (1 + b)w_p - bw_c$$

where $w_p$ and $w_c$ are wage rates for permanent labor and casual labor, respectively, $b$ is a constant, and $w_p$ is a function of $w_c$. Eswaran and Kotwal claim that

$$\frac{dz}{dw_c} = (1 + b)\left[\frac{dw_p}{dw_c} - \frac{b}{1+b}\right]$$

Verify this.

**91.** Find an equation of the tangent line to the graph of $y = x^3 - 3x$ at the point $(2, 2)$. Graph both the function and the tangent line on the same screen. Notice that the line passes through $(2, 2)$ and the line appears to be tangent to the curve.

**92.** Find an equation of the tangent line to the graph of $y = \sqrt[3]{x}$, at the point $(-8, -2)$. Graph both the function and the tangent line on the same screen. Notice that the line passes through $(-8, -2)$ and the line appears to be tangent to the curve.

## 11.3  The Derivative as a Rate of Change

**OBJECTIVE**

To motivate the instantaneous rate of change of a function by means of velocity and to interpret the derivative as an instantaneous rate of change. To develop the "marginal" concept, which is frequently used in business and economics.

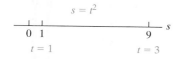

FIGURE 11.14  Motion along a number line.

We have given a geometric interpretation of the derivative as being the slope of the tangent line to a curve at a point. Historically, an important application of the derivative involves the motion of an object traveling in a straight line. This gives us a convenient way to interpret the derivative as a *rate of change.*

To denote the change in a variable such as $x$, the symbol $\Delta x$ (read "delta $x$") is commonly used. For example, if $x$ changes from 1 to 3, then the change in $x$ is $\Delta x = 3 - 1 = 2$. The new value of $x(= 3)$ is the old value plus the change, or $1 + \Delta x$. Similarly, if $t$ increases by $\Delta t$, the new value is $t + \Delta t$. We will use $\Delta$-notation in the discussion that follows.

Suppose an object moves along the number line in Figure 11.14 according to the equation

$$s = f(t) = t^2$$

where $s$ is the position of the object at time $t$. This equation is called an *equation of motion,* and $f$ is called a **position function.** Assume that $t$ is in seconds and $s$ is in meters. At $t = 1$ the position is $s = f(1) = 1^2 = 1$, and at $t = 3$ the position is $s = f(3) = 3^2 = 9$. Over this two-second time interval, the object has a change in position, or a *displacement,* of $9 - 1 = 8$ m, and the *average velocity* of the object is defined as

$$v_{ave} = \frac{\text{displacement}}{\text{length of time interval}} \tag{1}$$

$$= \frac{8}{2} = 4 \text{ m/s}$$

To say that the average velocity is 4 m/s from $t = 1$ to $t = 3$ means that, *on the average,* the position of the object changed by 4 m to the right each second during that time interval. Let us denote the changes in $s$-values and $t$-values by $\Delta s$ and $\Delta t$, respectively. Then the average velocity is given by

$$v_{ave} = \frac{\Delta s}{\Delta t} = 4 \text{ m/s} \quad \text{(for the interval } t = 1 \text{ to } t = 3)$$

The ratio $\Delta s / \Delta t$ is also called the **average rate of change of $s$ with respect to** $t$ over the interval from $t = 1$ to $t = 3$.

Now, let the time interval be only 1 second long (that is, $\Delta t = 1$). Then, for the *shorter* interval from $t = 1$ to $t = 1 + \Delta t = 2$, we have $f(2) = 2^2 = 4$, so

$$v_{ave} = \frac{\Delta s}{\Delta t} = \frac{f(2) - f(1)}{\Delta t} = \frac{4 - 1}{1} = 3 \text{ m/s}$$

More generally, over the time interval from $t = 1$ to $t = 1 + \Delta t$, the object moves from position $f(1)$ to position $f(1 + \Delta t)$. Thus, its displacement is

$$\Delta s = f(1 + \Delta t) - f(1)$$

Since the time interval has length $\Delta t$, the object's average velocity is given by

$$v_{ave} = \frac{\Delta s}{\Delta t} = \frac{f(1 + \Delta t) - f(1)}{\Delta t}$$

**TABLE 11.2**

| Length of Time Interval $\Delta t$ | Time Interval $t = 1$ to $t = 1 + \Delta t$ | Average Velocity, $\dfrac{\Delta s}{\Delta t} = \dfrac{f(1 + \Delta t) - f(1)}{\Delta t}$ |
|---|---|---|
| 0.1 | $t = 1$ to $t = 1.1$ | 2.1   m/s |
| 0.07 | $t = 1$ to $t = 1.07$ | 2.07  m/s |
| 0.05 | $t = 1$ to $t = 1.05$ | 2.05  m/s |
| 0.03 | $t = 1$ to $t = 1.03$ | 2.03  m/s |
| 0.01 | $t = 1$ to $t = 1.01$ | 2.01  m/s |
| 0.001 | $t = 1$ to $t = 1.001$ | 2.001 m/s |

If $\Delta t$ were to become smaller and smaller, the average velocity over the interval from $t = 1$ to $t = 1 + \Delta t$ would be close to what we might call the *instantaneous velocity* at time $t = 1$, that is, the velocity at a *point* in time ($t = 1$), as opposed to the velocity over an *interval* of time. For some typical values of $\Delta t$ between 0.1 and 0.001, we get the average velocities in Table 11.2, which you can verify.

The table suggests that as the length of the time interval approaches zero, the average velocity approaches the value 2 m/s. In other words, as $\Delta t$ approaches 0, $\Delta s / \Delta t$ approaches 2 m/s. We define the limit of the average velocity as $\Delta t \to 0$ to be the **instantaneous velocity** (or simply the **velocity**), $v$, at time $t = 1$. This limit is also called the **instantaneous rate of change** of $s$ with respect to $t$ at $t = 1$:

$$v = \lim_{\Delta t \to 0} v_{\text{ave}} = \lim_{\Delta t \to 0} \frac{\Delta s}{\Delta t} = \lim_{\Delta t \to 0} \frac{f(1 + \Delta t) - f(1)}{\Delta t}$$

If we think of $\Delta t$ as $h$, then the limit on the right is simply the derivative of $s$ with respect to $t$ at $t = 1$. Thus, the instantaneous velocity of the object at $t = 1$ is just $ds/dt$ at $t = 1$. Because $s = t^2$ and

$$\frac{ds}{dt} = 2t$$

the velocity at $t = 1$ is

$$v = \left. \frac{ds}{dt} \right|_{t=1} = 2(1) = 2 \text{ m/s}$$

which confirms our previous conclusion.

In summary, if $s = f(t)$ is the position function of an object moving in a straight line, then the average velocity of the object over the time interval $[t, t + \Delta t]$ is given by

$$v_{\text{ave}} = \frac{\Delta s}{\Delta t} = \frac{f(t + \Delta t) - f(t)}{\Delta t}$$

and the velocity at time $t$ is given by

$$v = \lim_{\Delta t \to 0} \frac{f(t + \Delta t) - f(t)}{\Delta t} = \frac{ds}{dt}$$

Selectively combining equations for $v$, we have

$$\frac{ds}{dt} = \lim_{\Delta t \to 0} \frac{\Delta s}{\Delta t}$$

which provides motivation for the otherwise bizarre Leibniz notation. (After all, $\Delta$ is the [uppercase] Greek letter corresponding to $d$.)

● **EXAMPLE 1**  **Finding Average Velocity and Velocity**

*Suppose the position function of an object moving along a number line is given by $s = f(t) = 3t^2 + 5$, where $t$ is in seconds and $s$ is in meters.*

**a.** Find the average velocity over the interval $[10, 10.1]$.

**b.** Find the velocity when $t = 10$.

**Solution:**

**a.** Here $t = 10$ and $\Delta t = 10.1 - 10 = 0.1$. So we have

$$
\begin{aligned}
v_{\text{ave}} = \frac{\Delta s}{\Delta t} &= \frac{f(t + \Delta t) - f(t)}{\Delta t} \\
&= \frac{f(10 + 0.1) - f(10)}{0.1} \\
&= \frac{f(10.1) - f(10)}{0.1} \\
&= \frac{311.03 - 305}{0.1} = \frac{6.03}{0.1} = 60.3 \text{ m/s}
\end{aligned}
$$

**b.** The velocity at time $t$ is given by

$$
v = \frac{ds}{dt} = 6t
$$

When $t = 10$, the velocity is

$$
\left.\frac{ds}{dt}\right|_{t=10} = 6(10) = 60 \text{ m/s}
$$

Notice that the average velocity over the interval $[10, 10.1]$ is close to the velocity at $t = 10$. This is to be expected because the length of the interval is small.

NOW WORK PROBLEM 1

Our discussion of the rate of change of $s$ with respect to $t$ applies equally well to *any* function $y = f(x)$. This means that we have the following:

If $y = f(x)$, then

$$
\frac{\Delta y}{\Delta x} = \frac{f(x + \Delta x) - f(x)}{\Delta x} = \begin{cases} \text{average rate of change} \\ \text{of } y \text{ with respect to } x \\ \text{over the interval from} \\ x \text{ to } x + \Delta x \end{cases}
$$

and

$$
\frac{dy}{dx} = \lim_{\Delta x \to 0} \frac{\Delta y}{\Delta x} = \begin{cases} \text{instantaneous rate of change} \\ \text{of } y \text{ with respect to } x \end{cases} \tag{2}
$$

Because the instantaneous rate of change of $y = f(x)$ at a point is a derivative, it is also the *slope of the tangent line* to the graph of $y = f(x)$ at that point. For convenience, we usually refer to the instantaneous rate of change simply as the **rate of change.** The interpretation of a derivative as a rate of change is extremely important.

Let us now consider the significance of the rate of change of $y$ with respect to $x$. From Equation (2), if $\Delta x$ (a change in $x$) is close to 0, then $\Delta y / \Delta x$ is close to $dy/dx$. That is,

$$
\frac{\Delta y}{\Delta x} \approx \frac{dy}{dx}
$$

Therefore,

$$
\Delta y \approx \frac{dy}{dx} \Delta x \tag{3}
$$

That is, if $x$ changes by $\Delta x$, then the change in $y$, $\Delta y$, is approximately $dy/dx$ times the change in $x$. In particular,

if $x$ changes by 1, an estimate of the change in $y$ is $\dfrac{dy}{dx}$

ESTIMATING $\Delta P$ BY USING $dP/dP$

Suppose that the profit $P$ made by selling a certain product at a price of $p$ per unit is given by $P = f(p)$ and the rate of change of that profit with respect to change in price is $\frac{dP}{dp} = 5$ at $p = 25$. Estimate the change in the profit $P$ if the price changes from 25 to 25.5.

FINDING A RATE OF CHANGE

The position of an object thrown upward at a speed of 16 feet/s from a height of 0 feet is given by $y(t) = 16t - 16t^2$. Find the rate of change of $y$ with respect to $t$, and evaluate it when $t = 0.5$. Use your graphing calculator to graph $y(t)$. Use the graph to interpret the behavior of the object when $t = 0.5$.

● EXAMPLE 2  **Estimating $\Delta y$ by Using $dy/dx$**

*Suppose that $y = f(x)$ and $\frac{dy}{dx} = 8$ when $x = 3$. Estimate the change in y if x changes from 3 to 3.5.*

**Solution:** We have $dy/dx = 8$ and $\Delta x = 3.5 - 3 = 0.5$. The change in $y$ is given by $\Delta y$, and, from Equation (3),

$$\Delta y \approx \frac{dy}{dx}\Delta x = 8(0.5) = 4$$

We remark that, since $\Delta y = f(3.5) - f(3)$, we have $f(3.5) = f(3) + \Delta y$. For example, if $f(3) = 5$, then $f(3.5)$ can be estimated by $5 + 4 = 9$.

● EXAMPLE 3  **Finding a Rate of Change**

*Find the rate of change of $y = x^4$ with respect to x, and evaluate it when $x = 2$ and when $x = -1$. Interpret your results.*

**Solution:** The rate of change is

$$\frac{dy}{dx} = 4x^3.$$

When $x = 2, dy/dx = 4(2)^3 = 32$. This means that if $x$ increases, from 2, by a small amount, then $y$ increases approximately 32 times as much. More simply, we say that, when $x = 2$, $y$ is increasing 32 times as fast as $x$ does. When $x = -1$, $dy/dx = 4(-1)^3 = -4$. The significance of the minus sign on $-4$ is that, when $x = -1$, $y$ is *decreasing* 4 times as fast as $x$ increases.

NOW WORK PROBLEM 11

● EXAMPLE 4  **Rate of Change of Price with Respect to Quantity**

*Let $p = 100 - q^2$ be the demand function for a manufacturer's product. Find the rate of change of price p per unit with respect to quantity q. How fast is the price changing with respect to q when $q = 5$? Assume that p is in dollars.*

**Solution:** The rate of change of $p$ with respect to $q$ is

$$\frac{dp}{dq} = \frac{d}{dq}(100 - q^2) = -2q$$

Thus,

$$\left.\frac{dp}{dq}\right|_{q=5} = -2(5) = -10$$

This means that when five units are demanded, an *increase* of one extra unit demanded corresponds to a decrease of approximately \$10 in the price per unit that consumers are willing to pay.

● EXAMPLE 5  **Rate of Change of Volume**

*A spherical balloon is being filled with air. Find the rate of change of the volume of air in the balloon with respect to its radius. Evaluate this rate of change when the radius is 2 ft.*

**Solution:** The formula for the volume $V$ of a ball of radius $r$ is $V = \frac{4}{3}\pi r^3$. The rate of change of $V$ with respect to $r$ is

$$\frac{dV}{dr} = \frac{4}{3}\pi(3r^2) = 4\pi r^2$$

When $r = 2$ ft, the rate of change is

$$\left.\frac{dV}{dr}\right|_{r=2} = 4\pi(2)^2 = 16\pi \, \frac{\text{ft}^3}{\text{ft}}$$

This means that when the radius is 2 ft, changing the radius by 1 ft will change the volume by approximately $16\pi$ ft³.

● **EXAMPLE 6   Rate of Change of Enrollment**

*A sociologist is studying various suggested programs that can aid in the education of preschool-age children in a certain city. The sociologist believes that x years after the beginning of a particular program, f(x) thousand preschoolers will be enrolled, where*

$$f(x) = \frac{10}{9}(12x - x^2) \quad 0 \le x \le 12$$

*At what rate would enrollment change (a) after three years from the start of this program and (b) after nine years?*

**Solution:** The rate of change of $f(x)$ is

$$f'(x) = \frac{10}{9}(12 - 2x)$$

a. After three years, the rate of change is

$$f'(3) = \frac{10}{9}(12 - 2(3)) = \frac{10}{9} \cdot 6 = \frac{20}{3} = 6\frac{2}{3}$$

Thus, enrollment would be increasing at the rate of $6\frac{2}{3}$ thousand preschoolers per year.

b. After nine years, the rate is

$$f'(9) = \frac{10}{9}(12 - 2(9)) = \frac{10}{9}(-6) = -\frac{20}{3} = -6\frac{2}{3}$$

Thus, enrollment would be *decreasing* at the rate of $6\frac{2}{3}$ thousand preschoolers per year.

NOW WORK PROBLEM 9 ●●

## Applications of Rate of Change to Economics

A manufacturer's **total-cost function,** $c = f(q)$, gives the total cost $c$ of producing and marketing $q$ units of a product. The rate of change of $c$ with respect to $q$ is called the **marginal cost.** Thus,

$$\text{marginal cost} = \frac{dc}{dq}$$

For example, suppose $c = f(q) = 0.1q^2 + 3$ is a cost function, where $c$ is in dollars and $q$ is in pounds. Then

$$\frac{dc}{dq} = 0.2q$$

The marginal cost when 4 lb are produced is $dc/dq$, evaluated when $q = 4$:

$$\left.\frac{dc}{dq}\right|_{q=4} = 0.2(4) = 0.80$$

This means that if production is increased by 1 lb, from 4 lb to 5 lb, then the change in cost is approximately $0.80. That is, the additional pound costs about $0.80. In general, *we interpret marginal cost as the approximate cost of one additional unit of output.* After all, the difference $f(q+1) - f(q)$ can be seen as a difference quotient

$$\frac{f(q+1) - f(q)}{1}$$

(the case where $h = 1$). Any difference quotient can be regarded as an approximation of the corresponding derivative and, conversely, any derivative can be regarded as an approximation of any of its corresponding difference quotients. Thus, for any function $f$ of $q$ we can always regard $f'(q)$ and $f(q + 1) - f(q)$ as approximations of each other. In economics, the latter can usually be regarded as the exact value of the cost, or profit depending upon the function, of the $(q + 1)$th item when $q$ are produced. The derivative is often easier to compute than the exact value. (In the case at hand, the actual cost of producing one more pound beyond 4 lb is $f(5) - f(4) = 5.5 - 4.6 = \$0.90$.)

If $c$ is the total cost of producing $q$ units of a product, then the **average cost per unit**, $\bar{c}$, is

$$\bar{c} = \frac{c}{q} \tag{4}$$

For example, if the total cost of 20 units is \$100, then the average cost per unit is $\bar{c} = 100/20 = \$5$. By multiplying both sides of Equation (4) by $q$, we have

$$c = q\bar{c}$$

That is, total cost is the product of the number of units produced and the average cost per unit.

### ●EXAMPLE 7   Marginal Cost

*If a manufacturer's average-cost equation is*

$$\bar{c} = 0.0001q^2 - 0.02q + 5 + \frac{5000}{q}$$

*find the marginal-cost function. What is the marginal cost when 50 units are produced?*

**Solution:**

> **Strategy**   The marginal-cost function is the derivative of the total-cost function $c$. Thus, we first find $c$ by multiplying $\bar{c}$ by $q$. We have

$$c = q\bar{c}$$

$$= q \left( 0.0001q^2 - 0.02q + 5 + \frac{5000}{q} \right)$$

$$c = 0.0001q^3 - 0.02q^2 + 5q + 5000$$

Differentiating $c$, we have the marginal-cost function:

$$\frac{dc}{dq} = 0.0001(3q^2) - 0.02(2q) + 5(1) + 0$$

$$= 0.0003q^2 - 0.04q + 5$$

The marginal cost when 50 units are produced is

$$\left. \frac{dc}{dq} \right|_{q=50} = 0.0003(50)^2 - 0.04(50) + 5 = 3.75$$

If $c$ is in dollars and production is increased by one unit, from $q = 50$ to $q = 51$, then the cost of the additional unit is approximately \$3.75. If production is increased by $\frac{1}{3}$ unit, from $q = 50$, then the cost of the additional output is approximately $\left( \frac{1}{3} \right)(3.75) = \$1.25$.

NOW WORK PROBLEM 21 ●●●

Suppose $r = f(q)$ is the **total-revenue function** for a manufacturer. The equation $r = f(q)$ states that the total dollar value received for selling $q$ units of a product is $r$. The **marginal revenue** is defined as the rate of change of the total dollar value received with respect to the total number of units sold. Hence, marginal revenue is merely the derivative of $r$ with respect to $q$:

$$\text{marginal revenue} = \frac{dr}{dq}$$

Marginal revenue indicates the rate at which revenue changes with respect to units sold. We interpret it as *the approximate revenue received from selling one additional unit of output.*

### ● EXAMPLE 8   Marginal Revenue

Suppose a manufacturer sells a product at $2 per unit. If $q$ units are sold, the total revenue is given by

$$r = 2q$$

The marginal-revenue function is

$$\frac{dr}{dq} = \frac{d}{dq}(2q) = 2$$

which is a constant function. Thus, the marginal revenue is 2 regardless of the number of units sold. This is what we would expect, because the manufacturer receives $2 for each unit sold.

NOW WORK PROBLEM 23 ●●

### Relative and Percentage Rates of Change

For the total-revenue function in Example 8, namely, $r = f(q) = 2q$, we have

$$\frac{dr}{dq} = 2$$

This means that revenue is changing at the rate of $2 per unit, regardless of the number of units sold. Although this is valuable information, it may be more significant when compared to $r$ itself. For example, if $q = 50$, then $r = 2(50) = 100$. Thus, the rate of change of revenue is $2/100 = 0.02$ *of* $r$. On the other hand, if $q = 5000$, then $r = 2(5000) = \$10,000$, so the rate of change of $r$ is $2/10,000 = 0.0002$ *of* $r$. Although $r$ changes at the same rate at each level, compared to $r$ itself, this rate is relatively smaller when $r = 10,000$ than when $r = 100$. By considering the ratio

$$\frac{dr/dq}{r}$$

we have a means of comparing the rate of change of $r$ with $r$ itself. This ratio is called the *relative rate of change* of $r$. We have shown that the relative rate of change when $q = 50$ is

$$\frac{dr/dq}{r} = \frac{2}{100} = 0.02$$

and when $q = 5000$, it is

$$\frac{dr/dq}{r} = \frac{2}{10,000} = 0.0002$$

**CAUTION**

Percentages can be confusing! Remember that *percent* means "per hundred." Thus $100\% = \frac{100}{100} = 1$, $2\% = \frac{2}{100} = 0.02$ and so on.

By multiplying relative rates by 100%, we obtain the so-called *percentage rates of change.* The percentage rate of change when $q = 50$ is $(0.02)(100\%) = 2\%$; when $q = 5000$, it is $(0.0002)(100\%) = 0.02\%$. For example, if an additional unit beyond 50 is sold, then revenue increases by approximately 2%.

In general, for any function $f$, we have the following definition:

**DEFINITION**

The *relative rate of change* of $f(x)$ is

$$\frac{f'(x)}{f(x)}$$

The *percentage rate of change* of $f(x)$ is

$$\frac{f'(x)}{f(x)} \cdot 100\%$$

**PRINCIPLES IN PRACTICE 3**

**RELATIVE AND PERCENTAGE RATES OF CHANGE**

The volume $V$ enclosed by a capsule-shaped container with a cylindrical height of 4 feet and radius $r$ is given by

$$V(r) = \frac{4}{3}\pi r^3 + 4\pi r^2$$

Determine the relative and percentage rates of change of volume with respect to the radius when the radius is 2 feet.

● **EXAMPLE 9    Relative and Percentage Rates of Change**

*Determine the relative and percentage rates of change of*

$$y = f(x) = 3x^2 - 5x + 25$$

*when $x = 5$.*

**Solution:**  Here

$$f'(x) = 6x - 5$$

Since $f'(5) = 6(5) - 5 = 25$ and $f(5) = 3(5)^2 - 5(5) + 25 = 75$, the relative rate of change of $y$ when $x = 5$ is

$$\frac{f'(5)}{f(5)} = \frac{25}{75} \approx 0.333$$

Multiplying 0.333 by 100% gives the percentage rate of change: $(0.333)(100) = 33.3\%$.

NOW WORK PROBLEM 35  ●●●

## Problems 11.3

**\*1.** Suppose that the position function of an object moving along a straight line is $s = f(t) = 2t^2 + 3t$, where $t$ is in seconds and $s$ is in meters. Find the average velocity $\Delta s/\Delta t$ over the interval $[1, 1 + \Delta t]$, where $\Delta t$ is given in the following table:

| $\Delta t$ | 1 | 0.5 | 0.2 | 0.1 | 0.01 | 0.001 |
|---|---|---|---|---|---|---|
| $\Delta s/\Delta t$ | | | | | | |

From your results, estimate the velocity when $t = 1$. Verify your estimate by using differentiation.

**2.** If $y = f(x) = \sqrt{2x + 5}$, find the average rate of change of $y$ with respect to $x$ over the interval $[3, 3 + \Delta x]$, where $\Delta x$ is given in the following table:

| $\Delta x$ | 1 | 0.5 | 0.2 | 0.1 | 0.01 | 0.001 |
|---|---|---|---|---|---|---|
| $\Delta y/\Delta x$ | | | | | | |

From your result, estimate the rate of change of $y$ with respect to $x$ when $x = 3$.

*In each of Problems 3–8, a position function is given, where $t$ is in seconds and $s$ is in meters.*

(a) *Find the position at the given t-value.*
(b) *Find the average velocity over the given interval.*
(c) *Find the velocity at the given t-value.*

**3.** $s = 2t^2 - 4t$; $[7, 7.5]$; $t = 7$

**4.** $s = \frac{1}{2}t + 1$; $[2, 2.1]$; $t = 2$

**5.** $s = 2t^3 + 6$; $[1, 1.02]$; $t = 1$

**6.** $s = -3t^2 + 2t + 1$; $[1, 1.25]$; $t = 1$

**7.** $s = t^4 - 2t^3 + t$; $[2, 2.1]$; $t = 2$

**8.** $s = 3t^4 - t^{7/2}$; $[0, \frac{1}{4}]$; $t = 0$

**\*9. Income–Education**  Sociologists studied the relation between income and number of years of education for members of a particular urban group. They found that a person with $x$ years of education before seeking regular employment can expect to receive an average yearly income of $y$ dollars per year, where

$$y = 5x^{5/2} + 5900 \qquad 4 \le x \le 16$$

Find the rate of change of income with respect to number of years of education. Evaluation the expression when $x = 9$.

**10.** Find the rate of change of the area $A$ of a disc, with respect to its radius $r$, when $r = 3$ m. The area $A$ of a disc as a function of its radius $r$ is given by

$$A = A(r) = \pi r^2$$

**\*11. Skin Temperature**  The approximate temperature $T$ of the skin in terms of the temperature $T_e$ of the environment is given by

$$T = 32.8 + 0.27(T_e - 20)$$

where $T$ and $T_e$ are in degrees Celsius.[3] Find the rate of change of $T$ with respect to $T_e$.

**12. Biology**   The volume $V$ of a spherical cell is given by $V = \frac{4}{3}\pi r^3$, where $r$ is the radius. Find the rate of change of volume with respect to the radius when $r = 6.3 \times 10^{-4}$ cm.

*In Problems 13–18, cost functions are given, where c is the cost of producing q units of a product. In each case, find the marginal-cost function. What is the marginal cost at the given value(s) of q?*

**13.** $c = 500 + 10q; q = 100$

**14.** $c = 5000 + 6q; q = 36$

**15.** $c = 0.1q^2 + 3q + 450; q = 5$

**16.** $c = 0.1q^2 + 3q + 2; q = 3$

**17.** $c = q^2 + 50q + 1000; q = 15, q = 16, q = 17$

**18.** $c = 0.04q^3 - 0.5q^2 + 4.4q + 7500; q = 5, q = 25, q = 1000$

*In Problems 19–22, $\bar{c}$ represents average cost per unit, which is a function of the number q of units produced. Find the marginal-cost function and the marginal cost for the indicated values of q.*

**19.** $\bar{c} = 0.01q + 5 + \dfrac{500}{q}; q = 50, q = 100$

**20.** $\bar{c} = 2 + \dfrac{1000}{q}; q = 25, q = 235$

**\*21.** $\bar{c} = 0.00002q^2 - 0.01q + 6 + \dfrac{20,000}{q}; q = 100, q = 500$

**22.** $\bar{c} = 0.002q^2 - 0.5q + 60 + \dfrac{7000}{q}; q = 15, q = 25$

*In Problems 23–26, r represents total revenue and is a function of the number q of units sold. Find the marginal-revenue function and the marginal revenue for the indicated values of q.*

**\*23.** $r = 0.8q; q = 9, q = 300, q = 500$

**24.** $r = q\left(15 - \frac{1}{30}q\right); q = 5, q = 15, q = 150$

**25.** $r = 250q + 45q^2 - q^3; q = 5, q = 10, q = 25$

**26.** $r = 2q(30 - 0.1q); q = 10, q = 20$

**27. Hosiery Mill**   The total-cost function for a hosiery mill is estimated by Dean[4] to be

$$c = -10,484.69 + 6.750q - 0.000328q^2$$

where $q$ is output in dozens of pairs and $c$ is total cost in dollars. Find the marginal-cost function and the average cost function and evaluate each when $q = 2000$.

**28. Light and Power Plant**   The total-cost function for an electric light and power plant is estimated by Nordin[5] to be

$$c = 32.07 - 0.79q + 0.02142q^2 - 0.0001q^3 \quad 20 \le q \le 90$$

where $q$ is the eight-hour total output (as a percentage of capacity) and $c$ is the total fuel cost in dollars. Find the marginal-cost function and evaluate it when $q = 70$.

**29. Urban Concentration**   Suppose the 100 largest cities in the United States in 1920 are ranked according to magnitude (areas of cities). From Lotka,[6] the following relation holds approximately:

$$PR^{0.93} = 5,000,000$$

Here, $P$ is the population of the city having respective rank $R$. This relation is called the *law of urban concentration* for 1920. Solve for $P$ in terms of $R$, and then find how fast the population is changing with respect to rank.

**30. Depreciation**   Under the straight-line method of depreciation, the value $v$ of a certain machine after $t$ years have elapsed is given by

$$v = 85,000 - 10,500t$$

where $0 \le t \le 9$. How fast is $v$ changing with respect to $t$ when $t = 2$? $t = 3$? at any time?

**31. Winter Moth**   A study of the winter moth was made in Nova Scotia (adapted from Embree).[7] The prepupae of the moth fall onto the ground from host trees. At a distance of $x$ ft from the base of a host tree, the prepupal density (number of prepupae per square foot of soil) was $y$, where

$$y = 59.3 - 1.5x - 0.5x^2 \quad 1 \le x \le 9$$

**(a)** At what rate is the prepupal density changing with respect to distance from the base of the tree when $x = 6$?

**(b)** For what value of $x$ is the prepupal density decreasing at the rate of 6 prepupae per square foot per foot?

**32. Cost Function**   For the cost function

$$c = 0.4q^2 + 4q + 5$$

find the rate of change of $c$ with respect to $q$ when $q = 2$. Also, what is $\Delta c/\Delta q$ over the interval $[2, 3]$?

*In Problems 33–38, find (a) the rate of change of y with respect to x and (b) the relative rate of change of y. At the given value of x, find (c) the rate of change of y, (d) the relative rate of change of y, and (e) the percentage rate of change of y.*

**33.** $y = f(x) = x + 4; x = 5$

**34.** $y = f(x) = 7 - 3x; x = 6$

**\*35.** $y = 3x^2 + 7; x = 2$

**36.** $y = 5 - 3x^3; x = 1$

**37.** $y = 8 - x^3; x = 1$

**38.** $y = x^2 + 3x - 4; x = -1$

**39. Cost Function**   For the cost function

$$c = 0.3q^2 + 3.5q + 9$$

how fast does $c$ change with respect to $q$ when $q = 10$? Determine the percentage rate of change of $c$ with respect to $q$ when $q = 10$.

---

[3]R. W. Stacy et al., *Essentials of Biological and Medical Physics* (New York: McGraw-Hill Book Company, 1955).

[4]J. Dean, "Statistical Cost Functions of a Hosiery Mill," *Studies in Business Administration*, XI, no. 4 (Chicago: University of Chicago Press, 1941).

[5]J. A. Nordin, "Note on a Light Plant's Cost Curves," *Econometrica*, 15 (1947), 231–35.

[6]A. J. Lotka, *Elements of Mathematical Biology* (New York: Dover Publications, Inc., 1956).

[7]D. G. Embree, "The Population Dynamics of the Winter Moth in Nova Scotia, 1954–1962," *Memoirs of the Entomological Society of Canada*, no. 46 (1965).

**40. Organic Matters/Species Diversity** In a discussion of contemporary waters of shallows seas, Odum[8] claims that in such waters the total organic matter $y$ (in milligrams per liter) is a function of species diversity $x$ (in number of species per thousand individuals). If $y = 100/x$, at what rate is the total organic matter changing with respect to species diversity when $x = 10$? What is the percentage rate of change when $x = 10$?

**41. Revenue** For a certain manufacturer, the revenue obtained from the sale of $q$ units of a product is given by

$$r = 30q - 0.3q^2$$

(a) How fast does $r$ change with respect to $q$? When $q = 10$, (b) find the relative rate of change of $r$, and (c) to the nearest percent, find the percentage rate of change of $r$.

**42. Revenue** Repeat Problem 43 for the revenue function given by $r = 10q - 0.2q^2$ and $q = 25$.

**43. Weight of Limb** The weight of a limb of a tree is given by $W = 2t^{0.432}$, where $t$ is time. Find the relative rate of change of $W$ with respect to $t$.

**44. Response to Shock** A psychological experiment[9] was conducted to analyze human responses to electrical shocks (stimuli). The subjects received shocks of various intensities. The response $R$ to a shock of intensity $I$ (in microamperes) was to be a number that indicated the perceived magnitude relative to that of a "standard" shock. The standard shock was assigned a magnitude of 10. Two groups of subjects were tested under slightly different conditions. The responses $R_1$ and $R_2$ of the first and second groups to a shock of intensity $I$ were given by

$$R_1 = \frac{I^{1.3}}{1855.24} \quad 800 \le I \le 3500$$

and

$$R_2 = \frac{I^{1.3}}{1101.29} \quad 800 \le I \le 3500$$

(a) For each group, determine the relative rate of change of response with respect to intensity.
(b) How do these changes compare with each other?
(c) In general, if $f(x) = C_1 x^n$ and $g(x) = C_2 x^n$, where $C_1$ and $C_2$ are constants, how do the relative rates of change of $f$ and $g$ compare?

**45. Cost** A manufacturer of mountain bikes has found that when 20 bikes are produced per day, the average cost is $150 and the marginal cost is $125. Based on that information, approximate the total cost of producing 21 bikes per day.

**46. Marginal and Average Costs** Suppose that the cost function for a certain product is $c = f(q)$. If the relative rate of change of $c$ (with respect to $q$) is $\dfrac{1}{q}$, prove that the marginal-cost function and the average-cost function are equal.

*In Problems 47 and 48, use the numerical derivative feature of your graphing calculator.*

**47.** If the total-cost function for a manufacturer is given by

$$c = \frac{5q^2}{\sqrt{q^2 + 3}} + 5000$$

where $c$ is in dollars, find the marginal cost when 10 units are produced. Round your answer to the nearest cent.

**48.** The population of a city $t$ years from now is given by

$$P = 250{,}000e^{0.04t}$$

Find the rate of change of population with respect to time $t$ three years from now. Round your answer to the nearest integer.

---

To find derivatives by applying the product and quotient rules, and to develop the concepts of marginal propensity to consume and marginal propensity to save.

# 11.4 The Product Rule and the Quotient Rule

The equation $F(x) = (x^2 + 3x)(4x + 5)$ expresses $F(x)$ as a product of two functions: $x^2 + 3x$ and $4x + 5$. To find $F'(x)$ by using only our previous rules, we first multiply the functions. Then we differentiate the result, term by term:

$$F(x) = (x^2 + 3x)(4x + 5) = 4x^3 + 17x^2 + 15x$$

$$F'(x) = 12x^2 + 34x + 15 \tag{1}$$

However, in many problems that involve differentiating a product of functions, the multiplication is not as simple as it is here. At times, it is not even practical to attempt it. Fortunately, there is a rule for differentiating a product, and the rule avoids such multiplications. Since the derivative of a sum of functions is the sum of their derivatives, you might expect a similar rule for products. However, the situation is rather subtle.

---

[8]H. T. Odum, "Biological Circuits and the Marine Systems of Texas," in *Pollution and Marine Biology*, ed. T. A. Olsen and F. J. Burgess (New York: Interscience Publishers, 1967).

[9]H. Babkoff, "Magnitude Estimation of Short Electrocutaneous Pulses," *Psychological Research*, 39, no. 1 (1976), 39–49.

**RULE 1   The Product Rule**

If $f$ and $g$ are differentiable functions, then the product $fg$ is differentiable, and

$$\frac{d}{dx}(f(x)g(x)) = f'(x)g(x) + f(x)g'(x)$$

That is, the derivative of the product of two functions is the derivative of the first function times the second, plus the first function times the derivative of the second.

$$\frac{d}{dx}(\text{product}) = \begin{pmatrix}\text{derivative}\\ \text{of first}\end{pmatrix}(\text{second}) + (\text{first})\begin{pmatrix}\text{derivative}\\ \text{of second}\end{pmatrix}$$

*Proof.* If $F(x) = f(x)g(x)$, then, by the definition of the derivative of $F$,

$$F'(x) = \lim_{h\to 0}\frac{F(x+h) - F(x)}{h}$$

$$= \lim_{h\to 0}\frac{f(x+h)g(x+h) - f(x)g(x)}{h}$$

Now we use a "trick." Adding and subtracting $f(x)g(x+h)$ in the numerator, we have

$$F'(x) = \lim_{h\to 0}\frac{f(x+h)g(x+h) - f(x)g(x) + f(x)g(x+h) - f(x)g(x+h)}{h}$$

Regrouping gives

$$F'(x) = \lim_{h\to 0}\frac{(f(x+h)g(x+h) - f(x)g(x+h)) + (f(x)g(x+h) - f(x)g(x))}{h}$$

$$= \lim_{h\to 0}\frac{(f(x+h) - f(x))g(x+h) + f(x)(g(x+h) - g(x))}{h}$$

$$= \lim_{h\to 0}\frac{(f(x+h) - f(x))g(x+h)}{h} + \lim_{h\to 0}\frac{f(x)(g(x+h) - g(x))}{h}$$

$$= \lim_{h\to 0}\frac{f(x+h) - f(x)}{h}\cdot\lim_{h\to 0}g(x+h) + \lim_{h\to 0}f(x)\cdot\lim_{h\to 0}\frac{g(x+h) - g(x)}{h}$$

Since we assumed that $f$ and $g$ are differentiable,

$$\lim_{h\to 0}\frac{f(x+h) - f(x)}{h} = f'(x)$$

and

$$\lim_{h\to 0}\frac{g(x+h) - g(x)}{h} = g'(x)$$

The differentiability of $g$ implies that $g$ is continuous, so from Section 10.3,

$$\lim_{h\to 0}g(x+h) = g(x)$$

Thus,

$$F'(x) = f'(x)g(x) + f(x)g'(x)$$

●**EXAMPLE 1   Applying the Product Rule**

*If* $F(x) = (x^2 + 3x)(4x + 5)$, *find* $F'(x)$.

**Solution:** We will consider $F$ as a product of two functions:

$$F(x) = \underbrace{(x^2 + 3x)}_{f(x)}\underbrace{(4x + 5)}_{g(x)}$$

Therefore, we can apply the product rule:

$$F'(x) = f'(x)g(x) + f(x)g'(x)$$

$$= \underbrace{\frac{d}{dx}(x^2 + 3x)}_{\substack{\text{Derivative} \\ \text{of first}}} \underbrace{(4x + 5)}_{\text{Second}} + \underbrace{(x^2 + 3x)}_{\text{First}} \underbrace{\frac{d}{dx}(4x + 5)}_{\substack{\text{Derivative} \\ \text{of second}}}$$

$$= (2x + 3)(4x + 5) + (x^2 + 3x)(4)$$

$$= 12x^2 + 34x + 15 \qquad \text{(simplifying)}$$

This agrees with our previous result. (See Equation (1).) Although there doesn't seem to be much advantage to using the product rule here, you will see that there are times when it is impractical to avoid it.

NOW WORK PROBLEM 1 ●●

●**EXAMPLE 2    Applying the Product Rule**

*If $y = (x^{2/3} + 3)(x^{-1/3} + 5x)$, find $dy/dx$.*

**Solution:** Applying the product rule gives

$$\frac{dy}{dx} = \frac{d}{dx}(x^{2/3} + 3)(x^{-1/3} + 5x) + (x^{2/3} + 3)\frac{d}{dx}(x^{-1/3} + 5x)$$

$$= \left(\frac{2}{3}x^{-1/3}\right)(x^{-1/3} + 5x) + (x^{2/3} + 3)\left(\frac{-1}{3}x^{-4/3} + 5\right)$$

$$= \frac{25}{3}x^{2/3} + \frac{1}{3}x^{-2/3} - x^{-4/3} + 15$$

Alternatively, we could have found the derivative without the product rule by first finding the product $(x^{2/3} + 3)(x^{-1/3} + 5x)$ and then differentiating the result, term by term.

NOW WORK PROBLEM 15 ●●

●**EXAMPLE 3    Differentiating a Product of Three Factors**

*If $y = (x + 2)(x + 3)(x + 4)$, find $y'$.*

**Solution:**

**Strategy**    We would like to use the product rule, but as given it applies only to *two* factors. By treating the first two factors as a single factor, we can consider $y$ to be a product of two functions:

$$y = [(x + 2)(x + 3)](x + 4)$$

The product rule gives

$$y' = \frac{d}{dx}[(x + 2)(x + 3)](x + 4) + [(x + 2)(x + 3)]\frac{d}{dx}(x + 4)$$

$$= \frac{d}{dx}[(x + 2)(x + 3)](x + 4) + [(x + 2)(x + 3)](1)$$

Applying the product rule again, we have

$$y' = \left(\frac{d}{dx}(x + 2)(x + 3) + (x + 2)\frac{d}{dx}(x + 3)\right)(x + 4) + (x + 2)(x + 3)$$

$$= [(1)(x + 3) + (x + 2)(1)](x + 4) + (x + 2)(x + 3)$$

After simplifying, we obtain

$$y' = 3x^2 + 18x + 26$$

Two other ways of finding the derivative are as follows:

**1.** Multiply the first two factors of $y$ to obtain

$$y = (x^2 + 5x + 6)(x + 4)$$

and then apply the product rule.

**2.** Multiply all three factors to obtain

$$y = x^3 + 9x^2 + 26x + 24$$

and then differentiate term by term.

NOW WORK PROBLEM 19

It is sometimes helpful to remember differentiation rules in more streamlined notation. For example,

$$(fg)' = f'g + fg'$$

is a correct equality of functions that expresses the product rule. We can then calculate

$$(fgh)' = ((fg)h)'$$
$$= (fg)'h + (fg)h'$$
$$= (f'g + fg')h + (fg)h'$$
$$= f'gh + fg'h + fgh'$$

It is not suggested that you try to commit to memory derived rules like

$$(fgh)' = f'gh + fg'h + fgh'$$

Because $f'g + fg' = gf' + fg'$, using commutativity of the product of functions, we can express the product rule with the derivatives as second factors:

$$(fg)' = gf' + fg'$$

and using commutativity of addition

$$(fg)' = fg' + gf'$$

Some people prefer these forms.

**DERIVATIVE OF A PRODUCT WITHOUT THE PRODUCT RULE**

One hour after $x$ milligrams of a particular drug are given to a person, the change in body temperature $T(x)$, in degrees Fahrenheit, is given approximately by $T(x) = x^2 \left(1 - \frac{x}{3}\right)$. The rate at which $T$ changes with respect to the size of the dosage $x$, $T'(x)$, is called the *sensitivity* of the body to the dosage. Find the sensitivity when the dosage is 1 milligram. Do not use the product rule.

● **EXAMPLE 4   Using the Product Rule to Find Slope**

*Find the slope of the graph of $f(x) = (7x^3 - 5x + 2)(2x^4 + 7)$ when $x = 1$.*

**Solution:**

**Strategy**   We find the slope by evaluating the derivative when $x = 1$. Because $f$ is a product of two functions, we can find the derivative by using the product rule.

We have

$$f'(x) = (7x^3 - 5x + 2)\frac{d}{dx}(2x^4 + 7) + (2x^4 + 7)\frac{d}{dx}(7x^3 - 5x + 2)$$
$$= (7x^3 - 5x + 2)(8x^3) + (2x^4 + 7)(21x^2 - 5)$$

Since we must compute $f'(x)$ when $x = 1$, *there is no need to simplify $f'(x)$ before evaluating it.* Substituting into $f'(x)$, we obtain

$$f'(1) = 4(8) + 9(16) = 176$$

NOW WORK PROBLEM 49

The product rule (and quotient rule that follows) should not be applied when a more direct and efficient method is available.

Usually, we do not use the product rule when simpler ways are obvious. For example, if $f(x) = 2x(x+3)$, then it is quicker to write $f(x) = 2x^2 + 6x$, from which $f'(x) = 4x + 6$. Similarly, we do not usually use the product rule to differentiate $y = 4(x^2 - 3)$. Since the 4 is a constant factor, by the constant-factor rule we have $y' = 4(2x) = 8x$.

The next rule is used for differentiating a *quotient* of two functions.

**RULE 2    The Quotient Rule**

If $f$ and $g$ are differentiable functions and $g(x) \neq 0$, then the quotient $f/g$ is also differentiable, and

$$\frac{d}{dx}\left(\frac{f(x)}{g(x)}\right) = \frac{g(x)\,f'(x) - f(x)g'(x)}{(g(x))^2}$$

With the understanding about the denominator not being zero, we can write

$$\left(\frac{f}{g}\right)' = \frac{gf' - fg'}{g^2}$$

That is, the derivative of the quotient of two functions is the denominator times the derivative of the numerator, minus the numerator times the derivative of the denominator, all divided by the square of the denominator.

$$\frac{d}{dx}(\text{quotient})$$

$$= \frac{(\text{denominator})\left(\begin{array}{c}\text{derivative}\\\text{of numerator}\end{array}\right) - (\text{numerator})\left(\begin{array}{c}\text{derivative}\\\text{of denominator}\end{array}\right)}{(\text{denominator})^2}$$

*Proof.* If $F(x) = \dfrac{f(x)}{g(x)}$, then

$$F(x)g(x) = f(x)$$

By the product rule,

$$F(x)g'(x) + g(x)F'(x) = f'(x)$$

Solving for $F'(x)$, we have

$$F'(x) = \frac{f'(x) - F(x)g'(x)}{g(x)}$$

But $F(x) = f(x)/g(x)$. Thus,

$$F'(x) = \frac{f'(x) - \dfrac{f(x)g'(x)}{g(x)}}{g(x)}$$

 **C A U T I O N**

The derivative of the quotient of two functions is trickier still than the product rule. One must remember where the minus sign goes!

Simplifying gives[10]

$$F'(x) = \frac{g(x)\,f'(x) - f(x)g'(x)}{(g(x))^2}$$

● **EXAMPLE 5    Applying the Quotient Rule**

*If* $F(x) = \dfrac{4x^2 + 3}{2x - 1}$, *find* $F'(x)$.

**Solution:**

**Strategy**   We recognize $F$ as a quotient, so we can apply the quotient rule.

---

[10]You may have observed that this proof assumes the existence of $F'(x)$. However, the rule can be proven without this assumption.

Let $f(x) = 4x^2 + 3$ and $g(x) = 2x - 1$. Then

$$F'(x) = \frac{g(x)f'(x) - f(x)g'(x)}{(g(x))^2}$$

$$= \frac{\overset{\text{Denominator}}{\overbrace{(2x-1)}}\,\overset{\substack{\text{Derivative}\\\text{of numerator}}}{\overbrace{\dfrac{d}{dx}(4x^2+3)}} - \overset{\text{Numerator}}{\overbrace{(4x^2+3)}}\,\overset{\substack{\text{Derivative of}\\\text{numerator}}}{\overbrace{\dfrac{d}{dx}(2x-1)}}}{\underset{\substack{\text{Square of}\\\text{denominator}}}{\underbrace{(2x-1)^2}}}$$

$$= \frac{(2x-1)(8x) - (4x^2+3)(2)}{(2x-1)^2}$$

$$= \frac{8x^2 - 8x - 6}{(2x-1)^2} = \frac{2(2x+1)(2x-3)}{(2x-1)^2}$$

NOW WORK PROBLEM 21

## EXAMPLE 6   Rewriting before Differentiating

*Differentiate* $y = \dfrac{1}{x + \dfrac{1}{x+1}}$.

**Solution:**

**Strategy**   To simplify the differentiation, we will rewrite the function so that no fraction appears in the denominator.

We have

$$y = \frac{1}{x + \dfrac{1}{x+1}} = \frac{1}{\dfrac{x(x+1)+1}{x+1}} = \frac{x+1}{x^2+x+1}$$

$$\frac{dy}{dx} = \frac{(x^2+x+1)(1) - (x+1)(2x+1)}{(x^2+x+1)^2} \qquad \text{(quotient rule)}$$

$$= \frac{(x^2+x+1) - (2x^2+3x+1)}{(x^2+x+1)^2}$$

$$= \frac{-x^2-2x}{(x^2+x+1)^2} = -\frac{x^2+2x}{(x^2+x+1)^2}$$

NOW WORK PROBLEM 45

Although a function may have the form of a quotient, this does not necessarily mean that the quotient rule must be used to find the derivative. The next example illustrates some typical situations in which, although the quotient rule can be used, a simpler and more efficient method is available.

## EXAMPLE 7   Differentiating Quotients without Using the Quotient Rule

*Differentiate the following functions.*

**a.** $f(x) = \dfrac{2x^3}{5}$

**Solution:** Rewriting, we have $f(x) = \frac{2}{5}x^3$. By the constant-factor rule,

$$f'(x) = \frac{2}{5}(3x^2) = \frac{6x^2}{5}$$

**b.** $f(x) = \dfrac{4}{7x^3}$

**Solution:** Rewriting, we have $f(x) = \frac{4}{7}(x^{-3})$. Thus,

$$f'(x) = \frac{4}{7}(-3x^{-4}) = -\frac{12}{7x^4}$$

**c.** $f(x) = \dfrac{5x^2 - 3x}{4x}$

**Solution:** Rewriting, we have $f(x) = \dfrac{1}{4}\left(\dfrac{5x^2 - 3x}{x}\right) = \dfrac{1}{4}(5x - 3)$ for $x \neq 0$. Thus,

$$f'(x) = \frac{1}{4}(5) = \frac{5}{4} \qquad \text{for } x \neq 0$$

Since the function $f$ is not defined for $x = 0$, $f'$ is not defined for $x = 0$ either.

NOW WORK PROBLEM 17

**CAUTION**

To differentiate $f(x) = \dfrac{1}{x^2 - 2}$, you might be tempted first to rewrite the quotient as $(x^2 - 2)^{-1}$. It would be a mistake to do this because we presently have no rule for differentiating that form. In short, we have no choice but to use the quotient rule. However, in the next section we will develop a rule that allows us to differentiate $(x^2 - 2)^{-1}$ in a direct and efficient way.

## EXAMPLE 8    Marginal Revenue

*If the demand equation for a manufacturer's product is*

$$p = \frac{1000}{q + 5}$$

*where $p$ is in dollars, find the marginal-revenue function and evaluate it when $q = 45$.*

**Solution:**

**Strategy**   First we must find the revenue function. The revenue $r$ received for selling $q$ units when the price per unit is $p$ is given by

**revenue = (price)(quantity)**,    that is,    $r = pq$

Using the demand equation, we will express $r$ in terms of $q$ only. Then we will differentiate to find the marginal-revenue function, $dr/dq$.

The revenue function is

$$r = \left(\frac{1000}{q + 5}\right)q = \frac{1000q}{q + 5}$$

Thus, the marginal-revenue function is given by

$$\frac{dr}{dq} = \frac{(q + 5)\dfrac{d}{dq}(1000q) - (1000q)\dfrac{d}{dq}(q + 5)}{(q + 5)^2}$$

$$= \frac{(q + 5)(1000) - (1000q)(1)}{(q + 5)^2} = \frac{5000}{(q + 5)^2}$$

and

$$\left.\frac{dr}{dq}\right|_{q=45} = \frac{5000}{(45 + 5)^2} = \frac{5000}{2500} = 2$$

This means that selling one additional unit beyond 45 results in approximately $2 more in revenue.

NOW WORK PROBLEM 59

## Consumption Function

A function that plays an important role in economic analysis is the **consumption function.** The consumption function $C = f(I)$ expresses a relationship between the total national income $I$ and the total national consumption $C$. Usually, both $I$ and $C$ are expressed in billions of dollars and $I$ is restricted to some interval. The *marginal propensity to consume* is defined as the rate of change of consumption with respect to income. It is merely the derivative of $C$ with respect to $I$:

$$\text{Marginal propensity to consume} = \frac{dC}{dI}$$

If we assume that the difference between income $I$ and consumption $C$ is savings $S$, then

$$S = I - C$$

Differentiating both sides with respect to $I$ gives

$$\frac{dS}{dI} = \frac{d}{dI}(I) - \frac{d}{dI}(C) = 1 - \frac{dC}{dI}$$

We define $dS/dI$ as the **marginal propensity to save.** Thus, the marginal propensity to save indicates how fast savings change with respect to income, and

$$\begin{matrix}\text{Marginal propensity} \\ \text{to save}\end{matrix} = 1 - \begin{matrix}\text{Marginal propensity} \\ \text{to consume}\end{matrix}$$

### ● EXAMPLE 9  Finding Marginal Propensities to Consume and to Save

*If the consumption function is given by*

$$C = \frac{5(2\sqrt{I^3} + 3)}{I + 10}$$

*determine the marginal propensity to consume and the marginal propensity to save when $I = 100$.*

Solution:

$$\frac{dC}{dI} = 5\left(\frac{(I + 10)\frac{d}{dI}(2I^{3/2} + 3) - (2\sqrt{I^3} + 3)\frac{d}{dI}(I + 10)}{(I + 10)^2}\right)$$

$$= 5\left(\frac{(I + 10)(3I^{1/2}) - (2\sqrt{I^3} + 3)(1)}{(I + 10)^2}\right)$$

When $I = 100$, the marginal propensity to consume is

$$\frac{dC}{dI}\bigg|_{I=100} = 5\left(\frac{1297}{12,100}\right) \approx 0.536$$

The marginal propensity to save when $I = 100$ is $1 - 0.536 = 0.464$. This means that if a current income of \$100 billion increases by \$1 billion, the nation consumes approximately 53.6% (536/1000) and saves 46.4% (464/1000) of that increase.

NOW WORK PROBLEM 69 ●●●

## Problems 11.4

*In Problems 1–48, differentiate the functions.*

**\*1.** $f(x) = (4x + 1)(6x + 3)$  **2.** $f(x) = (3x - 1)(7x + 2)$

**3.** $s(t) = (5 - 3t)(t^3 - 2t^2)$  **4.** $Q(x) = (3 + x)(5x^2 - 2)$

**5.** $f(r) = (3r^2 - 4)(r^2 - 5r + 1)$

**6.** $C(I) = (2I^2 - 3)(3I^2 - 4I + 1)$

**7.** $f(x) = x^2(2x^2 - 5)$  **8.** $f(x) = 3x^3(x^2 - 2x + 2)$

**9.** $y = (x^2 + 3x - 2)(2x^2 - x - 3)$

**10.** $\phi(x) = (3 - 5x + 2x^2)(2 + x - 4x^2)$

11. $f(w) = (w^2 + 3w - 7)(2w^3 - 4)$

12. $f(x) = (3x - x^2)(3 - x - x^2)$

13. $y = (x^2 - 1)(3x^3 - 6x + 5) - 4(4x^2 + 2x + 1)$

14. $h(x) = 4(x^5 - 3) + 3(8x^2 - 5)(2x + 2)$

*15. $F(p) = \frac{3}{2}(5\sqrt{p} - 2)(3p - 1)$

16. $g(x) = (\sqrt{x} + 5x - 2)(\sqrt[3]{x} - 3\sqrt{x})$

*17. $y = 7 \cdot \frac{2}{3}$

18. $y = (x - 1)(x - 2)(x - 3)$

*19. $y = (2x - 1)(3x + 4)(x + 7)$

20. $y = \dfrac{2x - 3}{4x + 1}$

*21. $f(x) = \dfrac{5x}{x - 1}$

22. $H(x) = \dfrac{-5x}{5 - x}$

23. $f(x) = \dfrac{-13}{3x^5}$

24. $f(x) = \dfrac{5(x^2 - 2)}{7}$

25. $y = \dfrac{x + 2}{x - 1}$

26. $h(w) = \dfrac{3w^2 + 5w - 1}{w - 3}$

27. $h(z) = \dfrac{6 - 2z}{z^2 - 4}$

28. $z = \dfrac{2x^2 + 5x - 2}{3x^2 + 5x + 3}$

29. $y = \dfrac{8x^2 - 2x + 1}{x^2 - 5x}$

30. $f(x) = \dfrac{x^3 - x^2 + 1}{x^2 + 1}$

31. $y = \dfrac{x^2 - 4x + 3}{2x^2 - 3x + 2}$

32. $F(z) = \dfrac{z^4 + 4}{3z}$

33. $g(x) = \dfrac{1}{x^{100} + 7}$

34. $y = \dfrac{-9}{2x^5}$

35. $u(v) = \dfrac{v^3 - 8}{v}$

36. $y = \dfrac{x - 5}{8\sqrt{x}}$

37. $y = \dfrac{3x^2 - x - 1}{\sqrt[3]{x}}$

38. $y = \dfrac{x^{0.3} - 2}{2x^{2.1} + 1}$

39. $y = 7 - \dfrac{4}{x - 8} + \dfrac{2x}{3x + 1}$

40. $q(x) = 2x^3 + \dfrac{5x + 1}{3x - 5} - \dfrac{2}{x^3}$

41. $y = \dfrac{x - 5}{(x + 2)(x - 4)}$

42. $y = \dfrac{(9x - 1)(3x + 2)}{4 - 5x}$

43. $s(t) = \dfrac{t^2 + 3t}{(t^2 - 1)(t^3 + 7)}$

44. $f(s) = \dfrac{17}{s(5s^2 - 10s + 4)}$

*45. $y = 3x - \dfrac{\frac{2}{x} - \frac{3}{x - 1}}{x - 2}$

46. $y = 3 - 12x^3 + \dfrac{1 - \frac{5}{x^2 + 2}}{x^2 + 5}$

47. $f(x) = \dfrac{a + x}{a - x}$, where $a$ is a constant

48. $f(x) = \dfrac{x^{-1} + a^{-1}}{x^{-1} - a^{-1}}$, where $a$ is a constant

*49. Find the slope of the curve $y = (4x^2 + 2x - 5)(x^3 + 7x + 4)$ at $(-1, 12)$.

50. Find the slope of the curve $y = \dfrac{x^3}{x^4 + 1}$ at $(-1, -\frac{1}{2})$.

*In Problems 51–54, find an equation of the tangent line to the curve at the given point.*

51. $y = \dfrac{6}{x - 1}$; $(3, 3)$

52. $y = \dfrac{x + 5}{x^2}$; $(1, 6)$

53. $y = (2x + 3)[2(x^4 - 5x^2 + 4)]$; $(0, 24)$

54. $y = \dfrac{x + 1}{x^2(x - 4)}$; $\left(2, -\dfrac{3}{8}\right)$

*In Problems 55 and 56, determine the relative rate of change of y with respect to x for the given value of x.*

55. $y = \dfrac{x}{2x - 6}$; $x = 1$

56. $y = \dfrac{1 - x}{1 + x}$; $x = 5$

57. **Motion** The position function for an object moving in a straight line is

$$s = \dfrac{2}{t^3 + 1}$$

where $t$ is in seconds and $s$ is in meters. Find the position and velocity of the object at $t = 1$.

58. **Motion** The position function for an object moving in a straight-line path is

$$s = \dfrac{t + 3}{t^2 + 7}$$

where $t$ is in seconds and $s$ is in meters. Find the positive value(s) of $t$ for which the velocity of the object is 0.

*In Problems 59–62, each equation represents a demand function for a certain product, where p denotes the price per unit for q units. Find the marginal-revenue function in each case. Recall that revenue = pq.*

*59. $p = 50 - 0.01q$

60. $p = 500/q$

61. $p = \dfrac{108}{q + 2} - 3$

62. $p = \dfrac{q + 750}{q + 50}$

63. **Consumption Function** For the United States (1922–1942), the consumption function is estimated by[11]

$$C = 0.672I + 113.1$$

Find the marginal propensity to consume.

64. **Consumption Function** Repeat Problem 63 if $C = 0.712I + 95.05$ for the United States for 1929–1941.[12]

*In Problems 65–68, each equation represents a consumption function. Find the marginal propensity to consume and the marginal propensity to save for the given value of I.*

65. $C = 3 + \sqrt{I} + 2\sqrt[3]{I}$; $I = 1$

66. $C = 6 + \dfrac{3I}{4} - \dfrac{\sqrt{I}}{3}$; $I = 25$

67. $C = \dfrac{16\sqrt{I} + 0.8\sqrt{I^3} - 0.2I}{\sqrt{I} + 4}$; $I = 36$

68. $C = \dfrac{20\sqrt{I} + 0.5\sqrt{I^3} - 0.4I}{\sqrt{I} + 5}$; $I = 100$

*69. **Consumption Function** Suppose that a country's consumption function is given by

$$C = \dfrac{10\sqrt{I} + 0.7\sqrt{I^3} - 0.2I}{\sqrt{I}}$$

where $C$ and $I$ are expressed in billions of dollars.

(a) Find the marginal propensity to save when income is 25 billion dollars.

(b) Determine the relative rate of change of $C$ with respect to $I$ when income is 25 billion dollars.

---

[11]T. Haavelmo, "Methods of Measuring the Marginal Propensity to Consume," *Journal of the American Statistical Association*, XLII (1947), 105–22.

[12]Ibid.

**70. Marginal Propensities to Consume and to Save**   Suppose that the savings function of a country is

$$S = \frac{I - 2\sqrt{I} - 8}{\sqrt{I} + 2}$$

where the national income ($I$) and the national savings ($S$) are measured in billions of dollars. Find the country's marginal propensity to consume and its marginal propensity to save when the national income is $150 billion. (*Hint:* It may be helpful to first factor the numerator.)

**71. Marginal Cost**   If the total-cost function for a manufacturer is given by

$$c = \frac{6q^2}{q + 2} + 6000$$

find the marginal-cost function.

**72. Marginal and Average Costs**   Given the cost function $c = f(q)$, show that if $\frac{d}{dq}(\bar{c}) = 0$, then the marginal-cost function and average-cost function are equal.

**73. Host–Parasite Relation**   For a particular host–parasite relationship, it is determined that when the host density (number of hosts per unit of area) is $x$, the number of hosts that are parasitized is $y$, where

$$y = \frac{900x}{10 + 45x}$$

At what rate is the number of hosts parasitized changing with respect to host density when $x = 2$?

**74. Acoustics**   The persistence of sound in a room after the source of the sound is turned off is called *reverberation*. The *reverberation time* RT of the room is the time it takes for the intensity level of the sound to fall 60 decibels. In the acoustical design of an auditorium, the following formula may be used to compute the RT of the room:[13]

$$RT = \frac{0.05V}{A + xV}$$

Here $V$ is the room volume, $A$ is the total room absorption, and $x$ is the air absorption coefficient. Assuming that $A$ and $x$ are positive constants, show that the rate of change of RT with respect to $V$ is always positive. If the total room volume increases by one unit, does the reverberation time increase or decrease?

**75. Predator–Prey**   In a predator-prey experiment,[14] it was statistically determined that the number of prey consumed, $y$, by an individual predator was a function of the prey density $x$ (the number of prey per unit of area), where

$$y = \frac{0.7355x}{1 + 0.02744x}$$

Determine the rate of change of prey consumed with respect to prey density.

**76. Social Security Benefits**   In a discussion of social security benefits, Feldstein[15] differentiates a function of the form

$$f(x) = \frac{a(1 + x) - b(2 + n)x}{a(2 + n)(1 + x) - b(2 + n)x}$$

where $a$, $b$, and $n$ are constants. He determines that

$$f'(x) = \frac{-1(1 + n)ab}{(a(1 + x) - bx)^2(2 + n)}$$

Verify this. (*Hint:* For convenience, let $2 + n = c$.) Next observe that Feldstein's function $f$ is of the form

$$g(x) = \frac{A + Bx}{C + Dx} \quad \text{where } A, B, C, \text{ and } D \text{ are constants}$$

Show that $g'(x)$ is a constant divided by a nonnegative function of $x$. What does this mean?

**77. Business**   The manufacturer of a product has found that when 20 units are produced per day, the average cost is $150 and the marginal cost is $125. What is the relative rate of change of average cost with respect to quantity when $q = 20$?

**78.** Use the result $(fgh)' = f'gh + fg'h + fgh'$ to find $dy/dx$ if

$$y = (3x + 1)(2x - 1)(x - 4)$$

OBJECTIVE

To introduce and apply the chain rule, to derive the power rule as a special case of the chain rule, and to develop the concept of the marginal-revenue product as an application of the chain rule.

# 11.5 The Chain Rule and the Power Rule

Our next rule, the *chain rule*, is ultimately the most important rule for finding derivatives. It involves a situation in which $y$ is a function of the variable $u$, but $u$ is a function of $x$, and we want to find the derivative of $y$ with respect to $x$. For example, the equations

$$y = u^2 \quad \text{and} \quad u = 2x + 1$$

define $y$ as a function of $u$ and $u$ as a function of $x$. If we substitute $2x + 1$ for $u$ in the first equation, we can consider $y$ to be a function of $x$:

$$y = (2x + 1)^2$$

To find $dy/dx$, we first expand $(2x + 1)^2$:

$$y = 4x^2 + 4x + 1$$

Then

$$\frac{dy}{dx} = 8x + 4$$

---

[13] L. L. Doelle, *Environmental Acoustics* (New York: McGraw-Hill Book Company, 1972).

[14] C. S. Holling, "Some Characteristics of Simple Types of Predation and Parasitism," *The Canadian Entomologist*, XCI, no. 7 (1959), 385–98.

[15] M. Feldstein, "The Optimal Level of Social Security Benefits," *The Quarterly Journal of Economics*, C, no. 2 (1985), 303–20.

From this example, you can see that finding $dy/dx$ by first performing a substitution *could* be quite involved. For instance, if originally we had been given $y = u^{100}$ instead of $y = u^2$, we wouldn't even want to try substituting. Fortunately, the chain rule will allow us to handle such situations with ease.

**RULE 1    The Chain Rule**

If $y$ is a differentiable function of $u$ and $u$ is a differentiable function of $x$, then $y$ is a differentiable function of $x$ and

$$\frac{dy}{dx} = \frac{dy}{du} \cdot \frac{du}{dx}$$

We can show you why the chain rule is reasonable by considering rates of change. Suppose

$$y = 8u + 5 \quad \text{and} \quad u = 2x - 3$$

Let $x$ change by one unit. How does $u$ change? To answer this question, we differentiate and find $du/dx = 2$. But for *each* one-unit change in $u$, there is a change in $y$ of $dy/du = 8$. Therefore, what is the change in $y$ if $x$ changes by one unit; that is, what is $dy/dx$? The answer is $8 \cdot 2$, which is $\dfrac{dy}{du} \cdot \dfrac{du}{dx}$. Thus, $\dfrac{dy}{dx} = \dfrac{dy}{du} \cdot \dfrac{du}{dx}$.

We will now use the chain rule to redo the problem at the beginning of this section. If

$$y = u^2 \quad \text{and} \quad u = 2x + 1$$

then

$$\frac{dy}{dx} = \frac{dy}{du} \cdot \frac{du}{dx} = \frac{d}{du}(u^2) \cdot \frac{d}{dx}(2x + 1)$$
$$= (2u)2 = 4u$$

Replacing $u$ by $2x + 1$ gives

$$\frac{dy}{dx} = 4(2x + 1) = 8x + 4$$

which agrees with our previous result.

**PRINCIPLES IN PRACTICE 1**

**USING THE CHAIN RULE**

If an object moves horizontally according to $x = 6t$, where $t$ is in seconds, and vertically according to $y = 4x^2$, find its vertical velocity $\dfrac{dy}{dt}$.

● **EXAMPLE 1    Using the Chain Rule**

**a.** If $y = 2u^2 - 3u - 2$ and $u = x^2 + 4$, find $dy/dx$.

Solution:  By the chain rule,

$$\frac{dy}{dx} = \frac{dy}{du} \cdot \frac{du}{dx} = \frac{d}{du}(2u^2 - 3u - 2) \cdot \frac{d}{dx}(x^2 + 4)$$
$$= (4u - 3)(2x)$$

We can write our answer in terms of $x$ alone by replacing $u$ by $x^2 + 4$.

$$\frac{dy}{dx} = [4(x^2 + 4) - 3](2x) = [4x^2 + 13](2x) = 8x^3 + 26x$$

**b.** If $y = \sqrt{w}$ and $w = 7 - t^3$, find $dy/dt$.

Solution:  Here, $y$ is a function of $w$ and $w$ is a function of $t$, so we can view $y$ as a function of $t$. By the chain rule,

$$\frac{dy}{dt} = \frac{dy}{dw} \cdot \frac{dw}{dt} = \frac{d}{dw}(\sqrt{w}) \cdot \frac{d}{dt}(7 - t^3)$$
$$= \left(\frac{1}{2}w^{-1/2}\right)(-3t^2) = \frac{1}{2\sqrt{w}}(-3t^2)$$
$$= -\frac{3t^2}{2\sqrt{w}} = -\frac{3t^2}{2\sqrt{7 - t^3}}$$

NOW WORK PROBLEM 1  ●●

● **EXAMPLE 2    Using the Chain Rule**

*If $y = 4u^3 + 10u^2 - 3u - 7$ and $u = 4/(3x - 5)$, find dy/dx when $x = 1$.*

**Solution:** By the chain rule,

$$\frac{dy}{dx} = \frac{dy}{du} \cdot \frac{du}{dx} = \frac{d}{du}(4u^3 + 10u^2 - 3u - 7) \cdot \frac{d}{dx}\left(\frac{4}{3x-5}\right)$$

$$= (12u^2 + 20u - 3) \cdot \frac{(3x-5)\dfrac{d}{dx}(4) - 4\dfrac{d}{dx}(3x-5)}{(3x-5)^2}$$

$$= (12u^2 + 20u - 3) \cdot \frac{-12}{(3x-5)^2}$$

**Do not simply replace** $x$ **by 1 and leave your answer in terms of** $u$.

Even though $dy/dx$ is in terms of $x$'s and $u$'s, we can evaluate it when $x = 1$ if we determine the corresponding value of $u$. When $x = 1$,

$$u = \frac{4}{3(1) - 5} = -2$$

Thus,

$$\left.\frac{dy}{dx}\right|_{x=1} = [12(-2)^2 + 20(-2) - 3] \cdot \frac{-12}{[3(1)-5]^2}$$

$$= 5 \cdot (-3) = -15$$

NOW WORK PROBLEM 5 ●●●

The chain rules states that if $y = f(u)$ and $u = g(x)$, then

$$\frac{dy}{dx} = \frac{dy}{du} \cdot \frac{du}{dx}$$

Actually, the chain rule applies to a composite function, because

$$y = f(u) = f(g(x)) = (f \circ g)(x)$$

Thus $y$, as a function of $x$, is $f \circ g$. This means that we can use the chain rule to differentiate a function when we recognize the function as a composition. However, we must first break down the function into composite parts.

For example, to differentiate

$$y = (x^3 - x^2 + 6)^{100}$$

we think of the function as a composition. Let

$$y = f(u) = u^{100} \quad \text{and} \quad u = g(x) = x^3 - x^2 + 6$$

Then $y = (x^3 - x^2 + 6)^{100} = (g(x))^{100} = f(g(x))$. Now that we have a composite, we differentiate. Since $y = u^{100}$ and $u = x^3 - x^2 + 6$, by the chain rule we have

$$\frac{dy}{dx} = \frac{dy}{du} \cdot \frac{du}{dx}$$

$$= (100u^{99})(3x^2 - 2x)$$

$$= 100(x^3 - x^2 + 6)^{99}(3x^2 - 2x)$$

We have just used the chain rule to differentiate $y = (x^3 - x^2 + 6)^{100}$, which is a power of a *function* of $x$, not simply a power of $x$. The following rule, called the *power rule*, generalizes our result and is a special case of the chain rule:

**RULE 2    The Power Rule**

If $u$ is a differentiable function of $x$ and $n$ is any real number, then

$$\frac{d}{dx}(u^n) = nu^{n-1}\frac{du}{dx}$$

*Proof.* Let $y = u^n$. Since $y$ is a differentiable function of $u$ and $u$ is a differentiable function of $x$, the chain rule gives

$$\frac{dy}{dx} = \frac{dy}{du} \cdot \frac{du}{dx}$$

But $dy/du = nu^{n-1}$. Thus,

$$\frac{dy}{dx} = nu^{n-1}\frac{du}{dx}$$

which is the power rule.

Another way of writing the power-rule formula is

$$\frac{d}{dx}((u(x))^n) = n(u(x))^{n-1}u'(x)$$

● EXAMPLE 3  **Using the Power Rule**

*If $y = (x^3 - 1)^7$, find $y'$.*

**Solution:** Since $y$ is a power of a *function* of $x$, the power rule applies. Letting $u(x) = x^3 - 1$ and $n = 7$, we have

$$y' = n[u(x)]^{n-1}u'(x)$$
$$= 7(x^3 - 1)^{7-1}\frac{d}{dx}(x^3 - 1)$$
$$= 7(x^3 - 1)^6(3x^2) = 21x^2(x^3 - 1)^6$$

NOW WORK PROBLEM 9

● EXAMPLE 4  **Using the Power Rule**

*If $y = \sqrt[3]{(4x^2 + 3x - 2)^2}$, find $dy/dx$ when $x = -2$.*

**Solution:** Since $y = (4x^2 + 3x - 2)^{2/3}$, we use the power rule with

$$u = 4x^2 + 3x - 2$$

and $n = \frac{2}{3}$. We have

$$\frac{dy}{dx} = \frac{2}{3}(4x^2 + 3x - 2)^{(2/3)-1}\frac{d}{dx}(4x^2 + 3x - 2)$$
$$= \frac{2}{3}(4x^2 + 3x - 2)^{-1/3}(8x + 3)$$
$$= \frac{2(8x + 3)}{3\sqrt[3]{4x^2 + 3x - 2}}$$

Thus,

$$\frac{dy}{dx}\bigg|_{x=-2} = \frac{2(-13)}{3\sqrt[3]{8}} = -\frac{13}{3}$$

NOW WORK PROBLEM 19

● EXAMPLE 5  **Using the Power Rule**

*If $y = \dfrac{1}{x^2 - 2}$, find $\dfrac{dy}{dx}$.*

The technique used in Example 5 is frequently used when the numerator of a quotient is a constant and the denominator is not.

**Solution:** Although the quotient rule can be used here, a more efficient approach is to treat the right side as the power $(x^2 - 2)^{-1}$ and use the power rule. Let $u = x^2 - 2$.

Then $y = u^{-1}$, and

$$\frac{dy}{dx} = (-1)(x^2 - 2)^{-1-1}\frac{d}{dx}(x^2 - 2)$$

$$= (-1)(x^2 - 2)^{-2}(2x)$$

$$= -\frac{2x}{(x^2 - 2)^2}$$

NOW WORK PROBLEM 27

● **EXAMPLE 6   Differentiating a Power of a Quotient**

*If* $z = \left(\dfrac{2s + 5}{s^2 + 1}\right)^4$, *find* $\dfrac{dz}{ds}$.

The problem here is to recognize the basic form of the function to be differentiated. In this case it is a power, not a quotient.

**Solution:**  Since $z$ is a power of a function, we first use the power rule:

$$\frac{dz}{ds} = 4\left(\frac{2s + 5}{s^2 + 1}\right)^{4-1}\frac{d}{ds}\left(\frac{2s + 5}{s^2 + 1}\right)$$

Now we use the quotient rule:

$$\frac{dz}{ds} = 4\left(\frac{2s + 5}{s^2 + 1}\right)^3\left(\frac{(s^2 + 1)(2) - (2s + 5)(2s)}{(s^2 + 1)^2}\right)$$

Simplifying, we have

$$\frac{dz}{ds} = 4 \cdot \frac{(2s + 5)^3}{(s^2 + 1)^3}\left(\frac{-2s^2 - 10s + 2}{(s^2 + 1)^2}\right)$$

$$= -\frac{8(s^2 + 5s - 1)(2s + 5)^3}{(s^2 + 1)^5}$$

NOW WORK PROBLEM 41

● **EXAMPLE 7   Differentiating a Product of Powers**

*If* $y = (x^2 - 4)^5(3x + 5)^4$, *find* $y'$.

**Solution:**  Since $y$ is a product, we first apply the product rule:

$$y' = (x^2 - 4)^5\frac{d}{dx}((3x + 5)^4) + (3x + 5)^4\frac{d}{dx}((x^2 - 4)^5)$$

Now we use the power rule:

$$y' = (x^2 - 4)^5(4(3x + 5)^3(3)) + (3x + 5)^4(5(x^2 - 4)^4(2x))$$

$$= 12(x^2 - 4)^5(3x + 5)^3 + 10x(3x + 5)^4(x^2 - 4)^4$$

In differentiating a product in which at least one factor is a power, simplifying the derivative usually involves factoring.

To simplify, we first remove common factors:

$$y' = 2(x^2 - 4)^4(3x + 5)^3[6(x^2 - 4) + 5x(3x + 5)]$$

$$= 2(x^2 - 4)^4(3x + 5)^3(21x^2 + 25x - 24)$$

NOW WORK PROBLEM 39

Usually, the power rule should be used to differentiate $y = [u(x)]^n$. Although a function such as $y = (x^2 + 2)^2$ can be written $y = x^4 + 4x^2 + 4$ and differentiated easily, this method is impractical for a function such as $y = (x^2 + 2)^{1000}$. Since $y = (x^2 + 2)^{1000}$ is of the form $y = [u(x)]^n$, we have

$$y' = 1000(x^2 + 2)^{999}(2x)$$

## Marginal-Revenue Product

Let us now use our knowledge of calculus to develop a concept relevant to economic studies. Suppose a manufacturer hires $m$ employees who produce a total of $q$ units of a product per day. We can think of $q$ as a function of $m$. If $r$ is the total revenue the manufacturer receives for selling these units, then $r$ can also be considered a function of $m$. Thus, we can look at $dr/dm$, the rate of change of revenue with respect to the number of employees. The derivative $dr/dm$ is called the **marginal-revenue product.** It approximates the change in revenue that results when a manufacturer hires an extra employee.

● EXAMPLE 8   **Marginal-Revenue Product**

*A manufacturer determines that m employees will produce a total of q units of a product per day, where*

$$q = \frac{10m^2}{\sqrt{m^2 + 19}} \tag{1}$$

*If the demand equation for the product is $p = 900/(q + 9)$, determine the marginal-revenue product when $m = 9$.*

Solution:   We must find $dr/dm$, where $r$ is revenue. Note that, by the chain rule,

$$\frac{dr}{dm} = \frac{dr}{dq} \cdot \frac{dq}{dm}$$

Thus, we must find both $dr/dq$ and $dq/dm$ when $m = 9$. We begin with $dr/dq$. The revenue function is given by

$$r = pq = \left(\frac{900}{q+9}\right)q = \frac{900q}{q+9} \tag{2}$$

so, by the quotient rule,

$$\frac{dr}{dq} = \frac{(q+9)(900) - 900q(1)}{(q+9)^2} = \frac{8100}{(q+9)^2}$$

In order to evaluate this expression when $m = 9$, we first use the given equation $q = 10m^2/\sqrt{m^2 + 19}$ to find the corresponding value of $q$:

$$q = \frac{10(9)^2}{\sqrt{9^2 + 19}} = 81$$

Hence,

$$\left.\frac{dr}{dq}\right|_{m=9} = \left.\frac{dr}{dq}\right|_{q=81} = \frac{8100}{(81+9)^2} = 1$$

Now we turn to $dq/dm$. From the quotient and power rules, we have

$$\frac{dq}{dm} = \frac{d}{dm}\left(\frac{10m^2}{\sqrt{m^2 + 19}}\right)$$

$$= \frac{(m^2+19)^{1/2}\frac{d}{dm}(10m^2) - (10m^2)\frac{d}{dm}[(m^2+19)^{1/2}]}{[(m^2+19)^{1/2}]^2}$$

$$= \frac{(m^2+19)^{1/2}(20m) - (10m^2)[\frac{1}{2}(m^2+19)^{-1/2}(2m)]}{m^2 + 19}$$

so

$$\left.\frac{dq}{dm}\right|_{m=9} = \frac{(81+19)^{1/2}(20 \cdot 9) - (10 \cdot 81)[\frac{1}{2}(81+19)^{-1/2}(2 \cdot 9)]}{81 + 19}$$

$$= 10.71$$

A direct formula for the marginal-revenue product is

$$\frac{dr}{dm} = \frac{dq}{dm}\left(p + q\frac{dp}{dq}\right)$$

Therefore, from the chain rule,

$$\left.\frac{dr}{dm}\right|_{m=9} = (1)(10.71) = 10.71$$

This means that if a tenth employee is hired, revenue will increase by approximately $10.71 per day.

NOW WORK PROBLEM 80 ●●●

In Example 8 the marginal-revenue product, $dr/dm$, was found by using the chain rule. Another method, which is well suited to a graphing calculator, is to use substitution to express $r$ as a function of $m$ and then differentiate directly. First we take Equation (1) and substitute for $q$ in the revenue function, Equation (2); this gives $r$ as a function of $m$. Here are the details: In our function menu, we

enter

$$Y_1 = 10X^2/\sqrt{(X^2 + 19)}$$

$$Y_2 = 900Y_1/(Y_1 + 9)$$

$Y_2$ expresses revenue as a function of the number of employees. Finally, to find the marginal-revenue product when $m = 9$, we compute nDeriv($Y_2$, X, 9). You should verify that this method gives (approximately) 10.71.

## Problems 11.5

*In Problems 1–8, use the chain rule.*

*1. If $y = u^2 - 2u$ and $u = x^2 - x$, find $dy/dx$.

2. If $y = 2u^3 - 8u$ and $u = 7x - x^3$, find $dy/dx$.

3. If $y = \dfrac{1}{w^2}$ and $w = 2 - x$, find $dy/dx$.

4. If $y = \sqrt[5]{z}$ and $z = x^5 - x^4 + 3$, find $dy/dx$.

*5. If $w = u^3$ and $u = \dfrac{t-1}{t+1}$, find $dw/dt$ when $t = 1$.

6. If $z = u^2 + \sqrt{u} + 9$ and $u = 2s^2 - 1$, find $dz/ds$ when $s = -1$.

7. If $y = 3w^2 - 8w + 4$ and $w = 2x^2 + 1$, find $dy/dx$ when $x = 0$.

8. If $y = 3u^3 - u^2 + 7u - 2$ and $u = 5x - 2$, find $dy/dx$ when $x = 1$.

*In Problems 9–52, find $y'$.*

*9. $y = (3x + 2)^6$

10. $y = (x^2 - 4)^4$

11. $y = (3 + 2x^3)^5$

12. $y = (x^2 + x)^4$

13. $y = 2(x^3 - 8x^2 + x)^{100}$

14. $y = \dfrac{(2x^2 + 1)^4}{2}$

15. $y = (x^2 - 2)^{-3}$

16. $y = (2x^3 - 8x)^{-12}$

17. $y = 2(x^2 + 5x - 2)^{-5/7}$

18. $y = 4(7x - x^4)^{-3/2}$

*19. $y = \sqrt{5x^2 - x}$

20. $y = \sqrt{3x^2 - 7}$

21. $y = \sqrt[4]{2x - 1}$

22. $y = \sqrt[3]{8x^2 - 1}$

23. $y = 2\sqrt[5]{(x^3 + 1)^2}$

24. $y = 7\sqrt[3]{(x^5 - 3)^5}$

25. $y = \dfrac{6}{2x^2 - x + 1}$

26. $y = \dfrac{3}{x^4 + 2}$

*27. $y = \dfrac{1}{(x^2 - 3x)^2}$

28. $y = \dfrac{1}{(2 + x)^4}$

29. $y = \dfrac{4}{\sqrt{9x^2 + 1}}$

30. $y = \dfrac{3}{(3x^2 - x)^{2/3}}$

31. $y = \sqrt[3]{7x} + \sqrt[3]{7x}$

32. $y = \sqrt{2x} + \dfrac{1}{\sqrt{2x}}$

33. $y = x^2(x - 4)^5$

34. $y = x(x + 4)^4$

35. $y = 4x^2\sqrt{5x + 1}$

36. $y = 4x^3\sqrt{1 - x^2}$

37. $y = (x^2 + 2x - 1)^3(5x)$

38. $y = x^2(x^3 - 1)^4$

*39. $y = (8x - 1)^3(2x + 1)^4$

40. $y = (3x + 2)^5(4x - 5)^2$

*41. $y = \left(\dfrac{x - 3}{x + 2}\right)^{12}$

42. $y = \left(\dfrac{2x}{x + 2}\right)^4$

43. $y = \sqrt{\dfrac{x - 2}{x + 3}}$

44. $y = \sqrt[3]{\dfrac{8x^2 - 3}{x^2 + 2}}$

45. $y = \dfrac{2x - 5}{(x^2 + 4)^3}$

46. $y = \dfrac{(4x - 2)^4}{3x^2 + 7}$

47. $y = \dfrac{(8x - 1)^5}{(3x - 1)^3}$

48. $y = \sqrt[3]{(x - 2)^2(x + 2)}$

49. $y = 6(5x^2 + 2)\sqrt{x^4 + 5}$

50. $y = 6 + 3x - 4x(7x + 1)^2$

51. $y = 8t + \dfrac{t - 1}{t + 4} - \left(\dfrac{8t - 7}{4}\right)^2$

52. $y = \dfrac{(2x^3 + 6)(7x - 5)}{(2x + 4)^2}$

*In Problems 53 and 54, use the quotient rule and power rule to find $y'$. Do not simplify your answer.*

53. $y = \dfrac{(2x + 1)^3(x + 3)^2}{(x^3 - 5)^5}$

54. $y = \dfrac{\sqrt{x + 2}(4x^2 - 1)^2}{9x - 3}$

55. If $y = (5u + 6)^3$ and $u = (x^2 + 1)^4$, find $dy/dx$ when $x = 0$.

56. If $z = 2y^2 - 4y + 5$, $y = 6x - 5$, and $x = 2t$, find $dz/dt$ when $t = 1$.

57. Find the slope of the curve $y = (x^2 - 7x - 8)^3$ at the point $(8, 0)$.

58. Find the slope of the curve $y = \sqrt{x + 1}$ at the point $(8, 3)$.

*In Problems 59–62, find an equation of the tangent line to the curve at the given point.*

59. $y = \sqrt[3]{(x^2 - 8)^2}$; $(3, 1)$

60. $y = (x + 3)^3$; $(-1, 8)$

61. $y = \dfrac{\sqrt{7x + 2}}{x + 1}$; $\left(1, \dfrac{3}{2}\right)$

62. $y = \dfrac{-3}{(3x^2 + 1)^3}$; $(0, -3)$

*In Problems 63 and 64, determine the percentage rate of change of $y$ with respect to $x$ for the given value of $x$.*

63. $y = (x^2 + 9)^3$; $x = 4$

64. $y = \dfrac{1}{(x^2 - 1)^3}$; $x = 2$

*In Problems 65–68, $q$ is the total number of units produced per day by $m$ employees of a manufacturer, and $p$ is the price per unit at which the $q$ units are sold. In each case, find the marginal-revenue product for the given value of $m$.*

65. $q = 5m$, $p = -0.4q + 50$; $m = 6$

66. $q = (200m - m^2)/20$, $p = -0.1q + 70$; $m = 40$

67. $q = 10m^2/\sqrt{m^2 + 9}$, $p = 525/(q + 3)$; $m = 4$

68. $q = 100m/\sqrt{m^2 + 19}$, $p = 4500/(q + 10)$; $m = 9$

**69. Demand Equation** Suppose $p = 100 - \sqrt{q^2 + 20}$ is a demand equation for a manufacturer's product.

  (a) Find the rate of change of $p$ with respect to $q$.
  (b) Find the relative rate of change of $p$ with respect to $q$.
  (c) Find the marginal-revenue function.

**70. Marginal-Revenue Product** If $p = k/q$, where $k$ is a constant, is the demand equation for a manufacturer's product and $q = f(m)$ defines a function that gives the total number of units produced per day by $m$ employees, show that the marginal-revenue product is always zero.

**71. Cost Function** The cost $c$ of producing $q$ units of a product is given by

$$c = 5500 + 12q + 0.2q^2$$

If the price per unit $p$ is given by the equation

$$q = 900 - 1.5p$$

use the chain rule to find the rate of change of cost with respect to price per unit when $p = 85$.

**72. Hospital Discharges** A governmental health agency examined the records of a group of individuals who were hospitalized with a particular illness. It was found that the total proportion that had been discharged at the end of $t$ days of hospitalization was given by

$$f(t) = 1 - \left(\frac{250}{250 + t}\right)^3$$

Find $f'(100)$ and interpret your answer.

**73. Marginal Cost** If the total-cost function for a manufacturer is given by

$$c = \frac{5q^2}{\sqrt{q^2 + 3}} + 5000$$

find the marginal-cost function.

**74. Salary/Education** For a certain population, if $E$ is the number of years of a person's education and $S$ represents average annual salary in dollars, then for $E \geq 7$,

$$S = 340E^2 - 4360E + 42{,}800$$

  (a) How fast is salary changing with respect to education when $E = 16$?
  (b) At what level of education does the rate of change of salary equal $5000 per year of education?

**75. Biology** The volume of a spherical cell is given by $V = \frac{4}{3}\pi r^3$, where $r$ is the radius. At time $t$ seconds, the radius (in centimeters) is given by

$$r = 10^{-8}t^2 + 10^{-7}t$$

Use the chain rule to find $dV/dt$ when $t = 10$.

**76. Pressure in Body Tissue** Under certain conditions, the pressure $p$ developed in body tissue by ultrasonic beams is given as a function of the beam's intensity via the equation[16]

$$p = (2\rho V I)^{1/2}$$

where $\rho$ (a Greek letter read "rho") is density of the affected tissue and $V$ is the velocity of propagation of the

beam. Here $\rho$ and $V$ are constants. (a) Find the rate of change of $p$ with respect to $I$. (b) Find the relative rate of change of $p$ with respect to $I$.

**77. Demography** Suppose that, for a certain group of 20,000 births, the number of people surviving to age $x$ years is

$$l_x = -0.000354x^4 + 0.00452x^3 + 0.848x^2 - 34.9x + 20{,}000$$
$$0 \leq x \leq 95.2$$

  (a) Find the rate of change of $l_x$ with respect to $x$, and evaluate your answer for $x = 65$.
  (b) Find the relative rate of change and the percentage rate of change of $l_x$ when $x = 65$. Round your answers to three decimal places.

**78. Muscle Contraction** A muscle has the ability to shorten when a load, such as a weight, is imposed on it. The equation

$$(P + a)(v + b) = k$$

is called the "fundamental equation of muscle contraction."[17] Here $P$ is the load imposed on the muscle, $v$ is the velocity of the shortening of the muscle fibers, and $a$, $b$, and $k$ are positive constants. Express $v$ as a function of $P$. Use your result to find $dv/dP$.

**79. Economics** Suppose $pq = 100$ is the demand equation for a manufacturer's product. Let $c$ be the total cost, and assume that the marginal cost is 0.01 when $q = 200$. Use the chain rule to find $dc/dp$ when $q = 200$.

**\*80. Marginal-Revenue Product** A monopolist who employs $m$ workers finds that they produce

$$q = 2m(2m + 1)^{3/2}$$

units of product per day. The total revenue $r$ (in dollars) is given by

$$r = \frac{50q}{\sqrt{1000 + 3q}}$$

  (a) What is the price per unit (to the nearest cent) when there are 12 workers?
  (b) Determine the marginal revenue when there are 12 workers.
  (c) Determine the marginal-revenue product when $m = 12$.

**81.** Suppose $y = f(x)$, where $x = g(t)$. Given that $g(2) = 3$, $g'(2) = 4$, $f(2) = 5$, $f'(2) = 6$, $g(3) = 7$, $g'(3) = 8$, $f(3) = 9$, and $f'(3) = 10$, determine the value of $\frac{dy}{dt}\big|_{t=2}$.

**82. Business** A manufacturer has determined that, for his product, the daily average cost (in hundreds of dollars) is given by

$$\bar{c} = \frac{324}{\sqrt{q^2 + 35}} + \frac{5}{q} + \frac{19}{18}$$

  (a) As daily production increases, the average cost approaches a constant dollar amount. What is this amount?
  (b) Determine the manufacturer's marginal cost when 17 units are produced per day.
  (c) The manufacturer determines that if production (and sales) were increased to 18 units per day, revenue would increase by $275. Should this move be made? Why?

[16]R. W. Stacy et al., *Essentials of Biological and Medical Physics* (New York: McGraw-Hill Book Company, 1955).

[17]Ibid.

**83.** If

$$y = (u + 1)\sqrt{u + 5}$$

and

$$u = x(x^2 + 5)^5$$

find $dy/dx$ when $x = 0.1$. Round your answer to two decimal places.

**84.** If

$$y = \frac{2u + 3}{u^3 - 2}$$

and

$$u = \frac{x + 4}{(2x + 3)^3}$$

find $dy/dx$ when $x = -1$. Round your answer to two decimal places.

## 11.6 Review

### Important Terms and Symbols

## Summary

The tangent line (or tangent) to a curve at point $P$ is the limiting position of secant lines $PQ$ as $Q$ approaches $P$ along the curve. The slope of the tangent at $P$ is called the slope of the curve at $P$.

If $y = f(x)$, the derivative of $f$ at $x$ is the function $f'(x)$ defined by the limit in the equation

$$f'(x) = \lim_{h \to 0} \frac{f(x + h) - f(x)}{h}$$

Geometrically, the derivative gives the slope of the curve $y = f(x)$ at the point $(x, f(x))$. An equation of the tangent line at a particular point $(a, f(a))$ is obtained by evaluating $f'(a)$, which is the slope of the tangent line, and using the point–slope form of a line: $y - f(a) = f'(a)(x - a)$. Any function that is differentiable at a point must also be continuous there.

The basic rules for finding derivatives are as follows, where we assume that all functions are differentiable:

$$\frac{d}{dx}(c) = 0, \text{ where } c \text{ is any constant}$$

$$\frac{d}{dx}(x^n) = nx^{n-1}, \text{ where } n \text{ is any real number}$$

$$\frac{d}{dx}(cf(x)) = cf'(x), \text{ where } c \text{ is a constant}$$

$$\frac{d}{dx}(f(x) + g(x)) = f'(x) + g'(x)$$

$$\frac{d}{dx}(f(x) - g(x)) = f'(x) - g'(x)$$

$$\frac{d}{dx}(f(x)g(x)) = f(x)g'(x) + g(x)f'(x)$$

$$\frac{d}{dx}\left(\frac{f(x)}{g(x)}\right) = \frac{g(x)f'(x) - f(x)g'(x)}{(g(x))^2}$$

$$\frac{dy}{dx} = \frac{dy}{du} \cdot \frac{du}{dx}, \text{ where } y \text{ is a function of } u \text{ and } u \text{ is a function of } x$$

$$\frac{d}{dx}(u^n) = nu^{n-1}\frac{du}{dx}, \text{ where } u \text{ is a function of } x \text{ and } n \text{ is any real number}$$

The derivative $dy/dx$ can also be interpreted as giving the (instantaneous) rate of change of $y$ with respect to $x$:

$$\frac{dy}{dx} = \lim_{\Delta x \to 0} \frac{\Delta y}{\Delta x} = \lim_{\Delta x \to 0} \frac{\text{change in } y}{\text{change in } x}$$

In particular, if $s = f(t)$ is a position function, where $s$ is position at time $t$, then

$$\frac{ds}{dt} = \text{velocity at time } t$$

In economics, the term *marginal* is used to describe derivatives of specific types of functions. If $c = f(q)$ is a total-cost function ($c$ is the total cost of $q$ units of a product), then the rate of change

$$\frac{dc}{dq} \text{ is called marginal cost}$$

We interpret marginal cost as the approximate cost of one additional unit of output. (Average cost per unit, $\bar{c}$, is related to total cost $c$ by $\bar{c} = c/q$, or $c = \bar{c}q$.)

A total-revenue function $r = f(q)$ gives a manufacturer's revenue $r$ for selling $q$ units of product. (Revenue $r$ and price $p$ are related by $r = pq$.) The rate of change

$$\frac{dr}{dq} \text{ is called marginal revenue}$$

which is interpreted as the approximate revenue obtained from selling one additional unit of output.

If $r$ is the revenue that a manufacturer receives when the total output of $m$ employees is sold, then the derivative $dr/dm$ is called the marginal-revenue product and gives the approximate change in revenue that results when the manufacturer hires an extra employee.

If $C = f(I)$ is a consumption function, where $I$ is national income and $C$ is national consumption, then

$$\frac{dC}{dI} \text{ is marginal propensity to consume}$$

and

$$1 - \frac{dC}{dI} \text{ is marginal prospensity to save}$$

For any function, the relative rate of change of $f(x)$ is

$$\frac{f'(x)}{f(x)}$$

which compares the rate of change of $f(x)$ with $f(x)$ itself. The percentage rate of change is

$$\frac{f'(x)}{f(x)} \cdot 100\%$$

## Review Problems

*Problem numbers shown in color indicate problems suggested for use as a practice chapter test.*

*In Problems 1–4, use the definition of the derivative to find $f'(x)$.*

**1.** $f(x) = 2 - x^2$

**2.** $f(x) = 2x^2 - 3x + 1$

**3.** $f(x) = \sqrt{3x}$

**4.** $f(x) = \dfrac{2}{1 + 4x}$

*In Problems 5–38, differentiate.*

**5.** $y = 7^4$

**6.** $y = ex$

**7.** $y = 7x^4 - 6x^3 + 5x^2 + 1$

**8.** $y = 4(x^2 + 5) - 7x$

**9.** $f(s) = s^2(s^2 + 2)$

**10.** $y = \sqrt{x + 3}$

**11.** $y = \dfrac{x^2 + 1}{5}$

**12.** $y = -\dfrac{2}{2x^2}$

**13.** $y = (x^3 + 7x^2)(x^3 - x^2 + 5)$

**14.** $y = (x^2 + 1)^{100}(x - 6)$

**15.** $f(x) = (2x^2 + 4x)^{100}$

**16.** $f(w) = w\sqrt{w} + w^2$

**17.** $y = \dfrac{3}{2x + 1}$

**18.** $y = \dfrac{5x^2 - 8x}{2x}$

**19.** $y = (8 + 2x)(x^2 + 1)^4$

**20.** $g(z) = (2z)^{3/5} + 5$

**21.** $f(z) = \dfrac{z^2 - 1}{z^2 + 4}$

**22.** $y = \dfrac{x - 5}{(x + 2)^2}$

**23.** $y = \sqrt[3]{4x - 1}$

**24.** $f(x) = (1 + 2^3)^{12}$

**25.** $y = \dfrac{1}{\sqrt{1 - x^2}}$

**26.** $y = \dfrac{x(x + 1)}{2x^2 + 3}$

**27.** $h(x) = (x - 6)^4(x + 5)^3$

**28.** $y = \dfrac{(x + 3)^5}{x}$

**29.** $y = \dfrac{5x - 4}{x + 6}$

**30.** $f(x) = 5x^3\sqrt{3 + 2x^4}$

**31.** $y = 2x^{-3/8} + (2x)^{-3/8}$

**32.** $y = \sqrt{\dfrac{x}{2}} + \sqrt{\dfrac{2}{x}}$

**33.** $y = \dfrac{x^2 + 6}{\sqrt{x^2 + 5}}$

**34.** $y = \sqrt[3]{(7 - 3x^2)^2}$

**35.** $y = (x^3 + 6x^2 + 9)^{3/5}$

**36.** $z = 0.4x^2(x + 1)^{-3} + 0.5$

**37.** $g(z) = \dfrac{-z}{(z - 1)^{-2}}$

**38.** $g(z) = \dfrac{-3}{4(z^5 + 2z - 5)^4}$

*In Problems 39–42, find an equation of the tangent line to the curve at the point corresponding to the given value of x.*

**39.** $y = x^2 - 6x + 4, x = 1$

**40.** $y = -2x^3 + 6x + 1, x = 2$

**41.** $y = \sqrt[3]{x}, x = 8$

**42.** $y = \dfrac{x^2}{x - 12}, x = 13$

**43.** If $f(x) = 4x^2 + 2x + 8$ find the relative and percentage rates of change of $f(x)$ when $x = 1$.

**44.** If $f(x) = x/(x + 4)$, find the relative and percentage rates of change of $f(x)$ when $x = 1$.

**45. Marginal Revenue**  If $r = q(20 - 0.1q)$ is a total-revenue function, find the marginal-revenue function.

**46. Marginal Cost**  If

$$c = 0.0001q^3 - 0.02q^2 + 3q + 6000$$

is a total-cost function, find the marginal cost when $q = 100$.

**47. Consumption Function**  If

$$C = 7 + 0.6I - 0.25\sqrt{I}$$

is a consumption function, find the marginal propensity to consume and the marginal propensity to save when $I = 16$.

**48. Demand Equation**  If $p = \dfrac{q + 12}{q + 5}$ is a demand equation, find the rate of change of price $p$ with respect to quantity $q$.

**49. Demand Equation**  If $p = -0.1q + 500$ is a demand equation, find the marginal-revenue function.

**50. Average Cost**  If $\bar{c} = 0.03q + 1.2 + \dfrac{3}{q}$ is an average-cost function, find the marginal cost when $q = 100$.

**51. Power-Plant Cost Function**  The total-cost function of an electric light and power plant is estimated by[18]

$$c = 16.68 + 0.125q + 0.00439q^2 \qquad 20 \le q \le 90$$

[18]J. A. Nordin, "Note on a Light Plant's Cost Curves," *Econometrica*, 15 (1947), 231–55.

where $q$ is the eight-hour total output (as a percentage of capacity) and $c$ is the total fuel cost in dollars. Find the marginal-cost function and evaluate it when $q = 70$.

**52. Marginal-Revenue Product**   A manufacturer has determined that $m$ employees will produce a total of $q$ units of product per day, where

$$q = m(50 - m)$$

If the demand function is given by

$$p = -0.01q + 9$$

find the marginal-revenue product when $m = 10$.

**53. Winter Moth**   In a study of the winter moth in Nova Scotia,[19] it was determined that the average number of eggs, $y$, in a female moth was a function of the female's abdominal width $x$ (in millimeters), where

$$y = f(x) = 14x^3 - 17x^2 - 16x + 34$$

and $1.5 \le x \le 3.5$. At what rate does the number of eggs change with respect to abdominal width when $x = 2$?

**54. Host–Parasite Relation**   For a particular host–parasite relationship, it is found that when the host density (number of hosts per unit of area) is $x$, the number of hosts that are parasitized is

$$y = 12 \left(1 - \frac{1}{1 + 3x}\right) \qquad x \ge 0$$

For what value of $x$ does $dy/dx$ equal $\frac{1}{3}$?

**55. Bacteria Growth**   Bacteria are growing in a culture. The time $t$ (in hours) for the number of bacteria to double in number (the generation time) is a function of the temperature $T$ (in degrees Celsius) of the culture and is given by

$$t = f(T) = \begin{cases} \frac{1}{24}T + \frac{11}{4} & \text{if } 30 \le T \le 36 \\ \frac{4}{3}T - \frac{175}{4} & \text{if } 36 < T \le 39 \end{cases}$$

Find $dt/dT$ when (a) $T = 38$ and (b) $T = 35$.

**56. Motion**   The position function of a particle moving in a straight line is

$$s = \frac{9}{2t^2 + 3}$$

where $t$ is in seconds and $s$ is in meters. Find the velocity of the particle at $t = 1$.

**57. Rate of Change**   The volume of a sphere is given by $V = \frac{1}{6}\pi d^3$, where $d$ is the diameter. Find the rate of change of $V$ with respect to $d$ when $d = 4$ ft.

**58. Motion**   The position function for a ball thrown vertically upward from the ground is

$$s = 218t - 16t^2$$

where $s$ is the height in feet above the ground after $t$ seconds. For what value(s) of $t$ is the velocity 64 ft/s?

**59.** Find the marginal-cost function if the average-cost function is

$$\bar{c} = 2q + \frac{10{,}000}{q^2}$$

**60.** Find an equation of the tangent line to the curve

$$y = \frac{(x^3 + 2)\sqrt{x + 1}}{x^4 + 2x}$$

at the point on the curve where $x = 1$.

**61.** A manufacturer has found that when $m$ employees are working, the number of units of product produced per day is

$$q = 10\sqrt{m^2 + 4900} - 700$$

The demand equation for the product is

$$8q + p^2 - 19{,}300 = 0$$

where $p$ is the selling price when the demand for the product is $q$ units per day.

**(a)** Determine the manufacturer's marginal-revenue product when $m = 240$.

**(b)** Find the relative rate of change of revenue with respect to the number of employees when $m = 240$.

**(c)** Suppose it would cost the manufacturer $400 more per day to hire an additional employee. Would you advise the manufacturer to hire the 241st employee? Why?

**62.** If $f(x) = x^2 \ln x$, use the "limit of a difference quotient" approach to estimate $f'(5)$. Round your answer to three decimal places.

**63.** If $f(x) = \sqrt[3]{x^2 + 3x - 4}$, use the numerical derivative feature of your graphing calculator to estimate the derivative when $x = 10$. Round your answer to three decimal places.

**64.** The total-cost function for a manufacturer is given by

$$c = \frac{5q^2 + 4}{\sqrt{q^2 + 6}} + 2500$$

where $c$ is in dollars. Use the numerical derivative feature of your graphing calculator to estimate the marginal cost when 15 units are produced. Round your answer to the nearest cent.

**65.** If

$$y = (u + 3)\sqrt{u + 6}$$

and

$$u = \frac{x + 4}{x + 3}$$

find $dy/dx$ when $x = 0.3$. Round your answer to two decimal places.

[19]D. G. Embree, "The Population Dynamics of the Winter Moth in Nova Scotia, 1954–1962," *Memoirs of the Entomological Society of Canada,* no. 46 (1965).

# Mathematical Snapshot

## Marginal Propensity to Consume

A consumption function can be defined either for a nation, as in Section 11.4, or for an individual family. In either case, the function relates total consumption to total income. A savings function, similarly, relates total savings to total income, either at the national or at the family level.

Data about income, consumption, and savings for the United States as a whole can be found in the National Income and Product Accounts (NIPA) tables compiled by the Bureau of Economic Analysis, a division of the U.S. Department of Commerce. The tables are downloadable at www.bea.gov. For the years 1959–1999, the national consumption function is indicated by the scatterplot in Figure 11.15.

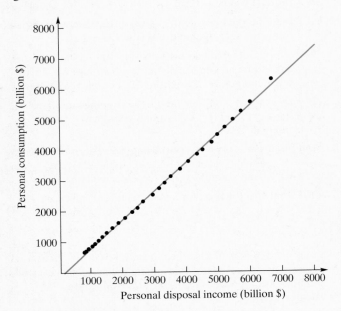

**FIGURE 11.15**  U.S. national consumption function.

Notice that the points lie more or less along a straight line. A linear regression gives the equation for this as $y = 0.9314x - 99.1936$.

The marginal propensity to consume derived from this graph is simply the slope of the line, that is, about 0.931 or 93.1%. At the national level, then, an increase of $1 billion in total disposable income produces an increase of $931 million in consumption. And if we assume that the rest is saved, there is an increase of $69 million in total savings.[20]

Perhaps somewhat easier to relate to, because of the smaller numbers involved, is the consumption function for an individual household. This function is documented in Consumer Expenditure Surveys conducted by the Bureau of Labor Statistics, which is part of the U.S. Department of Labor. The survey results for each year can be downloaded at www.bls.gov/cex/.

Each year's survey gives information for five quintiles, as they are called, where a quintile represents one-fifth of American households. The quintiles are ordered by income, so that the bottom quintile represents the poorest 20% of Americans and the top quintile represents the richest 20%.

**TABLE 11.3**  U.S. Family Income and Expenses, 1999

| After-Tax Income | Total Expenses |
|---|---|
| $7101 | $16,766 |
| $17,576 | $24,850 |
| $30,186 | $33,078 |
| $48,607 | $46,015 |
| $98,214 | $75,080 |

For the year 1999, income and consumption are as shown in Table 11.3. The numbers are average values within each quintile. If these data values are plotted using a graphing calculator, the points lie in a pattern that could be reasonably well approximated by a straight line but could be even better approximated by a curve—a curve shaped, qualitatively, like a square root function (Figure 11.16).

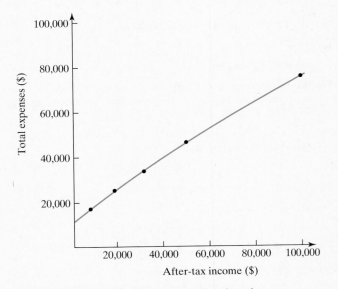

**FIGURE 11.16**  U.S. family consumption function.

[20]In reality, we must also account for interest payments and other outlays not counted as consumption. But we will ignore this complication from now on.

Most graphing calculators do not have a regression function for a square root–type function. They do, however, have a quadratic regression function—and the inverse of a quadratic function is a square root–type function. (Inverse functions were defined in Section 2.4.) So, we proceed as follows. First, using the statistics capabilities of a graphics calculator, enter the numbers in the *second* column in Table 11.3 as $x$-values and those in the *first* column as $y$-values. Second, perform a quadratic regression. The function obtained is given by

$$y = (4.4627 \times 10^{-6})x^2 + 1.1517x - 13{,}461$$

Third, swap the lists of $x$- and $y$-values in preparation for plotting. Fourth, replace $y$ with $x$ and $x$ with $y$ in the quadratic regression equation and solve the result for $y$ (using the quadratic formula) to obtain the equation

$$y = \frac{-1.1517 \pm \sqrt{1.1517^2 - 4(4.4627 \times 10^{-6})(-13{,}461 - x)}}{2(4.4627 \times 10^{-6})}$$

or, more simply,

$$y = -129{,}036 \pm \sqrt{1.9667 \times 10^{10} + 224{,}080x}$$

Finally, enter the upper half of the curve (corresponding to the + part of the ± sign) as a function to be graphed; then display it together with a plot of the data. The result looks as shown in Figure 11.17.

To find the marginal consumption for a given income level, we now use the $dy/dx$ function. To find the marginal consumption at \$50,000, for instance, we select $dy/dx$, then enter 50000. The calculator returns the value 0.637675, which represents a marginal consumption of about 63.8%. In other words, a family earning \$50,000 per year will, if given an extra \$1000, spend \$638 of it and save the rest.

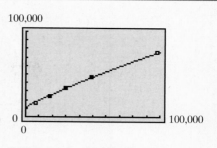

100,000

0
0                                     100,000

**FIGURE 11.17** Graph of regression curve.

## Problems

1. Compare the consumption function for Figure 11.15 with the consumption functions in Problems 63 and 64 of Section 11.5. Give two ways that these consumption functions differ significantly and interpret the differences qualitatively.

2. The first row in Table 11.3 has \$7101 in the first column and \$16,766 in the second column. What does this mean?

3. Suppose a family earning \$25,000 per year in 1999 received an unexpected bonus check for \$1000. How much of that check would you expect the family to spend? How much to save?

4. Suppose a family earning \$90,000 per year in 1999 received an unexpected \$1000 bonus check. How much would it spend?

5. What are the likely real-life reasons for the different answers in Problems 3 and 4?

# 12

# ADDITIONAL DIFFERENTIATION TOPICS

**Mathematical Snapshot**  Economic Order Quantity

After an uncomfortable trip in a vehicle, passengers sometimes describe the ride as "jerky." But what is jerkiness, exactly? What does it mean for, say, an engineer designing a new transportation system?

Travel in a straight line at a constant speed is called *uniform motion,* and there is nothing jerky about it. But if either the path or the speed changes, the ride may become jerky. Change in velocity over time is, formally, the derivative of velocity. Called acceleration, the change in velocity is the *second derivative* of position with respect to time—the derivative of the derivative of position. One of the important concepts covered in this chapter is that of a higher-order derivative, of which acceleration is an example.

But is acceleration responsible for jerkiness? The feeling of being jerked back and forth on a roller coaster is certainly related to acceleration. On the other hand, automotive magazines often praise a car for having *smooth* acceleration. So apparently acceleration has something to do with jerkiness but is not itself the cause.

The derivative of acceleration is the *third* derivative of position with respect to time. When this third derivative is large, the acceleration is changing rapidly. A roller coaster in a steady turn to the left is undergoing steady leftward acceleration. But when the coaster changes abruptly from a hard left turn to a hard right turn, the acceleration changes directions—and the riders experience a jerk. The third derivative of position is, in fact, so apt a measure of jerkiness that it is customarily called the *jerk,* just as the second derivative is called the acceleration.

Jerk has implications not only for passenger comfort in vehicles but also for equipment reliability. Engineers designing equipment for spacecraft, for instance, follow guidelines about the maximum jerk the equipment must be able to survive without damage to its internal components.

To develop a differentiation formula for $y = \ln u$, to apply the formula, and to use it to differentiate a logarithmic function to a base other than $e$.

# 12.1  Derivatives of Logarithmic Functions

In this section, we develop formulas for differentiating logarithmic functions. We begin with the derivative of $f(x) = \ln x$, where $x > 0$. By the definition of the derivative,

$$\frac{d}{dx}(\ln x) = \lim_{h \to 0} \frac{f(x+h) - f(x)}{h} = \lim_{h \to 0} \frac{\ln(x+h) - \ln x}{h}$$

Using the property of logarithms that $\ln m - \ln n = \ln(m/n)$, we have

$$\frac{d}{dx}(\ln x) = \lim_{h \to 0} \frac{\ln\left(\dfrac{x+h}{x}\right)}{h}$$

$$= \lim_{h \to 0} \left(\frac{1}{h} \ln\left(\frac{x+h}{x}\right)\right) = \lim_{h \to 0} \left(\frac{1}{h} \ln\left(1 + \frac{h}{x}\right)\right)$$

Writing $\dfrac{1}{h}$ as $\dfrac{1}{x} \cdot \dfrac{x}{h}$ gives

$$\frac{d}{dx}(\ln x) = \lim_{h \to 0} \left(\frac{1}{x} \cdot \frac{x}{h} \ln\left(1 + \frac{h}{x}\right)\right)$$

$$= \lim_{h \to 0} \left(\frac{1}{x} \ln\left(1 + \frac{h}{x}\right)^{x/h}\right) \qquad (\text{since } r \ln m = \ln m^r)$$

$$= \frac{1}{x} \cdot \lim_{h \to 0} \left(\ln\left(1 + \frac{h}{x}\right)^{x/h}\right)$$

Recall from Section 4.2 the graph of the function $f(x) = \ln x$. It is manifestly unbroken on its domain, which is the set of all positive real numbers. It can be *proved* that the logarithm function is continuous, as suggested by the unbroken graph, and from continuity we have that the limit of a logarithm is the logarithm of the limit ($\lim \ln u = \ln \lim u$). Consequently, we have

$$\frac{d}{dx}(\ln x) = \frac{1}{x} \ln\left(\lim_{h \to 0}\left(1 + \frac{h}{x}\right)^{x/h}\right) \tag{1}$$

To evaluate $\lim_{h \to 0}\left(1 + \dfrac{h}{x}\right)^{x/h}$, first note that if $h \to 0$, then, for fixed $x$, $\dfrac{h}{x} \to 0$ and, conversely, if $\dfrac{h}{x} \to 0$, then $h \to 0$. Thus, if we replace $\dfrac{h}{x}$ by $k$, the limit becomes

$$\lim_{k \to 0}(1 + k)^{1/k} = e$$

as in Section 10.1. Hence, Equation (1) becomes

$$\frac{d}{dx}(\ln x) = \frac{1}{x} \ln e = \frac{1}{x}(1) = \frac{1}{x} \quad \text{for } x > 0$$

Some care is required with this equation because while the left-hand side is defined only for $x > 0$, the right-hand side is defined for all $x \neq 0$. For $x < 0$, $\ln(-x)$ is defined and by the chain rule we have

$$\frac{d}{dx}(\ln(-x)) = \frac{1}{-x}\frac{d}{dx}(-x) = \frac{-1}{-x} = \frac{1}{x} \quad \text{for } x < 0$$

We can combine the last two equations by using the absolute function to get

$$\frac{d}{dx}(\ln|x|) = \frac{1}{x} \quad \text{for } x \neq 0 \tag{2}$$

● EXAMPLE 1  **Differentiating Functions Involving** $\ln x$

**a.** *Differentiate* $f(x) = 5 \ln x$.

Solution: Here $f$ is a constant (5) times a function ($\ln x$), so by Equation (2), we have

$$f'(x) = 5 \frac{d}{dx}(\ln x) = 5 \cdot \frac{1}{x} = \frac{5}{x} \quad \text{for } x > 0$$

**b.** *Differentiate* $y = \dfrac{\ln x}{x^2}$.

Solution: By the quotient rule and Equation (2),

$$y' = \frac{x^2 \dfrac{d}{dx}(\ln x) - (\ln x) \dfrac{d}{dx}(x^2)}{(x^2)^2}$$

$$= \frac{x^2 \left(\dfrac{1}{x}\right) - (\ln x)(2x)}{x^4} = \frac{x - 2x \ln x}{x^4} = \frac{1 - 2 \ln x}{x^3} \quad \text{for } x > 0$$

NOW WORK PROBLEM 1 ●●

We will now extend Equation (2) to cover a broader class of functions. Let $y = \ln |u|$, where $u$ is a differentiable function of $x$. By the chain rule,

The chain rule is used to develop the differentiation formula for $\ln |u|$.

$$\frac{d}{dx}(\ln |u|) = \frac{dy}{du} \cdot \frac{du}{dx} = \frac{d}{du}(\ln |u|) \cdot \frac{du}{dx} = \frac{1}{u} \cdot \frac{du}{dx} \quad \text{for } u \neq 0$$

Thus,

$$\frac{d}{du}(\ln |u|) = \frac{1}{u} \cdot \frac{du}{dx} \quad \text{for } u \neq 0 \qquad (3)$$

Of course, Equation (3) gives us $\dfrac{d}{du}(\ln u) = \dfrac{1}{u} \cdot \dfrac{du}{dx}$ for $u > 0$.

**DIFFERENTIATING FUNCTIONS INVOLVING** $\ln u$

The supply of $q$ units of a product at a price of $p$ dollars per unit is given by $q(p) = 25 + 2 \ln(3p^2 + 4)$. Find the rate of change of supply with respect to price, $\dfrac{dq}{dp}$.

● EXAMPLE 2  **Differentiating Functions Involving** $\ln u$

**a.** *Differentiate* $y = \ln(x^2 + 1)$.

Solution: This function has the form $\ln u$ with $u = x^2 + 1$ and since $x^2 + 1 > 0$, for all $x$, $y = \ln(x^2 + 1)$ is defined for all $x$. Using Equation (3), we have

$$\frac{dy}{dx} = \frac{1}{x^2 + 1} \frac{d}{dx}(x^2 + 1) = \frac{1}{x^2 + 1}(2x) = \frac{2x}{x^2 + 1}$$

**b.** *Differentiate* $y = x^2 \ln(4x + 2)$.

Solution: Using the product rule gives

$$\frac{dy}{dx} = x^2 \frac{d}{dx}(\ln(4x + 2)) + (\ln(4x + 2)) \frac{d}{dx}(x^2)$$

By Equation (3) with $u = 4x + 2$,

$$\frac{dy}{dx} = x^2 \left(\frac{1}{4x + 2}\right)(4) + (\ln(4x + 2))(2x)$$

$$= \frac{2x^2}{2x + 1} + 2x \ln(4x + 2) \quad \text{for } 4x + 2 > 0$$

Since $4x + 2 > 0$ exactly when $x > -1/2$, we have

$$\frac{d}{dx}(x^2 \ln(4x + 2)) = \frac{2x^2}{2x + 1} + 2x \ln(4x + 2) \quad \text{for } x > -1/2$$

**c.** *Differentiate* $y = \ln|\ln|x||$.

Solution: This has the form $y = \ln|u|$ with $u = \ln|x|$. Using Equation (3), we obtain

$$y' = \frac{1}{\ln|x|}\frac{d}{dx}(\ln|x|) = \frac{1}{\ln|x|}\left(\frac{1}{x}\right) = \frac{1}{x\ln|x|} \quad \text{for } x, u \neq 0$$

Since $\ln|x| = 0$ when $x = -1, 1$, we have

$$\frac{d}{dx}(\ln|\ln|x||) = \frac{1}{x\ln|x|} \quad \text{for } x \neq -1, 0, 1$$

NOW WORK PROBLEM 9

Frequently, we can reduce the work involved in differentiating the logarithm of a product, quotient, or power by using properties of logarithms to rewrite the logarithm *before* differentiating. The next example will illustrate.

**EXAMPLE 3   Rewriting Logarithmic Functions before Differentiating**

**a.** *Find* $\dfrac{dy}{dx}$ *if* $y = \ln(2x+5)^3$.

Solution: Here we have the logarithm of a power. First we simplify the right side by using properties of logarithms. Then we differentiate. We have

$$y = \ln(2x+5)^3 = 3\ln(2x+5) \quad \text{for } 2x+5 > 0$$
$$\frac{dy}{dx} = 3\left(\frac{1}{2x+5}\right)(2) = \frac{6}{2x+5} \quad \text{for } x > -5/2$$

Comparing both methods, we note that the easier one is to simplify first and then differentiate.

Alternatively, if the simplification were not performed first, we would write

$$\frac{dy}{dx} = \frac{1}{(2x+5)^3}\frac{d}{dx}((2x+5)^3)$$
$$= \frac{1}{(2x+5)^3}(3)(2x+5)^2(2) = \frac{6}{2x+5}$$

**b.** *Find* $f'(p)$ *if* $f(p) = \ln((p+1)^2(p+2)^3(p+3)^4)$.

Solution: We simplify the right side and then differentiate:

$$f(p) = 2\ln(p+1) + 3\ln(p+2) + 4\ln(p+3)$$
$$f'(p) = 2\left(\frac{1}{p+1}\right)(1) + 3\left(\frac{1}{p+2}\right)(1) + 4\left(\frac{1}{p+3}\right)(1)$$
$$= \frac{2}{p+1} + \frac{3}{p+2} + \frac{4}{p+3}$$

NOW WORK PROBLEM 5

**EXAMPLE 4   Differentiating Functions Involving Logarithms**

**a.** *Find* $f'(w)$ *if* $f(w) = \ln\sqrt{\dfrac{1+w^2}{w^2-1}}$.

Solution: We simplify by using properties of logarithms and then differentiate:

$$f(w) = \frac{1}{2}(\ln(1+w^2) - \ln(w^2-1))$$
$$f'(w) = \frac{1}{2}\left(\frac{1}{1+w^2}(2w) - \frac{1}{w^2-1}(2w)\right)$$
$$= \frac{w}{1+w^2} - \frac{w}{w^2-1} = -\frac{2w}{w^4-1}$$

**b.** *Find* $f'(x)$ *if* $f(x) = \ln^3(2x + 5)$.

> **Solution:** The exponent 3 refers to the cubing of $\ln(2x + 5)$. That is,
>
> $$f(x) = \ln^3(2x + 5) = [\ln(2x + 5)]^3$$
>
> By the power rule,
>
> $$f'(x) = 3(\ln(2x + 5))^2 \frac{d}{dx}(\ln(2x + 5))$$
>
> $$= 3(\ln(2x + 5))^2 \left( \frac{1}{2x + 5}(2) \right)$$
>
> $$= \frac{6}{2x + 5}(\ln(2x + 5))^2$$

NOW WORK PROBLEM 39 ⬤⬤

**CAUTION**

Do not confuse $\ln^3(2x + 5)$ with $\ln(2x + 5)^3$, which occurred in Example 3(a). It is advisable to write $\ln^3(2x + 5)$ explicitly as $[\ln(2x + 5)]^3$ and avoid $\ln^3(2x + 5)$.

### Derivatives of Logarithmic Functions to the Base $b$

To differentiate a logarithmic function to a base different from $e$, we can first convert the logarithm to natural logarithms via the change-of-base formula and then differentiate the resulting expression. For example, consider $y = \log_b u$, where $u$ is a differentiable function of $x$. By the change-of-base formula,

$$y = \log_b u = \frac{\ln u}{\ln b} \quad \text{for } u > 0$$

Differentiating, we have

$$\frac{d}{dx}(\log_b u) = \frac{d}{dx}\left( \frac{\ln u}{\ln b} \right) = \frac{1}{\ln b}\frac{d}{dx}(\ln u) = \frac{1}{\ln b} \cdot \frac{1}{u}\frac{du}{dx}$$

Summarizing,

$$\frac{d}{dx}(\log_b u) = \frac{1}{(\ln b)u} \cdot \frac{du}{dx} \quad \text{for } u > 0$$

**CAUTION**

Note that $\ln b$ is just a constant!

Rather than memorize this rule, we suggest that you remember the procedure used to obtain it.

> **Procedure to Differentiate** $\log_b u$
>
> Convert $\log_b u$ to natural logarithms to obtain $\dfrac{\ln u}{\ln b}$, and then differentiate.

⬤ **EXAMPLE 5    Differentiating a Logarithmic Function to the Base 2**

*Differentiate* $y = \log_2 x$.

**Solution:** Following the foregoing procedure, we have

$$\frac{d}{dx}(\log_2 x) = \frac{d}{dx}\left( \frac{\ln x}{\ln 2} \right) = \frac{1}{\ln 2}\frac{d}{dx}(\ln x) = \frac{1}{(\ln 2)x}$$

It is worth mentioning that we can write our answer in terms of the original base. Because

$$\frac{1}{\ln b} = \frac{1}{\dfrac{\log_b b}{\log_b e}} = \frac{\log_b e}{1} = \log_b e$$

we can express $\dfrac{1}{(\ln 2)x}$ as $\dfrac{\log_2 e}{x}$. More generally, $\dfrac{d}{dx}(\log_b u) = \dfrac{\log_b e}{u} \cdot \dfrac{du}{dx}$.

NOW WORK PROBLEM 15 ⬤⬤

**DIFFERENTIATING A LOGARITHMIC FUNCTION TO THE BASE 10**

The intensity of an earthquake is measured on the Richter scale. The reading is given by $R = \log \dfrac{I}{I_0}$, where $I$ is the intensity and $I_0$ is a standard minimum intensity. If $I_0 = 1$, find $\dfrac{dR}{dI}$, the rate of change of the Richter-scale reading with respect to the intensity.

● EXAMPLE 6   **Differentiating a Logarithmic Function to the Base 10**

If $y = \log(2x + 1)$, *find the rate of change of y with respect to x.*

**Solution:** The rate of change is $dy/dx$, and the base involved is 10. Therefore, we have

$$\frac{dy}{dx} = \frac{d}{dx}(\log(2x+1)) = \frac{d}{dx}\left(\frac{\ln(2x+1)}{\ln 10}\right)$$

$$= \frac{1}{\ln 10}\cdot\frac{1}{2x+1}(2) = \frac{2}{\ln 10(2x+1)}$$

## Problems 12.1

*In Problems 1–44, differentiate the functions. If possible, first use properties of logarithms to simplify the given function.*

*1. $y = 4\ln x$
2. $y = \dfrac{5\ln x}{9}$
3. $y = \ln(3x - 7)$
4. $y = \ln(5x - 6)$
*5. $y = \ln x^2$
6. $y = \ln(3x^2 + 2x + 1)$
7. $y = \ln(1 - x^2)$
8. $y = \ln(-x^2 + 6x)$
*9. $f(X) = \ln(4X^6 + 2X^3)$
10. $f(r) = \ln(2r^4 - 3r^2 + 2r + 1)$
11. $f(t) = t\ln t$
12. $y = x^2\ln x$
13. $y = x^3\ln(2x + 5)$
14. $y = (ax + b)^3\ln(ax + b)$
*15. $y = \log_3(8x - 1)$
16. $f(w) = \log(w^2 + w)$
17. $y = x^2 + \log_2(x^2 + 4)$
18. $y = x^2\log_2 x$
19. $f(z) = \dfrac{\ln z}{z}$
20. $y = \dfrac{x^2}{\ln x}$
21. $y = \dfrac{x^2 + 3}{(\ln x)^2}$
22. $y = \ln x^{100}$
23. $y = \ln(x^2 + 4x + 5)^3$
24. $y = 6\ln\sqrt[3]{x}$
25. $y = 9\ln\sqrt{1 + x^2}$
26. $f(t) = \ln\left(\dfrac{t^5}{1 + 3t^2 + t^4}\right)$
27. $f(l) = \ln\left(\dfrac{1 + l}{1 - l}\right)$
28. $y = \ln\left(\dfrac{2x + 3}{3x - 4}\right)$
29. $y = \ln\sqrt[4]{\dfrac{1 + x^2}{1 - x^2}}$
30. $y = \ln\sqrt[3]{\dfrac{x^3 - 1}{x^3 + 1}}$
31. $y = \ln[(x^2 + 2)^2(x^3 + x - 1)]$
32. $y = \ln[(5x + 2)^4(8x - 3)^6]$
33. $y = 13\ln\left(x^2\sqrt[3]{5x + 2}\right)$
34. $y = 6\ln\dfrac{x}{\sqrt{2x + 1}}$
35. $y = (x^2 + 1)\ln(2x + 1)$
36. $y = (ax + b)\ln(ax)$
37. $y = \ln x^3 + \ln^3 x$
38. $y = x^{\ln 2}$
*39. $y = \ln^4(ax)$
40. $y = \ln^2(2x + 11)$
41. $y = x\ln\sqrt{x - 1}$
42. $y = \ln\left(x^3\sqrt[4]{2x + 1}\right)$
43. $y = \sqrt{4 + 3\ln x}$
44. $y = \ln\left(x + \sqrt{1 + x^2}\right)$

**45.** Find an equation of the tangent line to the curve
$$y = \ln(x^2 - 3x - 3)$$
when $x = 4$.

**46.** Find an equation of the tangent line to the curve
$$y = x[\ln(x) - 1]$$
at the point where $x = e$.

**47.** Find the slope of the curve $y = \dfrac{x}{\ln x}$ when $x = 3$.

**48. Marginal Revenue**   Find the marginal-revenue function if the demand function is $p = 25/\ln(q + 2)$.

**49. Marginal Cost**   A total-cost function is given by
$$c = 25\ln(q + 1) + 12$$
Find the marginal cost when $q = 6$.

**50. Marginal Cost**   A manufacturer's average-cost function, in dollars, is given by
$$\bar{c} = \frac{500}{\ln(q + 20)}$$
Find the marginal cost (rounded to two decimal places) when $q = 50$.

**51. Supply Change**   The supply of $q$ units of a product at a price of $p$ dollars per unit is given by $q(p) = 25 + 10\ln(2p + 1)$. Find the rate of change of supply with respect to price, $\dfrac{dq}{dp}$.

**52. Sound Perception**   The loudness of sound ($L$, measured in decibels) perceived by the human ear depends upon intensity levels ($I$) according to $L = 10\log\dfrac{I}{I_0}$, where $I_0$ is the standard threshold of audibility. If $I_0 = 17$, find $\dfrac{dL}{dI}$, the rate of change of the loudness with respect to the intensity.

**53. Biology**   In a certain experiment with bacteria, it is observed that the relative activeness of a given bacteria colony is described by
$$A = 6\ln\left(\frac{T}{a - T} - a\right)$$
where $a$ is a constant and $T$ is the surrounding temperature. Find the rate of change of $A$ with respect to $T$.

**54.** Show that the relative rate of change of $y = f(x)$ with respect to $x$ is equal to the derivative of $y = \ln f(x)$.

**55.** Show that $\dfrac{d}{dx}(\log_b u) = \dfrac{1}{u}(\log_b e)\dfrac{du}{dx}$.

*In Problems 56 and 57, use differentiation rules to find $f'(x)$. Then use your graphing calculator to find all zeros of $f'(x)$. Round your answers to two decimal places.*

**56.** $f(x) = x^3\ln x$
**57.** $f(x) = \dfrac{\ln(x^2)}{x^2}$

To develop a differentiation formula for $y = e^u$, to apply the formula, and to use it to differentiate an exponential function with a base other than $e$.

## 12.2 Derivatives of Exponential Functions

We now obtain a formula for the derivative of the exponential function

$$y = e^u$$

where $u$ is a differentiable function of $x$. In logarithmic form, we have

$$u = \ln y$$

Differentiating both sides with respect to $x$ gives

$$\frac{d}{dx}(u) = \frac{d}{dx}(\ln y)$$

$$\frac{du}{dx} = \frac{1}{y}\frac{dy}{dx}$$

Solving for $dy/dx$ and then replacing $y$ by $e^u$ gives

$$\frac{dy}{dx} = y\frac{du}{dx} = e^u\frac{du}{dx}$$

Thus,

$$\frac{d}{dx}(e^u) = e^u\frac{du}{dx} \tag{1}$$

As a special case, let $u = x$. Then $du/dx = 1$, and

$$\frac{d}{dx}(e^x) = e^x \tag{2}$$

**CAUTION**

The power rule does not apply to $e^x$ and other exponential functions, $b^x$. The power rule applies to power functions, $x^a$. Note the location of the variable.

Note that the function and its derivative are the same.

### ● EXAMPLE 1    Differentiating Functions Involving $e^x$

**a.** *Find* $\dfrac{d}{dx}(3e^x)$. Since 3 is a constant factor,

$$\frac{d}{dx}(3e^x) = 3\frac{d}{dx}(e^x)$$

$$= 3e^x \qquad \text{(by Equation (2))}$$

If a quotient can be easily rewritten as a product, then you can use the somewhat simpler product rule rather than the quotient rule.

**b.** *If* $y = \dfrac{x}{e^x}$, *find* $\dfrac{dy}{dx}$.

**Solution:** We could use first the quotient rule and then Equation (2), but it is a little easier to first rewrite the function as $y = xe^{-x}$ and use the product rule and Equation (1):

$$\frac{dy}{dx} = e^{-x}\frac{d}{dx}(x) + x\frac{d}{dx}(e^{-x}) = e^{-x}(1) + x(e^{-x})(-1) = e^{-x}(1-x) = \frac{1-x}{e^x}$$

**c.** *If* $y = e^2 + e^x + \ln 3$, *find* $y'$.

**Solution:** Since $e^2$ and $\ln 3$ are constants, $y' = 0 + e^x + 0 = e^x$.

NOW WORK PROBLEM 1 ●●●

**PRINCIPLES IN PRACTICE 1**

**DIFFERENTIATING FUNCTIONS INVOLVING $e^u$**

When an object is moved from one environment to another, the change in temperature of the object is given by $T = Ce^{kt}$, where $C$ is the temperature difference between the two environments, $t$ is the time in the new environment, and $k$ is a constant. Find the rate of change of temperature with respect to time.

### ● EXAMPLE 2    Differentiating Functions Involving $e^u$

**a.** *Find* $\dfrac{d}{dx}\left(e^{x^3+3x}\right)$.

**Solution:** The function has the form $e^u$ with $u = x^3 + 3x$. From Equation (1),

$$\frac{d}{dx}\left(e^{x^3+3x}\right) = e^{x^3+3x}\frac{d}{dx}(x^3 + 3x) = e^{x^3+3x}(3x^2 + 3)$$

$$= 3(x^2 + 1)e^{x^3+3x}$$

$\dfrac{d}{dx}(e^u) = e^u\dfrac{du}{dx}$. Don't forget the $\dfrac{du}{dx}$.

**b.** *Find* $\dfrac{d}{dx}(e^{x+1}\ln(x^2+1))$.

Solution:  By the product rule,

$$\frac{d}{dx}(e^{x+1}\ln(x^2+1)) = e^{x+1}\frac{d}{dx}(\ln(x^2+1)) + (\ln(x^2+1))\frac{d}{dx}(e^{x+1})$$

$$= e^{x+1}\left(\frac{1}{x^2+1}\right)(2x) + (\ln(x^2+1))e^{x+1}(1)$$

$$= e^{x+1}\left(\frac{2x}{x^2+1} + \ln(x^2+1)\right)$$

NOW WORK PROBLEM 3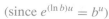

● **EXAMPLE 3   The Normal-Distribution Density Function**

*An important function used in the social sciences is the **normal-distribution density function***

$$y = f(x) = \frac{1}{\sigma\sqrt{2\pi}}e^{-(1/2)((x-\mu)/\sigma)^2}$$

*where $\sigma$ (a Greek letter read "sigma") and $\mu$ (a Greek letter read "mu") are constants. The graph of this function, called the normal curve, is bell shaped. (See Figure 12.1.) Determine the rate of change of $y$ with respect to $x$ when $x = \mu + \sigma$.*

Solution:  The rate of change of $y$ with respect to $x$ is $dy/dx$. We note that the factor $\dfrac{1}{\sigma\sqrt{2\pi}}$ is a constant and the second factor has the form $e^u$, where

$$u = -\frac{1}{2}\left(\frac{x-\mu}{\sigma}\right)^2$$

Thus,

$$\frac{dy}{dx} = \frac{1}{\sigma\sqrt{2\pi}}\left(e^{-(1/2)((x-\mu)/\sigma)^2}\right)\left(-\frac{1}{2}(2)\left(\frac{x-\mu}{\sigma}\right)\left(\frac{1}{\sigma}\right)\right)$$

Evaluating $dy/dx$ when $x = \mu + \sigma$, we obtain

$$\frac{dy}{dx}\bigg|_{x=\mu+\sigma} = \frac{1}{\sigma\sqrt{2\pi}}\left(e^{-(1/2)((\mu+\sigma-\mu)/\sigma)^2}\right)\left(-\frac{1}{2}(2)\left(\frac{\mu+\sigma-\mu}{\sigma}\right)\left(\frac{1}{\sigma}\right)\right)$$

$$= \frac{1}{\sigma\sqrt{2\pi}}\left(e^{-(1/2)}\right)\left(-\frac{1}{\sigma}\right)$$

$$= \frac{-e^{-(1/2)}}{\sigma^2\sqrt{2\pi}} = \frac{-1}{\sigma^2\sqrt{2\pi e}}$$

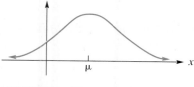

FIGURE 12.1   The normal-
distribution density function.

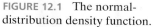

### Differentiating Exponential Functions to the Base $b$

Now that we are familiar with the derivative of $e^u$, we consider the derivative of the more general exponential function $b^u$. Because $b = e^{\ln b}$, we can express $b^u$ as an exponential function with the base $e$, a form we can differentiate. We have

$$\frac{d}{dx}(b^u) = \frac{d}{dx}((e^{\ln b})^u) = \frac{d}{dx}(e^{(\ln b)u})$$

$$= e^{(\ln b)u}\frac{d}{dx}((\ln b)u)$$

$$= e^{(\ln b)u}(\ln b)\left(\frac{du}{dx}\right)$$

$$= b^u(\ln b)\frac{du}{dx} \qquad \text{(since } e^{(\ln b)u} = b^u\text{)}$$

Summarizing,

$$\frac{d}{dx}(b^u) = b^u(\ln b)\frac{du}{dx} \tag{3}$$

Note that if $b = e$, then the factor $\ln b$ in Equation (3) is 1. Thus, if exponential functions to the base $e$ are used, we have a simpler differentiation formula with which to work. This is the reason natural exponential functions are used extensively in calculus. Rather than memorizing Equation (3), we suggest that you remember the procedure for obtaining it.

**Procedure to Differentiate $b^u$**

Convert $b^u$ to a natural exponential function by using the property that $b = e^{\ln b}$, and then differentiate.

The next example will illustrate this procedure.

⬤ **EXAMPLE 4**   **Differentiating an Exponential Function to the Base 4**

*Find* $\dfrac{d}{dx}(4^x)$.

**Solution:**  Using the preceding procedure, we have

$$\frac{d}{dx}(4^x) = \frac{d}{dx}((e^{\ln 4})^x)$$

$$= \frac{d}{dx}\left(e^{(\ln 4)x}\right) \qquad \left(\text{form}: \frac{d}{dx}(e^u)\right)$$

$$= e^{(\ln 4)x}(\ln 4) \qquad \text{(by Equation (1))}$$

$$= 4^x(\ln 4)$$

NOW WORK PROBLEM 15  ⬤⬤

*Verify the result by using Equation (3) directly.*

⬤ **EXAMPLE 5**   **Differentiating Different Forms**

*Find* $\dfrac{d}{dx}\left(e^2 + x^e + 2^{\sqrt{x}}\right)$.

**Solution:**  Here we must differentiate three different forms; do not confuse them! The first ($e^2$) is a constant base to a constant power, so it is a constant itself. Thus, its derivative is zero. The second ($x^e$) is a variable base to a constant power, so the power rule applies. The third ($2^{\sqrt{x}}$) is a constant base to a variable power, so we must differentiate an exponential function. Taken all together, we have

$$\frac{d}{dx}\left(e^2 + x^e + 2^{\sqrt{x}}\right) = 0 + ex^{e-1} + \frac{d}{dx}\left[e^{(\ln 2)\sqrt{x}}\right]$$

$$= ex^{e-1} + \left[e^{(\ln 2)\sqrt{x}}\right](\ln 2)\left(\frac{1}{2\sqrt{x}}\right)$$

$$= ex^{e-1} + \frac{2^{\sqrt{x}}\ln 2}{2\sqrt{x}}$$

NOW WORK PROBLEM 17  ⬤⬤

⬤ **EXAMPLE 6**   **Differentiating Inverse Functions**

We can apply the technique of this section to differentiate any inverse function $f^{-1}$ once we know the derivative of $f$. Suppose that

$$y = f^{-1}(u)$$

where, as usual, $u$ is a differentiable function of $x$ and we wish to find $dy/dx$. In terms of $f$, we have

$$f(y) = u$$

and differentiating both sides with respect to $x$, we obtain

$$f'(y)\frac{dy}{dx} = \frac{du}{dx}$$

using the chain rule for the left side. Solving for $dy/dx$ and replacing $y$ by $f^{-1}(u)$ gives

$$\frac{dy}{dx} = \frac{1}{f'(f^{-1}(u))}\frac{du}{dx}$$

so that

$$\frac{d}{dx}(f^{-1}(u)) = \frac{1}{f'(f^{-1}(u))}\frac{du}{dx} \quad \text{for } f'(f^{-1}(u)) \neq 0 \qquad (4)$$

and, in particular,

$$\frac{d}{dx}(f^{-1}(x)) = \frac{1}{f'(f^{-1}(x))} \quad \text{for } f'(f^{-1}(x)) \neq 0 \qquad (5)$$

The reader may have noticed here, and in our treatment of the derivative of the exponential function, that we have assumed that $f^{-1}$ is differentiable. The assumption can be avoided since it follows from the differentiability of $f$. A geometric plausibility argument can be given as follows. At each point $(x, f(x))$ on the graph of $f$ there is a nonvertical tangent line whose slope is $f'(x)$. Since the graph of $f^{-1}$ is obtained from the graph of $f$ by reflection in the line $y = x$, it seems clear that at each point $(x, f^{-1}(x)$ on the graph of $f^{-1}$ there will also be a tangent line—whose slope is $(f^{-1})'(x)$. Of course, if the tangent at $(f^{-1}(x), f(f^{-1}(x))) = (f^{-1}(x), x)$ is horizontal, then the tangent line at the reflected point $(x, f^{-1}(x))$ is vertical so that there the derivative of $f^{-1}$ does not exist. Observe that our algebraic derivation accounts for those exceptions!

As with the chain rule, Leibniz notation is well suited for inverse functions. Indeed, if $y = f^{-1}(x)$, then $\frac{d}{dx}(f^{-1}(x)) = \frac{dy}{dx}$. Now since $f(y) = x$, $\frac{dx}{dy} = f'(y)$ and we see that Equation (5) can be rewritten as

$$\frac{dy}{dx} = \frac{1}{\dfrac{dx}{dy}} \qquad (6)$$

## ● EXAMPLE 7   Differentiating Power Functions Again

We have often used the rule $d/dx(x^a) = ax^{a-1}$, but we have only *proved* it for $a$ a positive integer and a few other special cases. At least for $x > 0$, we can now improve our understanding of power functions, using Equation (1).

For $x > 0$, we can write $x^a = e^{a \ln x}$. So we have

$$\frac{d}{dx}(x^a) = \frac{d}{dx}e^{a \ln x} = e^{a \ln x}\frac{d}{dx}(a \ln x) = x^a(ax^{-1}) = ax^{a-1}$$

# Problems 12.2

*In Problems 1–28, differentiate the functions.*

*1. $y = 5e^x$

2. $y = \dfrac{2e^x}{5}$

*3. $y = e^{2x^2+3}$

4. $y = e^{2x^2+5}$

5. $y = e^{9-5x}$

6. $f(q) = e^{-q^3+6q-1}$

7. $f(r) = e^{3r^2+4r+4}$

8. $y = e^{x^2+6x^3+1}$

9. $y = xe^x$

10. $y = 3x^4 e^{-x}$

11. $y = x^2 e^{-x^2}$

12. $y = xe^{3x}$

13. $y = \dfrac{e^x + e^{-x}}{3}$

14. $y = \dfrac{e^x - e^{-x}}{e^x + e^{-x}}$

*15. $y = 5^{2x^3}$

16. $y = 2^x x^2$

*17. $f(w) = \dfrac{e^{2w}}{w^2}$

18. $y = e^{x-\sqrt{x}}$

19. $y = e^{1+\sqrt{x}}$

20. $y = (e^{2x} + 1)^3$

21. $y = x^5 - 5^x$

22. $f(z) = e^{-1/z^2}$

23. $y = \dfrac{e^x - 1}{e^x + 1}$

24. $y = e^{2x}(x + 6)$

**25.** $y = \ln e^x$

**26.** $y = e^{-x} \ln x$

**27.** $y = e^{x^2 \ln x^2}$

**28.** $y = \ln e^{4x+1}$

**29.** If $f(x) = e e^x e^{x^2}$, find $f'(-1)$.

**30.** If $f(x) = 5^{x^2 \ln x}$, find $f'(1)$.

**31.** Find an equation of the tangent line to the curve $y = e^x$ when $x = -2$.

**32.** Find an equation of the tangent line to the curve $y = e^x$ at the point $(1, e)$.

*For each of the demand equations in Problems 33 and 34, find the rate of change of price p with respect to quantity q. What is the rate of change for the indicated value of q?*

**33.** $p = 15e^{-0.001q}$; $q = 500$

**34.** $p = 9e^{-5q/750}$; $q = 300$

*In Problems 35 and 36, $\bar{c}$ is the average cost of producing q units of a product. Find the marginal-cost function and the marginal cost for the given values of q.*

**35.** $\bar{c} = \dfrac{7000e^{q/700}}{q}$; $q = 350, q = 700$

**36.** $\bar{c} = \dfrac{850}{q} + 4000\dfrac{e^{(2q+6)/800}}{q}$; $q = 97, q = 197$

**37.** If $w = e^{x^3 - 4x} + x \ln(x-1)$ and $x = \dfrac{t+1}{t-1}$, find $\dfrac{dw}{dt}$ when $t = 3$.

**38.** If $f'(x) = x^3$ and $u = e^x$, show that

$$\frac{d}{dx}[f(u)] = e^{4x}$$

**39.** Determine the value of the positive constant $c$ if

$$\frac{d}{dx}(c^x - x^c)\bigg|_{x=1} = 0$$

**40.** Calculate the relative rate of change of

$$f(x) = 10^{-x} + \ln(8 + x) + 0.01e^{x-2}$$

when $x = 2$. Round your answer to four decimal places.

**41. Production Run**   For a firm, the daily output on the $t$th day of a production run is given by

$$q = 500(1 - e^{-0.2t})$$

Find the rate of change of output $q$ with respect to $t$ on the tenth day.

**42. Normal-Density Function**   For the normal-density function

$$f(x) = \frac{1}{\sqrt{2\pi}} e^{-x^2/2}$$

find $f'(1)$.

**43. Population**   The population, in millions, of the greater Seattle area $t$ years from 1970 is estimated by $P = 1.92e^{0.0176t}$. Show that $dP/dt = kP$, where $k$ is a constant. This means that the rate of change of population at any time is proportional to the population at that time.

**44. Market Penetration**   In a discussion of diffusion of a new process into a market, Hurter and Rubenstein[1] refer to an equation of the form

$$Y = k\alpha^{\beta^t}$$

where $Y$ is the cumulative level of diffusion of the new process at time $t$ and $k$, $\alpha$, and $\beta$ are positive constants. Verify their claim that

$$\frac{dY}{dt} = k\alpha^{\beta^t}(\beta^t \ln \alpha) \ln \beta$$

**45. Finance**   After $t$ years, the value $S$ of a principal of $P$ dollars invested at the annual rate of $r$ compounded continuously is given by $S = Pe^{rt}$. Show that the relative rate of change of $S$ with respect to $t$ is $r$.

**46. Predator–Prey Relationship**   In an article concerning predators and prey, Holling[2] refers to an equation of the form

$$y = K(1 - e^{-ax})$$

where $x$ is the prey density, $y$ is the number of prey attacked, and $K$ and $a$ are constants. Verify his statement that

$$\frac{dy}{dx} = a(K - y)$$

**47. Earthquakes**   According to Richter,[3] the number of earthquakes of magnitude $M$ or greater per unit of time is given by $N = 10^A 10^{-bM}$, where $A$ and $b$ are constants. Find $dN/dM$.

**48. Psychology**   Short-term retention was studied by Peterson and Peterson.[4] The two researchers analyzed a procedure in which an experimenter verbally gave a subject a three-letter consonant syllable, such as CHJ, followed by a three-digit number, such as 309. The subject then repeated the number and counted backward by 3's, such as 309, 306, 303, .... After a period of time, the subject was signaled by a light to recite the three-letter consonant syllable. The time between the experimenter's completion of the last consonant to the onset of the light was called the *recall interval*. The time between the onset of the light and the completion of a response was referred to as *latency*. After many trials, it was determined that, for a recall interval of $t$ seconds, the approximate proportion of correct recalls with latency below 2.83 seconds was

$$p = 0.89[0.01 + 0.99(0.85)^t]$$

**(a)** Find $dp/dt$ and interpret your result.

**(b)** Evaluate $dp/dt$ when $t = 2$. Round your answer to two decimal places.

**49. Medicine**   Suppose a tracer, such as a colored dye, is injected instantly into the heart at time $t = 0$ and mixes uniformly with blood inside the heart. Let the initial concentration of the tracer in the heart be $C_0$, and assume that the heart has constant volume $V$. Also assume that, as

[1]A. P. Hurter, Jr., A. H. Rubenstein, et al., "Market Penetration by New Innovations: The Technological Literature," *Technological Forecasting and Social Change*, 11 (1978), 197–221.

[2]C. S. Holling, "Some Characteristics of Simple Types of Predation and Parasitism," *The Canadian Entomologist*, XCI, no. 7 (1959), 385–98.

[3]C. F. Richter, *Elementary Seismology* (San Francisco: W. H. Freeman and Company, Publishers, 1958).

[4]L. R. Peterson and M. J. Peterson, "Short-Term Retention of Individual Verbal Items," *Journal of Experimental Psychology*, 58 (1959), 193–98.

fresh blood flows into the heart, the diluted mixture of blood and tracer flows out at the constant positive rate $r$. Then the concentration of the tracer in the heart at time $t$ is given by

$$C(t) = C_0 e^{-(r/V)t}$$

Show that $dC/dt = (-r/V)C(t)$.

**50. Medicine** In Problem 49, suppose the tracer is injected at a constant rate $R$. Then the concentration at time $t$ is

$$C(t) = \frac{R}{r}\left[1 - e^{-(r/V)t}\right]$$

**(a)** Find $C(0)$.

**(b)** Show that $\dfrac{dC}{dt} = \dfrac{R}{V} - \dfrac{r}{V}C(t)$.

**51. Schizophrenia** Several models have been used to analyze the length of stay in a hospital. For a particular group of schizophrenics, one such model is[5]

$$f(t) = 1 - e^{-0.008t}$$

where $f(t)$ is the proportion of the group that was discharged at the end of $t$ days of hospitalization. Find the rate of discharge (the proportion discharged per day) at the end of 100 days. Round your answer to four decimal places.

**52. Savings and Consumption** A country's savings $S$ (in billions of dollars) is related to its national income $I$ (in billions of dollars) by the equation

$$S = \ln \frac{5}{3 + e^{-I}}$$

**(a)** Find the marginal propensity to consume as a function of income.

**(b)** To the nearest million dollars, what is the national income when the marginal propensity to save is $\dfrac{1}{8}$? (*Hint:* 1 billion = 1000 million).

*In Problems 53 and 54, use differentiation rules to find $f'(x)$. Then use your graphing calculator to find all real zeros of $f'(x)$. Round your answers to two decimal places.*

**53.** $f(x) = e^{2x^3+x^2-3x}$

**54.** $f(x) = x + e^{-x}$

## 12.3 Elasticity of Demand

OBJECTIVE

To give a mathematical analysis of the economic concept of elasticity.

*Elasticity of demand* is a means by which economists measure how a change in the price of a product will affect the quantity demanded. That is, it refers to consumer response to price changes. Loosely speaking, elasticity of demand is the ratio of the resulting percentage change in quantity demanded to a given percentage change in price:

$$\frac{\text{percentage change in quantity}}{\text{percentage change in price}}$$

For example, if, for a price increase of 5%, quantity demanded were to decrease by 2%, we would loosely say that elasticity of demand is $-2/5$.

To be more general, suppose $p = f(q)$ is the demand function for a product. Consumers will demand $q$ units at a price of $f(q)$ per unit and will demand $q + h$ units at a price of $f(q + h)$ per unit (Figure 12.2). The *percentage* change in quantity demanded from $q$ to $q + h$ is

$$\frac{(q+h) - q}{q} \cdot 100\% = \frac{h}{q} \cdot 100\%$$

The corresponding percentage change in price per unit is

$$\frac{f(q+h) - f(q)}{f(q)} \cdot 100\%$$

The ratio of these percentage changes is

$$\frac{\dfrac{h}{q} \cdot 100\%}{\dfrac{f(q+h) - f(q)}{f(q)} \cdot 100\%} = \frac{h}{q} \cdot \frac{f(q)}{f(q+h) - f(q)}$$

$$= \frac{f(q)}{q} \cdot \frac{h}{f(q+h) - f(q)}$$

$$= \frac{\dfrac{f(q)}{q}}{\dfrac{f(q+h) - f(q)}{h}} \quad \textbf{(1)}$$

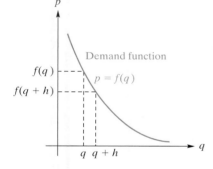

FIGURE 12.2 Change in demand.

[5]W. W. Eaton and G. A. Whitmore, "Length of Stay as a Stochastic Process: A General Approach and Application to Hospitalization for Schizophrenia," *Journal of Mathematical Sociology*, 5 (1977), 273–92.

If $f$ is differentiable, then as $h \to 0$, the limit of $[f(q+h) - f(q)]/h$ is $f'(q) = dp/dq$. Thus, the limit of (1) is

$$\frac{\dfrac{f(q)}{q}}{f'(q)} = \frac{\dfrac{p}{q}}{\dfrac{dp}{dq}} \qquad (\text{since } p = f(q))$$

which is called the *point elasticity of demand*.

---

**DEFINITION**

If $p = f(q)$ is a differentiable demand function, the ***point elasticity of demand,*** denoted by the Greek letter $\eta$ (eta), at $(q, p)$ is given by

$$\eta = \eta(q) = \frac{\dfrac{p}{q}}{\dfrac{dp}{dq}}$$

---

**CAUTION**

Since $p$ is a function of $q$, $dp/dq$ is a function of $q$ and thus the ratio that defines $\eta$ is a function of $q$. That is why we write $\eta = \eta(q)$.

To illustrate, let us find the point elasticity of demand for the demand function $p = 1200 - q^2$. We have

$$\eta = \frac{\dfrac{p}{q}}{\dfrac{dp}{dq}} = \frac{\dfrac{1200 - q^2}{q}}{-2q} = -\frac{1200 - q^2}{2q^2} = -\left(\frac{600}{q^2} - \frac{1}{2}\right) \qquad (2)$$

For example, if $q = 10$, then $\eta = -\left((600/10^2) - \frac{1}{2}\right) = -5\frac{1}{2}$. Since

$$\eta \approx \frac{\%\ \text{change in demand}}{\%\ \text{change in price}}$$

we have

$$(\%\ \text{change in price})(\eta) \approx \%\ \text{change in demand}$$

Thus, if price were increased by 1% when $q = 10$, then quantity demanded would change by approximately

$$(1\%)\left(-5\frac{1}{2}\right) = -5\frac{1}{2}\%$$

That is, demand would decrease $5\frac{1}{2}\%$. Similarly, decreasing price by $\frac{1}{2}\%$ when $q = 10$ results in a change in demand of approximately

$$\left(-\frac{1}{2}\%\right)\left(-5\frac{1}{2}\right) = 2\frac{3}{4}\%$$

Hence, demand increases by $2\frac{3}{4}\%$.

Note that when elasticity is evaluated, no units are attached to it—it is nothing more than a real number. In fact, the 100%'s arising from the word *percentage* cancel, so that elasticity is really an approximation of the ratio

$$\frac{\text{relative change in quantity}}{\text{relative change in price}}$$

and each of the relative changes is no more than a real number. For usual behavior of demand, an increase (decrease) in price corresponds to a decrease (increase) in quantity. This means that if price is plotted as a function of quantity then the graph will have a negative slope at each point. Thus, $dp/dq$ will typically be negative, and since $p$ and $q$ are positive, $\eta$ will typically be negative too. Some economists disregard the minus sign; in the preceding situation, they would consider the elasticity to be $5\frac{1}{2}$. We will not adopt this practice.

There are three categories of elasticity:

1. When $|\eta| > 1$, demand is *elastic*.
2. When $|\eta| = 1$, demand has *unit elasticity*.
3. When $|\eta| < 1$, demand is *inelastic*.

For example, in Equation (2), since $|\eta| = 5\frac{1}{2}$ when $q = 10$, demand is elastic. If $q = 20$, then $|\eta| = \left|-\left[(600/20^2) - \frac{1}{2}\right]\right| = 1$ so demand has unit elasticity. If $q = 25$, then $|\eta| = \left|-\frac{23}{50}\right|$, and demand is inelastic.

Loosely speaking, for a given percentage change in price, there is a greater percentage change in quantity demanded if demand is elastic, a smaller percentage change if demand is inelastic, and an equal percentage change if demand has unit elasticity. To better understand elasticity, it is helpful to think of typical examples. Demand for an essential utlity such as electricity tends to be inelastic through a wide range of prices. If electricity prices are increased by 10%, consumers can be expected to reduce their consumption somewhat but a full 10% decrease may not be possible if most of their electricity usage is for essentials of life such as heating and food preparation. On the other hand, demand for luxury goods tends to be quite elastic. A 10% increase in the price of jewelry, for example, may result in a 50% decrease in demand.

### ● EXAMPLE 1   Finding Point Elasticity of Demand

*Determine the point elasticity of the demand equation*

$$p = \frac{k}{q} \quad \text{where } k > 0 \text{ and } q > 0$$

**Solution:** From the definition, we have

$$\eta = \frac{\dfrac{p}{q}}{\dfrac{dp}{dq}} = \frac{\dfrac{k}{q^2}}{\dfrac{-k}{q^2}} = -1$$

Thus, the demand has unit elasticity for all $q > 0$. The graph of $p = k/q$ is called an *equilateral hyperbola* and is often found in economics texts in discussions of elasticity. (See Figure 2.14 for a graph of such a curve.)

NOW WORK PROBLEM 1 ●●

If we are given $p = f(q)$ for our demand equation, as in our discussion thus far, then it is usually straightforward to calculate $dp/dq = f'(q)$. However, if instead we are given $q$ as a function of $p$, then we will have $q = f^{-1}(p)$ and from Example 6 in Section 12.2,

$$\frac{dp}{dq} = \frac{1}{\dfrac{dq}{dp}}$$

It follows that

$$\eta = \frac{\dfrac{p}{q}}{\dfrac{dp}{dq}} = \frac{p}{q} \cdot \frac{dq}{dp} \tag{3}$$

provides another useful expression for $\eta$. Notice too that if $q = g(p)$, then

$$\eta = \eta(p) = \frac{p}{q} \cdot \frac{dq}{dp} = \frac{p}{g(p)} \cdot g'(p) = p \cdot \frac{g'(p)}{g(p)}$$

and thus

elasticity = price · relative rate of change of quantity as a function of price   (4)

### ● EXAMPLE 2   Finding Point Elasticity of Demand

*Determine the point elasticity of the demand equation*

$$q = p^2 - 40p + 400 \quad \text{where } q > 0$$

**Solution:** Here we have $q$ given as a function of $p$ and it is easy to see that $dq/dp = 2p - 40$. Thus,

$$\eta(p) = \frac{p}{q} \cdot \frac{dq}{dp} = \frac{p}{q(p)}(2p - 40)$$

For example, if $p = 15$, then $q = q(15) = 25$; hence, $\eta(15) = (15(-10))/25 = -6$, so demand is elastic for $p = 15$.

NOW WORK PROBLEM 13   ●●

Here we analyze elasticity for linear demand.

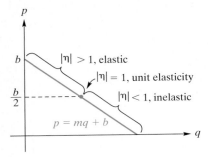

**FIGURE 12.3**   Elasticity for linear demand.

Point elasticity for a *linear* demand equation is quite interesting. Suppose the equation has the form

$$p = mq + b \quad \text{where } m < 0 \text{ and } b > 0$$

(See Figure 12.3.) We assume that $q > 0$; thus, $p < b$. The point elasticity of demand is

$$\eta = \frac{\dfrac{p}{q}}{\dfrac{dp}{dq}} = \frac{\dfrac{p}{q}}{m} = \frac{p}{mq} = \frac{p}{p - b}$$

By considering $d\eta/dp$, we will show that $\eta$ is a decreasing function of $p$. By the quotient rule,

$$\frac{d\eta}{dp} = \frac{(p - b) - p}{(p - b)^2} = -\frac{b}{(p - b)^2}$$

Since $b > 0$ and $(p - b)^2 > 0$, it follows that $d\eta/dp < 0$, meaning that the graph of $\eta = \eta(p)$ has a negative slope. This means that as price $p$ increases, elasticity $\eta$ decreases. However, $p$ ranges between 0 and $b$, and at the midpoint of this range, $b/2$,

$$\eta = \eta(b) = \frac{\dfrac{b}{2}}{\dfrac{b}{2} - b} = \frac{\dfrac{b}{2}}{-\dfrac{b}{2}} = -1$$

Therefore, if $p < b/2$, then $\eta > -1$; if $p > b/2$, then $\eta < -1$. Because we typically have $\eta < 0$, we can state these facts another way: When $p < b/2$, $|\eta| < 1$, and demand is inelastic; when $p = b/2$, $|\eta| = 1$, and demand has unit elasticity; when $p > b/2$, $|\eta| > 1$ and demand is elastic. This shows that the slope of a demand curve is not a measure of elasticity. The slope of the line in Figure 12.3 is $m$ everywhere, but elasticity varies with the point on the line. Of course, this is in accord with Equation (4).

### Elasticity and Revenue

Here we analyze the relationship between elasticity and the rate of change of revenue.

Turning to a different situation, we can relate how elasticity of demand affects changes in revenue (marginal revenue). If $p = f(q)$ is a manufacturer's demand function, the total revenue is given by

$$r = pq$$

To find the marginal revenue, $dr/dq$, we differentiate $r$ by using the product rule:

$$\frac{dr}{dq} = p + q\frac{dp}{dq}. \tag{5}$$

Factoring the right side of Equation (5), we have

$$\frac{dr}{dq} = p\left(1 + \frac{q}{p}\frac{dp}{dq}\right)$$

But

$$\frac{q}{p}\frac{dp}{dq} = \frac{\dfrac{dp}{dq}}{\dfrac{p}{q}} = \frac{1}{\eta}$$

Thus,

$$\frac{dr}{dq} = p\left(1 + \frac{1}{\eta}\right) \tag{6}$$

If demand is elastic, then $\eta < -1$, so $1 + \dfrac{1}{\eta} > 0$. If demand is inelastic, then $\eta > -1$, so $1 + \dfrac{1}{\eta} < 0$. We can assume that $p > 0$. From Equation (6) we can conclude that $dr/dq > 0$ on intervals for which demand is elastic. As we will soon see, a function is increasing on intervals for which its derivative is positive and a function is decreasing on intervals for which its derivative is negative. Hence, total revenue $r$ is increasing on intervals for which demand is elastic and total revenue is decreasing on intervals for which demand is inelastic.

Thus, we conclude from the preceding argument that as more units are sold, a manufacturer's total revenue increases if demand is elastic, but decreases if demand is inelastic. That is, if demand is elastic, a lower price will increase revenue. This means that a lower price will cause a large enough increase in demand to actually increase revenue. If demand is inelastic, a lower price will decrease revenue. For unit elasticity, a lower price leaves total revenue unchanged.

## Problems 12.3

*In Problems 1–14, find the point elasticity of the demand equations for the indicated values of q or p, and determine whether demand is elastic, is inelastic, or has unit elasticity.*

*1. $p = 40 - 2q$; $q = 5$

2. $p = 10 - 0.04q$; $q = 100$

3. $p = \dfrac{3500}{q}$; $q = 288$

4. $p = \dfrac{500}{q^2}$; $q = 52$

5. $p = \dfrac{500}{q+2}$; $q = 104$

6. $p = \dfrac{800}{2q+1}$; $q = 24$

7. $p = 150 - e^{q/100}$; $q = 100$

8. $p = 100e^{-q/200}$; $q = 200$

9. $q = 1200 - 150p$; $p = 4$

10. $q = 100 - p$; $p = 50$

11. $q = \sqrt{500 - p}$; $p = 400$

12. $q = \sqrt{2500 - p^2}$; $p = 20$

*13. $q = \dfrac{(p - 100)^2}{2}$; $p = 20$

14. $q = p^2 - 50p + 850$; $p = 20$

15. For the linear demand equation $p = 13 - 0.05q$, verify that demand is elastic when $p = 10$, is inelastic when $p = 3$, and has unit elasticity when $p = 6.50$.

16. For what value (or values) of $q$ do the following demand equations have unit elasticity?

   (a) $p = 36 - 0.25q$
   (b) $p = 300 - q^2$

17. The demand equation for a product is

$$q = 500 - 40p + p^2$$

where $p$ is the price per unit (in dollars) and $q$ is the quantity of units demanded (in thousands). Find the point elasticity of demand when $p = 15$. If this price of 15 is increased by $\frac{1}{2}$%, what is the approximate change in demand?

18. The demand equation for a certain product is

$$q = \sqrt{2500 - p^2}$$

where $p$ is in dollars. Find the point elasticity of demand when $p = 30$, and use this value to compute the approximate percentage change in demand if the price of \$30 is decreased to \$28.50.

19. For the demand equation $p = 500 - 2q$, verify that demand is elastic and total revenue is increasing for $0 < q < 125$. Verify that demand is inelastic and total revenue is decreasing for $125 < q < 250$.

20. Verify that $\dfrac{dr}{dq} = p\left(1 + \dfrac{1}{\eta}\right)$ if $p = 50 - 3q$.

21. Repeat Problem 20 for $p = \dfrac{1000}{q^2}$.

22. Suppose $p = mq + b$ is a linear demand equation, where $m \neq 0$ and $b > 0$.

   (a) Show that $\lim_{p \to b^-} \eta = -\infty$.
   (b) Show that $\eta = 0$ when $p = 0$.

23. The demand equation for a manufacturer's product has the form

$$p = \frac{a}{\sqrt{b + cq^2}}$$

where $a$, $b$, and $c$ are constants, with $c \neq 0$.

   (a) Show that elasticity does not depend on $a$.
   (b) Show that if $b$ and $c$ are positive, then demand is elastic for all $q > 0$.
   (c) For which value or values of the constants is unit elasticity possible?

24. Given the demand equation $q^2(1 + p)^2 = p$, determine the point elasticity of demand when $p = 9$.

**25.** The demand equation for a product is

$$q = \frac{60}{p} + \ln(65 - p^3)$$

   **(a)** Determine the point elasticity of demand when $p = 4$, and classify the demand as elastic, inelastic, or of unit elasticity at this price level.

   **(b)** If the price is lowered by 2% (from $4.00 to $3.92), use the answer to part (a) to estimate the corresponding percentage change in quantity sold.

   **(c)** Will the changes in part (b) result in an increase or decrease in revenue? Explain.

**26.** The demand equation for a manufacturer's product is

$$p = 50(151 - q)^{0.02\sqrt{q+19}}$$

   **(a)** Find the value of $dp/dq$ when 150 units are demanded.

   **(b)** Using the result in part (a), determine the point elasticity of demand when 150 units are demanded. At this level, is demand elastic, inelastic, or of unit elasticity?

   **(c)** Use the result in part (b) to approximate the price per unit if demand decreases from 150 to 140 units.

   **(d)** If the current demand is 150 units, should the manufacturer increase or decrease price in order to increase revenue? (Justify your answer.)

**27.** A manufacturer of aluminum doors currently is able to sell 500 doors per week at a price of $80 each. If the price were lowered to $75 each, an additional 50 doors per week could be sold. Estimate the current elasticity of demand for the doors, and also estimate the current value of the manufacturer's marginal-revenue function.

**28.** Given the demand equation

$$p = 2000 - q^2$$

   where $5 \le q \le 40$, for what value of $q$ is $|\eta|$ a maximum? For what value is it a minimum?

**29.** Repeat Problem 28 for

$$p = \frac{200}{q + 5}$$

   such that $5 \le q \le 95$.

To discuss the notion of a function defined implicitly and to determine derivatives by means of implicit differentiation.

## 12.4 Implicit Differentiation

Implicit differentiation is a technique for differentiating functions that are not given in the usual form $y = f(x)$ (nor in the form $x = g(y)$). To introduce this technique, we will find the slope of a tangent line to a circle. Let us take the circle of radius 2 whose center is at the origin (Figure 12.4). Its equation is

$$x^2 + y^2 = 4$$

$$x^2 + y^2 - 4 = 0 \tag{1}$$

The point $(\sqrt{2}, \sqrt{2})$ lies on the circle. To find the slope at this point, we need to find $dy/dx$ there. Until now, we have always had $y$ given explicitly (directly) in terms of $x$ before determining $y'$; that is, our equation was always in the form $y = f(x)$ (or in the form $x = g(y)$). In Equation (1), this is not so. We say that Equation (1) has the form $F(x, y) = 0$, where $F(x, y)$ denotes a function of two variables. The obvious thing to do is solve Equation (1) for $y$ in terms of $x$:

$$x^2 + y^2 - 4 = 0$$

$$y^2 = 4 - x^2$$

$$y = \pm\sqrt{4 - x^2} \tag{2}$$

A problem now occurs: Equation (2) may give two values of $y$ for a value of $x$. It does not define $y$ explicitly as a function of $x$. We can, however, suppose that Equation (1) defines $y$ as one of two different functions of $x$,

$$y = +\sqrt{4 - x^2} \quad \text{and} \quad y = -\sqrt{4 - x^2}$$

whose graphs are given in Figure 12.5. Since the point $(\sqrt{2}, \sqrt{2})$ lies on the graph of $y = \sqrt{4 - x^2}$, we should differentiate that function:

$$y = \sqrt{4 - x^2}$$

$$\frac{dy}{dx} = \frac{1}{2}(4 - x^2)^{-1/2}(-2x)$$

$$= -\frac{x}{\sqrt{4 - x^2}}$$

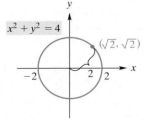

**FIGURE 12.4** The circle $x^2 + y^2 = 4$.

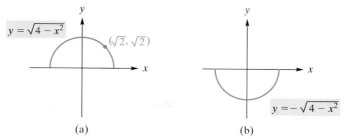

FIGURE 12.5   $x^2 + y^2 = 4$ gives rise to two different functions of $x$.

So

$$\left.\frac{dy}{dx}\right|_{x=\sqrt{2}} = -\frac{\sqrt{2}}{\sqrt{4-2}} = -1$$

Thus, the slope of the circle $x^2 + y^2 - 4 = 0$ at the point $(\sqrt{2}, \sqrt{2})$ is $-1$.

Let us summarize the difficulties we had. First, $y$ was not originally given explicitly in terms of $x$. Second, after we tried to find such a relation, we ended up with more than one function of $x$. In fact, depending on the equation given, it may be very complicated or even impossible to find an explicit expression for $y$. For example, it would be difficult to solve $ye^x + \ln(x + y) = 0$ for $y$. We will now consider a method that avoids such difficulties.

An equation of the form $F(x, y) = 0$, such as we had originally, is said to express $y$ *implicitly* as a function of $x$. The word *implicitly* is used, since $y$ is not given explicitly as a function of $x$. However, it is assumed or *implied* that the equation defines $y$ as at least one differentiable function of $x$. Thus, we assume that Equation (1), $x^2 + y^2 - 4 = 0$, defines some differentiable function of $x$, say, $y = f(x)$. Next, we treat $y$ as a function of $x$ and differentiate both sides of Equation (1) with respect to $x$. Finally, we solve the result for $dy/dx$. Applying this procedure, we obtain

$$\frac{d}{dx}(x^2 + y^2 - 4) = \frac{d}{dx}(0)$$

$$\frac{d}{dx}(x^2) + \frac{d}{dx}(y^2) - \frac{d}{dx}(4) = \frac{d}{dx}(0) \tag{3}$$

We know that $\dfrac{d}{dx}(x^2) = 2x$ and that both $\dfrac{d}{dx}(4)$ and $\dfrac{d}{dx}(0)$ are 0. But $\dfrac{d}{dx}(y^2)$ is **not** $2y$, because we are differentiating with respect to $x$, not $y$. That is, $y$ is not the independent variable. Since $y$ is assumed to be a function of $x$, $y^2$ has the form $u^n$, where $y$ plays the role of $u$. Just as the power rule states that $\dfrac{d}{dx}(u^2) = 2u\dfrac{du}{dx}$, we have $\dfrac{d}{dx}(y^2) = 2y\dfrac{dy}{dx}$. Hence, Equation (3) becomes

$$2x + 2y\frac{dy}{dx} = 0$$

Solving for $dy/dx$ gives

$$2y\frac{dy}{dx} = -2x$$

$$\frac{dy}{dx} = -\frac{x}{y} \quad \text{for } y \neq 0 \tag{4}$$

Notice that the expression for $dy/dx$ involves the variable $y$ as well as $x$. This means that to find $dy/dx$ at a point, both coordinates of the point must be substituted into $dy/dx$. Thus,

$$\left.\frac{dy}{dx}\right|_{(\sqrt{2}, \sqrt{2})} = -\frac{\sqrt{2}}{\sqrt{2}} = -1$$

as before. This method of finding $dy/dx$ is called **implicit differentiation.** We note that Equation (4) is not defined when $y = 0$. Geometrically, this is clear, since the tangent line to the circle at either $(2, 0)$ or $(-2, 0)$ is vertical, and the slope is not defined.

Here are the steps to follow when differentiating implicitly:

### Implicit Differentiation Procedure

For an equation that we assume defines $y$ implicitly as a differentiable function of $x$, the derivative $\dfrac{dy}{dx}$ can be found as follows:

1. Differentiate both sides of the equation with respect to $x$.
2. Collect all terms involving $\dfrac{dy}{dx}$ on one side of the equation, and collect all other terms on the other side.
3. Factor $\dfrac{dy}{dx}$ from the side involving the $\dfrac{dy}{dx}$ terms.
4. Solve for $\dfrac{dy}{dx}$, noting any restrictions.

### ● EXAMPLE 1   Implicit Differentiation

*Find $\dfrac{dy}{dx}$ by implicit differentiation if $y + y^3 - x = 7$.*

**Solution:** Here $y$ is not given as an explicit function of $x$ [that is, not in the form $y = f(x)$]. Thus, we assume that $y$ is an implicit (differentiable) function of $x$ and apply the preceding four-step procedure:

1. Differentiating both sides with respect to $x$, we have

$$\frac{d}{dx}(y + y^3 - x) = \frac{d}{dx}(7)$$

$$\frac{d}{dx}(y) + \frac{d}{dx}(y^3) - \frac{d}{dx}(x) = \frac{d}{dx}(7)$$

Now, $\dfrac{d}{dx}(y)$ can be written $\dfrac{dy}{dx}$, and $\dfrac{d}{dx}(x) = 1$. By the power rule,

$$\frac{d}{dx}(y^3) = 3y^2\frac{dy}{dx}$$

Hence, we obtain

$$\frac{dy}{dx} + 3y^2\frac{dy}{dx} - 1 = 0$$

2. Collecting all $\dfrac{dy}{dx}$ terms on the left side and all other terms on the right side gives

$$\frac{dy}{dx} + 3y^2\frac{dy}{dx} = 1$$

3. Factoring $\dfrac{dy}{dx}$ from the left side, we have

$$\frac{dy}{dx}(1 + 3y^2) = 1$$

4. We solve for $\dfrac{dy}{dx}$ by dividing both sides by $1 + 3y^2$:

$$\frac{dy}{dx} = \frac{1}{1 + 3y^2}$$

Because step 4 of the process often involves division by an expression involving the variables, the answer obtained must often be restricted to exclude those values of the variables that would make the denominator zero. Here the denominator is always greater than or equal to 1, so there is no restriction.

**CAUTION**
The derivative of $y^3$ with respect to $x$ is $3y^2\dfrac{dy}{dx}$, not $3y^2$.

In an implicit-differentiation problem, we are able to find the derivative of a function without knowing the function.

NOW WORK PROBLEM 3 ●●

**IMPLICIT DIFFERENTIATION**

Suppose that $P$, the proportion of people affected by a certain disease, is described by $\ln\left(\dfrac{P}{1-P}\right) = 0.5t$, where $t$ is the time in months. Find $\dfrac{dP}{dt}$, the rate at which $P$ grows with respect to time.

● **EXAMPLE 2   Implicit Differentiation**

*Find* $\dfrac{dy}{dx}$ *if* $x^3 + 4xy^2 - 27 = y^4$.

**Solution:** Since $y$ is not given explicitly in terms of $x$, we will use the method of implicit differentiation:

1. Assuming that $y$ is a function of $x$ and differentiating both sides with respect to $x$, we get

$$\frac{d}{dx}(x^3 + 4xy^2 - 27) = \frac{d}{dx}(y^4)$$

$$\frac{d}{dx}(x^3) + 4\frac{d}{dx}(xy^2) - \frac{d}{dx}(27) = \frac{d}{dx}(y^4)$$

To find $\dfrac{d}{dx}(xy^2)$, we use the product rule:

$$3x^2 + 4\left[x\frac{d}{dx}(y^2) + y^2\frac{d}{dx}(x)\right] - 0 = 4y^3\frac{dy}{dx}$$

$$3x^2 + 4\left[x\left(2y\frac{dy}{dx}\right) + y^2(1)\right] = 4y^3\frac{dy}{dx}$$

$$3x^2 + 8xy\frac{dy}{dx} + 4y^2 = 4y^3\frac{dy}{dx}$$

2. Collecting $\dfrac{dy}{dx}$ terms on the left side and other terms on the right gives

$$8xy\frac{dy}{dx} - 4y^3\frac{dy}{dx} = -3x^2 - 4y^2$$

3. Factoring $\dfrac{dy}{dx}$ from the left side yields

$$\frac{dy}{dx}(8xy - 4y^3) = -3x^2 - 4y^2$$

4. Solving for $\dfrac{dy}{dx}$, we have

$$\frac{dy}{dx} = \frac{-3x^2 - 4y^2}{8xy - 4y^3} = \frac{3x^2 + 4y^2}{4y^3 - 8xy}$$

which gives the value of $dy/dx$ at points $(x, y)$ for which $4y^3 - 8xy \neq 0$.

NOW WORK PROBLEM 11  ●●

**IMPLICIT DIFFERENTIATION**

The volume $V$ enclosed by a spherical balloon of radius $r$ is given by the equation $V = \dfrac{4}{3}\pi r^3$. If the radius is increasing at a rate of 5 inches/minute $\left(\text{that is, } \dfrac{dr}{dt} = 5\right)$, then find $\dfrac{dV}{dt}\bigg|_{r=12}$, the rate of increase of the volume, when the radius is 12 inches.

● **EXAMPLE 3   Implicit Differentiation**

*Find the slope of the curve* $x^3 = (y - x^2)^2$ *at* $(1, 2)$.

**Solution:** The slope at $(1, 2)$ is the value of $dy/dx$ at that point. Finding $dy/dx$ by implicit differentiation, we have

$$\frac{d}{dx}(x^3) = \frac{d}{dx}[(y - x^2)^2]$$

$$3x^2 = 2(y - x^2)\left(\frac{dy}{dx} - 2x\right)$$

$$3x^2 = 2\left(y\frac{dy}{dx} - 2xy - x^2\frac{dy}{dx} + 2x^3\right)$$

$$3x^2 = 2y\frac{dy}{dx} - 4xy - 2x^2\frac{dy}{dx} + 4x^3$$

$$3x^2 + 4xy - 4x^3 = 2y\frac{dy}{dx} - 2x^2\frac{dy}{dx}$$

$$3x^2 + 4xy - 4x^3 = 2\frac{dy}{dx}(y - x^2)$$

$$\frac{dy}{dx} = \frac{3x^2 + 4xy - 4x^3}{2(y - x^2)} \qquad \text{for } y - x^2 \neq 0$$

For the point $(1, 2)$, $y - x^2 = 2 - 1^2 = 1 \neq 0$. Thus, the slope of the curve at $(1, 2)$ is

$$\frac{dy}{dx}\bigg|_{(1,2)} = \frac{3(1)^2 + 4(1)(2) - 4(1)^3}{2(2 - (1)^2)} = \frac{7}{2}$$

NOW WORK PROBLEM 25 ●●

---

**IMPLICIT DIFFERENTIATION**

A 10-foot ladder is placed against a vertical wall. Suppose the bottom of the ladder slides away from the wall at a constant rate of 3 ft/s. $\left(\text{That is, } \dfrac{dx}{dt} = 3.\right)$ How fast is the top of the ladder sliding down the wall when the top of the ladder is 8 feet from the ground (that is, when $y = 8$)? (That is, what is $\dfrac{dy}{dt}$?) (Use the Pythagorean theorem for right triangles, $x^2 + y^2 = z^2$, where $x$ and $y$ are the legs of the triangle and $z$ is the hypotenuse.)

● **EXAMPLE 4** **Implicit Differentiation**

*If $q - p = \ln q + \ln p$, find $dq/dp$.*

**Solution:** We assume that $q$ is a function of $p$ and differentiate both sides with respect to $p$:

$$\frac{d}{dp}(q) - \frac{d}{dp}(p) = \frac{d}{dp}(\ln q) + \frac{d}{dp}(\ln p)$$

$$\frac{dq}{dp} - 1 = \frac{1}{q}\frac{dq}{dp} + \frac{1}{p}$$

$$\frac{dq}{dp} - \frac{1}{q}\frac{dq}{dp} = \frac{1}{p} + 1$$

$$\frac{dq}{dp}\left(1 - \frac{1}{q}\right) = \frac{1}{p} + 1$$

$$\frac{dq}{dp}\left(\frac{q - 1}{q}\right) = \frac{1 + p}{p}$$

$$\frac{dq}{dp} = \frac{(1 + p)q}{p(q - 1)} \qquad \text{for } p(q - 1) \neq 0$$

NOW WORK PROBLEM 19 ●●

---

## Problems 12.4

*In Problems 1–24, find $dy/dx$ by implicit differentiation.*

**1.** $x^2 + 4y^2 = 4$

**2.** $3x^2 + 6y^2 = 1$

**\*3.** $2y^3 - 7x^2 = 5$

**4.** $2x^2 - 3y^2 = 4$

**5.** $\sqrt[3]{x} + \sqrt[3]{y} = 3$

**6.** $x^{1/5} + y^{1/5} = 4$

**7.** $x^{3/4} + y^{3/4} = 5$

**8.** $y^3 = 4x$

**9.** $xy = 4$

**10.** $x^2 + xy - 2y^2 = 0$

**\*11.** $xy - y - 11x = 5$

**12.** $x^3 - y^3 = 3x^2y - 3xy^2$

**13.** $2x^3 + y^3 - 12xy = 0$

**14.** $2x^3 + 3xy + y^3 = 0$

**15.** $x = \sqrt{y} + \sqrt[4]{y}$

**16.** $x^3y^3 + x = 9$

**17.** $5x^3y^4 - x + y^2 = 25$

**18.** $y^2 + y = \ln x$

**\*19.** $y \ln x = xe^y$

**20.** $\ln(xy) + x = 4$

**21.** $xe^y + y = 13$

**22.** $4x^2 + 9y^2 = 16$

**23.** $(1 + e^{3x})^2 = 3 + \ln(x + y)$  **24.** $e^{x+y} = \ln(x + y)$

**\*25.** If $x + xy + y^2 = 7$, find $dy/dx$ at $(1, 2)$.

**26.** If $x\sqrt{y + 1} = y\sqrt{x + 1}$, find $dy/dx$ at $(3, 3)$.

**27.** Find the slope of the curve $4x^2 + 9y^2 = 1$ at the point $\left(0, \frac{1}{3}\right)$; at the point $(x_0, y_0)$.

**28.** Find the slope of the curve $(x^2 + y^2)^2 = 4y^2$ at the point $(0, 2)$.

**29.** Find an equation of the tangent line to the curve of

$$x^3 + xy + y^2 = -1$$

at the point $(-1, 1)$.

**30.** Repeat Problem 29 for the curve

$$y^2 + xy - x^2 = 5$$

at the point $(4, 3)$.

*For the demand equations in Problems 31–34, find the rate of change of $q$ with respect to $p$.*

**31.** $p = 100 - q^2$

**32.** $p = 400 - \sqrt{q}$

**33.** $p = \dfrac{20}{(q + 5)^2}$

**34.** $p = \dfrac{10}{q^2 + 3}$

**35. Radioactivity**   The relative activity $I/I_0$ of a radioactive element varies with elapsed time according to the equation

$$\ln\left(\frac{I}{I_0}\right) = -\lambda t$$

where $\lambda$ (a Greek letter read "lambda") is the disintegration constant and $I_0$ is the initial intensity (a constant). Find the rate of change of the intensity $I$ with respect to the elapsed time $t$.

**36. Earthquakes**   The magnitude $M$ of an earthquake and its energy $E$ are related by the equation[6]

$$1.5M = \log\left(\frac{E}{2.5 \times 10^{11}}\right)$$

Here $M$ is given in terms of Richter's preferred scale of 1958 and $E$ is in ergs. Determine the rate of change of energy with respect to magnitude and the rate of change of magnitude with respect to energy.

**37. Physical Scale**   The relationship between the speed ($v$), frequency ($f$), and wavelength ($\lambda$) of any wave is given by

$$v = f\lambda$$

Find $df/d\lambda$ by differentiating implicitly. (Treat $v$ as a constant.) Then show that the same result is obtained if you first solve the equation for $f$ and then differentiate with respect to $\lambda$.

**38. Biology**   The equation $(P + a)(v + b) = k$ is called the "fundamental equation of muscle contraction."[7] Here $P$ is

the load imposed on the muscle, $v$ is the velocity of the shortening of the muscle fibers, and $a$, $b$, and $k$ are positive constants. Use implicit differentiation to show that, in terms of $P$,

$$\frac{dv}{dP} = -\frac{k}{(P + a)^2}$$

**39. Marginal Propensity to Consume**   A country's savings $S$ is defined implicitly in terms of its national income $I$ by the equation

$$S^2 + \frac{1}{4}I^2 = SI + I$$

where both $S$ and $I$ are in billions of dollars. Find the marginal propensity to consume when $I = 16$ and $S = 12$.

**40. Technological Substitution**   New products or technologies often tend to replace old ones. For example, today most commercial airlines use jet engines rather than prop engines. In discussing the forecasting of technological substitution, Hurter and Rubenstein[8] refer to the equation

$$\ln\frac{f(t)}{1 - f(t)} + \sigma\frac{1}{1 - f(t)} = C_1 + C_2 t$$

where $f(t)$ is the market share of the substitute over time $t$ and $C_1$, $C_2$, and $\sigma$ (a Greek letter read "sigma") are constants. Verify their claim that the rate of substitution is

$$f'(t) = \frac{C_2 f(t)[1 - f(t)]^2}{\sigma f(t) + [1 - f(t)]}$$

OBJECTIVE

To describe the method of logarithmic differentiation and to show how to differentiate a function of the form $u^v$.

## 12.5 Logarithmic Differentiation

A technique called **logarithmic differentiation** often simplifies the differentiation of $y = f(x)$ when $f(x)$ involves products, quotients, or powers. The procedure is as follows:

### Logarithmic Differentiation

To differentiate $y = f(x)$,

1. Take the natural logarithm of both sides. This results in
$$\ln y = \ln(f(x))$$
2. Simplify $\ln(f(x))$ by using properties of logarithms.
3. Differentiate both sides with respect to $x$.
4. Solve for $\frac{dy}{dx}$.
5. Express the answer in terms of $x$ only. This requires substituting $f(x)$ for $y$.

There are a couple of points worth noting. First, irrespective of any simplification, the procedure produces

$$\frac{y'}{y} = \frac{d}{dx}(\ln(f(x)))$$

[6] K. E. Bullen, *An Introduction to the Theory of Seismology* (Cambridge, U.K.: Cambridge at the University Press, 1963).

[7] R. W. Stacy et al., *Essentials of Biological and Medical Physics* (New York: McGraw-Hill Book Company, 1955).

[8] A. P. Hurter, Jr., A. H. Rubenstein et al., "Market Penetration by New Innovations: The Technological Literature," *Technological Forecasting and Social Change*, 11 (1978), 197–221.

so that

$$\frac{dy}{dx} = y\frac{d}{dx}(\ln(f(x)))$$

is a formula that you can memorize, if you prefer. Second, the quantity $\frac{f'(x)}{f(x)}$, which results from differentiating $\ln(f(x))$, is what was called the *relative rate of change of* $f(x)$ in Section 11.3.

The next example illustrates the procedure.

● EXAMPLE 1   **Logarithmic Differentiation**

*Find $y'$ if* $y = \dfrac{(2x-5)^3}{x^2\sqrt[4]{x^2+1}}$.

·**Solution:** Differentiating this function in the usual way is messy because it involves the quotient, power, and product rules. Logarithmic differentiation makes the work less of a chore.

**1.** We take the natural logarithm of both sides:

$$\ln y = \ln \frac{(2x-5)^3}{x^2\sqrt[4]{x^2+1}}$$

**2.** Simplifying by using properties of logarithms, we have

$$\ln y = \ln(2x-5)^3 - \ln\left(x^2\sqrt[4]{x^2+1}\right)$$
$$= 3\ln(2x-5) - (\ln x^2 + \ln(x^2+1)^{1/4})$$
$$= 3\ln(2x-5) - 2\ln x - \frac{1}{4}\ln(x^2+1)$$

**3.** Differentiating with respect to $x$ gives

$$\frac{y'}{y} = 3\left(\frac{1}{2x-5}\right)(2) - 2\left(\frac{1}{x}\right) - \frac{1}{4}\left(\frac{1}{x^2+1}\right)(2x)$$
$$= \frac{6}{2x-5} - \frac{2}{x} - \frac{x}{2(x^2+1)}$$

**4.** Solving for $y'$ yields

$$y' = y\left(\frac{6}{2x-5} - \frac{2}{x} - \frac{x}{2(x^2+1)}\right)$$

**5.** Substituting the original expression for $y$ gives $y'$ in terms of $x$ only:

$$y' = \frac{(2x-5)^3}{x^2\sqrt[4]{x^2+1}}\left[\frac{6}{2x-5} - \frac{2}{x} - \frac{x}{2(x^2+1)}\right]$$

NOW WORK PROBLEM 1  ●●

**CAUTION**

Since $y$ is a function of $x$, differentiating $\ln y$ with respect to $x$ gives $\dfrac{y'}{y}$.

Logarithmic differentiation can also be used to differentiate a function of the form $y = u^v$, where both $u$ and $v$ are differentiable functions of $x$. Because neither the base nor the exponent is necessarily a constant, the differentiation techniques for $u^n$ and $a^u$ do not apply here.

● EXAMPLE 2   **Differentiating the Form $u^v$**

*Differentiate $y = x^x$ by using logarithmic differentiation.*

**Solution:** This example is a good candidate for the *formula* approach to logarithmic differentiation.

$$y' = y\frac{d}{dx}(\ln x^x) = x^x\frac{d}{dx}(x\ln x) = x^x\left((1)(\ln x) + (x)\left(\frac{1}{x}\right)\right) = x^x(\ln x + 1)$$

It is worthwhile mentioning that an alternative technique for differentiating a function of the form $y = u^v$ is to convert it to an exponential function to the base $e$.

To illustrate, for the function in this example, we have

$$y = x^x = (e^{\ln x})^x = e^{x \ln x}$$

$$y' = e^{x \ln x} \left( 1 \ln x + x \frac{1}{x} \right) = x^x (\ln x + 1)$$

NOW WORK PROBLEM 15

## EXAMPLE 3  Relative Rate of Change of a Product

*Show that the relative rate of change of a product is the sum of the relative rates of change of its factors. Use this result to express the percentage rate of change in revenue in terms of the percentage rate of change in price.*

**Solution:** Recall that the relative rate of change of a function $r$ is $\dfrac{r'}{r}$. We are to show that if $r = pq$, then $\dfrac{r'}{r} = \dfrac{p'}{p} + \dfrac{q'}{q}$. From $r = pq$ we have $\ln r = \ln p + \ln q$, which, when both sides are differentiated, gives

$$\frac{r'}{r} = \frac{p'}{p} + \frac{q'}{q}$$

as required. Multiplying both sides by 100% gives an expression for the percentage rate of change of $r$ in terms of those of $p$ and $q$:

$$\frac{r'}{r}100\% = \frac{p'}{p}100\% + \frac{q'}{q}100\%$$

If $p$ is *price* per item and $q$ is *quantity* sold, then $r = pq$ is total *revenue*. In this case we take differentiation to be with respect to $p$ and note that now $\dfrac{q'}{q} = \eta \dfrac{p'}{p}$, where $\eta$ is the elasticity of demand as in Section 12.3. It follows that in this case we have

$$\frac{r'}{r}100\% = (1 + \eta)\frac{p'}{p}100\%$$

expressing the percentage rate of change in revenue in terms of the percentage rate of change in price. For example, if at a given price and quantity, $\eta = -5$, then a 1% increase in price will result in a $(1 - 5)\% = -4\%$ increase in revenue, which is to say a 4% *decrease* in revenue, while a 3% decrease in price—that is, a $-3\%$ *increase* in price—will result in a $(1 - 5)(-3)\% = 12\%$ increase in revenue. It is also clear that at points at which there is unit elasticity ($\eta = -1$), any percentage change in price produces no percentage change in revenue.

NOW WORK PROBLEM 29

## EXAMPLE 4  Differentiating the Form $u^v$

*Find the derivative of $y = (1 + e^x)^{\ln x}$.*

**Solution:** This has the form $y = u^v$, where $u = 1 + e^x$ and $v = \ln x$. Using logarithmic differentiation, we have

$$\ln y = \ln((1 + e^x)^{\ln x})$$

$$\ln y = (\ln x) \ln(1 + e^x)$$

$$\frac{y'}{y} = \left(\frac{1}{x}\right)(\ln(1 + e^x)) + (\ln x)\left(\frac{1}{1 + e^x} \cdot e^x\right)$$

$$\frac{y'}{y} = \frac{\ln(1 + e^x)}{x} + \frac{e^x \ln x}{1 + e^x}$$

$$y' = y \left( \frac{\ln(1 + e^x)}{x} + \frac{e^x \ln x}{1 + e^x} \right)$$

$$y' = (1 + e^x)^{\ln x} \left( \frac{\ln(1 + e^x)}{x} + \frac{e^x \ln x}{1 + e^x} \right)$$

NOW WORK PROBLEM 17

Alternatively, we can differentiate even a general function of the form $y = u(x)^{v(x)}$ with $u(x) > 0$ by using the equation

$$u^v = e^{v \ln u}$$

Indeed, if $y = u(x)^{v(x)} = e^{v(x) \ln u(x)}$ for $u(x) > 0$, then

$$\frac{dy}{dx} = \frac{d}{dx}\left(e^{v(x) \ln u(x)}\right) = e^{v(x) \ln u(x)}\frac{d}{dx}(v(x) \ln u(x)) = u^v\left(v'(x) \ln u(x) + v(x)\frac{u'(x)}{u(x)}\right)$$

which could be summarized as

$$(u^v)' = u^v\left(v' \ln u + v\frac{u'}{u}\right)$$

As is often the case, there is no suggestion that you should memorize the preceding formula. The point here is that we have shown *any* function of the form $u^v$ can be differentiated using the equation $u^v = e^{v \ln u}$. The same result will be obtained from logarithmic differentiation:

$$\ln y = \ln(u^v)$$

$$\ln y = v \ln u$$

$$\frac{y'}{y} = v' \ln u + v\frac{u'}{u}$$

$$y' = y\left(v' \ln u + v\frac{u'}{u}\right)$$

$$(u^v)' = u^v\left(v' \ln u + v\frac{u'}{u}\right)$$

After completing this section, you should understand how to differentiate each of the following forms:

$$y = \begin{cases} (f(x))^a & \text{(a)} \\ b^{f(x)} & \text{(b)} \\ (f(x))^{g(x)} & \text{(c)} \end{cases}$$

For type (a), use the power rule. For type (b), use the differentiation formula for exponential functions. [If $b \neq e$, you can first convert $b^{f(x)}$ to an $e^u$ function.] For type (c), use logarithmic differentiation or first convert to an $e^u$ function. Do not apply a rule in a situation where the rule does not apply. For example, the power rule does not apply to $x^x$.

# Problems 12.5

*In Problems 1–12, find $y'$ by using logarithmic differentiation.*

*1. $y = (x + 1)^2(x - 2)(x^2 + 3)$

2. $y = (3x + 4)(8x - 1)^2(3x^2 + 1)^4$

3. $y = (3x^3 - 1)^2(2x + 5)^3$

4. $y = (2x^2 + 1)\sqrt{8x^2 - 1}$

5. $y = \sqrt{x + 1}\sqrt{x^2 - 2}\sqrt{x + 4}$

6. $y = (2x + 1)\sqrt{x^3 + 2}\sqrt[3]{2x + 5}$

7. $y = \frac{\sqrt{1 - x^2}}{1 - 2x}$

8. $y = \sqrt{\frac{x^2 + 5}{x + 9}}$

9. $y = \frac{(2x^2 + 2)^2}{(x + 1)^2(3x + 2)}$

10. $y = \frac{x(1 + x^2)^2}{\sqrt{2 + x^2}}$

11. $y = \sqrt{\frac{(x + 3)(x - 2)}{2x - 1}}$

12. $y = \sqrt[3]{\frac{6(x^3 + 1)^2}{x^6 e^{-4x}}}$

*In Problems 13–20, find $y'$.*

13. $y = x^{x^2+1}$

14. $y = (2x)^{\sqrt{x}}$

*15. $y = x^{1/x}$

16. $y = \left(\frac{3}{x^2}\right)^x$

*17. $y = (3x + 1)^{2x}$

18. $y = (x^2 + 1)^{x+1}$

19. $y = 4e^x x^{3x}$

20. $y = (\ln x)^{e^x}$

21. If $y = (4x - 3)^{2x+1}$, find $dy/dx$ when $x = 1$.

22. If $y = (\ln x)^{\ln x}$, find $dy/dx$ when $x = e$.

23. Find an equation of the tangent line to
$$y = (x + 1)(x + 2)^2(x + 3)^2$$
at the point where $x = 0$.

24. Find an equation of the tangent line to the graph of
$$y = x^x$$
at the point where $x = 1$.

**25.** Find an equation of the tangent line to the graph of

$$y = e^x(x^2 + 1)^x$$

at the point where $x = 1$.

**26.** If $y = x^x$, find the relative rate of change of $y$ with respect to $x$ when $x = 1$.

**27.** If $y = (3x)^{-2x}$, find the value of $x$ for which the *percentage* rate of change of $y$ with respect to $x$ is 60.

**28.** Suppose $f(x)$ is a positive differentiable function and $g$ is a differentiable function and $y = (f(x))^{g(x)}$. Use logarithmic differentiation to show that

$$\frac{dy}{dx} = (f(x))^{g(x)} \left( f'(x)\frac{g(x)}{f(x)} + g'(x)\ln(f(x)) \right)$$

***29.** The demand equation for a compact disc is

$$q = 500 - 40p + p^2$$

If the price of \$15 is increased by 1/2%, find the corresponding percentage change in revenue.

**30.** Repeat Problem 29 with the same information except for a 10% *decrease* in price.

## 12.6  Newton's Method

OBJECTIVE

To approximate real roots of an equation by using calculus. The method shown is suitable for calculators.

It is quite easy to solve equations of the form $f(x) = 0$ when $f$ is a linear or quadratic function. For example, we can solve $x^2 + 3x - 2 = 0$ by the quadratic formula. However, if $f(x)$ has degree greater than 2 (or is not a polynomial), it may be difficult, or even impossible, to find solutions (or roots) of $f(x) = 0$ by the methods to which you are accustomed. For this reason, we may settle for approximate solutions, which can be obtained in a variety of efficient ways. For example, a graphing calculator may be used to estimate the real roots of $f(x) = 0$. In this section, you will learn how the derivative may be so used (provided that $f$ is differentiable). The procedure we will develop, called *Newton's method,* is well suited to a calculator or computer.

Newton's method requires an initial estimate for a root of $f(x) = 0$. One way of obtaining this estimate is by making a rough sketch of the graph of $y = f(x)$ and estimating the root from the graph. A point on the graph where $y = 0$ is an $x$-intercept, and the $x$-value of this point is a root of $f(x) = 0$. Another way of locating a root is based on the following fact:

If $f$ is continuous on the interval $[a, b]$ and $f(a)$ and $f(b)$ have opposite signs, then the equation $f(x) = 0$ has at least one real root between $a$ and $b$.

Figure 12.6 depicts this situation. The $x$-intercept between $a$ and $b$ corresponds to a root of $f(x) = 0$, and we can use either $a$ or $b$ to approximate this root.

Assuming that we have an estimated (but incorrect) value for a root, we turn to a way of getting a better approximation. In Figure 12.7, you can see that $f(r) = 0$, so $r$ is a root of the equation $f(x) = 0$. Suppose $x_1$ is an initial approximation to $r$ (and one that is close to $r$). Observe that the tangent line to the curve at $(x_1, f(x_1))$ intersects the $x$-axis at the point $(x_2, 0)$, and $x_2$ is a better approximation to $r$ than is $x_1$.

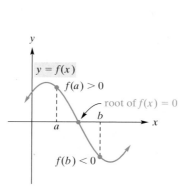

**FIGURE 12.6**    Root of $f(x) = 0$ between $a$ and $b$, where $f(a)$ and $f(b)$ have opposite signs.

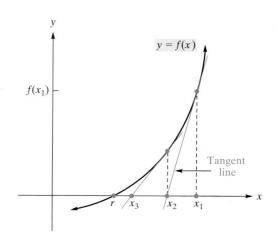

**FIGURE 12.7**    Improving approximation of root via tangent line.

We can find $x_2$ from the equation of the tangent line. The slope of the tangent line is $f'(x_1)$, so a point–slope form for this line is

$$y - f(x_1) = f'(x_1)(x - x_1) \tag{1}$$

Since $(x_2, 0)$ is on the tangent line, its coordinates must satisfy Equation (1). This gives

$$0 - f(x_1) = f'(x_1)(x_2 - x_1)$$
$$-\frac{f(x_1)}{f'(x_1)} = x_2 - x_1 \qquad [\text{if } f'(x_1) \neq 0]$$

Thus,

$$x_2 = x_1 - \frac{f(x_1)}{f'(x_1)} \tag{2}$$

To get a better approximation to $r$, we again perform the procedure described, but this time we use $x_2$ as our starting point. This gives the approximation

$$x_3 = x_2 - \frac{f(x_2)}{f'(x_2)} \tag{3}$$

Repeating (or *iterating*) this computation over and over, we hope to obtain better approximations, in the sense that the sequence of values

$$x_1, x_2, x_3, \ldots$$

will approach $r$. In practice, we terminate the process when we have reached a desired degree of accuracy.

If you analyze Equations (2) and (3), you can see how $x_2$ is obtained from $x_1$ and how $x_3$ is obtained from $x_2$. In general, $x_{n+1}$ is obtained from $x_n$ by means of the following general formula, called **Newton's method:**

**Newton's Method**

$$x_{n+1} = x_n - \frac{f(x_n)}{f'(x_n)} \quad n = 1, 2, 3, \ldots \tag{4}$$

A formula, like Equation (4), that indicates how one number in a sequence is obtained from the preceding one is called a **recursion formula,** or an *iteration equation.*

● **EXAMPLE 1   Approximating a Root by Newton's Method**

*Approximate the root of $x^4 - 4x + 1 = 0$ that lies between 0 and 1. Continue the approximation procedure until two successive approximations differ by less than 0.0001.*

**Solution:** Letting $f(x) = x^4 - 4x + 1$, we have

$$f(0) = 0 - 0 + 1 = 1$$

and

$$f(1) = 1 - 4 + 1 = -2$$

(Note the change in sign.) Since $f(0)$ is closer to 0 than is $f(1)$, we choose 0 to be our first approximation, $x_1$. Now,

$$f'(x) = 4x^3 - 4$$

so

$$f(x_n) = x_n^4 - 4x_n + 1 \quad \text{and} \quad f'(x_n) = 4x_n^3 - 4$$

Substituting into Equation (4) gives the recursion formula

$$x_{n+1} = x_n - \frac{f(x_n)}{f'(x_n)} = x_n - \frac{x_n^4 - 4x_n + 1}{4x_n^3 - 4}$$

$$= \frac{4x_n^4 - 4x_n - x_n^4 + 4x_n - 1}{4x_n^3 - 4}$$

so

$$x_{n+1} = \frac{3x_n^4 - 1}{4x_n^3 - 4} \tag{5}$$

Since $x_1 = 0$, letting $n = 1$ in Equation (5) gives

$$x_2 = \frac{3x_1^4 - 1}{4x_1^3 - 4} = \frac{3(0)^4 - 1}{4(0)^3 - 4} = 0.25$$

Letting $n = 2$ in Equation (5) gives

$$x_3 = \frac{3x_2^4 - 1}{4x_2^3 - 4} = \frac{3(0.25)^4 - 1}{4(0.25)^3 - 4} \approx 0.25099$$

Letting $n = 3$ in Equation (5) gives

$$x_4 = \frac{3x_3^4 - 1}{4x_3^3 - 4} = \frac{3(0.25099)^4 - 1}{4(0.25099)^3 - 4} \approx 0.25099$$

The data obtained thus far are displayed in Table 12.1. Since the values of $x_3$ and $x_4$ differ by less than 0.0001, we take the root to be 0.25099 (that is, $x_4$).

NOW WORK PROBLEM 1

**TABLE 12.1**

| $n$ | $x_n$ | $x_{n+1}$ |
|---|---|---|
| 1 | 0.00000 | 0.25000 |
| 2 | 0.25000 | 0.25099 |
| 3 | 0.25099 | 0.25099 |

● **EXAMPLE 2**   **Approximating a Root by Newton's Method**

*Approximate the root of $x^3 = 3x - 1$ that lies between $-1$ and $-2$. Continue the approximation procedure until two successive approximations differ by less than 0.0001.*

**Solution:**  Letting $f(x) = x^3 - 3x + 1$ (we need the form $f(x) = 0$), we find that

$$f(-1) = (-1)^3 - 3(-1) + 1 = 3$$

and

$$f(-2) = (-2)^3 - 3(-2) + 1 = -1$$

(Note the change in sign.) Since $f(-2)$ is closer to 0 than is $f(-1)$, we choose $-2$ to be our first approximation, $x_1$. Now,

$$f'(x) = 3x^2 - 3$$

so

$$f(x_n) = x_n^3 - 3x_n + 1 \quad \text{and} \quad f'(x_n) = 3x_n^2 - 3$$

Substituting into Equation (4) gives the recursion formula

$$x_{n+1} = x_n - \frac{f(x_n)}{f'(x_n)} = x_n - \frac{x_n^3 - 3x_n + 1}{3x_n^2 - 3}$$

so

$$x_{n+1} = \frac{2x_n^3 - 1}{3x_n^2 - 3} \tag{6}$$

Since $x_1 = -2$, letting $n = 1$ in Equation (6) gives

$$x_2 = \frac{2x_1^3 - 1}{3x_1^2 - 3} = \frac{2(-2)^3 - 1}{3(-2)^2 - 3} \approx -1.88889$$

Continuing in this way, we obtain Table 12.2. Because the values of $x_3$ and $x_4$ differ by 0.00006, which is less than 0.0001, we take the root to be $-1.87939$ (that is, $x_4$).

NOW WORK PROBLEM 3

**TABLE 12.2**

| $n$ | $x_n$ | $x_n + 1$ |
|---|---|---|
| 1 | −2.00000 | −1.88889 |
| 2 | −1.88889 | −1.87945 |
| 3 | −1.87945 | −1.87939 |

The situation where $x_1$ leads to a derivative of 0 occurs in Problems 2 and 8 of Problems 12.6. In case your choice for the initial approximation, $x_1$, gives the derivative a value of zero, choose a different number that is close to the desired root. A graph of $f$ could be helpful in this situation. Finally, we remark that there are times when the sequence of approximations does not approach the root. A discussion of such situations is beyond the scope of this book.

## TECHNOLOGY

Figure 12.8 gives a short TI-83 Plus program for Newton's method. Before the program is executed, the first approximation to the root of $f(x) = 0$ is stored as X, and $f(x)$ and $f'(x)$ are stored as $Y_1$ and $Y_2$, respectively.

When executed, the program computes the first iteration and pauses. Successive iterations are obtained by successively pressing ENTER. Figure 12.9 shows the iterations for the problem in Example 2.

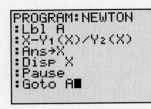

FIGURE 12.8 Calculator program for Newton's method.

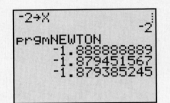

FIGURE 12.9 Iterations for problem in Example 2.

## Problems 12.6

*In Problems 1–10, use Newton's method to approximate the indicated root of the given equation. Continue the approximation procedure until the difference of two successive approximations is less than 0.0001.*

*1. $x^3 - 4x + 1 = 0$;  root between 0 and 1

2. $x^3 + 2x^2 - 1 = 0$;  root between 0 and 1

*3. $x^3 - x - 1 = 0$;  root between 1 and 2

4. $x^3 - 9x + 6 = 0$;  root between 2 and 3

5. $x^3 + x + 1 = 0$;  root between −1 and 0

6. $x^3 = 2x + 5$;  root between 2 and 3

7. $x^4 = 3x - 1$;  root between 0 and 1

8. $x^4 + 4x - 1 = 0$;  root between −2 and −1

9. $x^4 - 2x^3 + x^2 - 3 = 0$;  root between 1 and 2

10. $x^4 - x^3 + x - 2 = 0$;  root between 1 and 2

11. Estimate, to three-decimal-place accuracy, the cube root of 71. (*Hint:* Show that the problem is equivalent to finding a root of $f(x) = x^3 - 71 = 0$.) Choose 4 as the initial estimate. Continue the iteration until two successive approximations, rounded to three decimal places, are the same.

12. Estimate $\sqrt[4]{19}$, to two-decimal-place accuracy. Use 2 as your initial estimate.

13. Find, to two-decimal-place accuracy, all real solutions of the equation $e^x = x + 5$. (*Hint:* A rough sketch of the graphs of $y = e^x$ and $y = x + 5$ makes it clear how many solutions there are. Use nearby integer values for your initial estimates.)

14. Find, to three-decimal-place accuracy, all real solutions of the equation $\ln x = 5 - x$.

15. **Break-Even Quantity**    The cost of manufacturing $q$ tons of a certain product is given by

$$c = 250 + 2q - 0.1q^3$$

and the revenue obtained by selling the $q$ tons is given by

$$r = 3q$$

Approximate, to two-decimal-place accuracy, the break-even quantity. (*Hint:* Approximate a root of $r - c = 0$ by choosing 13 as your initial estimate.)

16. **Break-Even Quantity**    The total cost of manufacturing $q$ hundred pencils is $c$ dollars, where

$$c = 40 + 3q + \frac{q^2}{1000} + \frac{1}{q}$$

Pencils are sold for $7 per hundred.

(a) Show that the break-even quantity is a solution of the equation

$$f(q) = \frac{q^3}{1000} - 4q^2 + 40q + 1 = 0$$

(b) Use Newton's method to approximate the solution of $f(q) = 0$, where $f(q)$ is given in part (a). Use 10 as your initial approximation, and give your answer to two-decimal-place accuracy.

17. **Equilibrium**    Given the supply equation $p = 2q + 5$ and the demand equation $p = \dfrac{100}{q^2 + 1}$, use Newton's method to

estimate the market equilibrium quantity. Give your answer to three-decimal-place accuracy.

**18. Equilibrium**  Given the supply equation

$$p = 0.2q^3 + 0.5q + 2$$

and the demand equation $p = 10 - q$, use Newton's method to estimate the market equilibrium quantity, and find the corresponding equilibrium price. Use 5 as an initial estimate

for the required value of $q$, and give your answer to two-decimal-place accuracy.

**19.** Use Newton's method to approximate (to two-decimal-place accuracy) a critical value of the function

$$f(x) = \frac{x^3}{3} - x^2 - 5x + 1$$

on the interval [3, 4].

## 12.7  Higher-Order Derivatives

We know that the derivative of a function $y = f(x)$ is itself a function, $f'(x)$. If we differentiate $f'(x)$, the resulting function is called the **second derivative** of $f$ at $x$. It is denoted $f''(x)$, which is read " $f$ double prime of $x$." Similarly, the derivative of the second derivative is called the **third derivative,** written $f'''(x)$. Continuing in this way, we get *higher-order derivatives*. Some notations for higher-order derivatives are given in Table 12.3. To avoid clumsy notation, primes are not used beyond the third derivative.

**CAUTION**

The symbol $d^2y/dx^2$ represents the second derivative of $y$. It is not the same as $(dy/dx)^2$, the square of the first derivative of $y$.

**TABLE 12.3**

| First derivative: | $y'$ | $f'(x)$ | $\dfrac{dy}{dx}$ | $\dfrac{d}{dx}(f(x))$ | $D_x y$ |
|---|---|---|---|---|---|
| Second derivative: | $y''$ | $f''(x)$ | $\dfrac{d^2 y}{dx^2}$ | $\dfrac{d^2}{dx^2}(f(x))$ | $D_x^2 y$ |
| Third derivative: | $y'''$ | $f'''(x)$ | $\dfrac{d^3 y}{dx^3}$ | $\dfrac{d^3}{dx^3}(f(x))$ | $D_x^3 y$ |
| Fourth derivative: | $y^{(4)}$ | $f^{(4)}(x)$ | $\dfrac{d^4 y}{dx^4}$ | $\dfrac{d^4}{dx^4}(f(x))$ | $D_x^4 y$ |

**EXAMPLE 1  Finding Higher-Order Derivatives**

**a.** If $f(x) = 6x^3 - 12x^2 + 6x - 2$, *find* all *higher-order derivatives.*

**Solution:**  Differentiating $f(x)$ gives

$$f'(x) = 18x^2 - 24x + 6$$

Differentiating $f'(x)$ yields

$$f''(x) = 36x - 24$$

Similarly,

$$f'''(x) = 36$$
$$f^{(4)}(x) = 0$$

All successive derivatives are also 0: $f^{(5)}(x) = 0$, and so on.

**b.** If $f(x) = 7$, *find* $f''(x)$.

**Solution:**
$$f'(x) = 0$$
$$f''(x) = 0$$

NOW WORK PROBLEM 1

**EXAMPLE 2  Finding a Second-Order Derivative**

If $y = e^{x^2}$, *find* $\dfrac{d^2 y}{dx^2}$.

**Solution:**

$$\frac{dy}{dx} = e^{x^2}(2x) = 2xe^{x^2}$$

By the product rule,

$$\frac{d^2y}{dx^2} = 2[x(e^{x^2})(2x) + e^{x^2}(1)] = 2e^{x^2}(2x^2 + 1)$$

NOW WORK PROBLEM 5 ●●●

**PRINCIPLES IN PRACTICE 2**

EVALUATING A SECOND-ORDER
DERIVATIVE

If the cost to produce $q$ units of a product is

$$c(q) = 7q^2 + 11q + 19$$

and the marginal cost function is $c'(q)$, find the rate of change of the marginal cost function with respect to $q$ when $q = 3$.

● **EXAMPLE 3   Evaluating a Second-Order Derivative**

*If* $y = f(x) = \dfrac{16}{x+4}$, *find* $\dfrac{d^2y}{dx^2}$ *and evaluate it when* $x = 4$.

**Solution:**  Since $y = 16(x + 4)^{-1}$, the power rule gives

$$\frac{dy}{dx} = -16(x+4)^{-2}$$

$$\frac{d^2y}{dx^2} = 32(x+4)^{-3} = \frac{32}{(x+4)^3}$$

Evaluating when $x = 4$, we obtain

$$\left.\frac{d^2y}{dx^2}\right|_{x=4} = \frac{32}{8^3} = \frac{1}{16}$$

The second derivative evaluated at $x = 4$ is also denoted $f''(4)$ or $y''(4)$.

NOW WORK PROBLEM 21 ●●●

● **EXAMPLE 4   Finding the Rate of Change of $f''(x)$**

*If* $f(x) = x \ln x$, *find the rate of change of* $f''(x)$.

**Solution:**  To find the rate of change of any function, we must find its derivative. Thus, we want the derivative of $f''(x)$, which is $f'''(x)$. Accordingly,

The rate of change of $f''(x)$ is $f'''(x)$.

$$f'(x) = x\left(\frac{1}{x}\right) + (\ln x)(1) = 1 + \ln x$$

$$f''(x) = 0 + \frac{1}{x} = \frac{1}{x}$$

$$f'''(x) = \frac{d}{dx}(x^{-1}) = (-1)x^{-2} = -\frac{1}{x^2}$$

NOW WORK PROBLEM 17 ●●●

## Higher-Order Implicit Differentiation

We will now find a higher-order derivative by means of implicit differentiation. Keep in mind that we will assume $y$ to be a function of $x$.

● **EXAMPLE 5   Higher-Order Implicit Differentiation**

*Find* $\dfrac{d^2y}{dx^2}$ *if* $x^2 + 4y^2 = 4$.

**Solution:**  Differentiating both sides with respect to $x$, we obtain

$$2x + 8y\frac{dy}{dx} = 0$$

$$\frac{dy}{dx} = \frac{-x}{4y} \tag{1}$$

$$\frac{d^2y}{dx^2} = \frac{4y\dfrac{d}{dx}(-x) - (-x)\dfrac{d}{dx}(4y)}{(4y)^2}$$

$$= \frac{4y(-1) - (-x)\left(4\dfrac{dy}{dx}\right)}{16y^2}$$

$$= \frac{-4y + 4x\dfrac{dy}{dx}}{16y^2}$$

$$\frac{d^2y}{dx^2} = \frac{-y + x\dfrac{dy}{dx}}{4y^2} \qquad (2)$$

Although we have found an expression for $d^2y/dx^2$, our answer involves the derivative $dy/dx$. It is customary to express the answer without the derivative—that is, in terms of $x$ and $y$ only. This is easy to do. From Equation (1), $\dfrac{dy}{dx} = \dfrac{-x}{4y}$, so by substituting into Equation (2), we have

In Example 5, the simplification of $d^2y/dx^2$ by making use of the original equation is not unusual.

$$\frac{d^2y}{dx^2} = \frac{-y + x\left(\dfrac{-x}{4y}\right)}{4y^2} = \frac{-4y^2 - x^2}{16y^3} = -\frac{4y^2 + x^2}{16y^3}$$

We can further simplify the answer. Since $x^2 + 4y^2 = 4$ (the original equation),

$$\frac{d^2y}{dx^2} = -\frac{4}{16y^3} = -\frac{1}{4y^3}$$

NOW WORK PROBLEM 23   ⬤⬤

### ⬤ EXAMPLE 6   Higher-Order Implicit Differentiation

*Find* $\dfrac{d^2y}{dx^2}$ *if* $y^2 = e^{x+y}$.

**Solution:** Differentiating both sides with respect to $x$ gives

$$2y\frac{dy}{dx} = e^{x+y}\left(1 + \frac{dy}{dx}\right)$$

Solving for $dy/dx$, we obtain

$$2y\frac{dy}{dx} = e^{x+y} + e^{x+y}\frac{dy}{dx}$$

$$2y\frac{dy}{dx} - e^{x+y}\frac{dy}{dx} = e^{x+y}$$

$$(2y - e^{x+y})\frac{dy}{dx} = e^{x+y}$$

$$\frac{dy}{dx} = \frac{e^{x+y}}{2y - e^{x+y}}$$

Since $y^2 = e^{x+y}$ (the original equation),

$$\frac{dy}{dx} = \frac{y^2}{2y - y^2} = \frac{y}{2 - y}$$

$$\frac{d^2y}{dx^2} = \frac{(2-y)\dfrac{dy}{dx} - y\left(-\dfrac{dy}{dx}\right)}{(2-y)^2} = \frac{2\dfrac{dy}{dx}}{(2-y)^2}$$

Now we express our answer without $dy/dx$. Since $\dfrac{dy}{dx} = \dfrac{y}{2-y}$,

$$\frac{d^2y}{dx^2} = \frac{2\left(\dfrac{y}{2-y}\right)}{(2-y)^2} = \frac{2y}{(2-y)^3}$$

NOW WORK PROBLEM 31   ⬤⬤⬤

## Problems 12.7

*In Problems 1–20, find the indicated derivatives.*

*1. $y = 4x^3 - 12x^2 + 6x + 2$, $y'''$

2. $y = x^5 - 2x^4 + 7x^2 - 2$, $y'''$

3. $y = 8 - x$, $\dfrac{d^2 y}{dx^2}$

4. $y = -x - x^2$, $\dfrac{d^2 y}{dx^2}$

*5. $y = x^3 + e^x$, $y^{(4)}$

6. $F(q) = \ln(q + 1)$, $\dfrac{d^3 F}{dq^3}$

7. $f(x) = x^2 \ln x$, $f''(x)$

8. $y = \dfrac{1}{x}$, $y'''$

9. $f(q) = \dfrac{1}{2q^4}$, $f'''(q)$

10. $f(x) = \sqrt{x}$, $f''(x)$

11. $f(r) = \sqrt{9 - r}$, $f''(r)$

12. $y = e^{-4x^2}$, $y''$

13. $y = \dfrac{1}{2x + 3}$, $\dfrac{d^2 y}{dx^2}$

14. $y = (3x + 7)^5$, $y''$

15. $y = \dfrac{x + 1}{x - 1}$, $y''$

16. $y = 2x^{1/2} + (2x)^{1/2}$, $y''$

*17. $y = \ln[x(x + 6)]$, $y''$

18. $y = \ln \dfrac{(2x + 5)(5x - 2)}{x + 1}$, $y''$

19. $f(z) = z^2 e^z$, $f''(z)$

20. $y = \dfrac{x}{e^x}$, $\dfrac{d^2 y}{dx^2}$

*21. If $y = e^{2x} + e^{3x}$, find $\left.\dfrac{d^5 y}{dx^5}\right|_{x=0}$.

22. If $y = e^{2\ln(x^3 + 1)}$, find $y''$ when $x = 1$.

*In Problems 23–32, find $y''$.*

*23. $x^2 + 4y^2 - 16 = 0$

24. $x^2 - y^2 = 16$

25. $y^2 = 4x$

26. $9x^2 + 16y^2 = 25$

27. $\sqrt{x} + 4\sqrt{y} = 4$

28. $y^2 - 6xy = 4$

29. $xy + y - x = 4$

30. $x^2 + 2xy + y^2 = 1$

*31. $y = e^{x+y}$

32. $e^x - e^y = x^2 + y^2$

33. If $x^2 + 3x + y^2 = 4y$, find $d^2 y/dx^2$ when $x = 0$ and $y = 0$.

34. Show that the equation

$$f''(x) + 4f'(x) + 4f(x) = 0$$

is satisfied if $f(x) = (3x - 5)e^{-2x}$.

35. Find the rate of change of $f'(x)$ if $f(x) = (5x - 3)^4$.

36. Find the rate of change of $f''(x)$ if

$$f(x) = 6\sqrt{x} + \dfrac{1}{6\sqrt{x}}$$

37. **Marginal Cost**  If $c = 0.3q^2 + 2q + 850$ is a cost function, how fast is marginal cost changing when $q = 100$?

38. **Marginal Revenue**  If $p = 400 - 40q - q^2$ is a demand equation, how fast is marginal revenue changing when $q = 4$?

39. If $f(x) = x^4 - 6x^2 + 5x - 6$, determine the values of $x$ for which $f''(x) = 0$.

40. Suppose that $e^y = y^2 e^x$. (a) Determine $dy/dx$, and express your answer in terms of $y$ only. (b) Determine $d^2 y/dx^2$, and express your answer in terms of $y$ only.

*In Problems 41 and 42, determine $f''(x)$. Then use your graphing calculator to find all real zeros of $f''(x)$. Round your answers to two decimal places.*

41. $f(x) = 6e^x - x^3 - 15x^2$

42. $f(x) = \dfrac{x^5}{20} + \dfrac{x^4}{12} + \dfrac{5x^3}{6} + \dfrac{x^2}{2}$

## 12.8 Review

### Important Terms and Symbols

| | | Examples |
|---|---|---|
| Section 12.1 | **Derivatives of Logarithmic Functions**<br>derivative of $\ln x$ and of $\log_b u$ | Ex. 5, p. 532 |
| Section 12.2 | **Derivatives of Exponential Functions**<br>derivative of $e^x$ and of $b^u$ | Ex. 4, p. 536 |
| Section 12.3 | **Elasticity of Demand**<br>point elasticity of demand, $\eta$    elastic    unit elasticity    inelastic | Ex. 2, p. 542 |
| Section 12.4 | **Implicit Differentiation**<br>implicit function | Ex. 1, p. 546 |
| Section 12.5 | **Logarithmic Differentiation**<br>logarithmic differentiation    relative rate of change of revenue | Ex. 3, p. 551 |
| Section 12.6 | **Newton's Method**<br>recursion formula, $x_{n+1} = x_n - \dfrac{f(x_n)}{f'(x_n)}$ | Ex. 1, p. 554 |
| Section 12.7 | **Higher-Order Derivatives**<br>higher-order derivatives,    $f''(x)$,    $\dfrac{d^3 y}{dx^3}$,    $\dfrac{d^4}{dx^4}[f(x)], \ldots$ | Ex. 1, p. 557 |

# Summary

The derivative formulas for natural logarithmic and exponential functions are

$$\frac{d}{dx}(\ln u) = \frac{1}{u}\frac{du}{dx}$$

and

$$\frac{d}{dx}(e^u) = e^u\frac{du}{dx}$$

To differentiate logarithmic and exponential functions in bases other than $e$, you can first transform the function to base $e$ and then differentiate the result. Alternatively, differentiation formulas can be applied:

$$\frac{d}{dx}(\log_b u) = \frac{1}{(\ln b)u}\cdot\frac{du}{dx}$$

$$\frac{d}{dx}(b^u) = b^u(\ln b)\cdot\frac{du}{dx}$$

Point elasticity of demand is a function that measures how consumer demand is affected by a change in price. It is given by

$$\eta = \frac{p}{q}\frac{dq}{dp}$$

where $p$ is the price per unit at which $q$ units are demanded. The three categories of elasticity are as follows:

$|\eta(p)| > 1$   demand is elastic

$|\eta(p)| = 1$   unit elasticity

$|\eta(p)| < 1$   demand is inelastic

For a given percentage change in price, if there is a greater (respectively lesser) percentage change in quantity demanded, then demand is elastic (respectively, inelastic) and conversely.

The relationship between elasticity and the rate of change of revenue is given by

$$\frac{dr}{dq} = p\left(1 + \frac{1}{\eta}\right)$$

If an equation implicitly defines $y$ as a function of $x$ (rather than defining it explicitly in the form $y = f(x)$, then $dy/dx$ can be found by implicit differentiation. With this method, we treat $y$ as a function of $x$ and differentiate both sides of the equation with respect to $x$. When doing this, remember that

$$\frac{d}{dx}(y^n) = ny^{n-1}\frac{dy}{dx}$$

and, more generally, that

$$\frac{d}{dx}(f(y)) = f'(y)\frac{dy}{dx}$$

Finally, we solve the resulting equation for $dy/dx$.

Suppose that $f(x)$ consists of products, quotients, or powers. To differentiate $y = \log_b(f(x))$, it may be helpful to use properties of logarithms to rewrite $\log_b(f(x))$ in terms of simpler logarithms and then differentiate that form. To differentiate $y = f(x)$, where $f(x)$ consists of products, quotients, or powers, the method of logarithmic differentiation may be used. In that method, we take the natural logarithm of both sides of $y = f(x)$ to obtain $\ln y = \ln(f(x))$. After simplifying $\ln(f(x))$ by using properties of logarithms, we differentiate both sides of $\ln y = \ln(f(x))$ with respect to $x$ and then solve for $y'$. Logarithmic differentiation can also be used to differentiate $y = u^v$, where both $u$ and $v$ are functions of $x$.

Newton's method is the name given to the following formula, which is used to approximate the roots of the equation $f(x) = 0$, provided that $f$ is differentiable:

$$x_{n+1} = x_n - \frac{f(x_n)}{f'(x_n)}, \quad n = 1, 2, 3, \ldots$$

In most cases you might encounter, the approximation improves as $n$ increases.

Because the derivative $f'(x)$ of a function $y = f(x)$ is itself a function, it can be successively differentiated to obtain the second derivative $f''(x)$, the third derivative $f'''(x)$, and other higher-order derivatives.

# Review Problems

*Problem numbers shown in color indicate problems suggested for use as a practice chapter test.*

*In Problems 1–30, differentiate.*

**1.** $y = 3e^x + e^2 + e^{x^2} + x^{e^2}$

**2.** $f(w) = we^w + w^2$

**3.** $f(r) = \ln(3r^2 + 7r + 1)$

**4.** $y = e^{\ln x}$

**5.** $y = e^{x^2 + 4x + 5}$

**6.** $f(t) = \log_6\sqrt{t^2 + 1}$

**7.** $y = e^x(x^2 + 2)$

**8.** $y = 3^{5x^3}$

**9.** $y = \sqrt{(x - 6)(x + 5)(9 - x)}$

**10.** $f(t) = e^{1/t}$

**11.** $y = \dfrac{\ln x}{e^x}$

**12.** $y = \dfrac{e^x + e^{-x}}{x^2}$

**13.** $f(q) = \ln[(q + 1)^2(q + 2)^3]$

**14.** $y = (x + 2)^3(x + 1)^4(x - 2)^2$

**15.** $y = 2^{2x^2 + 2x - 5}$

**16.** $y = (e + e^2)^0$

**17.** $y = \dfrac{4e^{3x}}{xe^{x-1}}$

**18.** $y = \dfrac{e^x}{\ln x}$

**19.** $y = \log_2(8x + 5)^2$

**20.** $y = \ln\left(\dfrac{5}{x^2}\right)$

**21.** $f(l) = \ln(1 + l + l^2 + l^3)$

**22.** $y = (x^2)^{x^2}$

**23.** $y = (x + 1)^{x+1}$

**24.** $y = \dfrac{1 + e^x}{1 - e^x}$

**25.** $\phi(t) = \ln\left(t\sqrt{4 - t^2}\,\right)$

**26.** $y = (x + 3)^{\ln x}$

**27.** $y = \dfrac{(x^2 + 1)^{1/2}(x^2 + 2)^{1/3}}{(2x^3 + 6x)^{2/5}}$

**28.** $y = \dfrac{\ln x}{\sqrt{x}}$

**29.** $y = (x^x)^x$

**30.** $y = x^{(x^x)}$

*In Problems 31–34, evaluate $y'$ at the given value of $x$.*

**31.** $y = (x + 1)\ln x^2,\ x = 1$

**32.** $y = \dfrac{e^{x^2+1}}{\sqrt{x^2 + 1}},\ x = 1$

**33.** $y = e^{e + x\ln(1/x)},\ x = e$

**34.** $y = \left[\dfrac{2^{5x}(x^2 - 3x + 5)^{1/3}}{(x^2 - 3x + 7)^3}\right]^{-1},\ x = 0$

*In Problems 35 and 36, find an equation of the tangent line to the curve at the point corresponding to the given value of x.*

**35.** $y = 3e^x,\ x = \ln 2$

**36.** $y = x + x^2\ln x,\ x = 1$

**37.** Find the $y$-intercept of the tangent line to the graph of $y = x(2^{2-x^2})$ at the point where $x = 1$.

**38.** If $w = 2^{x+1} + \ln(1 + x^2)$ and

$$x = \log_2(t^2 + 1) - e^{(t-1)^2}$$

find $w$ and $dw/dt$ when $t = 1$.

*In Problems 39–42, find the indicated derivative at the given point.*

**39.** $y = e^{x^2-2x+1},\ y'',\ (1, 1)$

**40.** $y = x^2e^x,\ y''',\ (1, e)$

**41.** $y = \ln(2x),\ y''',\ (1, \ln 2)$

**42.** $y = x\ln x,\ y'',\ (1, 0)$

*In Problems 43–46, find dy/dx.*

**43.** $2xy + y^2 = 10$

**44.** $x^3y^3 = 3$

**45.** $\ln(xy^2) = xy$

**46.** $y^2e^{y\ln x} = e^2$

*In Problems 47 and 48, find $d^2y/dx^2$ at the given point.*

**47.** $x + xy + y = 5,\ (2, 1)$

**48.** $xy + y^2 = 2,\ (-1, 2)$

**49.** If $y$ is defined implicitly by $e^y = (y + 1)e^x$, determine both $dy/dx$ and $d^2y/dx^2$ as explicit functions of $y$ only.

**50.** If $\sqrt{x} + \sqrt{y} = 1$, find $\dfrac{d^2y}{dx^2}$.

**51. Schizophrenia** Several models have been used to analyze the length of stay in a hospital. For a particular group of schizophrenics, one such model is[9]

$$f(t) = 1 - (0.8e^{-0.01t} + 0.2e^{-0.0002t})$$

where $f(t)$ is the proportion of the group that was discharged at the end of $t$ days of hospitalization. Determine the discharge rate (proportion discharged per day) at the end of $t$ days.

**52. Earthquakes** According to Richter,[10] the number $N$ of earthquakes of magnitude $M$ or greater per unit of time is given by $\log N = A - bM$, where $A$ and $b$ are constants. He claims that

$$\log\left(-\dfrac{dN}{dM}\right) = A + \log\left(\dfrac{b}{q}\right) - bM$$

where $q = \log e$. Verify this statement.

**53.** If $f(x) = e^{3x^4+2x^3-25x}$, find all real zeros of $f'(x)$. Round your answers to two decimal places.

**54.** If $f(x) = \dfrac{x^5}{10} + \dfrac{x^4}{6} + \dfrac{2x^3}{3} + x^2 + 1$, find all zeros of $f''(x)$. Round your answers to two decimal places.

*For the demand equations in Problems 55–57, determine whether demand is elastic, is inelastic, or has unit elasticity for the indicated value of q.*

**55.** $p = \dfrac{500}{q};\quad q = 200$

**56.** $p = 900 - q^2;\quad q = 10$

**57.** $p = 18 - 0.02q;\quad q = 600$

**58.** The demand equation for a product is

$$p = 20 - 2\sqrt{q}$$

**(a)** Find the point elasticity of demand when $p = 8$.

**(b)** Find all values of $p$ for which demand is elastic.

---

[9]Adapted from W. W. Eaton and G. A. Whitmore, "Length of Stay as a Stochastic Process: A General Approach and Application to Hospitalization for Schizophrenia," *Journal of Mathematical Sociology*, 5 (1977) 273–92.

[10]C. F. Richter, *Elementary Seismology* (San Francisco: W. H. Freeman and Company, Publishers, 1958).

**59.** The demand equation of a product is
$$q = \sqrt{2500 - p^2}$$
Find the point elasticity of demand when $p = 30$. If the price of 30 decreases $\frac{2}{3}$%, what is the approximate change in demand?

**60.** The demand equation for a product is
$$q = \sqrt{100 - p}, \quad \text{where } 0 < p < 100$$

(a) Find all prices that correspond to elastic demand.

(b) Compute the point elasticity of demand when $p = 40$. Use your answer to estimate the percentage increase or decrease in demand when price is increased by 5% to $p = 42$.

**61.** The equation $x^3 - 2x - 2 = 0$ has a root between 1 and 2. Use Newton's method to estimate the root. Continue the approximation procedure until the difference of two successive approximations is less than 0.0001. Round your answer to four decimal places.

**62.** Find, to an accuracy of three decimal places, all real solutions of the equation $e^x = 3x$.

# Mathematical Snapshot

## Economic Order Quantity

I n inventory management, the economic order quantity is the most cost-efficient size for resupply orders. To find this optimum size, we need to have an idea of how stock depletion and resupply take place, and of how costs accrue.

Here are the classic assumptions:

1. Inventory is depleted through purchases at a constant rate $D$, which is measured in units per year.
2. Resupply orders are all the same size, and each arrives in a single lump shipment just as stock is running out.
3. Besides the cost per item, each order also involves a fixed cost per order, $F$.
4. Each unit in stock has a constant value, $V$, measured in dollars.
5. The cost of inventory storage is a fixed fraction, $R$, of total current inventory value. This carrying cost factor is measured in dollars per dollar per year.

Assumptions 1 and 2 entail a graph of inventory over time that looks like Figure 12.10.

We now wish to minimize the cost, in dollars per year, of managing an inventory in the way Figure 12.10 depicts. If resupply is ordered in lots of $q$ units each, then there are $\dfrac{D}{q}$ orders per year, for an annual ordering cost of $\dfrac{FD}{q}$. (The yearly expense due to the per-item ordering cost cannot be adjusted by changing the order size, so this cost is ignored in our calculations.) With an average inventory level of $\dfrac{q}{2}$, the annual carrying cost is $\dfrac{RVq}{2}$. The annual inventory-related cost, $C$, is then the sum of the ordering cost and the carrying cost:

$$C = C(q) = \frac{FD}{q} + \frac{RVq}{2}$$

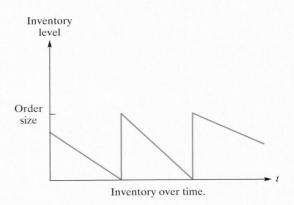

FIGURE 12.10   Inventory over time.

This function $C$ clearly takes on large values both when $q$ gets large and when $q$ approaches zero. It follows from arguments that we will study in detail in the next chapter that if there is a unique value of $q$ where $\dfrac{dC}{dq}$ equals zero then this value of $q$ will provide a minimum value of $C$. Let us try to find such a $q$.

$$\frac{dC}{dq} = \frac{-FD}{q^2} + \frac{RV}{2} = 0$$

$$q^2 = \frac{2FD}{RV}$$

$$q = \sqrt{\frac{2FD}{RV}}$$

This formula is called the Wilson lot size formula, after an industry consultant who popularized its use. If we substitute $F = \$10$ per order, $D = 1500$ units per year, $R = \$0.10$ dollars per dollar per year, and $V = \$10$, then $q$ comes out as

$$q = \sqrt{\frac{2(10)(1500)}{(0.10)(10)}} \approx 173.2$$

The most cost-efficient order size is 173 units.

Variations of the Wilson formula relax one or more of the five assumptions on which it is based. One assumption that can be relaxed is assumption 5. Suppose that carrying cost as a percentage of inventory value rises when inventory is low. (Think of a large warehouse sitting nearly empty.) We will model this by replacing $R$ with $R(1+ke^{-sq})$. $R$ is the per-dollar annual carrying cost for large inventory levels, and the term $ke^{-sq}$ ($k, s > 0$) raises the cost for low inventory levels. The total annual inventory cost now becomes

$$C = \frac{FD}{q} + \frac{RVq(1 + ke^{-sq})}{2}$$

Again, we wish to minimize this quantity, and again $C$ gets large both as $q$ gets large and as $q$ approaches zero. The minimum is where

$$\frac{dC}{dq} = \frac{-FD}{q^2} + \frac{RV(1 + ke^{-sq} - ksqe^{-sq})}{2} = 0$$

Suppose $k = 1$, $s = \dfrac{\ln 2}{1000} \approx 0.000693$. Then the per-dollar carrying cost is twice as great as for a small inventory as for a very large one and is midway between those two costs at an inventory level of 1000. If we keep $F$, $D$, $R$, and $V$ the same as before and then use a graphing calculator or other numeric solution technique, we find that $\dfrac{dC}{dq} = 0$ when $q \approx 127.9$. The optimum order size is 128 units. Note that even though the assumptions now include economies of scale, the carrying cost is greater at all inventory levels and has led to a lower economic order quantity.

## Problems

1. Use the Wilson lot size formula to calculate the economic order quantity for an item that is worth $36.50, costs 5% of its value annually to store, sells at a rate of 3400 units per year, and is purchased from a supplier that charges a flat $25 processing fee for every order.

2. Suppose that assumptions 1 and 3–5 are kept but 2 is modified: A manager never allows inventory to drop to zero but instead maintains a safety margin of a certain number of units. What difference does this make to the calculation of the economic order quantity?

3. What other assumptions, besides assumptions 2 and 5, might realistically be relaxed? Explain.

# 13

# CURVE SKETCHING

**Mathematical Snapshot**   Population Change over Time

In the mid-1970s, economist Arthur Laffer was explaining his views on taxes to a politician—as the story goes, it was either presidential aspirant Ronald Reagan or Ford administration staff member Richard Cheney (later Vice President under George W. Bush). To illustrate his argument, Laffer grabbed a paper napkin and sketched the graph that now bears his name: the Laffer curve.[1]

The Laffer curve describes total government tax revenue as a function of the tax rate. Obviously, if the tax rate is zero, the government gets nothing. But if the tax rate is 100%, revenue would again equal zero, because there is no incentive to earn money if it will all be taken away. Since tax rates between 0% and 100% do generate revenue, Laffer reasoned, the curve relating revenue to tax rate must look, qualitatively, more or less as shown in the figure below.

Laffer's argument was not meant to show that the optimal tax rate was 50%. It was meant to show that under some circumstances, namely when the tax rate is to the right of the peak of the curve, it is possible to *raise government revenue by lowering taxes*. This was a key argument made for the tax cuts passed by Congress during the first term of the Reagan presidency.

Because the Laffer curve is only a qualitative picture, it does not actually give an optimal tax rate. Revenue-based arguments for tax cuts involve the claim that the point of peak revenue lies to the left of the current taxation scheme on the horizontal axis. By the same token, those who urge raising taxes to raise government income are assuming either a different relationship between rates and revenues or a different location of the curve's peak.

By itself, then, the Laffer curve is too abstract to be of much help in determining the optimal tax rate. But even very simple sketched curves, like supply and demand curves and the Laffer curve, can help economists describe the causal factors that drive an economy. In this chapter, we will discuss techniques for sketching and interpreting curves.

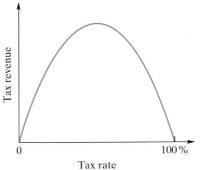

[1]For one version of the story, see Jude Wanniski, *The Way the World Works,* 3rd ed. (Morristown, NJ: Polyconomics, 1989), p. 299.

OBJECTIVE

To find when a function is increasing or decreasing, to find critical values, to locate relative maxima and relative minima, and to state the first-derivative test. Also, to sketch the graph of a function by using the information obtained from the first derivative.

# 13.1 Relative Extrema

## Increasing or Decreasing Nature of a Function

Examining the graphical behavior of functions is a basic part of mathematics and has applications to many areas of study. When we sketch a curve, just plotting points may not give enough information about its shape. For example, the points $(-1, 0)$, $(0, -1)$, and $(1, 0)$ satisfy the equation given by $y = (x + 1)^3(x - 1)$. On the basis of these points, you might hastily conclude that the graph should appear as in Figure 13.1(a), but in fact the true shape is given in Figure 13.1(b). In this chapter we will explore the powerful role that differentiation plays in analyzing a function, so that we can determine the true shape and behavior of its graph.

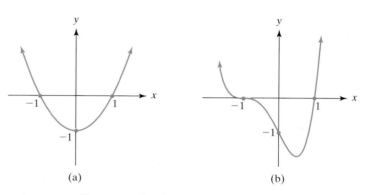

(a)      (b)

FIGURE 13.1   Curves passing through $(-1, 0)$, $(0, -1)$, and $(1, 0)$.

We begin by analyzing the graph of the function $y = f(x)$ in Figure 13.2. Notice that as $x$ increases (goes from left to right) on the interval $I_1$, between $a$ and $b$, the values of $f(x)$ increase and the curve is rising. Mathematically, this observation means that if $x_1$ and $x_2$ are any two points in $I_1$ such that $x_1 < x_2$, then $f(x_1) < f(x_2)$. Here $f$ is said to be an *increasing function* on $I_1$. On the other hand, as $x$ increases on the interval $I_2$ between $c$ and $d$, the curve is falling. On this interval, $x_3 < x_4$ implies that $f(x_3) > f(x_4)$, and $f$ is said to be a *decreasing function* on $I_2$. We summarize these observations in the following definition.

### DEFINITION

A function $f$ is said to be ***increasing*** on an interval $I$ when, for any two numbers $x_1, x_2$ in $I$, if $x_1 < x_2$, then $f(x_1) < f(x_2)$. A function $f$ is ***decreasing*** on an interval $I$ when, for any two numbers $x_1, x_2$ in $I$, if $x_1 < x_2$, then $f(x_1) > f(x_2)$.

In terms of the graph of the function, $f$ is increasing on $I$ if the curve rises to the right and $f$ is decreasing on $I$ if the curve falls to the right. Recall that a straight line

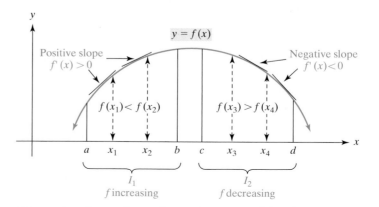

FIGURE 13.2   Increasing or decreasing nature of function.

with positive slope rises to the right while a straight line with negative slope falls to the right.

Turning again to Figure 13.2, we note that over the interval $I_1$, tangent lines to the curve have positive slopes, so $f'(x)$ must be positive for all $x$ in $I_1$. A positive derivative implies that the curve is rising. Over the interval $I_2$, the tangent lines have negative slopes, so $f'(x) < 0$ for all $x$ in $I_2$. The curve is falling where the derivative is negative. We thus have the following rule, which allows us to use the derivative to determine when a function is increasing or decreasing:

> **RULE 1  Criteria for Increasing or Decreasing Function**
>
> Let $f$ be differentiable on the interval $(a, b)$. If $f'(x) > 0$ for all $x$ in $(a, b)$, then $f$ is increasing on $(a, b)$. If $f'(x) < 0$ for all $x$ in $(a, b)$, then $f$ is decreasing on $(a, b)$.

To illustrate these ideas, we will use Rule 1 to find the intervals on which $y = 18x - \frac{2}{3}x^3$ is increasing and the intervals on which $y$ is decreasing. Letting $y = f(x)$, we must determine when $f'(x)$ is positive and when $f'(x)$ is negative. We have

$$f'(x) = 18 - 2x^2 = 2(9 - x^2) = 2(3 + x)(3 - x)$$

Using the technique of Section 10.4, we can find the sign of $f'(x)$ by testing the intervals determined by the roots of $2(3 + x)(3 - x) = 0$, namely, $-3$ and $3$. These should be arranged in increasing order on the top of a sign chart for $f'$ so as to divide the domain of $f$ into intervals. (See Figure 13.3.) In each interval, the sign of $f'(x)$ is determined by the signs of its factors:

|          | $-3$ |      | $3$  |      |
|----------|:----:|:----:|:----:|:----:|
| $3 + x$  | $-$  | $0$  | $+$  | $+$  |
| $3 - x$  | $+$  | $+$  | $0$  | $-$  |
| $f'(x)$  | $-$  | $0$  | $+$  | $0$  | $-$ |
| $f(x)$   |      |      |      |      |

FIGURE 13.3  Sign chart for $f'(x) = 18 - 9x^2$ and its interpretation for $f(x)$.

If $x < -3$,        then sign($f'(x)$) $= 2(-)(+) = -$, so $f$ is *decreasing*.

If $-3 < x < 3$,    then sign($f'(x)$) $= 2(+)(+) = +$, so $f$ is *increasing*.

If $x > 3$,         then sign($f'(x)$) $= 2(+)(-) = -$, so $f$ is *decreasing*.

These results are indicated in the sign chart given by Figure 13.3, where the bottom line is a schematic version of what the signs of $f'$ say about $f$ itself. Notice that the horizontal line segments in the bottom row indicate horizontal tangents for $f$ at $-3$ and at $3$. Thus, $f$ is decreasing on $(-\infty, -3)$ and $(3, \infty)$, and is increasing on $(-3, 3)$. This corresponds to the rising and falling nature of the graph of $f$ shown in Figure 13.4. Indeed, the point of a well-constructed sign chart is to provide a schematic for subsequent construction of the graph itself.

## Extrema

Look now at the graph of $y = f(x)$ in Figure 13.5. Some observations can be made. First, there is something special about the points $P$, $Q$, and $R$. Notice that $P$ is *higher* than any other "nearby" point on the curve—and likewise for $R$. The point $Q$ is *lower* than any other "nearby" point on the curve. Since $P$, $Q$, and $R$ may not necessarily be the highest or lowest points on the *entire* curve, we say that the graph of $f$ *has relative maxima at a and at c; and has a relative minimum at b.* The function $f$ has

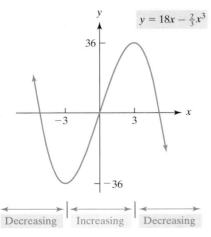

FIGURE 13.4  Increasing/ decreasing for $y = 18x - \frac{2}{3}x^3$.

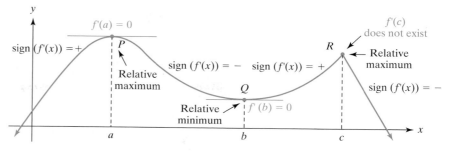

**FIGURE 13.5** Relative maxima and relative minima.

**CAUTION**

Be sure to note the difference between relative extreme *values* and *where* they occur.

relative maximum values of $f(a)$ at $a$ and $f(c)$ at $c$; and has a relative minimum value of $f(b)$ at $b$. We also say that $(a, f(a))$ and $(c, f(c))$ are relative maximum points and $(b, f(b))$ is a relative minimum point on the graph of $f$.

Turning back to the graph, we see that there is an *absolute maximum* (highest point on the entire curve) at $a$, but there is no *absolute minimum* (lowest point on the entire curve) because the curve is assumed to extend downward indefinitely. More precisely, we define these new terms as follows:

### DEFINITION

A function $f$ has a ***relative maximum*** at $a$ if there is an open interval containing $a$ on which $f(a) \geq f(x)$ for all $x$ in the interval. The relative maximum value is $f(a)$. A function $f$ has a ***relative minimum*** at $a$ if there is an open interval containing $a$ on which $f(a) \leq f(x)$ for all $x$ in the interval. The relative minimum value is $f(a)$.

### DEFINITION

A function $f$ has an ***absolute maximum*** at $a$ if $f(a) \geq f(x)$ for all $x$ in the domain of $f$. The absolute maximum value is $f(a)$. A function $f$ has an ***absolute minimum*** at $a$ if $f(a) \leq f(x)$ for all $x$ in the domain of $f$. The absolute minimum value is $f(a)$.

If it exists, an absolute maximum value is unique; however, it may occur at more than one value of $x$. A similar statement is true for an absolute minimum.

We refer to either a relative maximum or a relative minimum as a **relative extremum** (plural: *relative extrema*). Similarly, we speak of **absolute extrema.**

When dealing with relative extrema, we compare the function value at a point with values of nearby points; however, when dealing with absolute extrema, we compare the function value at a point with all other values determined by the domain. Thus, relative extrema are *local* in nature, whereas absolute extrema are *global* in nature.

Referring back to Figure 13.5, we notice that at a relative extremum the derivative may not be defined (as when $x = c$). But whenever it is defined at a relative extremum, it is 0 (as when $x = a$ and when $x = b$), and hence the tangent line is horizontal. We can state the following:

**RULE 2   A Necessary Condition for Relative Extrema**

If $f$ has a relative extremum at $a$, then $f'(a) = 0$ or $f'(a)$ does not exist.

The implication in Rule 2 goes in only one direction:

$$\left.\begin{array}{c}\text{relative extremum}\\\text{at } a\end{array}\right\} \quad \overset{\text{implies}}{\Longrightarrow} \quad \left\{\begin{array}{c}f'(a) = 0\\\text{or}\\f'(a) \text{ does not exist}\end{array}\right.$$

Rule 2 does *not* say that if $f'(a)$ is 0 or $f'(a)$ does not exist, then there must be a relative extremum at $a$. In fact, there may not be one at all. For example, in Figure 13.6(a), $f'(a)$ is 0 because the tangent line is horizontal at $a$, but there is no relative extremum

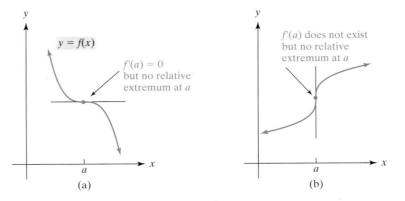

FIGURE 13.6   No relative extremum at $a$.

there. In Figure 13.6(b), $f'(a)$ does not exist because the tangent line is vertical at $a$, but again there is no relative extremum there.

But if we want to find all relative extrema of a function—and this is an important task—what Rule 2 *does* tell us is that we can limit our search to those values of $x$ in the domain of $f$ for which *either* $f'(x) = 0$ *or* $f'(x)$ does not exist. Typically, in applications, this cuts down our search for relative extrema from the infinitely many $x$ for which $f$ is defined to a small finite number of *possibilities*. Because these values of $x$ are so important for locating the relative extrema of $f$, they are called the *critical values* for $f$, and if $a$ is a critical value for $f$ then we also say that $(a, f(a))$ is a *critical point* on the graph of $f$. Thus, in Figure 13.5, the numbers $a$, $b$, and $c$ are critical values, and $P$, $Q$, and $R$ are critical points.

> ### DEFINITION
> For $a$ in the domain of $f$, if either $f'(a) = 0$ or $f'(a)$ does not exsit, then $a$ is called a ***critical value*** for $f$. If $a$ is a critical value, then the point $(a, f(a))$ is called a ***critical point*** for $f$.

At a critical point, there may be a relative maximum, a relative minimum, or neither. Moreover, from Figure 13.5, we observe that each relative extremum occurs at a point around which the sign of $f'(x)$ is changing. For the relative maximum at $a$, the sign of $f'(x)$ goes from $+$ for $x < a$ to $-$ for $x > a$, as long as $x$ is near $a$. For the relative minimum at $b$, the sign of $f'(x)$ goes from $-$ to $+$, and for the relative maximum at $c$, it again goes from $+$ to $-$. Thus, *around relative maxima, $f$ is increasing and then decreasing, and the reverse holds for relative minima*. More precisely, we have the following rule:

### RULE 3   Criteria for Relative Extrema

Suppose $f$ is continuous on an open interval $I$ that contains the critical value $a$ and $f$ is differentiable on $I$, except possibly at $a$.

1. If $f'(x)$ changes from positive to negative as $x$ increases through $a$, then $f$ has a relative maximum at $a$.

2. If $f'(x)$ changes from negative to positive as $x$ increases through $a$, then $f$ has a relative minimum at $a$.

To illustrate Rule 3 with a concrete example, refer again to Figure 13.3, the sign chart for $f'(x) = 18 - 2x^2$. The row labeled by $f'(x)$ shows clearly that $f(x) = 18x - \frac{2}{3}x^2$ has a relative minimum at $-3$ and a relative maximum at $3$. The row providing the interpretation of the chart for $f$, labeled $f(x)$, is immediately deduced from the row above it. The significance of the $f(x)$ row is that it provides

**CAUTION**

We point out again that not every critical value corresponds to a relative extremum. For example, if $y = f(x) = x^3$, then $f'(x) = 3x^2$. Since $f'(0) = 0$, 0 is a critical value. But if $x < 0$, then $3x^2 > 0$ and if $x > 0$, then $3x^2 > 0$. Since $f'(x)$ does not change sign at 0, there is no relative extremum at 0. Indeed, since $f'(x) \geq 0$ for all $x$, the graph of $f$ never falls, and $f$ is said to be *nondecreasing*. (See Figure 13.8.)

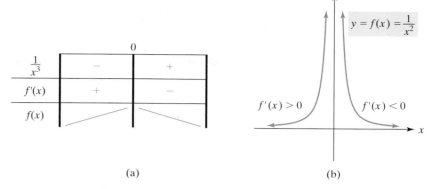

(a)                    (b)

**FIGURE 13.7**   $f'(0)$ is not defined, but 0 is not a critical value because 0 is not in the domain of $f$.

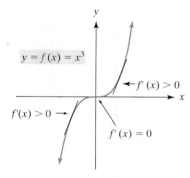

**FIGURE 13.8**   Zero is a critical value, but does not give a relative extremum.

an intermediate step in actually sketching the graph of $f$. In this row it stands out, visually, that $f$ has a relative minimum at $-3$ and a relative maximum at 3.

When searching for extrema of a function $f$, care must be paid to those $a$ that are not in the domain of $f$ but that are near values in the domain of $f$. Consider the following example. If

$$y = f(x) = \frac{1}{x^2} \quad \text{then} \quad f'(x) = -\frac{2}{x^3}$$

Although $f'(x)$ does not exist at 0, 0 is not a critical value, because 0 is not in the domain of $f$. Thus, a relative extremum cannot occur at 0. Nevertheless, the derivative may change sign around any $x$-value where $f'(x)$ is not defined, so such values are important in determining intervals over which $f$ is increasing or decreasing. In particular, such values should be included in a sign chart for $f'$. See Figure 13.7(a) and the accompanying graph Figure 13.7(b).

Observe that the thick vertical rule at 0 on the chart serves to indicate that 0 is not in the domain of $f$. Here there are no extrema of any kind.

In Rule 3 the hypotheses must be satisfied, or the conclusion need not hold. For example, consider the case-defined function

$$f(x) = \begin{cases} \dfrac{1}{x^2} & \text{if } x \neq 0 \\ 0 & \text{if } x = 0 \end{cases}$$

Here, 0 is explicitly in the domain of $f$ but $f$ is not continuous at 0. We recall from Section 11.1 that if a function $f$ is not continuous at $a$, then $f$ is not differentiable at $a$, meaning that $f'(a)$ does not exist. Thus $f'(0)$ does not exist and 0 is a critical value that must be included in the sign chart for $f'$ shown in Figure 13.9(a). We extend

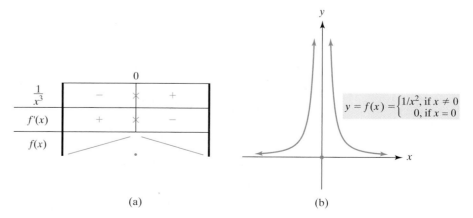

(a)                    (b)

**FIGURE 13.9**   Zero is a critical value but Rule 3 does not apply.

our sign chart conventions by indicating with a × symbol those values for which $f'$ does not exist. We see in this example that $f'(x)$ changes from positive to negative as $x$ increases through 0 but $f$ does *not* have a relative maximum at 0. Here Rule 3 does not apply because its continuity hypothesis is not met. In Figure 13.9(b), 0 is displayed in the domain of $f$. It is clear that $f$ has an absolute *minimum* at 0 because $f(0) = 0$ and, for all $x \neq 0$, $f(x) > 0$.

Summarizing the results of this section, we have the *first-derivative test* for the relative extrema of $y = f(x)$:

### First-Derivative Test for Relative Extrema

**Step 1.** Find $f'(x)$.

**Step 2.** Determine all critical values of $f$ (those $a$ where $f'(a) = 0$ or $f'(a)$ does not exist) and any $a$ that are not in the domain of $f$ but that are near values in the domain of $f$, and construct a sign chart that shows for each of the intervals determined by these values whether $f$ is increasing ($f'(x) > 0$) or decreasing ($f'(x) < 0$).

**Step 3.** For each critical value $a$ at which $f$ is continuous, determine whether $f'(x)$ changes sign as $x$ increases through $a$. There is a relative maximum at $a$ if $f'(x)$ changes from $+$ to $-$ going from left to right and a relative minimum if $f'(x)$ changes from $-$ to $+$ going from left to right. If $f'(x)$ does not change sign, there is no relative extremum at $a$.

**Step 4.** For critical values $a$ at which $f$ is not continuous, analyze the situation by using the definitions of extrema directly.

### ● EXAMPLE 1   First-Derivative Test

*If $y = f(x) = x + \dfrac{4}{x+1}$, for $x \neq 1$ use the first-derivative test to find where relative extrema occur.*

**Solution:**

**Step 1.**  $f(x) = x + 4(x + 1)^{-1}$, so

$$f'(x) = 1 + 4(-1)(x+1)^{-2} = 1 - \frac{4}{(x+1)^2}$$

$$= \frac{(x+1)^2 - 4}{(x+1)^2} = \frac{x^2 + 2x - 3}{(x+1)^2}$$

$$= \frac{(x+3)(x-1)}{(x+1)^2} \quad \text{for } x \neq -1$$

Note that we expressed $f'(x)$ as a quotient with numerator and denominator fully factored. This enables us in Step 2 to determine easily where $f'(x)$ is 0 or does not exist and the signs of $f'$.

**Step 2.** Setting $f'(x) = 0$ gives $x = -3, 1$. The denominator of $f'(x)$ is 0 when $x$ is $-1$. We note that $-1$ is not in the domain of $f$ but all values near $-1$ are in the domain of $f$. We construct a sign chart, headed by the values $-3, -1$, and 1 (which we have placed in increasing order). See Figure 13.10.

The three values lead us to test four intervals as shown in our sign chart. On each of these intervals, $f$ is differentiable and is not zero. We determine the sign of $f'$ on each interval by first determining the sign of each of its factors on each interval. For example, considering first the interval $(-\infty, -3)$, it is not easy to see immediately that $f'(x) > 0$ there; but it is easy to see that $x+3 < 0$ for $x < -3$, while $(x+1)^{-2} > 0$ for all $x \neq -1$, and $x-1 < 0$ for $x < 1$. These observations account for the signs of the factors in the $(-\infty, -3)$ column of the chart. The sign of $f'(x)$ in that column is obtained by "multiplying signs" (downward): $(-)(+)(-) = +$. We repeat these considerations for the other three intervals. Note that the thick vertical line at $-1$ in the chart indicates that $-1$ is not in the domain of $f$ and hence cannot give rise to any extrema.

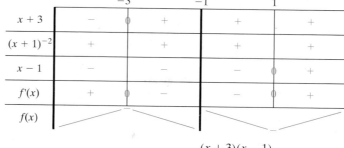

|              | $-3$ |   | $-1$ |   | $1$ |   |
|--------------|:---:|:---:|:---:|:---:|:---:|:---:|
| $x + 3$      | $-$ | 0 | $+$ |   | $+$ |   | $+$ |
| $(x + 1)^{-2}$ | $+$ |   | $+$ |   | $+$ |   | $+$ |
| $x - 1$      | $-$ |   | $-$ |   | $-$ | 0 | $+$ |
| $f'(x)$      | $+$ | 0 | $-$ |   | $-$ | 0 | $+$ |
| $f(x)$       |     |   |     |   |     |   |     |

**FIGURE 13.10**   Sign chart for $f'(x) = \dfrac{(x+3)(x-1)}{(x+1)^2}$.

In the bottom row of the sign chart we record, graphically, the nature of tangent lines to $f(x)$ in each interval and at the values where $f'$ is 0.

**Step 3.** From the sign chart alone we conclude that at $-3$ there is a relative maximum (since $f'(x)$ changes from $+$ to $-$ at $-3$). Going beyond the chart, we compute $f(-3) = -3 + (4/-2) = -5$ and this gives the relative maximum value of $-5$ at $-3$. We also conclude from the chart that there is a relative minimum at 1 (because $f'(x)$ changes from $-$ to $+$ at 1). From $f(1) = 1 + 4/2 = 3$ we see that at 1 the relative minimum value is 3.

**Step 4.** There are no critical values at which $f$ is not continuous, so our considerations above provide the whole story about the relative extrema of $f(x)$, whose graph is given in Figure 13.11. Note that the general shape of the graph was indeed forecast by the bottom row of the sign chart (Figure 13.10).

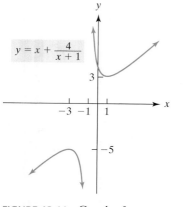

$$y = x + \frac{4}{x+1}$$

**FIGURE 13.11**   Graph of $y = x + \dfrac{4}{x+1}$.

NOW WORK PROBLEM 37

● **EXAMPLE 2    A Relative Extremum where $f'(x)$ Does Not Exist**

*Test $y = f(x) = x^{2/3}$ for relative extrema.*

**Solution:**  We have

$$f'(x) = \frac{2}{3}x^{-1/3}$$

$$= \frac{2}{3\sqrt[3]{x}}$$

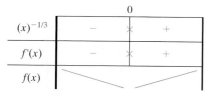

|            | $0$ |   |   |
|------------|:---:|:---:|:---:|
| $(x)^{-1/3}$ | $-$ | $\times$ | $+$ |
| $f'(x)$    | $-$ | $\times$ | $+$ |
| $f(x)$     |     |   |     |

**FIGURE 13.12**   Sign chart for $f'(x) = \dfrac{2}{3\sqrt[3]{x}}$.

and the sign chart is which requires little comment, except to note that again we use the symbol $\times$ on the vertical line at 0 to indicate that $f'(0)$ does not exist. Since $f$ is continuous at 0, we conclude from Rule 3 that $f$ has a relative minimum at 0 of $f(0) = 0$, and there are no other relative extrema. We note further, by inspection, that $f$ has an *absolute* minimum at 0. The graph of $f$ follows as Figure 13.13. Note that we could have predicted its shape from the the bottom line of line of the sign chart Figure 13.12, which shows there can be no tangent with a slope at 0. (Of course, the tangent does exist at 0 but it is a vertical line.)

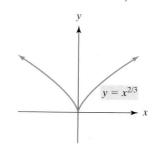

$$y = x^{2/3}$$

**FIGURE 13.13**
Derivative does not exist at 0 and there is a minimum at 0.

NOW WORK PROBLEM 41

● **EXAMPLE 3  Finding Relative Extrema**

*Test $y = f(x) = x^2 e^x$ for relative extrema.*

**Solution:** By the product rule,
$$f'(x) = x^2 e^x + e^x(2x) = xe^x(x + 2)$$
Noting that $e^x$ is always positive, we obtain the critical values $0$ and $-2$. From the sign chart of $f'(x)$ given in Figure 13.14, we conclude that there is a relative maximum when $x = -2$ and a relative minimum when $x = 0$.

| | $-2$ | | $0$ | |
|---|---|---|---|---|
| $x + 2$ | $-$ | $+$ | | $+$ |
| $x$ | $-$ | $-$ | | $+$ |
| $e^x$ | $+$ | $+$ | | $+$ |
| $f'(x)$ | $+$ | $-$ | | $+$ |
| $f(x)$ | | | | |

**FIGURE 13.14**  Sign chart for $f'(x) = x(x + 2)e^x$.

NOW WORK PROBLEM 49 ●●●

## Curve Sketching

In the next example we show how the first-derivative test, in conjunction with the notions of intercepts and symmetry, can be used as an aid in sketching the graph of a function.

● **EXAMPLE 4  Curve Sketching**

*Sketch the graph of $y = f(x) = 2x^2 - x^4$ with the aid of intercepts, symmetry, and the first-derivative test.*

**Solution:**

***Intercepts***  If $x = 0$, then $f(x) = 0$ so that the $y$-intercept is $(0, 0)$. Next note that
$$f(x) = 2x^2 - x^4 = x^2(2 - x^2) = x^2(\sqrt{2} + x)(\sqrt{2} - x)$$
So if $y = 0$, then $x = 0, \pm\sqrt{2}$ and the $x$-intercepts are $(-\sqrt{2}, 0)$, $(0, 0)$, and $(\sqrt{2}, 0)$. We have the sign chart *for $f$ itself* (Figure 13.15), which shows the intervals over which the graph of $y = f(x)$ is above the $x$-axis $(+)$ and the intervals over which the graph of $y = f(x)$ is below the $x$-axis $(-)$.

| | $-\sqrt{2}$ | | $0$ | | $\sqrt{2}$ | |
|---|---|---|---|---|---|---|
| $\sqrt{2} + x$ | $-$ | $+$ | | $+$ | | $+$ |
| $x^2$ | $+$ | $+$ | | $+$ | | $+$ |
| $\sqrt{2} - x$ | $+$ | $+$ | | $+$ | | $-$ |
| $f(x)$ | $-$ | $+$ | | $+$ | | $-$ |

**FIGURE 13.15**  Sign chart for $f(x) = (\sqrt{2} + x)x^2(\sqrt{2} - x)$.

***Symmetry***  Testing for $y$-axis symmetry, we have
$$f(-x) = 2(-x)^2 - (-x)^4 = 2x^2 - x^4 = f(x)$$
So the graph is symmetric with respect to the $y$-axis. Because $y$ is a function (and not the zero function), there is no $x$-axis symmetry and hence no symmetry about the origin.

***First-Derivative Test***

**Step 1.**  $y' = 4x - 4x^3 = 4x(1 - x^2) = 4x(1 + x)(1 - x)$.

| | −1 | | 0 | | 1 | |
|---|---|---|---|---|---|---|
| $1 + x$ | − | 0 | + | | + | | + |
| $4x$ | − | | − | 0 | + | | + |
| $1 − x$ | + | | + | | + | 0 | − |
| $f'(x)$ | + | 0 | − | 0 | + | 0 | − |
| $f(x)$ | | | | | | | |

**FIGURE 13.16**   Sign chart of $y' = (1 + x)4x(1 − x)$.

**Step 2.** Setting $y' = 0$ gives the critical values $x = 0, ±1$. Since $f$ is a polynomial, it is defined and differentiable for all $x$. Thus the only values to head the sign chart for $f'$ are $−1, 0, 1$ (in increasing order) and the sign chart is given in Figure 13.16. Since we are interested in the graph, the critical *points* are important to us. By substituting the critical values into the *original* equation, $y = 2x^2 − x^4$, we obtain the $y$-coordinates of these points. We find the critical points to be $(−1, 1)$, $(0, 0)$, and $(1, 1)$.

**Step 3.** From the sign chart and evaluations in step 2, it is clear that $f$ has relative maxima $(−1, 1)$ and $(1, 1)$ and relative minimum $(0, 0)$. (Step 4 does not apply here.)

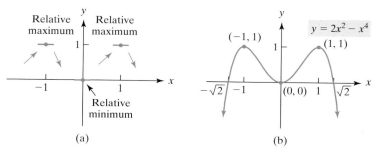

**FIGURE 13.17**   Putting together the graph of $y = 2x^2 − x^4$.

***Discussion***   In Figure 13.17(a), we have indicated the horizontal tangents at the relative maximum and minimum points. We know the curve rises from the left, has a relative maximum, then falls, has a relative minimum, then rises to a relative maximum, and falls thereafter. By symmetry, it suffices to sketch on one side of the $y$-axis and construct a mirror image on the other side. We also know, from the sign chart for $f$, where the graph crosses and touches the $x$-axis, and this adds further precision to our sketch, which is shown in Figure 13.17(b).

As a passing comment, we note that *absolute* maxima occur at $x = ±1$. See Figure 13.17(b). There is no absolute minimum.

NOW WORK PROBLEM 59

**T E C H N O L O G Y**

A graphing calculator is a powerful tool for investigating relative extrema. For example, consider the function

$$f(x) = 3x^4 − 4x^3 + 4$$

whose graph is shown in Figure 13.18. It appears that there is a relative minimum near $x = 1$. We can locate this minimum by either using "trace and zoom" or (on a TI-83 Plus) using the "minimum" feature. Figure 13.19 shows the latter approach. The relative minimum point is estimated to be $(1.00, 3)$.

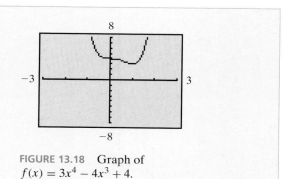

**FIGURE 13.18**   Graph of $f(x) = 3x^4 − 4x^3 + 4$.

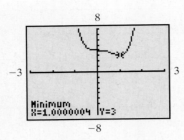

**FIGURE 13.19** Relative minimum at (1.00, 3).

Now let us see how the graph of $f'$ indicates when extrema occur. We have

$$f'(x) = 12x^3 - 12x^2$$

whose graph is shown in Figure 13.20. It appears that $f'(x)$ is 0 at two points. Using "trace and zoom" or the "zero" feature, we estimate the zeros of $f'$ (the critical values of $f$) to be 1 and 0. Around $x = 1$, we see that $f'(x)$ goes from negative values to positive values. (That is, the graph of $f'$ goes from below the $x$-axis to above it.) Thus, we conclude that $f$ has a relative minimum at $x = 1$, which confirms our previous result.

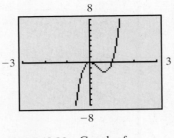

**FIGURE 13.20** Graph of $f'(x) = 12x^3 - 12x^2$.

Around the critical value $x = 0$, the values of $f'(x)$ are negative. Since $f'(x)$ does not change sign, we conclude that there is no relative extremum at $x = 0$. This is also apparent from the graph in Figure 13.18.

It is worthwhile to note that we can approximate the graph of $f'$ without determining $f'(x)$ itself. We make use of the "nDeriv" feature. First we enter the function $f$ as $Y_1$. Then we set

$$Y_2 = nDeriv(Y_1, X, X)$$

The graph of $Y_2$ approximates the graph of $f'(x)$.

## Problems 13.1

*In Problems 1–4, the graph of a function is given (Figures 13.21–13.24). Find the open intervals on which the function is increasing or decreasing, and find the coordinates of all relative extrema.*

**1.**

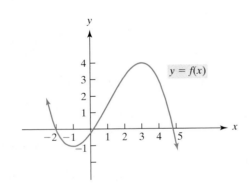

**FIGURE 13.21** Graph for Problem 1.

**2.**

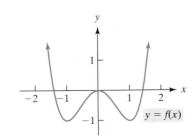

**FIGURE 13.22** Graph for Problem 2.

**3.**

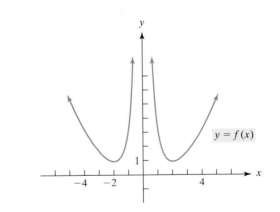

**FIGURE 13.23** Graph for Problem 3.

**4.**

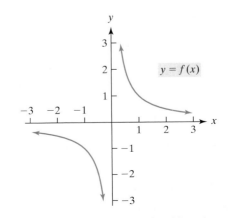

**FIGURE 13.24** Graph for Problem 4.

*In Problems 5–8, the derivative of a continuous function $f$ is given. Find the open intervals on which $f$ is increasing or decreasing, and find the x-values of all relative extrema.*

**5.** $f'(x) = (x + 3)(x - 1)(x - 2)$

**6.** $f'(x) = 2x(x - 1)^3$

**7.** $f'(x) = (x + 1)(x - 3)^2$    **8.** $f'(x) = \dfrac{x(x + 2)}{x^2 + 1}$

*In Problems 9–52, determine where the function is increasing or decreasing, and determine where relative maxima and minima occur. Do not sketch the graph.*

**9.** $y = 2x^3 + 1$

**10.** $y = x^2 + 4x + 3$

**11.** $y = x - x^2 + 2$

**12.** $y = x^3 - \dfrac{5}{2}x^2 - 2x + 6$

**13.** $y = -\dfrac{x^3}{3} - 2x^2 + 5x - 2$

**14.** $y = \dfrac{x^4}{4} + x^3$

**15.** $y = x^4 - 2x^2$

**16.** $y = -3 + 12x - x^3$

**17.** $y = x^3 - \dfrac{7}{2}x^2 + 2x - 5$

**18.** $y = x^3 - 6x^2 + 12x - 6$

**19.** $y = 2x^3 - \dfrac{11}{2}x^2 - 10x + 2$    **20.** $y = -5x^3 + x^2 + x - 7$

**21.** $y = \dfrac{x^3}{3} - 5x^2 + 22x + 1$    **22.** $y = \dfrac{9}{5}x^5 - \dfrac{47}{3}x^3 + 10x$

**23.** $y = 3x^5 - 5x^3$

**24.** $y = 3x - \dfrac{x^6}{2}$

**25.** $y = -x^5 - 5x^4 + 200$

**26.** $y = \dfrac{3x^4}{2} - 4x^3 + 17$

**27.** $y = 8x^4 - x^8$

**28.** $y = \dfrac{4}{5}x^5 - \dfrac{13}{3}x^3 + 3x + 4$

**29.** $y = (x^2 - 1)^4$

**30.** $y = \sqrt[3]{x}(x - 2)$

**31.** $y = \dfrac{5}{x - 1}$

**32.** $y = \dfrac{3}{x}$

**33.** $y = \dfrac{10}{\sqrt{x}}$

**34.** $y = \dfrac{3x}{2x + 5}$

**35.** $y = \dfrac{x^2}{2 - x}$

**36.** $y = 4x^2 + \dfrac{1}{x}$

**\*37.** $y = \dfrac{x^2 - 3}{x + 2}$

**38.** $y = \dfrac{2x^2}{4x^2 - 25}$

**39.** $y = \dfrac{5x + 2}{x^2 + 1}$

**40.** $y = \sqrt[3]{x^3 - 9x}$

**\*41.** $y = (x - 1)^{2/3}$

**42.** $y = x^2(x + 3)^4$

**43.** $y = x^3(x - 6)^4$

**44.** $y = x(1 - x)^{2/5}$

**45.** $y = e^{-\pi x} + \pi$

**46.** $y = x \ln x$

**47.** $y = x^2 - 9 \ln x$

**48.** $y = x^{-1}e^x$

**\*49.** $y = e^x + e^{-x}$

**50.** $y = e^{-x^2/2}$

**51.** $y = x \ln x - x$

**52.** $y = (x^2 + 1)e^{-x}$

*In Problems 53–64, determine intervals on which the function is increasing or decreasing, relative maxima and minima, symmetry, and those intercepts that can be obtained conveniently. Then sketch the graph.*

**53.** $y = x^2 - 3x - 10$    **54.** $y = 2x^2 - 5x - 12$

**55.** $y = 3x - x^3$    **56.** $y = x^4 - 16$

**57.** $y = 2x^3 - 9x^2 + 12x$    **58.** $y = 2x^3 - x^2 - 4x + 4$

**\*59.** $y = x^4 + 4x^3 + 4x^2$    **60.** $y = x^6 - \dfrac{6}{5}x^5$

**61.** $y = (x - 1)^2(x + 2)^2$    **62.** $y = \sqrt{x}(x^2 - x - 2)$

**63.** $y = 2\sqrt{x} - x$    **64.** $y = x^{5/3} + 5x^{2/3}$

**65.** Sketch the graph of a continuous function $f$ such that $f(2) = 2$, $f(4) = 6$, $f'(2) = f'(4) = 0$, $f'(x) < 0$ for $x < 2$, $f'(x) > 0$ for $2 < x < 4$, $f$ has a relative maximum at 4, and $\lim_{x \to \infty} f(x) = 0$.

**66.** Sketch the graph of a continuous function $f$ such that $f(1) = 2$, $f(4) = 5$, $f'(1) = 0$, $f'(x) \geq 0$ for $x < 4$, $f$ has a relative maximum when $x = 4$, and there is a vertical tangent line when $x = 4$.

**67. Average Cost**   If $c_f = 25{,}000$ is a fixed-cost function, show that the average fixed-cost function $\overline{c}_f = c_f/q$ is a decreasing function for $q > 0$. Thus, as output $q$ increases, each unit's portion of fixed cost declines.

**68. Marginal Cost**   If $c = 3q - 3q^2 + q^3$ is a cost function, when is marginal cost increasing?

**69. Marginal Revenue**   Given the demand function

$$p = 400 - 2q$$

find when marginal revenue is increasing.

**70. Cost Function**   For the cost function $c = \sqrt{q}$, show that marginal and average costs are always decreasing for $q > 0$.

**71. Revenue**   For a manufacturer's product, the revenue function is given by $r = 240q + 57q^2 - q^3$. Determine the output for maximum revenue.

**72. Labor Markets**   Eswaran and Kotwal[2] consider agrarian economies in which there are two types of workers, permanent and casual. Permanent workers are employed on long-term contracts and may receive benefits such as holiday gifts and emergency aid. Casual workers are hired on a daily basis and perform routine and menial tasks such as weeding, harvesting, and threshing. The difference $z$ in the present-value cost of hiring a permanent worker over that of hiring a casual worker is given by

$$z = (1 + b)w_p - bw_c$$

where $w_p$ and $w_c$ are wage rates for permanent labor and casual labor, respectively, $b$ is a positive constant, and $w_p$ is a function of $w_c$.

**(a)** Show that

$$\frac{dz}{dw_c} = (1 + b)\left[\frac{dw_p}{dw_c} - \frac{b}{1 + b}\right]$$

**(b)** If $dw_p/dw_c < b/(1 + b)$, show that $z$ is a decreasing function of $w_c$.

**73. Thermal Pollution**   In Shonle's discussion of thermal pollution,[3] the efficiency of a power plant is given by

$$E = 0.71\left(1 - \frac{T_c}{T_h}\right)$$

where $T_h$ and $T_c$ are the respective absolute temperatures of the hotter and colder reservoirs. Assume that $T_c$ is a positive constant and that $T_h$ is positive. Using calculus, show that as $T_h$ increases, the efficiency increases.

———
[2]M. Eswaran and A. Kotwal, "A Theory of Two-Tier Labor Markets in Agrarian Economics," *The American Economic Review*, 75, no. 1 (1985), 162–77.

[3]J. I. Shonle, *Environmental Applications of General Physics* (Reading, MA: Addison-Wesley Publishing Company, Inc., 1975).

**74. Telephone Service**  In a discussion of the pricing of local telephone service, Renshaw[4] determines that total revenue $r$ is given by

$$r = 2F + \left(1 - \frac{a}{b}\right)p - p^2 + \frac{a^2}{b}$$

where $p$ is an indexed price per call, and $a$, $b$, and $F$ are constants. Determine the value of $p$ that maximizes revenue.

**75. Storage and Shipping Costs**  In his model for storage and shipping costs of materials for a manufacturing process, Lancaster[5] derives the cost function

$$C(k) = 100\left(100 + 9k + \frac{144}{k}\right) \qquad 1 \le k \le 100$$

where $C(k)$ is the total cost (in dollars) of storage and transportation for 100 days of operation if a load of $k$ tons of material is moved every $k$ days.

**(a)** Find $C(1)$.
**(b)** For what value of $k$ does $C(k)$ have a minimum?
**(c)** What is the minimum value?

**76. Physiology—The Bends**  When a deep-sea diver undergoes decompression or a pilot climbs to a high altitude, nitrogen may bubble out of the blood, causing what is commonly called *the bends*. Suppose the percentage $P$ of people who suffer effects of the bends at an altitude of $h$ thousand feet is given by[6]

$$P = \frac{100}{1 + 100{,}000e^{-0.36h}}$$

Is $P$ an increasing function of $h$?

*In Problems 77–80, from the graph of the function, find the coordinates of all relative extrema. Round your answers to two decimal places.*

**77.** $y = 0.3x^2 + 2.3x + 5.1$

**78.** $y = 3x^4 - 4x^3 - 5x + 1$

**79.** $y = \dfrac{8.2x}{0.4x^2 + 3}$

**80.** $y = \dfrac{e^x(3 - x)}{7x^2 + 1}$

**81.** Graph the function

$$f(x) = [x(x-2)(2x-3)]^2$$

in the window $-1 \le x \le 3$, $-1 \le y \le 3$. Upon first glance, it may appear that this function has two relative minimum points and one relative maximum point. However, in reality, it has three relative minimum points and two relative maximum points. Determine the $x$-values of all these points. Round answers to two decimal places.

**82.** If $f(x) = 3x^3 - 7x^2 + 4x + 2$, display the graphs of $f$ and $f'$ on the same screen. Notice that $f'(x) = 0$ where relative extrema of $f$ occur.

**83.** Let $f(x) = 6 + 4x - 3x^2 - x^3$. (a) Find $f'(x)$. (b) Graph $f'(x)$. (c) Observe where $f'(x)$ is positive and where it is negative. Give the intervals (rounded to two decimal places) where $f$ is increasing and where $f$ is decreasing. (d) Graph $f$ and $f'$ on the same screen, and verify your results to part (c).

**84.** If $f(x) = x^4 - x^2 - (x + 2)^2$, find $f'(x)$. Determine the critical values of $f$. Round your answers to two decimal places.

## 13.2 Absolute Extrema on a Closed Interval

If a function $f$ is *continuous* on a *closed* interval $[a, b]$, it can be shown that of *all* the function values $f(x)$ for $x$ in $[a, b]$, there must be an (absolute) maximum value and an (absolute) minimum value. These two values are called **extreme values** of $f$ on that interval. This important property of continuous functions is called the *extreme-value theorem*.

### Extreme-Value Theorem

If a function is continuous on a closed interval, then the function has *both* a maximum value *and* a minimum value on that interval.

For example, each function in Figure 13.25 is continuous on the closed interval $[1, \ 3]$. Geometrically, the extreme-value theorem assures us that over this interval each graph has a highest point and a lowest point.

In the extreme-value theorem, you must realize that we are dealing with

1. a closed interval and
2. a function continuous on that interval

---

[4]E. Renshaw, "A Note on Equity and Efficiency in the Pricing of Local Telephone Services," *The American Economic Review*, 75, no. 3 (1985), 515–18.

[5]P. Lancaster, *Mathematics: Models of the Real World* (Englewood Cliffs, NJ: Prentice-Hall, Inc., 1976).

[6]Adapted from G. E. Folk, Jr., *Textbook of Environmental Physiology*, 2nd ed. (Philadelphia: Lea & Febiger, 1974).

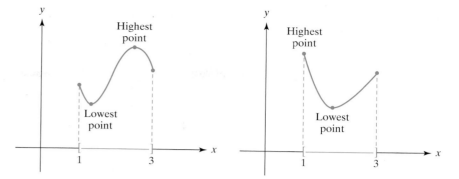

**FIGURE 13.25**   Illustrating the extreme-value theorem.

If either condition (1) or condition (2) is not met, then extreme values are not guaranteed. For example, Figure 13.26(a) shows the graph of the continuous function $f(x) = x^2$ on the *open* interval $(-1, 1)$. You can see that $f$ has no maximum value on the interval (although $f$ has a minimum value there). Now consider the function $f(x) = 1/x^2$ on the closed interval $[-1, 1]$. Here $f$ is *not continuous* at 0. From the graph of $f$ in Figure 13.26(b), you can see that $f$ has no maximum value (although there is a minimum value).

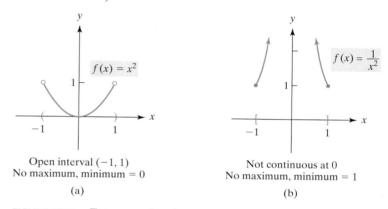

**FIGURE 13.26**   Extreme-value theorem does not apply.

In the previous section, our emphasis was on relative extrema. Now we will focus our attention on absolute extrema and make use of the extreme-value theorem where possible. If the domain of a function is a closed interval, to determine *absolute* extrema we must examine the function not only at critical values, but also at the endpoints. For example, Figure 13.27 shows the graph of the continuous function $y = f(x)$ over $[a, b]$. The extreme-value theorem guarantees absolute extrema over the interval. Clearly, the important points on the graph occur at $x = a, b, c,$ and $d,$

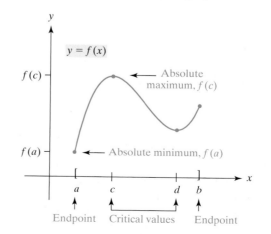

**FIGURE 13.27**   Absolute extrema.

which correspond to endpoints or critical values. Notice that the absolute maximum occurs at the critical value $c$ and the absolute minimum occurs at the endpoint $a$. These results suggest the following procedure:

**Procedure to Find Absolute Extrema for a Function $f$ That Is Continuous on $[a, b]$**

**Step 1.** Find the critical values of $f$.

**Step 2.** Evaluate $f(x)$ at the endpoints $a$ and $b$ and at the critical values in $(a, b)$.

**Step 3.** The maximum value of $f$ is the greatest of the values found in step 2. The minimum value of $f$ is the least of the values found in step 2.

● **EXAMPLE 1    Finding Extreme Values on a Closed Interval**

*Find absolute extrema for $f(x) = x^2 - 4x + 5$ over the closed interval $[1, 4]$.*

**Solution:** Since $f$ is continuous on $[1, 4]$, the foregoing procedure applies.

**Step 1.** To find the critical values of $f$, we first find $f'$:

$$f'(x) = 2x - 4 = 2(x - 2)$$

This gives the critical value $x = 2$.

**Step 2.** Evaluating $f(x)$ at the endpoints 1 and 4 and at the critical value 2, we have

$$\begin{aligned} f(1) &= 2 \\ f(4) &= 5 \end{aligned} \quad \text{values of } f \text{ at endpoints}$$

and

$$f(2) = 1 \quad \text{value of } f \text{ at critical value 2 in } (1, 4)$$

**Step 3.** From the function values in step 2, we conclude that the maximum is $f(4) = 5$ and the minimum is $f(2) = 1$. (See Figure 13.28.)

NOW WORK PROBLEM 1  ●●

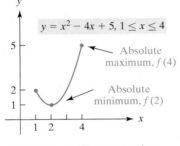

**FIGURE 13.28** Extreme values for Example 1.

## Problems 13.2

*In Problems 1–14, find the absolute extrema of the given function on the given interval.*

*1. $f(x) = x^2 - 2x + 3, [0, 3]$

2. $f(x) = -2x^2 - 6x + 5, [-3, 2]$

3. $f(x) = \frac{1}{3}x^3 + \frac{1}{2}x^2 - 2x + 1, [-1, 0]$

4. $f(x) = \frac{1}{4}x^4 - \frac{3}{2}x^2, [0, 1]$

5. $f(x) = 4x^3 + 3x^2 - 18x + 3, [\frac{1}{2}, 3]$

6. $f(x) = x^{2/3}, [-8, 8]$

7. $f(x) = -3x^5 + 5x^3, [-2, 0]$

8. $f(x) = \frac{7}{3}x^3 + 2x^2 - 3x + 1, [0, 3]$

9. $f(x) = 3x^4 - x^6, [-1, 2]$

10. $f(x) = \frac{1}{4}x^4 - \frac{1}{2}x^2 + 3, [-2, 3]$

11. $f(x) = x^4 - 9x^2 + 2, [-1, 3]$

12. $f(x) = \dfrac{x}{x^2 + 1}, [0, 2]$

13. $f(x) = (x - 1)^{2/3}, [-26, 28]$

14. $f(x) = 0.2x^3 - 3.6x^2 + 2x + 1, [-1, 2]$

15. Consider the function

$$f(x) = x^4 + 8x^3 + 21x^2 + 20x + 9$$

over the interval $[-4, 9]$.

**(a)** Determine the value(s) (rounded to two decimal places) of $x$ at which $f$ attains a minimum value.

**(b)** What is the minimum value (rounded to two decimal places) of $f$?

**(c)** Determine the value(s) of $x$ at which $f$ attains a maximum value.

**(d)** What is the maximum value of $f$?

OBJECTIVE

To test a function for concavity and inflection points. Also, to sketch curves with the aid of the information obtained from the first and second derivatives.

## 13.3 Concavity

You have seen that the first derivative provides much information for sketching curves. It is used to determine when a function is increasing or decreasing and to locate relative maxima and minima. However, to be sure we know the true shape of a curve, we may need more information. For example, consider the curve $y = f(x) = x^2$. Since $f'(x) = 2x$, $x = 0$ is a critical value. If $x < 0$, then $f'(x) < 0$, and $f$ is decreasing; if $x > 0$, then $f'(x) > 0$, and $f$ is increasing. Thus, there is a relative minimum when $x = 0$. In Figure 13.29, both curves meet the preceding conditions. But which one

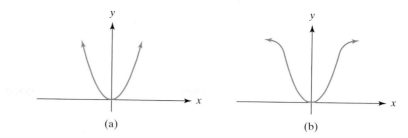

FIGURE 13.29   Two functions with $f'(x) < 0$ for $x < 0$ and $f'(x) > 0$ for $x > 0$.

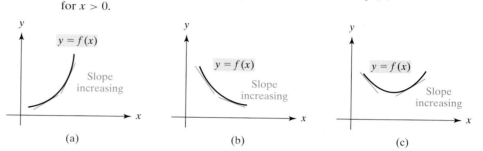

FIGURE 13.30   Each curve is concave up.

truly describes the curve $y = x^2$? This question will be settled easily by using the second derivative and the notion of *concavity*.

In Figure 13.30, note that each curve $y = f(x)$ "bends" (or opens) upward. This means that if tangent lines are drawn to each curve, the curves lie *above* them. Moreover, the slopes of the tangent lines *increase* in value as $x$ increases: In part (a), the slopes go from small positive values to larger values; in part (b), they are negative and approaching zero (and thus increasing); in part (c), they pass from negative values to positive values. Since $f'(x)$ gives the slope at a point, an increasing slope means that $f'$ must be an increasing function. To describe this property, each curve (or function $f$) in Figure 13.30 is said to be *concave up*.

In Figure 13.31, it can be seen that each curve lies *below* the tangent lines and the curves are bending downward. As $x$ increases, the slopes of the tangent lines are *decreasing*. Thus, $f'$ must be a decreasing function here, and we say that $f$ is *concave down*.

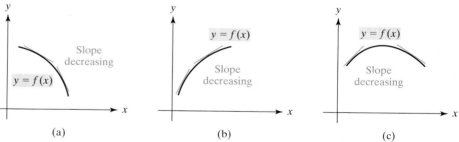

FIGURE 13.31   Each curve is concave down.

 **CAUTION**

Concavity relates to whether $f'$, not $f$, is increasing or decreasing. In Figure 13.30(b), note that $f$ is concave up and decreasing; however, in Figure 13.31(a), $f$ is concave down and decreasing.

## DEFINITION

Let $f$ be differentiable on the interval $(a, b)$. Then $f$ is said to be **concave up** [**concave down**] on $(a, b)$ if $f'$ is increasing [decreasing] on $(a, b)$.

*Remember:* If $f$ is concave up on an interval, then, geometrically, its graph is bending upward there. If $f$ is concave down, then its graph is bending downward.

Since $f'$ is increasing when its derivative $f''(x)$ is positive, and $f'$ is decreasing when $f''(x)$ is negative, we can state the following rule:

## RULE 1   Criteria for Concavity

Let $f'$ be differentiable on the interval $(a, b)$. If $f''(x) > 0$ for all $x$ in $(a, b)$, then $f$ is concave up on $(a, b)$. If $f''(x) < 0$ for all $x$ in $(a, b)$, then $f$ is concave down on $(a, b)$.

A function $f$ is also said to be concave up at a point $c$ if there exists an open interval around $c$ on which $f$ is concave up. In fact, for the functions that we will consider, if $f''(c) > 0$, then $f$ is concave up at $c$. Similarly, $f$ is concave down at $c$ if $f''(c) < 0$.

### ● EXAMPLE 1 Testing for Concavity

*Determine where the given function is concave up and where it is concave down.*

**a.** $y = f(x) = (x-1)^3 + 1$.

Solution: To apply Rule 1, we must examine the signs of $y''$. Now, $y' = 3(x-1)^2$, so

$$y'' = 6(x-1)$$

Thus, $f$ is concave up when $6(x-1) > 0$, that is, when $x > 1$. And $f$ is concave down when $6(x-1) < 0$, that is, when $x < 1$. We now use a sign chart for $f''$ (together with an interpretation line for $f$) to organize our findings. (See Figure 13.32.)

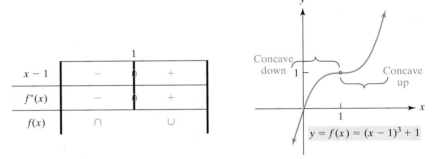

**FIGURE 13.32**  Sign chart for $f''$ and concavity for $f(x) = (x-1)^3 + 1$.

**b.** $y = x^2$.

Solution: We have $y' = 2x$ and $y'' = 2$. Because $y''$ is always positive, the graph of $y = x^2$ must always be concave up, as in Figure 13.29(a). The graph cannot appear as in Figure 13.29(b), for that curve is sometimes concave down.

NOW WORK PROBLEM 1 ●●

A point on a graph where concavity changes from concave down to concave up, or vice versa, such as $(1, 1)$ in Figure 13.32, is called an *inflection point* or a *point of inflection*. Around such a point, the sign of $f''(x)$ goes from $-$ to $+$ or from $+$ to $-$. More precisely, we have the following definition:

---

The definition of an inflection point implies that $a$ is in the domain of $f$.

### DEFINITION
A function $f$ has an ***inflection point*** at $a$ if and only if $f$ is continuous at $a$ and $f$ changes concavity at $a$.

---

To test a function for concavity and inflection points, first find the values of $x$ where $f''(x)$ is 0 or not defined. These values of $x$ determine intervals. On each interval, determine whether $f''(x) > 0$ ($f$ is concave up) or $f''(x) < 0$ ($f$ is concave down). If concavity changes around one of these $x$-values and $f$ is continuous there, then $f$ has an inflection point at this $x$-value. The continuity requirement implies that the $x$-value must be in the domain of the function. In brief, a *candidate* for an inflection point must satisfy two conditions:

1. $f''$ must be 0 or fail to exist at that point.
2. $f$ must be continuous at that point.

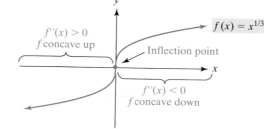

FIGURE 13.33    Inflection point for $f(x) = x^{1/3}$.

The candidate *will be* an inflection point if concavity changes around it. For example, if $f(x) = x^{1/3}$, then $f'(x) = \frac{1}{3}x^{-2/3}$ and

$$f''(x) = -\frac{2}{9}x^{-5/3} = -\frac{2}{9x^{5/3}}$$

Because $f''$ does not exist at 0, but $f$ is continuous at 0, there is a candidate for an inflection point at 0. If $x > 0$, then $f''(x) < 0$, so $f$ is concave down for $x > 0$; if $x < 0$, then $f''(x) > 0$, so $f$ is concave up for $x < 0$. Because concavity changes at 0, there is an inflection point there. (See Figure 13.33.)

### ● EXAMPLE 2    Concavity and Inflection Points

*Test $y = 6x^4 - 8x^3 + 1$ for concavity and inflection points.*

**Solution:** We have

$$y' = 24x^3 - 24x^2$$
$$y'' = 72x^2 - 48x = 24x(3x - 2)$$

|   |   | 0 |   | 2/3 |   |
|---|---|---|---|---|---|
| $x$ | $-$ | $0$ | $+$ | | $+$ |
| $3x - 2$ | $-$ | | $-$ | $0$ | $+$ |
| $y''$ | $+$ | $0$ | $-$ | $0$ | $+$ |
| $y$ | $\cup$ | | $\cap$ | | $\cup$ |

FIGURE 13.34    Sign chart of $y'' = 24x(3x - 2)$ for $y = 6x^4 - 8x^3 + 1$.

To find where $y'' = 0$, we set each factor in $y''$ equal to 0. This gives $x = 0, \frac{2}{3}$. We also note that $y''$ is never undefined. Thus, there are three intervals to consider, as recorded on the top of the sign chart in Figure 13.34. Since $y$ is continuous at 0 and $\frac{2}{3}$, these points are candidates for inflection points. Having completed the sign chart, we see that concavity changes at 0 and at $\frac{2}{3}$. Thus these candidates are indeed inflection points. (See Figure 13.35.) In summary, the curve is concave up on $(-\infty, 0)$ and $(\frac{2}{3}, \infty)$ and is concave down on $(0, \frac{2}{3})$. Inflection points occur at 0 and at $\frac{2}{3}$. These points are $(0, y(0)) = (0, 1)$ and $(\frac{2}{3}, y(\frac{2}{3})) = (\frac{2}{3}, -\frac{5}{27})$.

NOW WORK PROBLEM 13    ●●

As we did in the analysis of increasing and decreasing, so we must in concavity analysis consider also those points $a$ that are not in the domain of $f$ but that are near points in the domain of $f$. The next example will illustrate.

### ● EXAMPLE 3    A Change in Concavity with No Inflection Point

*Discuss concavity and find all inflection points for $f(x) = \dfrac{1}{x}$.*

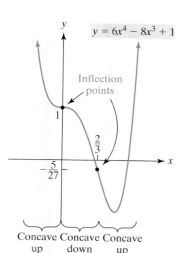

FIGURE 13.35    Graph of $y = 6x^4 - 8x^3 + 1$.

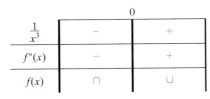

| $\dfrac{1}{x^3}$ | $-$ | $+$ |
|---|---|---|
| $f''(x)$ | $-$ | $+$ |
| $f(x)$ | $\cap$ | $\cup$ |

**FIGURE 13.36**    Sign chart for $f''(x)$.

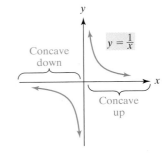

**FIGURE 13.37**    Graph of $y = \dfrac{1}{x}$.

**Solution:** Since $f(x) = x^{-1}$   for $x \neq 0$,

$$f'(x) = -x^{-2}   \text{ for } x \neq 0$$

$$f''(x) = 2x^{-3} = \frac{2}{x^3}   \text{ for } x \neq 0$$

We see that $f''(x)$ is never 0 but it is not defined when $x = 0$. Since $f$ is not continuous at 0, we conclude that 0 is not a candidate for an inflection point. Thus, the given function has no inflection point. However, 0 must be considered in an analysis of concavity. See the sign chart in Figure 13.36; note that we have a thick verical line at 0 to indicate that 0 is not in the domain of $f$ and cannot correspond to an inflection point. If $x > 0$, then $f''(x) > 0$; if $x < 0$, then $f''(x) < 0$. Hence, $f$ is concave up on $(0, \infty)$ and concave down on $(-\infty, 0)$. (See Figure 13.37.) Although concavity changes around $x = 0$, there is no inflection point there because $f$ is not continuous at 0 (nor is it even defined there).

**CAUTION**

A candidate for an inflection point may not necessarily be an inflection point. For example, if $f(x) = x^4$, then $f''(x) = 12x^2$ and $f''(0) = 0$. But $f''(x) > 0$ both when $x < 0$ and when $x > 0$. Thus, concavity does not change, and there are no inflection points. (See Figure 13.38.)

NOW WORK PROBLEM 23

## Curve Sketching

### EXAMPLE 4    Curve Sketching

*Sketch the graph of $y = 2x^3 - 9x^2 + 12x$.*

**Solution:**

***Intercepts***    If $x = 0$, then $y = 0$. Setting $y = 0$ gives $0 = x(2x^2 - 9x + 12)$. Clearly, $x = 0$ is a solution, and using the quadratic formula on $2x^2 - 9x + 12 = 0$ gives no real roots. Thus, the only intercept is $(0, 0)$. In fact, since $2x^2 - 9x + 12$ is a continuous function whose value at 0 is $2 \cdot 0^2 - 9 \cdot 0 + 12 = 12 > 0$, we conclude that $2x^2 - 9x + 12 > 0$ for all $x$, which gives the sign chart Figure 13.39 for $y$.

Note that this chart tells us the graph of $y = 2x^3 - 9x^2 + 12x$ is confined to the third and first quadrants of the $xy$-plane.

***Symmetry***    None.

***Maxima and Minima***    We have

$$y' = 6x^2 - 18x + 12 = 6(x^2 - 3x + 2) = 6(x - 1)(x - 2)$$

The critical values are $x = 1, 2$, so these and the factors $x - 1$ and $x - 2$ determine the sign chart of $y'$ (Figure 13.40).

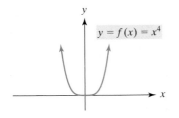

**FIGURE 13.38**    Graph of $f(x) = x^4$.

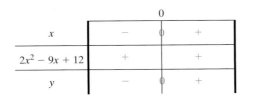

| | 0 | |
|---|---|---|
| $x$ | $-$ | $+$ |
| $2x^2 - 9x + 12$ | $+$ | $+$ |
| $y$ | $-$ | $+$ |

**FIGURE 13.39**    Sign chart for $y$.

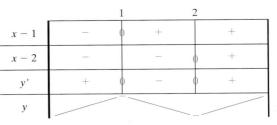

| | | 1 | | 2 | |
|---|---|---|---|---|---|
| $x - 1$ | $-$ | 0 | $+$ | | $+$ |
| $x - 2$ | $-$ | | $-$ | 0 | $+$ |
| $y'$ | $+$ | 0 | $-$ | 0 | $+$ |
| $y$ | | | | | |

**FIGURE 13.40**    Sign chart of $y' = 6(x - 1)(x - 2)$.

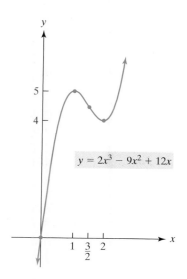

| $2x - 3$ | $-$ | $\underset{3/2}{0}$ | $+$ |
|---|---|---|---|
| $y''$ | $-$ | $0$ | $+$ |
| $y$ | $\cap$ | | $\cup$ |

**FIGURE 13.41** Sign chart of $y''$.

From the sign chart for $y'$ we see that there is a relative maximum at 1 and a relative minimum at 2. Note too that the bottom line of Figure 13.40, together with that of Figure 13.39, comes close to determining a precise graph of $y = 2x^3 - 9x^2 + 12x$. Of course, it will help to know the relative maximum $y(1) = 5$, which occurs at 1, and the relative minimum $y(2) = 4$, which occurs at 2, so that in addition to the intercept $(0, 0)$ we will actually plot also $(1, 5)$ and $(2, 4)$.

**Concavity**

$$y'' = 12x - 18 = 6(2x - 3)$$

Setting $y'' = 0$ gives a possible inflection point at $x = \frac{3}{2}$ from which we construct the simple sign chart for $y''$ in Figure 13.41.

Since concavity changes at $x = \frac{3}{2}$, at which point $f$ is certainly continuous, there is an inflection point at $\frac{3}{2}$.

**Discussion**  We know the coordinates of three of the important points on the graph. The only other important point from our perspective is the inflection point, and since $y(3/2) = 2(3/2)^3 - 9(3/2)^2 + 12(3/2) = 9/2$ the inflection point is $(3/2, 9/2)$.

We plot the four points noted above and observe from all three sign charts jointly that the curve increases through the third quadrant and passes through $(0, 0)$, all the while concave down until a relative maximum is attained at $(1, 5)$. The curve then falls until it reaches a relative minimum at $(2, 4)$. However, along the way the concavity changes at $(3/2, 9/2)$ from concave down to concave up and remains so for the rest of the curve. After $(2, 4)$ the curve increases through the first quadrant. The curve is shown in Figure 13.42.

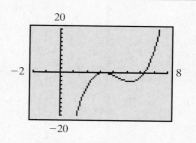

**FIGURE 13.42**  Graph of $y = 2x^3 - 9x^2 + 12x$.

NOW WORK PROBLEM 39

## TECHNOLOGY

Suppose that you need to find the inflection points for

$$f(x) = \frac{1}{20}x^5 - \frac{17}{16}x^4 + \frac{273}{32}x^3 - \frac{4225}{128}x^2 + \frac{750}{4}$$

The second derivative of $f$ is given by

$$f''(x) = x^3 - \frac{51}{4}x^2 + \frac{819}{16}x - \frac{4225}{64}$$

Here the zeros of $f''$ are not obvious. Thus, we will graph $f''$ using a graphing calculator. (See Figure 13.43.) We find that the zeros of $f''$ are 3.25 and 6.25. Around $x = 6.25$, $f''(x)$ goes from negative to positive values. Therefore, at $x = 6.25$, there is an inflection point. Around $x = 3.25$, $f''(x)$ does not change sign, so no inflection point exists at $x = 3.25$. Comparing our results with the graph of $f$ in Figure 13.44, we see that everything checks out.

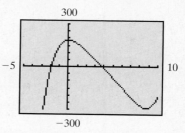

**FIGURE 13.43**  Graph of $f''$; zeros of $f''$ are 3.25 and 6.25.

**FIGURE 13.44**  Graph of $f$; inflection point at $x = 6.25$, but not at $x = 3.25$.

# Problems 13.3

*In Problems 1–6, a function and its second derivative are given. Determine the concavity of f and x-values where points of inflection occur.*

*1. $f(x) = 2x^4 + 3x^3 + 2x - 3$; $f''(x) = 6x(4x + 3)$

2. $f(x) = \dfrac{x^5}{20} + \dfrac{x^4}{4} - 2x^2$; $f''(x) = (x-1)(x+2)^2$

3. $f(x) = \dfrac{2 + x - x^2}{x^2 - 2x + 1}$; $f''(x) = \dfrac{2(7-x)}{(x-1)^4}$

4. $f(x) = \dfrac{x^2}{(x-1)^2}$; $f''(x) = \dfrac{2(2x+1)}{(x-1)^4}$

5. $f(x) = \dfrac{x^2 + 1}{x^2 - 2}$; $f''(x) = \dfrac{6(3x^2 + 2)}{(x^2 - 2)^3}$

6. $f(x) = x\sqrt{4 - x^2}$; $f''(x) = \dfrac{2x(x^2 - 6)}{(4 - x^2)^{3/2}}$

*In Problems 7–34, determine concavity and the x-values where points of inflection occur. Do not sketch the graphs.*

7. $y = -2x^2 + 4x$      8. $y = -74x^2 + 19x - 37$

9. $y = 4x^3 + 12x^2 - 12x$     10. $y = x^3 - 6x^2 + 9x + 1$

11. $y = 2x^3 - 5x^2 + 5x - 2$     12. $y = x^4 - 8x^2 - 6$

*13. $y = 2x^4 - 48x^2 + 7x + 3$     14. $y = -\dfrac{x^4}{4} + \dfrac{9x^2}{2} + 2x$

15. $y = 2x^{1/5}$     16. $y = \dfrac{7}{x^3}$

17. $y = \dfrac{x^4}{2} + \dfrac{19x^3}{6} - \dfrac{7x^2}{2} + x + 5$

18. $y = -\dfrac{5}{2}x^4 - \dfrac{1}{6}x^3 + \dfrac{1}{2}x^2 + \dfrac{1}{3}x - \dfrac{2}{5}$

19. $y = \dfrac{1}{20}x^5 - \dfrac{1}{4}x^4 + \dfrac{1}{6}x^3 - \dfrac{1}{2}x - \dfrac{2}{3}$

20. $y = \dfrac{1}{10}x^5 - 3x^3 + 17x + 43$

21. $y = \dfrac{1}{30}x^6 - \dfrac{7}{12}x^4 + 5x^2 + 2x - 1$

22. $y = x^6 - 3x^4$     *23. $y = \dfrac{x+1}{x-1}$

24. $y = 1 - \dfrac{1}{x^2}$     25. $y = \dfrac{x^2}{x^2 + 1}$

26. $y = \dfrac{4x^2}{x+3}$     27. $y = \dfrac{21x + 40}{6(x+3)^2}$

28. $y = 3(x^2 - 2)^2$     29. $y = 5e^x$

30. $y = e^x - e^{-x}$     31. $y = 3xe^x$

32. $y = xe^{x^2}$     33. $y = \dfrac{\ln x}{2x}$

34. $y = \dfrac{x^2 + 1}{3e^x}$

*In Problems 35–62, determine intervals on which the function is increasing, decreasing, concave up, and concave down; relative maxima and minima; inflection points; symmetry; and those intercepts that can be obtained conveniently. Then sketch the graph.*

35. $y = x^2 - x - 6$     36. $y = x^2 + 2$

37. $y = 5x - 2x^2$     38. $y = x - x^2 + 2$

*39. $y = x^3 - 9x^2 + 24x - 19$     40. $y = x^3 - 25x^2$

41. $y = \dfrac{x^3}{3} - 4x$     42. $y = x^3 - 6x^2 + 9x$

43. $y = x^3 - 3x^2 + 3x - 3$     44. $y = 2x^3 + \dfrac{5}{2}x^2 + 2x$

45. $y = 4x^3 - 3x^4$     46. $y = -x^3 + 2x^2 - x + 4$

47. $y = -2 + 12x - x^3$     48. $y = (3 + 2x)^3$

49. $y = 2x^3 - 6x^2 + 6x - 2$     50. $y = \dfrac{x^5}{100} - \dfrac{x^4}{20}$

51. $y = 5x - x^5$     52. $y = x^2(x-1)^2$

53. $y = 3x^4 - 4x^3 + 1$     54. $y = 3x^5 - 5x^3$

55. $y = 4x^2 - x^4$     56. $y = x^4 - x^2$

57. $y = x^{1/3}(x - 8)$     58. $y = (x-1)^2(x+2)^2$

59. $y = 4x^{1/3} + x^{4/3}$     60. $y = (x+1)\sqrt{x+4}$

61. $y = 6x^{2/3} - \dfrac{x}{2}$     62. $y = 5x^{2/3} - x^{5/3}$

63. Sketch the graph of a continuous function $f$ such that $f(2) = 4$, $f'(2) = 0$, $f'(x) < 0$ if $x < 2$, and $f''(x) > 0$ if $x > 2$.

64. Sketch the graph of a continuous function $f$ such that $f(4) = 4$, $f'(4) = 0$, $f''(x) < 0$ for $x < 4$, and $f''(x) > 0$ for $x > 4$.

65. Sketch the graph of a continuous function $f$ such that $f(1) = 1$, $f'(1) = 0$, and $f''(x) < 0$ for all $x$.

66. Sketch the graph of a continuous function $f$ such that $f(3) = 4$, both $f'(x) > 0$ and $f''(x) > 0$ for $x < 3$, and both $f'(x) < 0$ and $f''(x) > 0$ for $x > 3$.

67. **Demand Equation** Show that the graph of the demand equation $p = \dfrac{100}{q + 2}$ is decreasing and concave up for $q > 0$.

68. **Average Cost** For the cost function
$$c = q^2 + 2q + 1$$
show that the graph of the average-cost function $\bar{c}$ is always concave up for $q > 0$.

69. **Species of Plants** The number of species of plants on a plot may depend on the size of the plot. For example, in Figure 13.45, we see that on 1-m$^2$ plots there are three species (A, B, and C on the left plot, A, B, and D on the right plot), and on a 2-m$^2$ plot there are four species (A, B, C, and D).

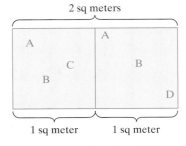

**FIGURE 13.45** Species of plants.

In a study of rooted plants in a certain geographic region,[7] it was determined that the average number of species, $S$, occurring on plots of size $A$ (in square meters) is given by

$$S = f(A) = 12\sqrt[4]{A} \quad 0 \le A \le 625$$

[7]Adapted from R. W. Poole, *An Introduction to Quantitative Ecology* (New York: McGraw-Hill Book Company, 1974).

Sketch the graph of $f$. (*Note:* Your graph should be rising and concave down. Thus, the number of species is increasing with respect to area, but at a decreasing rate.)

**70. Inferior Good** In a discussion of an inferior good, Persky[8] considers a function of the form

$$g(x) = e^{(U_0/A)}e^{-x^2/(2A)}$$

where $x$ is a quantity of a good, $U_0$ is a constant that represents utility, and $A$ is a positive constant. Persky claims that the graph of $g$ is concave down for $x < \sqrt{A}$ and concave up for $x > \sqrt{A}$. Verify this.

**71. Psychology** In a psychological experiment involving conditioned response,[9] subjects listened to four tones, denoted 0, 1, 2, and 3. Initially, the subjects were conditioned to tone 0 by receiving a shock whenever this tone was heard. Later, when each of the four tones (stimuli) were heard without shocks, the subjects' responses were recorded by means of a tracking device that measures galvanic skin reaction. The average response to each stimulus (without shock) was determined, and the results were plotted on a coordinate plane where the $x$- and $y$-axes represent the stimuli (0, 1, 2, 3) and the average galvanic responses, respectively. It was determined that the points fit a curve that is approximated by the graph of

$$y = 12.5 + 5.8(0.42)^x$$

Show that this function is decreasing and concave up.

**72. Entomology** In a study of the effects of food deprivation on hunger,[10] an insect was fed until its appetite was completely satisfied. Then it was deprived of food for $t$ hours (the deprivation period). At the end of this period, the insect was re-fed until its appetite was again completely satisfied. The weight $H$ (in grams) of the food that was consumed at this time was statistically found to be a function of $t$, where

$$H = 1.00[1 - e^{-(0.0464t + 0.0670)}]$$

Here $H$ is a measure of hunger. Show that $H$ is increasing with respect to $t$ and is concave down.

**73. Insect Dispersal** In an experiment on the dispersal of a particular insect,[11] a large number of insects are placed at a release point in an open field. Surrounding this point are traps that are placed in a concentric circular arrangement at a distance of 1 m, 2 m, 3 m, and so on from the release point. Twenty-four hours after the insects are released, the number of insects in each trap is counted. It is determined that at a distance of $r$ meters from the release point, the average number of insects contained in a trap is

$$n = f(r) = 0.1 \ln(r) + \frac{7}{r} - 0.8 \quad 1 \le r \le 10$$

(a) Show that the graph of $f$ is always falling and concave up. (b) Sketch the graph of $f$. (c) When $r = 5$, at what rate is the average number of insects in a trap decreasing with respect to distance?

**74.** Graph $y = -0.35x^3 + 4.1x^2 + 8.3x - 7.4$, and from the graph determine the number of (a) relative maximum points, (b) relative minimum points, and (c) inflection points.

**75.** Graph $y = x^5(x - 2.3)$, and from the graph determine the number of inflection points. Now, prove that for any $a \ne 0$, the curve $y = x^5(x - a)$ has two points of inflection.

**76.** Graph $y = 1 - 2^{-x^2}$, and from the graph determine the number of inflection points.

**77.** Graph the curve $y = x^3 - 2x^2 + x + 3$, and also graph the tangent line to the curve at $x = 2$. Around $x = 2$, does the curve lie above or below the tangent line? From your observation determine the concavity at $x = 2$.

**78.** If $f(x) = 2x^3 + 3x^2 - 6x + 1$, find $f'(x)$ and $f''(x)$. Note that where $f'$ has a relative minimum, $f$ changes its direction of bending. Why?

**79.** If $f(x) = x^6 + 3x^5 - 4x^4 + 2x^2 + 1$, find the $x$-values (rounded to two decimal places) of the inflection points of $f$.

**80.** If $f(x) = \dfrac{x+1}{x^2+1}$, find the $x$-values (rounded to two decimal places) of the inflection points of $f$.

---

OBJECTIVE

To locate relative extrema by applying the second-derivative test.

# 13.4 The Second-Derivative Test

The second derivative can be used to test certain critical values for relative extrema. Observe in Figure 13.46 that at $a$, there is a horizontal tangent; that is, $f'(a) = 0$. Furthermore, around $a$, the function is concave up (that is, $f''(a) > 0$). This leads us to conclude that there is a relative minimum at $a$. On the other hand, around $b$, the function is concave down (that is, $f''(b) < 0$). Because the tangent line is horizontal at $b$, we conclude that a relative maximum exists there. This technique of examining the second derivative at points where the first derivative is 0 is called the *second-derivative test* for relative extrema.

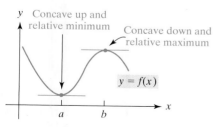

**FIGURE 13.46** Relating concavity to relative extrema.

[8]A. L. Persky, "An Inferior Good and a Novel Indifference Map," *The American Economist* XXIX, no. 1 (1985), 67–69.

[9]Adapted from C. I. Hovland, "The Generalization of Conditioned Responses: I. The Sensory Generalization of Conditioned Responses with Varying Frequencies of Tone," *Journal of General Psychology*, 17 (1937), 125–48.

[10]C. S. Holling, "The Functional Response of Invertebrate Predators to Prey Density," *Memoirs of the Entomological Society of Canada*, no. 48 (1966).

[11]Adapted from Poole, op. cit.

### Second-Derivative Test for Relative Extrema

Suppose $f'(a) = 0$.

If $f''(a) < 0$, then $f$ has a relative maximum at $a$.

If $f''(a) > 0$, then $f$ has a relative minimum at $a$.

We want to emphasize that *the second-derivative test does* not *apply when* $f''(a) = 0$. If both $f'(a) = 0$ and $f''(a) = 0$, then there may be a relative maximum, a relative minimum, or neither, at $a$. In such cases, the first-derivative test should be used to analyze what is happening at $a$. (Also, the second-derivative test does not apply when $f'(a)$ does not exist.)

### ● EXAMPLE 1    Second-Derivative Test

*Test the following for relative maxima and minima. Use the second-derivative test, if possible.*

**a.** $y = 18x - \frac{2}{3}x^3$.

Solution:

$$y' = 18 - 2x^2 = 2(9 - x^2) = 2(3 + x)(3 - x)$$

$$y'' = -4x \qquad \left(\text{taking } \frac{d}{dx} \text{ of } 18 - 2x^2\right)$$

Solving $y' = 0$ gives the critical values $x = \pm 3$.

$$\text{If } x = 3, \quad \text{then } y'' = -4(3) = -12 < 0.$$

There is a relative maximum when $x = 3$.

$$\text{If } x = -3, \quad \text{then } y'' = -4(-3) = 12 > 0.$$

There is a relative minimum when $x = -3$. (Refer back to Figure 13.4.)

**b.** $y = 6x^4 - 8x^3 + 1$.

**CAUTION**

Although the second-derivative test can be very useful, do not depend entirely on it. Not only may the test fail to apply, but also it may be awkward to find the second derivative.

Solution:

$$y' = 24x^3 - 24x^2 = 24x^2(x - 1)$$
$$y'' = 72x^2 - 48x$$

Solving $y' = 0$ gives the critical values $x = 0, 1$. We see that

$$\text{if } x = 0, \quad \text{then } y'' = 0$$

and

$$\text{if } x = 1, \quad \text{then } y'' > 0$$

By the second-derivative test, there is a relative minimum when $x = 1$. We cannot apply the test when $x = 0$ because $y'' = 0$ there. To analyze what is happening at 0, we turn to the first-derivative test:

$$\text{If } x < 0, \quad \text{then } y' < 0.$$

$$\text{If } 0 < x < 1, \quad \text{then } y' < 0.$$

Thus, no maximum or minimum exists when $x = 0$. (Refer back to Figure 13.35.)

NOW WORK PROBLEM 5 ●●●

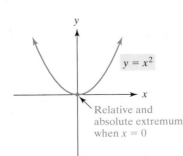

**FIGURE 13.47** Exactly one relative extremum implies an absolute extremum.

If a continuous function has *exactly one* relative extremum on an interval, it can be shown that the relative extremum must also be an *absolute* extremum on the interval. To illustrate, in Figure 13.47 the function $y = x^2$ has a relative minimum when $x = 0$, and there are no other relative extrema. Since $y = x^2$ is continuous, this relative minimum is also an absolute minimum for the function.

### ● EXAMPLE 2   Absolute Extrema

*If* $y = f(x) = x^3 - 3x^2 - 9x + 5$, *determine when absolute extrema occur on the interval* $(0, \infty)$.

**Solution:** We have

$$f'(x) = 3x^2 - 6x - 9 = 3(x^2 - 2x - 3)$$
$$= 3(x + 1)(x - 3)$$

The only critical value on the interval $(0, \infty)$ is 3. Applying the second-derivative test at this point gives

$$f''(x) = 6x - 6$$
$$f''(3) = 6(3) - 6 = 12 > 0$$

Thus, there is a relative minimum at 3. Since this is the only relative extremum on $(0, \infty)$ and $f$ is continuous there, we conclude by our previous discussion that there is an *absolute* minimum value at 3; this value is $f(3) = -22$. (See Figure 13.48.)

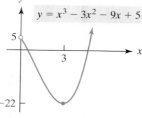

**FIGURE 13.48** On $(0, \infty)$, there is an absolute minimum at 3.

NOW WORK PROBLEM 3 ●●●

## Problems 13.4

*In Problems 1–14, test for relative maxima and minima. Use the second-derivative test, if possible. In Problems 1–4, state whether the relative extrema are also absolute extrema.*

**1.** $y = x^2 - 5x + 6$
**2.** $y = 5x^2 + 20x + 2$
*3.** $y = -4x^2 + 2x - 8$
**4.** $y = 3x^2 - 5x + 6$
*5.** $y = \frac{1}{3}x^3 + 2x^2 - 5x + 1$
**6.** $y = x^3 - 12x + 1$
**7.** $y = -x^3 + 3x^2 + 1$
**8.** $y = x^4 - 2x^2 + 4$
**9.** $y = 7 - 2x^4$
**10.** $y = -2x^7$
**11.** $y = 81x^5 - 5x$
**12.** $y = \frac{55}{3}x^3 - x^2 - 21x - 3$
**13.** $y = (x^2 + 7x + 10)^2$
**14.** $y = -x^3 + 3x^2 + 9x - 2$

OBJECTIVE

To determine horizontal and vertical asymptotes for a curve and to sketch the graphs of functions having asymptotes.

## 13.5 Asymptotes

### Vertical Asymptotes

In this section, we conclude our discussion of curve-sketching techniques by investigating functions having *asymptotes*. An asymptote is a line that a curve approaches arbitrarily closely. For example, in each part of Figure 13.49, the dashed line $x = a$ is an asymptote. But to be precise about it, we need to make use of infinite limits. In Figure 13.49(a), notice that as $x \to a^+$, $f(x)$ becomes positively infinite:

$$\lim_{x \to a^+} f(x) = \infty$$

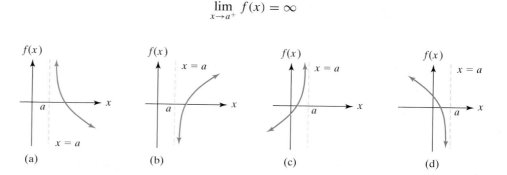

(a)   (b)   (c)   (d)

**FIGURE 13.49**   Vertical asymptotes $x = a$.

In Figure 13.49(b), as $x \to a^+$, $f(x)$ becomes negatively infinite:

$$\lim_{x \to a^+} f(x) = -\infty$$

In Figure. 13.49(c) and (d), we have

$$\lim_{x \to a^-} f(x) = \infty \quad \text{and} \quad \lim_{x \to a^-} f(x) = -\infty$$

respectively.

Loosely speaking, we can say that each graph in Figure 13.49 "blows up" around the dashed vertical line $x = a$, in the sense that a one-sided limit of $f(x)$ at $a$ is either $\infty$ or $-\infty$. The line $x = a$ is called a *vertical asymptote* for the graph. A vertical asymptote is not part of the graph but is a useful aid in sketching it because part of the graph approaches the asymptote. Because of the explosion around $x = a$, the function is *not* continuous at $a$.

### DEFINITION

The line $x = a$ is a ***vertical asymptote*** for the graph of the function $f$ if and only if at least one of the following is true:

$$\lim_{x \to a^+} f(x) = \pm\infty$$

or

$$\lim_{x \to a^-} f(x) = \pm\infty$$

To determine vertical asymptotes, we must find values of $x$ around which $f(x)$ increases or decreases without bound. For a rational function (a quotient of two polynomials) *expressed in lowest terms* these $x$-values are precisely those for which the denominator is zero but the numerator is not zero. For example, consider the rational function

$$f(x) = \frac{3x - 5}{x - 2}$$

When $x$ is 2, the denominator is 0, but the numerator is not. If $x$ is slightly larger than 2, then $x - 2$ is both close to 0 and positive, and $3x - 5$ is close to 1. Thus, $(3x - 5)/(x - 2)$ is very large, so

$$\lim_{x \to 2^+} \frac{3x - 5}{x - 2} = \infty$$

**CAUTION**

To see that the proviso about *lowest terms* is necessary, observe that
$$f(x) = \frac{3x - 5}{x - 2} = \frac{(3x - 5)(x - 2)}{(x - 2)^2} \text{ so}$$
that $x = 2$ is a vertical asymptote of $\frac{(3x - 5)(x - 2)}{(x - 2)^2}$, and here 2 makes both the denominator *and* the numerator 0.

This limit is sufficient to conclude that the line $x = 2$ is a vertical asymptote. Because we are ultimately interested in the behavior of a function around a vertical asymptote, it is worthwhile to examine what happens to this function as $x$ approaches 2 from the left. If $x$ is slightly less than 2, then $x - 2$ is very close to 0 but negative, and $3x - 5$ is close to 1. Hence, $(3x - 5)/(x - 2)$ is "very negative," so

$$\lim_{x \to 2^-} \frac{3x - 5}{x - 2} = -\infty$$

We conclude that the function increases without bound as $x \to 2^+$ and decreases without bound as $x \to 2^-$. The graph appears in Figure 13.50.

In summary, we have a rule for vertical asymptotes.

**Vertical-Asymptote Rule for Rational Functions**

Suppose that

$$f(x) = \frac{P(x)}{Q(x)}$$

where $P$ and $Q$ are polynomial functions and the quotient is in lowest terms. The line $x = a$ is a vertical asymptote for the graph of $f$ if and only if $Q(a) = 0$ and $P(a) \neq 0$.

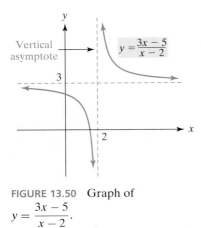

**FIGURE 13.50** Graph of $y = \dfrac{3x - 5}{x - 2}$.

(It might be thought here that "lowest terms" rules out the possibility of a value *a* making *both* denominator *and* numerator 0, but consider the rational function $\dfrac{(3x-5)(x-2)}{(x-2)}$. Here we cannot divide numerator and denominator by $x-2$, to obtain the polynomial $3x - 5$, because the domain of the latter is not equal to the domain of the former.)

### ● EXAMPLE 1  Finding Vertical Asymptotes

*Determine vertical asymptotes for the graph of*

$$f(x) = \frac{x^2 - 4x}{x^2 - 4x + 3}$$

**Solution:** Since *f* is a rational function, the vertical-asymptote rule applies. Writing

$$f(x) = \frac{x(x-4)}{(x-3)(x-1)} \quad \text{(factoring)}$$

makes it clear that the denominator is 0 when *x* is 3 or 1. Neither of these values makes the numerator 0. Thus, the lines $x = 3$ and $x = 1$ are vertical asymptotes. (See Figure 13.51.)

NOW WORK PROBLEM 1 ●●●

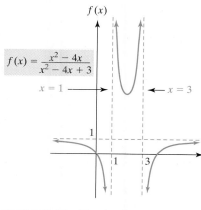

**FIGURE 13.51**  Graph of $f(x) = \dfrac{x^2 - 4x}{x^2 - 4x + 3}$.

Although the vertical-asymptote rule guarantees that the lines $x = 3$ and $x = 1$ are vertical asymptotes, it does not indicate the precise nature of the "blow-up" around these lines. A precise analysis requires the use of one-sided limits.

### Horizontal and Oblique Asymptotes

A curve $y = f(x)$ may have other kinds of asymptote. In Figure 13.52(a), as *x* increases without bound ($x \to \infty$), the graph approaches the horizontal line $y = b$. That is,

$$\lim_{x \to \infty} f(x) = b$$

In Figure 13.52(b), as *x* becomes negatively infinite, the graph approaches the horizontal line $y = b$. That is,

$$\lim_{x \to -\infty} f(x) = b$$

In each case, the dashed line $y = b$ is called a *horizontal asymptote* for the graph. It is a horizontal line around which the graph "settles" either as $x \to \infty$ or as $x \to -\infty$.

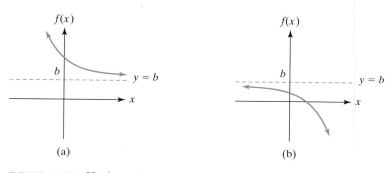

**FIGURE 13.52**  Horizontal asymptotes $y = b$.

In summary, we have the following definition:

### DEFINITION

Let *f* be a function. The line $y = b$ is a **horizontal asymptote** for the graph of *f* if and only if at least one of the following is true:

$$\lim_{x \to \infty} f(x) = b \quad \text{or} \quad \lim_{x \to -\infty} f(x) = b$$

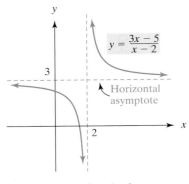

**FIGURE 13.53** Graph of $f(x) = \dfrac{3x - 5}{x - 2}$.

To test for horizontal asymptotes, we must find the limits of $f(x)$ as $x \to \infty$ and as $x \to -\infty$. To illustrate, we again consider

$$f(x) = \frac{3x - 5}{x - 2}$$

Since this is a rational function, we can use the procedures of Section 10.2 to find the limits. Because the dominant term in the numerator is $3x$ and the dominant term in the denominator is $x$, we have

$$\lim_{x \to \infty} \frac{3x - 5}{x - 2} = \lim_{x \to \infty} \frac{3x}{x} = \lim_{x \to \infty} 3 = 3$$

Thus, the line $y = 3$ is a horizontal asymptote. (See Figure 13.53.) Also,

$$\lim_{x \to -\infty} \frac{3x - 5}{x - 2} = \lim_{x \to -\infty} \frac{3x}{x} = \lim_{x \to -\infty} 3 = 3$$

Hence, the graph settles down near the horizontal line $y = 3$ both as $x \to \infty$ and as $x \to -\infty$.

● EXAMPLE 2   **Finding Horizontal Asymptotes**

*Find horizontal asymptotes for the graph of*

$$f(x) = \frac{x^2 - 4x}{x^2 - 4x + 3}$$

**Solution:**  We have

$$\lim_{x \to \infty} \frac{x^2 - 4x}{x^2 - 4x + 3} = \lim_{x \to \infty} \frac{x^2}{x^2} = \lim_{x \to \infty} 1 = 1$$

Therefore, the line $y = 1$ is a horizontal asymptote. The same result is obtained for $x \to -\infty$. (Refer back to Figure 13.51.)

NOW WORK PROBLEM 11   ●●●

Horizontal asymptotes arising from limits such as $\lim_{t \to \infty} f(t) = b$, where $t$ is thought of as *time,* can be important in business applications as expressions of long-term behavior. For example, in Section 9.3 we discussed long-term market share.

If we rewrite $\lim_{x \to \infty} f(x) = b$ as $\lim_{x \to \infty}(f(x) - b) = 0$, then another possibility is suggested. For it might be that the long-term behavior of $f$, while not constant, is linear. This leads us to the following:

**DEFINITION**

Let $f$ be a function. The line $y = mx + b$ is a **nonvertical asymptote** for the graph of $f$ if and only if at least one of the following is true:

$$\lim_{x \to \infty} (f(x) - (mx + b)) = 0 \quad \text{or} \quad \lim_{x \to -\infty} (f(x) - (mx + b)) = 0$$

Of course, if $m = 0$, then we have just repeated the definition of horizontal asymptote. But if $m \neq 0$ then $y = mx + b$ is the equation of a nonhorizontal (and nonvertical) line with slope $m$ that is sometimes described as *oblique.* Thus to say that $\lim_{x \to \infty}(f(x) - (mx + b)) = 0$ is to say that for large values of $x$, the graph settles down near the line $y = mx + b$, often called an *oblique asymptote* for the graph.

If $f(x) = \dfrac{P(x)}{Q(x)}$, where the degree of $P$ is one more than the degree of $Q$, then long division allows us to write $\dfrac{P(x)}{Q(x)} = (mx + b) + \dfrac{R(x)}{Q(x)}$, where $m \neq 0$ and where either $R(x)$ is the zero polynomial or the degree of $R$ is strictly less than the degree of $Q$. In this case, $y = mx + b$ will be an oblique asymptote for the graph of $f$. The next example will illustrate.

● EXAMPLE 3   **Finding an Oblique Asymptote**

*Find the oblique asyptote for the graph of the rational function*

$$y = f(x) = \frac{10x^2 + 9x + 5}{5x + 2}$$

**Solution:**  Since the degree of the numerator is 2, one greater than the degree of the denominator, we use long division to express

$$f(x) = \frac{10x^2 + 9x + 5}{5x + 2} = 2x + 1 + \frac{3}{5x + 2}$$

Thus

$$\lim_{x \to \pm\infty} (f(x) - (2x + 1)) = \lim_{x \to \pm\infty} \frac{3}{5x + 2} = 0$$

which shows that $y = 2x + 1$ is an oblique asymptote, in fact the only nonvertical asymptote, as we explain below. On the other hand, it is clear that $x = -\frac{2}{5}$ is a vertical asymptote—and the only one. (See Figure 13.54.)

NOW WORK PROBLEM 35 ●●

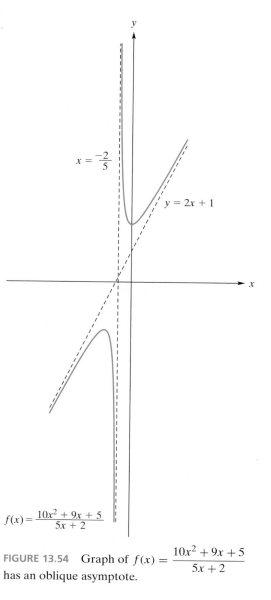

$x = \frac{-2}{5}$

$y = 2x + 1$

$f(x) = \dfrac{10x^2 + 9x + 5}{5x + 2}$

**FIGURE 13.54**   Graph of $f(x) = \dfrac{10x^2 + 9x + 5}{5x + 2}$ has an oblique asymptote.

A few remarks about asymptotes are appropriate now. With vertical asymptotes, we are examining the behavior of a graph around specific *x*-values. However, with nonvertical asymptotes we are examining the graph as *x* becomes unbounded. Although a graph may have numerous vertical asymptotes, it can have at most two different nonvertical asymptotes—possibly one for $x \to \infty$ and possibly one for $x \to -\infty$. If, for example, the graph has two horizontal asymptotes, then there can be no oblique asymptotes.

From Section 10.2, when the numerator of a rational function has degree greater than that of the denominator, no limit exists as $x \to \infty$ or $x \to -\infty$. From this observation, we conclude that *whenever the degree of the numerator of a rational function is greater than the degree of the denominator, the graph of the function cannot have a horizontal asymptote.* Similarly, it can be shown that if the degree of the numerator of a rational function is more than one greater than the degree of the denominator, the function cannot have an oblique asymptote.

### ● EXAMPLE 4  Finding Horizontal and Vertical Asymptotes

*Find vertical and horizontal asymptotes for the graph of the polynomial function*

$$y = f(x) = x^3 + 2x$$

**Solution:** We begin with vertical asymptotes. This is a rational function with denominator 1, which is never zero. By the vertical-asymptote rule, there are no vertical asymptotes. Because the degree of the numerator (3) is greater than the degree of the denominator (0), there are no horizontal asymptotes. However, let us examine the behavior of the graph of $f$ as $x \to \infty$ and $x \to -\infty$. We have

$$\lim_{x \to \infty} (x^3 + 2x) = \lim_{x \to \infty} x^3 = \infty$$

and

$$\lim_{x \to -\infty} (x^3 + 2x) = \lim_{x \to -\infty} x^3 = -\infty$$

Thus, as $x \to \infty$, the graph must extend indefinitely upward, and as $x \to -\infty$, the graph must extend indefinitely downward. (See Figure 13.55.)

NOW WORK PROBLEM 9 ●●

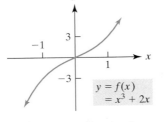

**FIGURE 13.55** Graph of $y = x^3 + 2x$ has neither horizontal nor vertical asymptotes.

The results in Example 3 can be generalized to any polynomial function:

A polynomial function of degree greater than 1 has no asymptotes.

### ● EXAMPLE 5  Finding Horizontal and Vertical Asymptotes

*Find horizontal and vertical asymptotes for the graph of $y = e^x - 1$.*

**Solution:** Testing for horizontal asymptotes, we let $x \to \infty$. Then $e^x$ increases without bound, so

$$\lim_{x \to \infty} (e^x - 1) = \infty$$

Thus, the graph does not settle down as $x \to \infty$. However, as $x \to -\infty$, we have $e^x \to 0$, so

$$\lim_{x \to -\infty} (e^x - 1) = \lim_{x \to -\infty} e^x - \lim_{x \to -\infty} 1 = 0 - 1 = -1$$

Therefore, the line $y = -1$ is a horizontal asymptote. The graph has no vertical asymptotes because $e^x - 1$ neither increases nor decreases without bound around any fixed value of *x*. (See Figure 13.56.)

NOW WORK PROBLEM 23 ●●

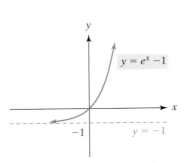

**FIGURE 13.56** Graph of $y = e^x - 1$ has a horizontal asymptote.

### Curve Sketching

In this section we show how to graph a function by making use of all the curve-sketching tools that we have developed.

● EXAMPLE 6    Curve Sketching

*Sketch the graph of* $y = \dfrac{1}{4 - x^2}$.

Solution:

***Intercepts***    When $x = 0$, $y = \frac{1}{4}$. If $y = 0$, then $0 = 1/(4 - x^2)$, which has no solution. Thus $(0, \frac{1}{4})$ is the only intercept. However, the factorization

$$y = \frac{1}{4 - x^2} = \frac{1}{(2 + x)(2 - x)}$$

allows us to construct the following sign chart for $y$, showing where the graph lies below the $x$-axis ($-$) and where it lies above the the $x$-axis ($+$).

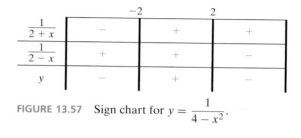

FIGURE 13.57    Sign chart for $y = \dfrac{1}{4 - x^2}$.

***Symmetry***    There is symmetry about the $y$-axis:

$$y(-x) = \frac{1}{4 - (-x)^2} = \frac{1}{4 - x^2} = y(x)$$

Since $y$ is a function of $x$ (and not the constant function 0), there can be no symmetry about the $x$-axis and hence no symmetry about the origin. Since $x$ is not a function of $y$ (and $y$ is a function of $x$), there can be no symmetry about $y = x$ either.

***Asymptotes***    From the factorization of $y$ above, we see that $x = -2$ and $x = 2$ are vertical asymptotes. Testing for horizontal asymptotes, we have

$$\lim_{x \to \pm\infty} \frac{1}{4 - x^2} = \lim_{x \to \pm\infty} \frac{1}{-x^2} = -\lim_{x \to \pm\infty} \frac{1}{x^2} = 0$$

Thus, $y = 0$ (the $x$-axis) is the only nonvertical asymptote.

***Maxima and Minima***    Since $y = (4 - x^2)^{-1}$,

$$y' = -1(4 - x^2)^{-2}(-2x) = \frac{2x}{(4 - x^2)^2}$$

We see that $y'$ is 0 when $x = 0$ and $y'$ is undefined when $x = \pm 2$. However, only 0 is a critical value, because $y$ is not defined at $\pm 2$. The sign chart for $y'$ follows. (See Figure 13.58.)

The sign chart shows clearly that the function is decreasing on $(-\infty, -2)$ and $(-2, 0)$, increasing on $(0, 2)$ and $(2, \infty)$, and that there is a relative minimum at 0.

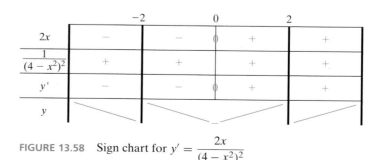

FIGURE 13.58    Sign chart for $y' = \dfrac{2x}{(4 - x^2)^2}$

***Concavity***

$$y'' = \frac{(4 - x^2)^2(2) - (2x)2(4 - x^2)(-2x)}{(4 - x^2)^4}$$

$$= \frac{2(4 - x^2)[(4 - x^2) - (2x)(-2x)]}{(4 - x^2)^4} = \frac{2(4 + 3x^2)}{(4 - x^2)^3}$$

Setting $y'' = 0$, we get no real roots. However, $y''$ is undefined when $x = \pm 2$. Although concavity may change around these values of $x$, the values cannot correspond to inflection points because they are not in the domain of the function. There are three intervals to test for concavity. (See the sign chart Figure 13.59.)

The sign chart shows that the graph is concave up on $(-2, 2)$ and concave down on $(-\infty, -2)$ and $(2, \infty)$.

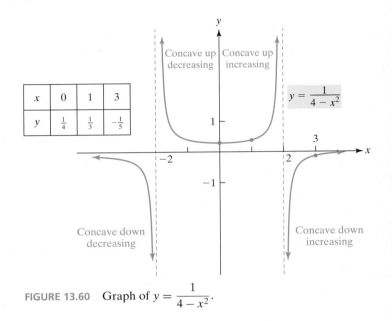

|               | | −2 | | 2 | |
|---------------|---|----|---|---|---|
| $4 + 3x^2$    | + | | + | | + |
| $\frac{1}{(4 - x^2)^3}$ | − | | + | | − |
| $y''$         | − | | + | | − |
| $y$           | ∩ | | ∪ | | ∩ |

**FIGURE 13.59**   Concavity analysis.

| $x$ | 0 | 1 | 3 |
|-----|---|---|---|
| $y$ | $\frac{1}{4}$ | $\frac{1}{3}$ | $-\frac{1}{5}$ |

**FIGURE 13.60**   Graph of $y = \dfrac{1}{4 - x^2}$.

***Discussion***   Only one point on the curve, $(0, 1/4)$, has arisen as a special point that must be plotted (both because it is an intercept and a local minimum). We might wish to plot a few more points as in the table in Figure 13.60, but note that any such extra points are only of value if they are on the same side of the $y$-axis (because of symmetry). Taking account of all the information gathered, we obtain the graph in Figure 13.60.

NOW WORK PROBLEM 31

● **EXAMPLE 7   Curve Sketching**

*Sketch the graph of* $y = \dfrac{4x}{x^2 + 1}$.

**Solution:**

***Intercepts***   When $x = 0$, $y = 0$; when $y = 0$, $x = 0$. Thus, $(0, 0)$ is the only intercept. Since the denominator of $y$ is always positive, we see that the sign of $y$ is that of $x$. Here we dispense with a sign chart for $y$. From the observations so far it follows that the graph proceeds from the third quadrant (negative $x$ and negative $y$), through $(0, 0)$ to the positive quadrant (positive $x$ and positive $y$).

***Symmetry***   There is symmetry about the origin:

$$y(-x) = \frac{4(-x)}{(-x)^2 + 1} = \frac{-4x}{x^2 + 1} = -y(x)$$

No other symmetry exists.

***Asymptotes*** The denominator of this rational function is never 0, so there are no vertical asymptotes. Testing for horizontal asymptotes, we have

$$\lim_{x \to \pm\infty} \frac{4x}{x^2 + 1} = \lim_{x \to \pm\infty} \frac{4x}{x^2} = \lim_{x \to \pm\infty} \frac{4}{x} = 0$$

Thus, $y = 0$ (the $x$-axis) is a horizontal asymptote and the only nonvertical asymptote.

***Maxima and Minima*** We have

$$y' = \frac{(x^2 + 1)(4) - 4x(2x)}{(x^2 + 1)^2} = \frac{4 - 4x^2}{(x^2 + 1)^2} = \frac{4(1 + x)(1 - x)}{(x^2 + 1)^2}$$

The critical values are $x = \pm 1$, so there are three intervals to consider in the sign chart. (See Figure 13.61.)

We see that $y$ is decreasing on $(-\infty, -1)$ and on $(1, \infty)$, increasing on $(-1, 1)$, with relative minimum at $-1$ and relative maximum at $1$. The relative minimum is $(-1, y(-1)) = (-1, -2)$; the relative maximum is $(1, y(1)) = (1, 2)$.

|  | | $-1$ | | $1$ | |
|---|---|---|---|---|---|
| $1 + x$ | $-$ | $0$ | $+$ | | $+$ |
| $1 - x$ | $+$ | | $+$ | $0$ | $-$ |
| $\dfrac{1}{(x^2 + 1)^2}$ | $+$ | | $+$ | | $+$ |
| $y'$ | $-$ | $0$ | $+$ | $0$ | $-$ |
| $y$ | | | | | |

**FIGURE 13.61** Sign chart for $y'$.

***Concavity*** Since $y' = \dfrac{4 - 4x^2}{(x^2 + 1)^2}$,

$$y'' = \frac{(x^2 + 1)^2(-8x) - (4 - 4x^2)(2)(x^2 + 1)(2x)}{(x^2 + 1)^4}$$

$$= \frac{8x(x^2 + 1)(x^2 - 3)}{(x^2 + 1)^4} = \frac{8x(x + \sqrt{3})(x - \sqrt{3})}{(x^2 + 1)^3}$$

Setting $y'' = 0$, we conclude that the possible points of inflection are when $x = \pm\sqrt{3}, 0$. There are four intervals to consider in the sign chart. (See Figure 13.62.)

|  | | $-\sqrt{3}$ | | $0$ | | $\sqrt{3}$ | |
|---|---|---|---|---|---|---|---|
| $x + \sqrt{3}$ | $-$ | $0$ | $+$ | | $+$ | | $+$ |
| $x$ | $-$ | | $-$ | $0$ | $+$ | | $+$ |
| $x - \sqrt{3}$ | $-$ | | $-$ | | $-$ | $0$ | $+$ |
| $\dfrac{1}{(x^2 + 1)^3}$ | $+$ | | $+$ | | $+$ | | $+$ |
| $y''$ | $-$ | $0$ | $+$ | $0$ | $-$ | $0$ | $+$ |
| $y$ | $\cap$ | | $\cup$ | | $\cap$ | | $\cup$ |

**FIGURE 13.62** Concavity analysis for $y = \dfrac{4x}{x^2 + 1}$.

Inflection points occur at $x = 0$ and $\pm\sqrt{3}$. The inflection points are

$$(-\sqrt{3}, y(\sqrt{3})) = (-\sqrt{3}, -\sqrt{3}) \quad (0, y(0)) = (0, 0) \quad (\sqrt{3}, y(\sqrt{3})) = (\sqrt{3}, \sqrt{3})$$

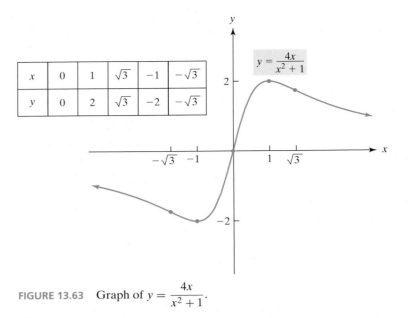

**FIGURE 13.63**    Graph of $y = \dfrac{4x}{x^2 + 1}$.

***Discussion***    After consideration of all of the preceding information, the graph of $y = 4x/(x^2 + 1)$ is given in Figure 13.63, together with a table of important points.

NOW WORK PROBLEM 39 ●●

## Problems 13.5

*In Problems 1–24, find the vertical asymptotes and the nonvertical asymptotes for the graphs of the functions. Do not sketch the graphs.*

*1. $y = \dfrac{x}{x - 1}$

2. $y = \dfrac{x + 1}{x}$

3. $f(x) = \dfrac{x + 2}{3x - 5}$

4. $y = \dfrac{2x + 1}{2x + 1}$

5. $y = \dfrac{4}{x}$

6. $y = 1 - \dfrac{2}{x^2}$

7. $y = \dfrac{1}{x^2 - 1}$

8. $y = \dfrac{x}{x^2 - 4}$

*9. $y = x^2 - 5x + 5$

10. $y = \dfrac{x^4}{x^3 - 4}$

*11. $f(x) = \dfrac{2x^2}{x^2 + x - 6}$

12. $f(x) = \dfrac{x^3}{5}$

13. $y = \dfrac{2x^2 + 3x + 1}{x^2 - 5}$

14. $y = \dfrac{2x^3 + 1}{3x(2x - 1)(4x - 3)}$

15. $y = \dfrac{2}{x - 3} + 5$

16. $f(x) = \dfrac{x^2 - 1}{2x^2 - 9x + 4}$

17. $f(x) = \dfrac{3 - x^4}{x^3 + x^2}$

18. $y = \dfrac{x^2 + 4x^3 + 6x^4}{3x^2}$

19. $y = \dfrac{x^2 - 3x - 4}{1 + 4x + 4x^2}$

20. $y = \dfrac{x^4 + 1}{1 - x^4}$

21. $y = \dfrac{9x^2 - 16}{2(3x + 4)^2}$

22. $y = \dfrac{2}{5} + \dfrac{2x}{12x^2 + 5x - 2}$

*23. $y = 2e^{x+2} + 4$

24. $f(x) = 12e^{-x}$

*In Problems 25–46, determine intervals on which the function is increasing, decreasing, concave up, and concave down; relative maxima and minima; inflection points; symmetry; vertical and nonvertical asymptotes; and those intercepts that can be obtained conveniently. Then sketch the curve.*

25. $y = \dfrac{3}{x}$

26. $y = \dfrac{2}{2x - 3}$

27. $y = \dfrac{x}{x - 1}$

28. $y = \dfrac{10}{\sqrt{x}}$

29. $y = x^2 + \dfrac{1}{x^2}$

30. $y = \dfrac{3x^2 - 5x - 1}{x - 2}$

*31. $y = \dfrac{1}{x^2 - 1}$

32. $y = \dfrac{1}{x^2 + 1}$

33. $y = \dfrac{1 + x}{1 - x}$

34. $y = \dfrac{1 + x}{x^2}$

*35. $y = \dfrac{x^2}{7x + 4}$

36. $y = \dfrac{x^3 + 1}{x}$

37. $y = \dfrac{9}{9x^2 - 6x - 8}$

38. $y = \dfrac{8x^2 + 3x + 1}{2x^2}$

*39. $y = \dfrac{3x + 1}{(3x - 2)^2}$

40. $y = \dfrac{3x + 1}{(6x + 5)^2}$

41. $y = \dfrac{x^2 - 1}{x^3}$

42. $y = \dfrac{3x}{(x - 2)^2}$

43. $y = x + \dfrac{1}{x + 1}$

44. $y = \dfrac{3x^4 + 1}{x^3}$

45. $y = \dfrac{-3x^2 + 2x - 5}{3x^2 - 2x - 1}$

46. $y = 3x + 2 + \dfrac{1}{3x + 2}$

47. Sketch the graph of a function $f$ such that $f(0) = 0$, there is a horizontal asymptote $y = 1$ for $x \to \pm\infty$, there is a vertical asymptote $x = 2$, both $f'(x) < 0$ and $f''(x) < 0$ for $x < 2$, and both $f'(x) < 0$ and $f''(x) > 0$ for $x > 2$.

48. Sketch the graph of a function $f$ such that $f(0) = 0$, there is a horizontal asymptote $y = 2$ for $x \to \pm\infty$, there is a vertical asymptote $x = -1$, both $f'(x) > 0$ and $f''(x) > 0$ for $x < -1$, and both $f'(x) > 0$ and $f''(x) < 0$ for $x > -1$.

49. Sketch the graph of a function $f$ such that $f(0) = 0$, there is a horizontal asymptote $y = 0$ for $x \to \pm\infty$, there are vertical asymptotes $x = -1$ and $x = 2$, $f'(x) < 0$ for $x < -1$ and $-1 < x < 2$, and $f''(x) < 0$ for $x > 2$.

**50.** Sketch the graph of a function $f$ such that $f(-2) = 2$, $f(0) = 0$, $f(2) = 0$, there is a horizontal asymptote $y = 1$ for $x \to \pm\infty$, there are vertical asymptotes $x = -1$ and $x = 1$, $f''(x) > 0$ for $x < -1$, and $f'(x) < 0$ for $-1 < x < 1$ and $f''(x) < 0$ for $1 < x$.

**51. Purchasing Power**    In discussing the time pattern of purchasing, Mantell and Sing[12] use the curve

$$y = \frac{x}{a + bx}$$

as a mathematical model. Find the asymptotes for their model.

**52.** Sketch the graphs of $y = 6 - 3e^{-x}$ and $y = 6 + 3e^{-x}$. Show that they are asymptotic to the same line. What is the equation of this line?

**53. Market for Product**    For a new product, the yearly number of thousand packages sold, $y$, $t$ years after its introduction is predicted to be given by

$$y = f(t) = 150 - 76e^{-t}$$

Show that $y = 150$ is a horizontal asymptote for the graph. This reveals that after the product is established with consumers, the market tends to be constant.

**54.** Graph $y = \dfrac{x^2 - 2}{x^3 + \frac{7}{2}x^2 + 12x + 1}$. From the graph, locate any horizontal or vertical asymptotes.

**55.** Graph $y = \dfrac{6x^3 - 2x^2 + 6x - 1}{3x^3 - 2x^2 - 18x + 12}$. From the graph, locate any horizontal or vertical asymptotes.

**56.** Graph $y = \dfrac{\ln(x + 4)}{x^2 - 8x + 5}$ in the standard window. The graph suggests that there are two vertical asymptotes of the form $x = k$, where $k > 0$. Also, it appears that the graph "begins" near $x = -4$. As $x \to -4^+$, $\ln(x + 4) \to -\infty$ and $x^2 - 8x + 5 \to 53$. Thus, $\lim_{x \to 4^+} y = -\infty$. This gives the vertical asymptote $x = -4$. So, in reality, there are *three* vertical asymptotes. Use the zoom feature to make the asymptote $x = -4$ apparent from the display.

**57.** Graph $y = \dfrac{0.34e^{0.7x}}{4.2 + 0.71e^{0.7x}}$, where $x > 0$. From the graph, determine an equation of the horizontal asymptote by examining the $y$-values as $x \to \infty$. To confirm this equation algebraically, find $\lim_{x \to \infty} y$ by first dividing both the numerator and denominator by $e^{0.7x}$.

## 13.6  Applied Maxima and Minima

To model situations involving maximizing or minimizing a quantity.

By using techniques from this chapter, we can solve problems that involve maximizing or minimizing a quantity. For example, we might want to maximize profit or minimize cost. The crucial part is expressing the quantity to be maximized or minimized as a function of some variable in the problem. Then we differentiate and test the resulting critical values. For this, the first-derivative test or the second-derivative test can be used, although it may be obvious from the nature of the problem whether or not a critical value represents an appropriate answer. Because our interest is in *absolute* maxima and minima, sometimes we must examine endpoints of the domain of the function. (Very often the function used to model the situation of a problem will be the restriction to a closed interval of a function that has a large natural domain. Such *real-world* limitations tend to generate endpoints.)

The aim of this example is to set up a cost function from which cost is minimized.

### EXAMPLE 1    Minimizing the Cost of a Fence

*For insurance purposes, a manufacturer plans to fence in a 10,800-ft² rectangular storage area adjacent to a building by using the building as one side of the enclosed area. The fencing parallel to the building faces a highway and will cost $3 per foot installed, whereas the fencing for the other two sides costs $2 per foot installed. Find the amount of each type of fence so that the total cost of the fence will be a minimum. What is the minimum cost?*

**Solution:** As a first step in a problem like this, it is a good idea to draw a diagram that reflects the situation. In Figure 13.64, we have labeled the length of the side parallel to the building as $x$ and the lengths of the other two sides as $y$, where $x$ and $y$ are in feet.

Since we want to minimize cost, our next step is to determine a function that gives cost. The cost obviously depends on how much fencing is along the highway and how much is along the other two sides. Along the highway the cost per foot is 3 (dollars), so the total cost of that fencing is $3x$. Similarly, along *each* of the other two sides, the cost is $2y$. Thus, the total cost of the fencing is given by the cost function

$$C = 3x + 2y + 2y$$

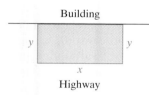

**FIGURE 13.64**  Fencing problem of Example 1.

Building

$y$                    $y$

$x$

Highway

---

[12]L. H. Mantell and F. P. Sing, *Economics for Business Decisions* (New York: McGraw-Hill Book Company, 1972), p. 107.

that is,

$$C = 3x + 4y \tag{1}$$

We need to find the absolute minimum value of $C$. To do this, we use the techniques discussed in this chapter; that is, we examine $C$ at critical values (and any endpoints) in the domain. But in order to differentiate, we need to first express $C$ as a function of one variable only. [Equation (1) gives $C$ as a function of *two* variables, $x$ and $y$.] We can accomplish this by first finding a relationship between $x$ and $y$. From the statement of the problem, we are told that the storage area, which is $xy$, must be 10,800:

$$xy = 10{,}800 \tag{2}$$

With this equation, we can express one variable (say, $y$) in terms of the other ($x$). Then, substitution into Equation (1) will give $C$ as a function of one variable only. Solving Equation (2) for $y$ gives

$$y = \frac{10{,}800}{x} \tag{3}$$

Substituting into Equation (1), we have

$$C = C(x) = 3x + 4\left(\frac{10{,}800}{x}\right)$$

$$C(x) = 3x + \frac{43{,}200}{x} \tag{4}$$

From the physical nature of the problem, the domain of $C$ is $x > 0$.

We now find $dC/dx$, set it equal to 0, and solve for $x$. We have

$$\frac{dC}{dx} = 3 - \frac{43{,}200}{x^2} \qquad \left(\frac{d}{dx}(43{,}200x^{-1}) = -43{,}200x^{-2}\right)$$

$$3 - \frac{43{,}200}{x^2} = 0$$

$$3 = \frac{43{,}200}{x^2}$$

from which it follows that

$$x^2 = \frac{43{,}200}{3} = 14{,}400$$

$$x = 120 \qquad\qquad \text{(since } x > 0\text{)}$$

Thus, 120 is the *only* critical value, and there are no endpoints to consider. To test this value, we will use the second-derivative test.

$$\frac{d^2C}{dx^2} = \frac{86{,}400}{x^3}$$

When $x = 120$, $d^2C/dx^2 > 0$, so we conclude that $x = 120$ gives a relative minimum. However, since 120 is the only critical value on the open interval $(0, \infty)$ and $C$ is continuous on that interval, this relative minimum must also be an absolute minimum.

We are not done yet! The questions posed in the problem must be answered. For minimum cost, the number of feet of fencing along the highway is 120. When $x = 120$, we have, from Equation (3), $y = 10{,}800/120 = 90$. Therefore, the number of feet of fencing for the other two sides is $2y = 180$. It follows that 120 ft of the \$3 fencing and 180 ft of the \$2 fencing are needed. The minimum cost can be obtained from the cost function, Equation (4), and is

$$C(120) = 3x + \left.\frac{43{,}200}{x}\right|_{x=120} = 3(120) + \frac{43{,}200}{120} = 720$$

NOW WORK PROBLEM 3

Based on Example 1, the following guide may be helpful in solving an applied maximum or minimum problem:

### Guide for Solving Applied Max–Min Problems

**Step 1.** When appropriate, draw a diagram that reflects the information in the problem.

**Step 2.** Set up a function for the quantity that you want to maximize or minimize.

**Step 3.** Express the function in step 2 as a function of one variable only, and note the domain of this function. The domain may be implied by the nature of the problem itself.

**Step 4.** Find the critical values of the function. After testing each critical value, determine which one gives the absolute extreme value you are seeking. If the domain of the function includes endpoints, be sure to also examine function values at these endpoints.

**Step 5.** Based on the results of step 4, answer the question(s) posed in the problem.

● EXAMPLE 2   **Maximizing Revenue**

This example involves maximizing revenue when a demand equation is known.

*The demand equation for a manufacturer's product is*

$$p = \frac{80 - q}{4} \quad 0 \le q \le 80$$

*where q is the number of units and p is the price per unit. At what value of q will there be maximum revenue? What is the maximum revenue?*

**Solution:**  Let $r$ represent total revenue, which is the quantity to be maximized. Since

$$\text{revenue} = (\text{price})(\text{quantity})$$

we have

$$r = pq = \frac{80 - q}{4} \cdot q = \frac{80q - q^2}{4} = r(q)$$

where $0 \le q \le 80$. Setting $dr/dq = 0$, we obtain

$$\frac{dr}{dq} = \frac{80 - 2q}{4} = 0$$

$$80 - 2q = 0$$

$$q = 40$$

Thus, 40 is the only critical value. Now we see whether this gives a maximum. Examining the first derivative for $0 \le q < 40$, we have $dr/dq > 0$, so $r$ is increasing. If $q > 40$, then $dr/dq < 0$, so $r$ is decreasing. Because to the left of 40 we have $r$ increasing, and to the right $r$ is decreasing, we conclude that $q = 40$ gives the *absolute* maximum revenue, namely

$$r(40) = (80(40) - (40)^2)/4 = 400$$

NOW WORK PROBLEM 7 ●●●

● EXAMPLE 3   **Minimizing Average Cost**

This example involves minimizing average cost when the cost function is known.

*A manufacturer's total-cost function is given by*

$$c = c(q) = \frac{q^2}{4} + 3q + 400$$

*where c is the total cost of producing q units. At what level of output will average cost per unit be a minimum? What is this minimum?*

**Solution:** The quantity to be minimized is the average cost $\bar{c}$. The average-cost function is

$$\bar{c} = \bar{c}(q) = \frac{c}{q} = \frac{\dfrac{q^2}{4} + 3q + 400}{q} = \frac{q}{4} + 3 + \frac{400}{q} \tag{5}$$

Here $q$ must be positive. To minimize $\bar{c}$, we differentiate:

$$\frac{d\bar{c}}{dq} = \frac{1}{4} - \frac{400}{q^2} = \frac{q^2 - 1600}{4q^2}$$

To get the critical values, we solve $d\bar{c}/dq = 0$:

$$q^2 - 1600 = 0$$

$$(q - 40)(q + 40) = 0$$

$$q = 40 \qquad \text{(since } q > 0)$$

To determine whether this level of output gives a relative minimum, we will use the second-derivative test. We have

$$\frac{d^2\bar{c}}{dq^2} = \frac{800}{q^3}$$

which is positive for $q = 40$. Thus, $\bar{c}$ has a relative minimum when $q = 40$. We note that $\bar{c}$ is continuous for $q > 0$. Since $q = 40$ is the only relative extremum, we conclude that this relative minimum is indeed an absolute minimum. Substituting $q = 40$ in Equation (5) gives the minimum average cost $\bar{c}(40) = \dfrac{40}{4} + 3 + \dfrac{400}{40} = 23$.

NOW WORK PROBLEM 5 ●◖◗

● **EXAMPLE 4**    **Maximization Applied to Enzymes**

*This example is a biological application involving maximizing the rate at which an enzyme is formed. The equation involved is a literal equation.*

*An enzyme is a protein that acts as a catalyst for increasing the rate of a chemical reaction that occurs in cells. In a certain reaction, an enzyme is converted to another enzyme called the product. The product acts as a catalyst for its own formation. The rate $R$ at which the product is formed (with respect to time) is given by*

$$R = kp(l - p)$$

*where $l$ is the total initial amount of both enzymes, $p$ is the amount of the product enzyme, and $k$ is a positive constant. For what value of $p$ will $R$ be a maximum?*

**Solution:** We can write $R = k(pl - p^2)$. Setting $dR/dp = 0$ and solving for $p$ gives

$$\frac{dR}{dp} = k(l - 2p) = 0$$

$$p = \frac{l}{2}$$

Now, $d^2R/dp^2 = -2k$. Since $k > 0$, the second derivative is always negative. Hence, $p = l/2$ gives a relative maximum. Moreover, since $R$ is a continuous function of $p$, we conclude that we indeed have an absolute maximum when $p = l/2$.

◖◗●

Calculus can be applied to inventory decisions, as the following example shows.

● **EXAMPLE 5**    **Economic Lot Size**

*This example involves determining the number of units in a production run in order to minimize certain costs.*

*A company annually produces and sells 10,000 units of a product. Sales are uniformly distributed throughout the year. The company wishes to determine the number of units to be manufactured in each production run in order to minimize total annual setup costs and carrying costs. The same number of units is produced in each run. This number is referred to as the **economic lot size or economic order quantity**. The production cost* *of each unit is $20, and carrying costs (insurance, interest, storage, etc.) are estimated to be 10% of the value of the average inventory. Setup costs per production run are $40. Find the economic lot size.*

**Solution:** Let $q$ be the number of units in a production run. Since sales are distributed at a uniform rate, we will assume that inventory varies uniformly from $q$ to 0 between production runs. Thus, we take the average inventory to be $q/2$ units. The production costs are $20 per unit, so the value of the average inventory is $20(q/2)$. Carrying costs are 10% of this value:

$$0.10(20)\left(\frac{q}{2}\right)$$

The number of production runs per year is $10{,}000/q$. Hence, the total setup costs are

$$40\left(\frac{10{,}000}{q}\right)$$

Therefore, the total of the annual carrying costs and setup costs is given by

$$C = 0.10(20)\left(\frac{q}{2}\right) + 40\left(\frac{10{,}000}{q}\right)$$

$$= q + \frac{400{,}000}{q} \qquad\qquad (q > 0)$$

$$\frac{dC}{dq} = 1 - \frac{400{,}000}{q^2} = \frac{q^2 - 400{,}000}{q^2}$$

Setting $dC/dq = 0$, we get

$$q^2 = 400{,}000$$

Since $q > 0$,

$$q = \sqrt{400{,}000} = 200\sqrt{10} \approx 632.5$$

To determine whether this value of $q$ minimizes $C$, we will examine the first derivative. If $0 < q < \sqrt{400{,}000}$, then $dC/dq < 0$. If $q > \sqrt{400{,}000}$, then $dC/dq > 0$. We conclude that there is an *absolute* minimum at $q = 632.5$. The number of production runs is $10{,}000/632.5 \approx 15.8$. For practical purposes, there would be 16 lots, each having the economic lot size of 625 units.

NOW WORK PROBLEM 29 ●●●

●**EXAMPLE 6  Maximizing TV Cable Company Revenue**

The aim of this example is to set up a revenue function from which revenue is maximized over a closed interval.

*The Vista TV Cable Co. currently has 100,000 subscribers who are each paying a monthly rate of $40. A survey reveals that there will be 1000 more subscribers for each $0.25 decrease in the rate. At what rate will maximum revenue be obtained, and how many subscribers will there be at this rate?*

**Solution:** Let $x$ be the number of $0.25 decreases. The monthly rate is then $40 - 0.25x$, where $0 \le x \le 160$ (the rate cannot be negative), and the number of *new* subscribers is $1000x$. Thus, the total number of subscribers is $100{,}000 + 1000x$. We want to maximize the revenue, which is given by

$$r = (\text{number of subscribers})(\text{rate per subscriber})$$

$$= (100{,}000 + 1000x)(40 - 0.25x)$$

$$= 1000(100 + x)(40 - 0.25x)$$

$$= 1000(4000 + 15x - 0.25x^2)$$

Setting $r' = 0$ and solving for $x$, we have

$$r' = 1000(15 - 0.5x) = 0$$

$$x = 30$$

Since the domain of $r$ is the closed interval $[0, 160]$, the absolute maximum value of $r$ must occur at $x = 30$ or at one of the endpoints of the interval. We now compute $r$ at these three points:

$$r(0) = 1000(4000 + 15(0) - 0.25(0)^{2)} = 4,000,000$$

$$r(30) = 1000(4000 + 15(30) - 0.25(30)^2) = 4,225,000$$

$$r(160) = 1000(4000 + 15(160) - 0.25(160)^2 = 0$$

Accordingly, the maximum revenue occurs when $x = 30$. This corresponds to thirty $0.25 decreases, for a total decrease of $7.50; that is, the monthly rate is $40 - $7.50 = $32.50. The number of subscribers at that rate is $100,000 + 30(1000) = 130,000$.

NOW WORK PROBLEM 19

### EXAMPLE 7  Maximizing the Number of Recipients of Health-Care Benefits

Here we maximize a function over a closed interval.

*An article in a sociology journal stated that if a particular health-care program for the elderly were initiated, then t years after its start, n thousand elderly people would receive direct benefits, where*

$$n = \frac{t^3}{3} - 6t^2 + 32t \quad 0 \le t \le 12$$

*For what value of t does the maximum number receive benefits?*

**Solution:** Setting $dn/dt = 0$, we have

$$\frac{dn}{dt} = t^2 - 12t + 32 = 0$$

$$(t - 4)(t - 8) = 0$$

$$t = 4 \quad \text{or} \quad t = 8$$

Since the domain of $n$ is the closed interval $[0, 12]$, the absolute maximum value of $n$ must occur at $t = 0, 4, 8$, or $12$:

$$n(0) = \frac{0^3}{3} - 6(0^2)0 + 32(0) = 0$$

$$n(4) = \frac{4^3}{3} - 6(4^2) + 32(4) = \frac{160}{3}$$

$$n(8) = \frac{8^3}{3} - 6(8^2) + 32(8) = \frac{128}{3}$$

$$n(12) = \frac{12^3}{3} - 6(12)^2 + 32(12) = \frac{288}{3} = 96$$

Thus, an absolute maximum occurs when $t = 12$. A graph of the function is given in Figure 13.65.

NOW WORK PROBLEM 15

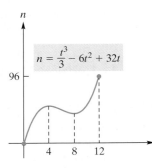

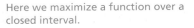

**FIGURE 13.65** Graph of $n = \frac{t^3}{3} - 6t^2 + 32t$ on $[0, 12]$.

**CAUTION**

The preceding example illustrates that you should not ignore endpoints when finding absolute extrema on a closed interval.

In the next example, we use the word *monopolist*. Under a situation of monopoly, there is only one seller of a product for which there are no similar substitutes, and the seller—that is, the monopolist—controls the market. By considering the demand equation for the product, the monopolist may set the price (or volume of output) so that maximum profit will be obtained.

This example involves maximizing profit when the demand and average-cost functions are known. In the last part, a tax is imposed on the monopolist, and a new profit function is analyzed.

### EXAMPLE 8  Profit Maximization

*Suppose that the demand equation for a monopolist's product is $p = 400 - 2q$ and the average-cost function is $\bar{c} = 0.2q + 4 + (400/q)$, where q is number of units, and both p and $\bar{c}$ are expressed in dollars per unit.*

a. *Determine the level of output at which profit is maximized.*

b. *Determine the price at which maximum profit occurs.*

c. *Determine the maximum profit.*

d. *If, as a regulatory device, the government imposes a tax of $22 per unit on the monopolist, what is the new price for profit maximization?*

**Solution:** We know that

$$\text{profit} = \text{total revenue} - \text{total cost}$$

Since total revenue $r$ and total cost $c$ are given by

$$r = pq = 400q - 2q^2$$

and

$$c = q\bar{c} = 0.2q^2 + 4q + 400$$

the profit is

$$P = r - c = 400q - 2q^2 - (0.2q^2 + 4q + 400)$$

so that

$$P(q) = 396q - 2.2q^2 - 400 \quad \text{for } q > 0 \tag{6}$$

a. To maximize profit, we set $dP/dq = 0$:

$$\frac{dP}{dq} = 396 - 4.4q = 0$$

$$q = 90$$

Now, $d^2P/dq^2 = -4.4$ is always negative, so it is negative at the critical value $q = 90$. By the second-derivative test, then, there is a relative maximum there. Since $q = 90$ is the only critical value on $(0, \infty)$, we must have an absolute maximum there.

b. The price at which maximum profit occurs is obtained by setting $q = 90$ in the demand equation:

$$p = 400 - 2(90) = 220$$

c. The maximum profit is obtained by evaluating $P(90)$. We have

$$P(90) = 396(90) - 2.2(90)^2 - 400 = 17{,}420$$

d. The tax of $22 per unit means that for $q$ units, the total cost increases by $22q$. The new cost function is $c_1 = 0.2q^2 + 4q + 400 + 22q$, and the new profit is given by

$$P_1 = 400q - 2q^2 - (0.2q^2 + 4q + 400 + 22q)$$

$$= 374q - 2.2q^2 - 400$$

Setting $dP_1/dq = 0$ gives

$$\frac{dP_1}{dq} = 374 - 4.4q = 0$$

$$q = 85$$

Since $d^2P_1/dq^2 = -4.4 < 0$, we conclude that, to maximize profit, the monopolist must restrict output to 85 units at a higher price of $p_1 = 400 - 2(85) = \$230$. Since this price is only $10 more than before, only part of the tax has been shifted to the consumer, and the monopolist must bear the cost of the balance. The profit now is $15,495, which is less than the former profit.

NOW WORK PROBLEM 13 ●●●

This discussion leads to the economic principle that when profit is maximum, marginal revenue is equal to marginal cost.

We conclude this section by using calculus to develop an important principle in economics. Suppose $p = f(q)$ is the demand function for a firm's product, where $p$ is price per unit and $q$ is the number of units produced and sold. Then the total revenue is given by $r = qp = qf(q)$, which is a function of $q$. Let the total cost of producing $q$ units be given by the cost function $c = g(q)$. Thus, the total profit, which is total revenue minus total cost, is also a function of $q$, namely,

$$P(q) = r - c = qf(q) - g(q)$$

Let us consider the most profitable output for the firm. Ignoring special cases, we know that profit is maximized when $dP/dq = 0$ and $d^2P/dq^2 < 0$. We have

$$\frac{dP}{dq} = \frac{d}{dq}(r - c) = \frac{dr}{dq} - \frac{dc}{dq}$$

Consequently, $dP/dq = 0$ when

$$\frac{dr}{dq} = \frac{dc}{dq}$$

That is, at the level of maximum profit, the slope of the tangent to the total-revenue curve must equal the slope of the tangent to the total-cost curve (Figure 13.66). But $dr/dq$ is the marginal revenue MR, and $dc/dq$ is the marginal cost MC. Thus, under typical conditions, to maximize profit, it is necessary that

$$MR = MC$$

For this to indeed correspond to a maximum, it is necessary that $d^2P/dq^2 < 0$:

$$\frac{d^2P}{dq^2} = \frac{d^2}{dq^2}(r - c) = \frac{d^2r}{dq^2} - \frac{d^2c}{dq^2} < 0 \quad \text{equivalently} \quad \frac{d^2r}{dq^2} < \frac{d^2c}{dq^2}$$

That is, when $MR = MC$, in order to ensure maximum profit, the slope of the marginal-revenue curve must be less than the slope of the marginal-cost curve.

The condition that $d^2P/dq^2 < 0$ when $dP/dq = 0$ can be viewed another way. Equivalently, to have $MR = MC$ correspond to a maximum, $dP/dq$ must go from $+$ to $-$; that is, it must go from $dr/dq - dc/dq > 0$ to $dr/dq - dc/dq < 0$. Hence, as output increases, we must have $MR > MC$ and then $MR < MC$. This means that at the point $q_1$ of maximum profit, *the marginal-cost curve must cut the marginal-revenue curve from below* (Figure 13.67). For production up to $q_1$, the revenue from additional output would be greater than the cost of such output, and the total profit would increase. For output beyond $q_1$, $MC > MR$, and each unit of output would add more to total costs than to total revenue. Hence, total profits would decline.

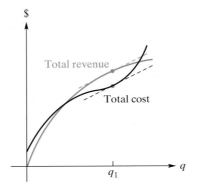

FIGURE 13.66 At maximum profit, marginal revenue equals marginal cost.

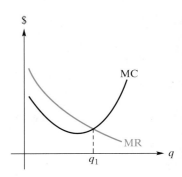

FIGURE 13.67 At maximum profit, the marginal-cost curve cuts the marginal-revenue curve from below.

# Problems 13.6

*In this set of problems, unless otherwise specified, p is price per unit (in dollars) and q is output per unit of time. Fixed costs refer to costs that remain constant at all levels of production during a given time period. (An example is rent.)*

1. Find two numbers whose sum is 82 and whose product is as big as possible.

2. Find two nonnegative numbers whose sum is 20 and for which the product of twice one number and the square of the other number will be a maximum.

*3. **Fencing**   A company has set aside $9000 to fence in a rectangular portion of land adjacent to a stream by using the stream for one side of the enclosed area. The cost of the fencing parallel to the stream is $15 per foot installed, and the fencing for the remaining two sides costs $9 per foot installed. Find the dimensions of the maximum enclosed area.

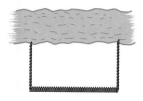

4. **Fencing**   The owner of the Laurel Nursery Garden Center wants to fence in 1200 ft$^2$ of land in a rectangular plot to be used for different types of shrubs. The plot is to be divided into five equal plots with four fences parallel to the same pair of sides, as shown in Figure 13.68. What is the least number of feet of fence needed?

FIGURE 13.68   Diagram for Problem 4.

*5. **Average Cost**   A manufacturer finds that the total cost $c$ of producing a product is given by the cost function

$$c = 0.05q^2 + 5q + 500$$

At what level of output will average cost per unit be a minimum?

6. **Automobile Expense**   The cost per hour (in dollars) of operating an automobile is given by

$$C = 0.12s - 0.0012s^2 + 0.08 \qquad 0 \le s \le 60$$

where $s$ is the speed in miles per hour. At what speed is the cost per hour a minimum?

*7. **Revenue**   The demand equation for a monopolist's product is

$$p = -5q + 30$$

At what price will revenue be maximized?

8. **Revenue**   Suppose that the demand function for a monopolist's product is of the form

$$q = Ae^{-Bp}$$

for positive constants $A$ and $B$. In terms of $A$ and $B$, find the value of $p$ for which maximum revenue is obtained. Can you explain why your answer does not depend on $A$?

9. **Weight Gain**   A group of biologists studied the nutritional effects on rats that were fed a diet containing 10% protein.[13] The protein consisted of yeast and cottonseed flour. By varying the percent $p$ of yeast in the protein mix, the group found that the (average) weight gain (in grams) of a rat over a period of time was

$$f(p) = 160 - p - \frac{900}{p + 10} \qquad 0 \le p \le 100$$

Find (a) the maximum weight gain and (b) the minimum weight gain.

10. **Drug Dose**   The severity of the reaction of the human body to an initial dose $D$ of a drug is given by[14]

$$R = f(D) = D^2 \left( \frac{C}{2} - \frac{D}{3} \right)$$

where the constant $C$ denotes the maximum amount of the drug that may be given. Show that $R$ has a maximum *rate of change* when $D = C/2$.

11. **Profit**   For a monopolist's product, the demand function is

$$p = 85 - 0.05q$$

and the cost function is

$$c = 600 + 35q$$

At what level of output will profit be maximized? At what price does this occur, and what is the profit?

12. **Profit**   For a monopolist, the cost per unit of producing a product is $3, and the demand equation is

$$p = \frac{10}{\sqrt{q}}$$

What price will give the greatest profit?

---

[13]Adapted from R. Bressani, "The Use of Yeast in Human Foods," in *Single-Cell Protein,* ed. R. I. Mateles and S. R. Tannenbaum (Cambridge, MA: MIT Press, 1968).

[14]R. M. Thrall, J. A. Mortimer. K. R. Rebman, and R. F. Baum, eds., *Some Mathematical Models in Biology,* rev. ed., Report No. 40241-R-7. Prepared at University of Michigan, 1967.

*13. **Profit**   For a monopolist's product, the demand equation is

$$p = 42 - 4q$$

and the average-cost function is

$$\bar{c} = 2 + \frac{80}{q}$$

Find the profit-maximizing price.

14. **Profit**   For a monopolist's product, the demand function is

$$p = \frac{40}{\sqrt{q}}$$

and the average-cost function is

$$\bar{c} = \frac{1}{3} + \frac{2000}{q}$$

Find the profit-maximizing price and output. At this level, show that marginal revenue is equal to marginal cost.

*15. **Profit**   A manufacturer can produce at most 120 units of a certain product each year. The demand equation for the product is

$$p = q^2 - 100q + 3200$$

and the manufacturer's average-cost function is

$$\bar{c} = \frac{2}{3}q^2 - 40q + \frac{10{,}000}{q}$$

Determine the profit-maximizing output $q$ and the corresponding maximum profit.

16. **Cost**   A manufacturer has determined that, for a certain product, the average cost (in dollars per unit) is given by

$$\bar{c} = 2q^2 - 42q + 228 + \frac{210}{q}$$

where $3 \le q \le 12$.

   (a) At what level within the interval [3, 12] should production be fixed in order to minimize total cost? What is the minimum total cost?
   (b) If production were required to lie within the interval [7, 12], what value of $q$ would minimize total cost?

17. **Profit**   For XYZ Manufacturing Co., total fixed costs are $1200, material and labor costs combined are $2 per unit, and the demand equation is

$$p = \frac{100}{\sqrt{q}}$$

What level of output will maximize profit? Show that this occurs when marginal revenue is equal to marginal cost. What is the price at profit maximization?

18. **Revenue**   A real-estate firm owns 100 garden-type apartments. At $400 per month, each apartment can be rented. However, for each $10-per-month increase, there will be two vacancies with no possibility of filling them. What rent per apartment will maximize monthly revenue?

*19. **Revenue**   A TV cable company has 4800 subscribers who are each paying $18 per month. It can get 150 more subscribers for each $0.50 decrease in the monthly fee. What rate will yield maximum revenue, and what will this revenue be?

20. **Profit**   A manufacturer of a product finds that, for the first 600 units that are produced and sold, the profit is $40 per unit. The profit on each of the units beyond 600 is decreased by $0.05 times the number of additional units produced. For example, the total profit when 602 units are produced and sold is 600(40) + 2(39.90). What level of output will maximize profit?

21. **Container Design**   A container manufacturer is designing a rectangular box, open at the top and with a square base, that is to have a volume of 32 ft³. If the box is to require the least amount of material, what must be its dimensions? (See Figure 13.69.)

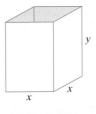

**FIGURE 13.69**
Open-top box
for Problems 21
and 22.

22. **Container Design**   An open-top box with a square base is to be constructed from 192 ft² of material. What should be the dimensions of the box if the volume is to be a maximum? What is the maximum volume? (See Figure 13.69.)

23. **Container Design**   An open box is to be made by cutting equal squares from each corner of a $L$-inch-square piece of cardboard and then folding up the sides. Find the length of the side of the square (in terms of $L$) that must be cut out if the volume of the box is to be maximized. What is the maximum volume? (See Figure 13.70.)

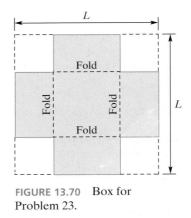

**FIGURE 13.70**   Box for
Problem 23.

24. **Poster Design**   A rectangular cardboard poster is to have 240 in² for printed matter. It is to have a 5-in. margin at the top and bottom and a 3-in. margin on each side. Find the dimensions of the poster so that the amount of cardboard used is minimized. (See Figure 13.71.)

(*Hint:* First find the values of $x$ and $y$ in Figure 13.71 that minimize the amount of cardboard.)

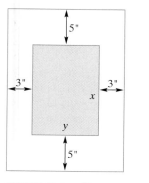

**FIGURE 13.71** Poster for Problem 24.

**25. Container Design** A cylindrical can, open at the top, is to have a fixed volume of $K$. Show that if the least amount of material is to be used, then both the radius and height are equal to $\sqrt[3]{K/\pi}$. (See Figure 13.72.)

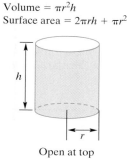

Volume $= \pi r^2 h$
Surface area $= 2\pi rh + \pi r^2$

Open at top

**FIGURE 13.72** Can for Problems 25 and 26.

**26. Container Design** A cylindrical can, open at the top, is to be made from a fixed amount of material, $K$. If the volume is to be a maximum, show that both the radius and height are equal to $\sqrt{K/(3\pi)}$. (See Figure 13.72.)

**27. Profit** The demand equation for a monopolist's product is

$$p = 600 - 2q$$

and the total-cost function is

$$c = 0.2q^2 + 28q + 200$$

Find the profit-maximizing output and price, and determine the corresponding profit. If the government were to impose a tax of $22 per unit on the manufacturer, what would be the new profit-maximizing output and price? What is the profit now?

**28. Profit** Use the *original* data in Problem 27, and assume that the government imposes a license fee of $1000 on the manufacturer. This is a lump-sum amount without regard to output. Show that the profit-maximizing price and output remain the same. Show, however, that there will be less profit.

**\*29. Economic Lot Size** A manufacturer has to produce 1000 units annually of a product that is sold at a uniform rate during the year. The production cost of each unit is $10, and carrying costs (insurance, interest, storage, etc.) are estimated to be 12.8% of the value of average inventory. Setup costs per production run are $40. Find the economic lot size.

**30. Profit** For a monopolist's product, the cost function is

$$c = 0.004q^3 + 20q + 5000$$

and the demand function is

$$p = 450 - 4q$$

Find the profit-maximizing output.

**31. Workshop Attendance** Imperial Educational Services (I.E.S.) is considering offering a workshop in resource allocation to key personnel at Acme Corp. To make the offering economically feasible, I.E.S. feels that at least 30 persons must attend at a cost of $50 each. Moreover, I.E.S. will agree to reduce the charge for *everybody* by $1.25 for each person over the 30 who attends. How many people should be in the group for I.E.S. to maximize revenue? Assume that the maximum allowable number in the group is 40.

**32. Cost of Leasing Motor** The Kiddie Toy Company plans to lease an electric motor that will be used 80,000 horsepower-hours per year in manufacturing. One horsepower-hour is the work done in 1 hour by a 1-horsepower motor. The annual cost to lease a suitable motor is $200, plus $0.40 per horsepower. The cost per horsepower-hour of operating the motor is $0.008/N$, where $N$ is the horsepower. What size motor, in horsepower, should be leased in order to minimize cost?

**33. Transportation Cost** The cost of operating a truck on a thruway (excluding the salary of the driver) is

$$0.165 + \frac{s}{200}$$

dollars per mile, where $s$ is the (steady) speed of the truck in miles per hour. The truck driver's salary is $18 per hour. At what speed should the truck driver operate the truck to make a 700-mile trip most economical?

**34. Cost** For a manufacturer, the cost of making a part is $30 per unit for labor and $10 per unit for materials; overhead is fixed at $20,000 per week. If more than 5000 units are made each week, labor is $45 per unit for those units in excess of 5000. At what level of production will average cost per unit be a minimum?

**35. Profit** Ms. Jones owns a small insurance agency that sells policies for a large insurance company. For each policy sold, Ms. Jones, who does not sell policies herself, is paid a commission of $50 by the insurance company. From previous experience, Ms. Jones has determined that, when she employs $m$ salespeople,

$$q = m^3 - 15m^2 + 92m$$

policies can be sold per week. She pays each of the $m$ salespeople a salary of $1000 per week, and her weekly fixed cost is $3000. Current office facilities can accommodate at most eight salespeople. Determine the number of salespeople that Ms. Jones should hire to maximize her weekly profit. What is the corresponding maximum profit?

36. **Profit** A manufacturing company sells high-quality jackets through a chain of specialty shops. The demand equation for these jackets is

$$p = 400 - 50q$$

where $p$ is the selling price (in dollars per jacket) and $q$ is the demand (in thousands of jackets). If this company's marginal-cost function is given by

$$\frac{dc}{dq} = \frac{800}{q + 5}$$

show that there is a maximum profit, and determine the number of jackets that must be sold to obtain this maximum profit.

37. **Chemical Production** Each day, a firm makes $x$ tons of chemical A ($x \leq 4$) and

$$y = \frac{24 - 6x}{5 - x}$$

tons of chemical B. The profit on chemical A is $2000 per ton, and on B it is $1000 per ton. How much of chemical A should be produced per day to maximize profit? Answer the same question if the profit on A is $P$ per ton and that on B is $P/2$ per ton.

38. **Rate of Return** To erect an office building, fixed costs are $1.44 million and include land, architect's fees, a basement, a foundation, and so on. If $x$ floors are constructed, the cost (excluding fixed costs) is

$$c = 10x[120,000 + 3000(x - 1)]$$

The revenue per month is $60,000 per floor. How many floors will yield a maximum rate of return on investment? (Rate of return = total revenue/total cost.)

39. **Gait and Power Output of an Animal** In a model by Smith,[15] the power output of an animal at a given speed as a

function of its movement or *gait j*, is found to be

$$P(j) = Aj\frac{L^4}{V} + B\frac{V^3 L^2}{1 + j}$$

where $A$ and $B$ are constants, $j$ is a measure of the "jumpiness" of the gait, $L$ is a constant representing linear dimension, and $V$ is a constant forward speed.

Assume that $P$ is a minimum when $dP/dj = 0$. Show that when this occurs,

$$(1 + j)^2 = \frac{BV^4}{AL^2}$$

As a passing comment, Smith indicates that "at top speed, $j$ is zero for an elephant, 0.3 for a horse, and 1 for a greyhound, approximately."

40. **Traffic Flow** In a model of traffic flow on a lane of a freeway, the number of cars the lane can carry per unit time is given by[16]

$$N = \frac{-2a}{-2at_r + v - \dfrac{2al}{v}}$$

where $a$ is the acceleration of a car when stopping ($a < 0$), $t_r$ is the reaction time to begin braking, $v$ is the average speed of the cars, and $l$ is the length of a car. Assume that $a$, $t_r$, and $l$ are constant. To find how many cars a lane can carry at most, we want to find the speed $v$ that maximizes $N$. To maximize $N$, it suffices to minimize the denominator

$$-2at_r + v - \frac{2al}{v}$$

**(a)** Find the value of $v$ that minimizes the denominator.
**(b)** Evaluate your answer in part (a) when $a = -19.6$ (ft/s$^2$), $l = 20$ (ft), and $t_r = 0.5$ (s). Your answer will be in feet per second.
**(c)** Find the corresponding value of $N$ to one decimal place. Your answer will be in cars per second. Convert your answer to cars per hour.
**(d)** Find the relative change in $N$ that results when $l$ is reduced from 20 ft to 15 ft, for the maximizing value of $v$.

41. **Average Cost** During the Christmas season, a promotional company purchases cheap red felt stockings, glues fake white fur and sequins onto them, and packages them for distribution. The total cost of producing $q$ cases of stockings is given by

$$c = 3q^2 + 50q - 18q \ln q + 120$$

Find the number of cases that should be processed in order to minimize the average cost per case. Determine (to two decimal places) this minimum average cost.

[15]J. M. Smith, *Mathematical Ideas in Biology* (London: Cambridge University Press, 1968).

[16]J. I. Shonle, *Environmental Applications of General Physics* (Reading, MA: Addison-Wesley Publishing Co., 1975).

**42. Profit**   A monopolist's demand equation is given by

$$p = q^2 - 20q + 160$$

where $p$ is the selling price (in thousands of dollars) per ton when $q$ tons of product are sold. Suppose that fixed cost is

$50,000 and that each ton costs $30,000 to produce. If current equipment has a maximum production capacity of 12 tons, use the graph of the profit function to determine at what production level the maximum profit occurs. Find the corresponding maximum profit and selling price per ton.

# 13.7 Review

## Important Terms and Symbols

**Examples**

| | | |
|---|---|---|
| Section 13.1 | **Relative Extrema** | |
| | increasing function     decreasing function | Ex. 1, p. 572 |
| | relative maximum     relative minimum | Ex. 2, p. 573 |
| | relative extrema     absolute extrema | Ex. 3, p. 574 |
| | critical value     critical point     first-derivative test | Ex. 4, p. 574 |
| Section 13.2 | **Absolute Extrema on a Closed Interval** | |
| | extreme-value theorem | Ex. 1, p. 580 |
| Section 13.3 | **Concavity** | |
| | concave up     concave down     inflection point | Ex. 1, p. 582 |
| Section 13.4 | **The Second-Derivative Test** | |
| | second-derivative test | Ex. 1, p. 588 |
| Section 13.5 | **Asymptotes** | |
| | vertical asymptote     horizontal asymptote | Ex. 1, p. 591 |
| | oblique asymptote | Ex. 3, p. 593 |
| Section 13.6 | **Applied Maxima and Minima** | |
| | economic lot size | Ex. 5, p. 602 |

## Summary

Calculus is a great aid in sketching the graph of a function. The first derivative is used to determine when a function is increasing or decreasing and to locate relative maxima and minima. If $f'(x)$ is positive throughout an interval, then over that interval, $f$ is increasing and its graph rises (from left to right). If $f'(x)$ is negative throughout an interval, then over that interval, $f$ is decreasing and its graph is falling.

A point $(a, f(a))$ on the graph at which $f'(a)$ is 0 or is not defined is a candidate for a relative extremum, and $a$ is called a critical value. For a relative extremum to occur at $a$, the first derivative must change sign around $a$. The following procedure is the first-derivative test for the relative extrema of $y = f(x)$:

### First-Derivative Test for Relative Extrema

**Step 1.** Find $f'(x)$.

**Step 2.** Determine all values $a$ where $f'(a) = 0$ or $f'(a)$ is not defined.

**Step 3.** On the intervals defined by the values in step 2, determine whether $f$ is increasing ($f'(x) > 0$) or decreasing ($f'(x) < 0$).

**Step 4.** For each critical value $a$ at which $f$ is continuous, determine whether $f'(x)$ changes sign as $x$ increases through $a$. There is a relative maximum at $a$ if $f'(x)$ changes from + to −, and a relative minimum if $f'(x)$ changes from − to +. If $f'(x)$ does not change sign, there is no relative extremum at $a$.

Under certain conditions, a function is guaranteed to have absolute extrema. The extreme-value theorem states that if $f$ is continuous on a closed interval, then $f$ has an absolute maximum value and an absolute minimum value over the interval. To locate absolute extrema, the following procedure can be used:

### Procedure to Find Absolute Extrema for a Function $f$ Continuous on $[a, b]$

**Step 1.** Find the critical values of $f$.

**Step 2.** Evaluate $f(x)$ at the endpoints $a$ and $b$ and at the critical values in $(a, b)$.

**Step 3.** The maximum value of $f$ is the greatest of the values found in step 2. The minimum value of $f$ is the least of the values found in step 2.

The second derivative is used to determine concavity and points of inflection. If $f''(x) > 0$ throughout an interval, then $f$ is concave up over that interval, and its graph bends upward. If $f''(x) < 0$ over an interval, then $f$ is concave down throughout that interval, and its graph bends downward. A point on the graph where $f$ is continuous and its concavity changes is an inflection point. The point $(a, f(a))$ on the graph is a possible point of inflection if either $f''(a) = 0$ or $f''(a)$ is not defined and $f$ is continuous at $a$.

The second derivative also provides a means for testing certain critical values for relative extrema:

## Second-Derivative Test for Relative Extrema

Suppose $f'(a) = 0$. Then

If $f''(a) < 0$, then $f$ has a relative maximum at $a$.

If $f''(a) > 0$, then $f$ has a relative minimum at $a$.

Asymptotes are also aids in curve sketching. Graphs "blow up" near vertical asymptotes, and they "settle" near horizontal asymptotes and oblique asymptotes. The line $x = a$ is a vertical asymptote for the graph of a function $f$ if $\lim f(x) = \infty$ or $-\infty$ as $x$ approaches $a$ from the right ($x \to a^+$) or the left ($x \to a^-$). For the case of a rational function, $f(x) = P(x)/Q(x)$ in lowest terms, we can find vertical asymptotes without evaluating limits. If $Q(a) = 0$ but $P(a) \neq 0$, then the line $x = a$ is a vertical asymptote.

The line $y = b$ is a horizontal asymptote for the graph of a function $f$ if at least one of the following is true:

$$\lim_{x \to \infty} f(x) = b \quad \text{or} \quad \lim_{x \to -\infty} f(x) = b$$

The line $y = mx + b$ is an oblique asymptote for the graph of a function $f$ if at least one of the following is true:

$$\lim_{x \to \infty} (f(x) - (mx + b)) = 0 \quad \text{or} \quad \lim_{x \to -\infty} (f(x) - (mx + b)) = 0$$

In particular, a polynomial function of degree greater than 1 has no asymptotes. Moreover, a rational function whose numerator has degree greater than that of the denominator does not have a horizontal asymptote and a rational function whose numerator has degree more than one greater than that of the denominator does not have an oblique asymptote.

## Applied Maxima and Minima

In applied work the importance of calculus in maximization and minimization problems can hardly be overstated. For example, in the area of economics, we can maximize profit or minimize cost. Some important relationships that are used in economics problems are the following:

$$\bar{c} = \frac{c}{q} \quad \text{average cost per unit} = \frac{\text{total cost}}{\text{quantity}}$$

$$r = pq \quad \text{revenue} = (\text{price})(\text{quantity})$$

$$P = r - c \quad \text{profit} = \text{total revenue} - \text{total cost}$$

## Review Problems

*Problem numbers shown in color indicate problems suggested for use as a practice chapter test.*

*In Problems 1–4, find horizontal and vertical asymptotes.*

1. $y = \dfrac{3x^2}{x^2 - 16}$

2. $y = \dfrac{x + 3}{9x - 3x^2}$

3. $y = \dfrac{5x^2 - 3}{(3x + 2)^2}$

4. $y = \dfrac{4x + 1}{3x - 5} - \dfrac{3x + 1}{2x - 11}$

*In Problems 5–8, find critical values.*

5. $f(x) = \dfrac{5x^2}{3 - x^2}$

6. $f(x) = 8(x - 1)^2(x + 6)^4$

7. $f(x) = \dfrac{\sqrt[3]{x + 1}}{3 - 4x}$

8. $f(x) = \dfrac{13xe^{-5x/6}}{6x + 5}$

*In Problems 9–12, find intervals on which the function is increasing or decreasing.*

9. $f(x) = -\frac{5}{3}x^3 + 15x^2 + 35x + 10$

10. $f(x) = \dfrac{2x^2}{(x + 1)^2}$

11. $f(x) = \dfrac{6x^4}{x^2 - 3}$

12. $f(x) = 4\sqrt[3]{5x^3 - 7x}$

*In Problems 13–18, find intervals on which the function is concave up or concave down.*

13. $f(x) = x^4 - x^3 - 14$

14. $f(x) = \dfrac{x - 2}{x + 2}$

15. $f(x) = \dfrac{1}{2x - 1}$

16. $f(x) = x^3 + 2x^2 - 5x + 2$

17. $f(x) = (2x + 1)^3(3x + 2)$

18. $f(x) = (x^2 - x - 1)^2$

*In Problems 19–24, test for relative extrema.*

19. $f(x) = 2x^3 - 9x^2 + 12x + 7$

20. $f(x) = \dfrac{2x + 1}{x^2}$

21. $f(x) = \dfrac{x^{10}}{10} + \dfrac{x^5}{5}$

22. $f(x) = \dfrac{x^2}{x^2 - 4}$

23. $f(x) = x^{2/3}(x + 1)$

24. $f(x) = x^3(x - 2)^4$

*In Problems 25–30, find the x-values where inflection points occur.*

25. $y = x^5 - 5x^4 + 3x$

26. $y = \dfrac{x^2 + 2}{5x}$

27. $y = 4(3x - 5)(x^4 + 2)$

28. $y = x^2 + 2\ln(-x)$

29. $y = \dfrac{x^3}{e^x}$

30. $y = 6(x^2 - 4)^3$

*In Problems 31–34, test for absolute extrema on the given interval.*

31. $f(x) = 3x^4 - 4x^3$, $[0, 2]$

32. $f(x) = 2x^3 - 15x^2 + 36x$, $[0, 3]$

33. $f(x) = \dfrac{x}{(5x - 6)^2}$, $[-2, 0]$

**34.** $f(x) = (x+1)^2(x-1)^{2/3}$, $[2, 3]$

**35.** Let $f(x) = (x^2 + 1)e^{-x}$.

(a) Determine the values of $x$ at which relative maxima and relative minima, if any, occur.

(b) Determine the interval(s) on which the graph of $f$ is concave down, and find the coordinates of all points of inflection.

**36.** Let $f(x) = \dfrac{x}{x^2 - 1}$.

(a) Determine whether the graph of $f$ is symmetric about the $x$-axis, $y$-axis, or origin.

(b) Find the interval(s) on which $f$ is increasing.

(c) Find the coordinates of all relative extrema of $f$.

(d) Determine $\lim_{x \to -\infty} f(x)$ and $\lim_{x \to \infty} f(x)$.

(e) Sketch the graph of $f$.

(f) State the absolute minimum and absolute maximum values of $f(x)$ (if they exist).

*In Problems 37–48, indicate intervals on which the function is increasing, decreasing, concave up, or concave down; indicate relative maximum points, relative minimum points, points of inflection, horizontal asymptotes, vertical asymptotes, symmetry, and those intercepts that can be obtained conveniently. Then sketch the graph.*

**37.** $y = x^2 - 2x - 24$

**38.** $y = 2x^3 + 15x^2 + 36x + 9$

**39.** $y = x^3 - 12x + 20$

**40.** $y = x^4 - 4x^3 - 20x^2 + 150$

**41.** $y = x^3 - x$

**42.** $y = \dfrac{x+2}{x-3}$

**43.** $f(x) = \dfrac{100(x+5)}{x^2}$

**44.** $y = \dfrac{x^2 - 4}{x^2 - 1}$

**45.** $y = \dfrac{2x}{(3x-1)^3}$

**46.** $y = 6x^{1/3}(2x - 1)$

**47.** $f(x) = \dfrac{e^x + e^{-x}}{2}$

**48.** $f(x) = 1 - \ln(x^3)$

**49.** Are the following statements true or false?

(a) If $f'(x_0) = 0$, then $f$ must have a relative extremum at $x_0$.

(b) Since the function $f(x) = 1/x$ is decreasing on the intervals $(-\infty, 0)$ and $(0, \infty)$, it is impossible to find $x_1$ and $x_2$ in the domain of $f$ such that $x_1 < x_2$ and $f(x_1) < f(x_2)$.

(c) On the interval $(-1, 1]$, the function $f(x) = x^4$ has an absolute maximum and an absolute minimum.

(d) If $f''(x_0) = 0$, then $(x_0, f(x_0))$ must be a point of inflection.

(e) A function $f$ defined on the interval $(-2, 2)$ with exactly one relative maximum must have an absolute maximum.

**50.** An important function in probability theory is the standard normal-density function

$$f(x) = \frac{1}{\sqrt{2\pi}} e^{-x^2/2}$$

(a) Determine whether the graph of $f$ is symmetric about the $x$-axis, $y$-axis, or origin.

(b) Find the intervals on which $f$ is increasing and those on which it is decreasing.

(c) Find the coordinates of all relative extrema of $f$.

(d) Find $\lim_{x \to -\infty} f(x)$ and $\lim_{x \to \infty} f(x)$.

(e) Find the intervals on which the graph of $f$ is concave up and those on which it is concave down.

(f) Find the coordinates of all points of inflection.

(g) Sketch the graph of $f$.

(h) Find all absolute extrema.

**51. Marginal Cost**  If $c = q^3 - 6q^2 + 12q + 18$ is a total-cost function, for what values of $q$ is marginal cost increasing?

**52. Marginal Revenue**  If $r = 320q^{3/2} - 2q^2$ is the revenue function for a manufacturer's product, determine the intervals on which the marginal-revenue function is increasing.

**53. Revenue Function**  The demand equation for a manufacturer's product is

$$p = 200 - \frac{\sqrt{q}}{5} \quad \text{where } q > 0$$

Show that the graph of the revenue function is concave down wherever it is defined.

**54. Contraception**  In a model of the effect of contraception on birthrate,[17] the equation

$$R = f(x) = \frac{x}{4.4 - 3.4x} \quad 0 \le x \le 1$$

gives the proportional reduction $R$ in the birthrate as a function of the efficiency $x$ of a contraception method. An efficiency of 0.2 (or 20%) means that the probability of becoming pregnant is 80% of the probability of becoming pregnant without the contraceptive. Find the reduction (as a percentage) when efficiency is (a) 0, (b) 0.5, and (c) 1. Find $dR/dx$ and $d^2 R/dx^2$, and sketch the graph of the equation.

**55. Learning and Memory**  If you were to recite members of a category, such as four-legged animals, the words that you utter would probably occur in "chunks," with distinct pauses between such chunks. For example, you might say the following for the category of four-legged animals:

dog, cat, mouse, rat,
(pause)
horse, donkey, mule,
(pause)
cow, pig, goat, lamb,
etc.

The pauses may occur because you must mentally search for subcategories (animals around the house, beasts of burden, farm animals, etc.).

The elapsed time between onsets of successive words is called *interresponse time*. A function has been used to analyze the length of time for pauses and the chunk size

---

[17]R. K. Leik and B. F. Meeker, *Mathematical Sociology* (Englewood Cliffs, NJ: Prentice-Hall, Inc., 1975).

(number of words in a chunk).[18] This function $f$ is such that

$$f(t) = \begin{cases} \text{the average number of words} \\ \text{that occur in succession with} \\ \text{interresponse times less than } t \end{cases}$$

The graph of $f$ has a shape similar to that in Figure 13.73 and is best fit by a third-degree polynomial, such as

$$f(t) = At^3 + Bt^2 + Ct + D$$

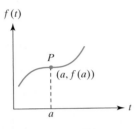

FIGURE 13.73 Diagram for Problem 55.

The point $P$ has special meaning. It is such that the value $a$ separates interresponse times *within* chunks from those *between* chunks. Mathematically, $P$ is a critical point that is also a point of inflection. Assume these two conditions, and show that (a) $a = -B/(3A)$ and (b) $B^2 = 3AC$.

**56. Market Penetration**   In a model for the market penetration of a new product, sales $S$ of the product at time $t$ are given by[19]

$$S = g(t) = \frac{m(p+q)^2}{p}\left[\frac{e^{-(p+q)t}}{\left(\frac{q}{p}e^{-(p+q)t} + 1\right)^2}\right]$$

where $p$, $q$, and $m$ are nonzero constants.

**(a)** Show that

$$\frac{dS}{dt} = \frac{\frac{m}{p}(p+q)^3 e^{-(p+q)t}\left[\frac{q}{p}e^{-(p+q)t} - 1\right]}{\left(\frac{q}{p}e^{-(p+q)t} + 1\right)^3}$$

**(b)** Determine the value of $t$ for which maximum sales occur. You may assume that $S$ attains a maximum when $dS/dt = 0$.

*In Problems 57–60, where appropriate, round your answers to two decimal places.*

**57.** From the graph of $y = 4x^3 + 5.3x^2 - 7x + 3$, find the coordinates of all relative extrema.

**58.** From the graph of $f(x) = x^4 - 2x^3 + 3x - 1$, determine the absolute extrema of $f$ over the interval $[-1, 1]$.

**59.** The graph of a function $f$ has exactly one inflection point. If

$$f''(x) = \frac{x^3 + 3x + 2}{5x^2 - 2x + 4}$$

use the graph of $f''$ to determine the $x$-value of the inflection point of $f$.

**60.** Graph $y = \dfrac{3x - 6x^2}{x^3 + 4x + 1}$. From the graph, locate any horizontal or vertical asymptotes.

**61. Maximization of Production**   A manufacturer determined that $m$ employees on a certain production line will produce $q$ units per month, where

$$q = 80m^2 - 0.1m^4$$

To obtain maximum monthly production, how many employees should be assigned to the production line?

**62. Revenue**   The demand function for a manufacturer's product is given by $p = 100e^{-0.1q}$. For what value of $q$ does the manufacturer maximize total revenue?

**63. Revenue**   The demand function for a monopolist's product is

$$p = \sqrt{500 - q}$$

If the monopolist wants to produce at least 100 units, but not more than 200 units, how many units should be produced to maximize total revenue?

**64. Average Cost**   If $c = 0.01q^2 + 5q + 100$ is a cost function, find the average-cost function. At what level of production $q$ is there a minimum average cost?

**65. Profit**   The demand function for a monopolist's product is

$$p = 500 - 3q$$

and the average cost per unit for producing $q$ units is

$$\bar{c} = q + 200 + \frac{1000}{q}$$

where $p$ and $\bar{c}$ are in dollars per unit. Find the maximum profit that the monopolist can achieve.

**66. Container Design**   A rectangular box is to be made by cutting out equal squares from each corner of a piece of cardboard 10 in. by 16 in. and then folding up the sides. What must be the length of the side of the square cut out if the volume of the box is to be maximum?

**67. Fencing**   A rectangular portion of a field is to be enclosed by a fence and divided equally into three parts by two fences parallel to one pair of the sides. If a total of 800 ft of fencing is to be used, find the dimensions that will maximize the fenced area.

**68. Poster Design**   A rectangular poster having an area of 500 in² is to have a 4-in. margin at each side and at the bottom and a 6-in. margin at the top. The remainder of the poster is for printed matter. Find the dimensions of the poster so that the area for the printed matter is maximized.

**69. Cost**   A furniture company makes personal-computer stands. For a certain model, the total cost (in thousands of dollars) when $q$ *hundred* stands are produced is given by

$$c = 2q^3 - 9q^2 + 12q + 20$$

[18]A. Graesser and G. Mandler, "Limited Processing Capacity Constrains the Storage of Unrelated Sets of Words and Retrieval from Natural Categories," *Human Learning and Memory*, 4, no. 1 (1978), 86–100.

[19]A. P. Hurter, Jr., A. H. Rubenstein et al., "Market Penetration by New Innovations: The Technological Literature," *Technological Forecasting and Social Change*, vol. 11 (1978), 197–221.

**(a)** The company is currently capable of manufacturing between 75 and 600 stands (inclusive) per week. Determine the number of stands that should be produced per week to minimize the total cost, and find the corresponding average cost per stand.

**(b)** Suppose that between 300 and 600 stands must be produced. How many should the company now produce in order to minimize total cost?

**70. Bacteria**   In a laboratory, an experimental antibacterial agent is applied to a population of 100 bacteria. Data indicate that the number of bacteria $t$ hours after the agent is introduced is given by

$$N = \frac{12{,}100 + 110t + 100t^2}{121 + t^2}$$

For what value of $t$ does the maximum number of bacteria in the population occur? What is this maximum number?

# Mathematical Snapshot

## Population Change Over Time

Now that we know how to find the derivative of a function, we might ask whether there is a way to run the process in reverse: to find a function, given its derivative. Ultimately, this is what integration (Chapters 14–15) is all about. Meanwhile, however, we can use the derivative of a function to find the function *approximately* even without knowing how to do integration.

To illustrate, suppose we wish to describe the population, over time, of a small town in a frontier area. Let use imagine that the things we know about the town are all facts about how its population, $P$, changes over time, $t$, with population measured in people and time in years:

1. Births exceed deaths, so that over the course of a year there is a 25% increase in the population before other factors are accounted for. Thus, the annual change due to the birth/death difference is $0.25P$.

2. Every year, of the travelers passing through, ten decide to stop and settle down. This contributes a constant 10 to the annual change.

3. Loneliness causes some people to leave when the town is too small for them. At the extreme, 99% of people will leave over the course of a year if they are all alone (population = 1). When the population is 100, 10% of the residents leave per year due to loneliness.

Assuming an exponential relationship, we write the likelihood that a given person leaves within a year due to loneliness as $Ae^{-kP}$, where $A$ and $k$ are positive constants. The numbers tell us that $Ae^{-k \cdot 1} = 0.99$ and $Ae^{-k \cdot 100} = 0.10$. Solving this pair of equations for $A$ and $k$ yields

$$k = \frac{\ln 9.9}{99} \approx 0.02316$$

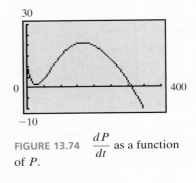

and

$$A = 0.99e^{(\ln 9.9)/99} \approx 1.01319$$

And if $Ae^{-kP}$ is the likelihood of a single person's leaving, the population change per year due to loneliness is $-P$ times that, namely $-1.01319Pe^{-0.02316P}$. (The negative sign is due to the fact that the change is downward.)

4. Crowding causes some people to leave when the town is too large for them. Nobody has a crowding problem when they are all alone (population = 1), but when the population is 100, 10% of the residents leave per year due to crowding.

Again assuming an exponential relationship, we write the likelihood that a given person leaves within a year due to crowding as $1 - Ae^{-kP}$. This time, the numbers tell us that $1 - Ae^{-k \cdot 1} = 0$ and $1 - Ae^{-k \cdot 100} = 0.10$. Solving this pair of equations for $A$ and $k$ yields

$$k = -\frac{\ln 0.9}{99} \approx 0.001064$$

and

$$A = e^{-(\ln 0.9)/99} \approx 1.001065$$

If $1 - Ae^{-kP}$ is the likelihood of a single person's leaving, the population change per year due to crowding is $-P$ times that, namely $-P(1 - 1.001065e^{-0.001064P})$.

The overall rate of change in the population now is the net effect of all these factors added together. In equation form,

$$\frac{dP}{dt} = 0.25P + 10 - 1.01319Pe^{-0.02316P}$$
$$- P(1 - 1.001065e^{-0.001064P})$$

Before we try to reconstruct the function $P(t)$, let us graph the derivative. On a graphing calculator, it looks as shown in Figure 13.74. Note that $\dfrac{dP}{dt}$ is depicted as a

**FIGURE 13.74** $\dfrac{dP}{dt}$ as a function of $P$.

function of $P$. This is a different graph from what we would get if we knew $P$ as a function of $t$, found its derivative, and graphed that in the standard manner, namely as a function of $t$. Nonetheless, this graph reveals some significant facts. First, the derivative is positive from $P = 0$ to $P = 311$; this means that the population will have positive growth in that entire range and thus can be expected to grow from nothing into a substantial community.

Growth does fall to near zero at around $P = 30$. Apparently departures due to loneliness nearly bring growth to a halt when the population is still small. But once the town has grown through that phase, its size increases steadily, at one point (around $P = 170$) adding 21 people per year.

Eventually, departures due to crowding start to take a toll. Above 312 the derivative is negative. This means that if the population ever fluctuated above 312, population losses would shrink it back down to that level. In short, the population of this town stabilizes at 311 or 312—not exactly a city, but this is, after all, a frontier environment.

If we now wish to graph the town's population as a function of time, here is how we do this: We approximate the graph with a string of line segments, each of which has a slope given by the expression we obtained for $dP/dt$. We begin with a known time and population and calculate the initial slope. Let us grow the town from nothing, setting $t = 0$ at $P = 0$. Then $\dfrac{dP}{dt} = 10$. Now we advance the clock forward by a convenient time interval—let us choose 1 year—and, since the slope at $(0, 0)$ equals 10, we increase the population from 0 to 10. The new values for $t$ and $P$ are 1 and 10, respectively, so we draw a line segment from $(0, 0)$ to $(1, 10)$. Now, with $t = 1$ and $P = 10$, we recalculate the slope and go through the same steps again, and we repeat this process until we have drawn as much of the curve as we want to see.

Obviously, this would be extremely tedious to do by hand. On a graphing calculator, however, we can use the programming and line-drawing features. For a TI-83 Plus, the following program does the job nicely, after the expression for $\dfrac{dP}{dt}$ is entered as $Y_1$ (keeping $P$ as the variable):

```
PROGRAM:POPLTN
:Input "P?",P
:Input "T?", T
:ClrDraw
:T → S
:For(I, S + 1, S + 55)
:Line(T,P,I,P + Y₁)
:I → T
:(P + Y₁) → P
:End
```

Deselect the function $Y_1$. Set the graphing window to display the coordinate plane from 0 to 55 horizontally and from 0 to 350 vertically. Then run the program and, at the prompt, give initial values for $P$ and $t$. The program will draw 55 line segments, enough to take the population to its final size from $P = 0, t = 0$. The result is shown in Figure 13.75.

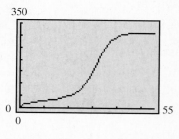

**FIGURE 13.75**    $P$ as a function of $t$.

## Problems

1. What information does Figure 13.75 give that is not evident from Figure 13.74?

2. What happens when an initial value of 450 is selected for $P$? (The display should be adjusted to run from 0 to 500 vertically.) Does this seem right?

3. Why is this procedure for obtaining a graph of $P(t)$ only approximate? How could the approximation be improved?

# 14

# INTEGRATION

 Delivered Price

Anyone who runs a business knows the need for accurate cost estimates. When jobs are individually contracted, determining how much a job will cost is generally the first step in deciding how much to bid.

For example, a painter must determine how much paint a job will take. Since a gallon of paint will cover a certain number of square feet, the key is to determine the area of the surfaces to be painted. Normally, even this requires only simple arithmetic—walls and ceilings are rectangular, and so total area is a sum of products of base and height.

But not all area calculations are as simple. Suppose, for instance, that the bridge shown below must be sandblasted to remove accumulated soot. How would the contractor who charges for sandblasting by the square foot calculate the area of the vertical face on each side of the bridge?

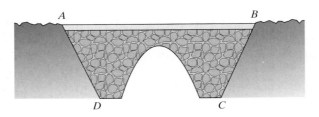

The area could be estimated as perhaps three-quarters of the area of the trapezoid formed by points $A$, $B$, $C$, and $D$. But a more accurate calculation—which might be desirable if the bid were for dozens of bridges of the same dimensions (as along a stretch of railroad)—would require a more refined approach.

If the shape of the bridge's arch can be described mathematically by a function, the contractor could use the method introduced in this chapter: integration. Integration has many applications, the simplest of which is finding areas of regions bounded by curves. Other applications include calculating the total deflection of a beam due to bending stress, calculating the distance traveled underwater by a submarine, and calculating the electricity bill for a company that consumes power at differing rates over the course of a month. Chapters 11–13 dealt with differential calculus. We differentiated a function and obtained another function, its derivative. *Integral calculus* is concerned with the reverse process: We are given the derivative of a function and must find the original function. The need for doing this arises in a natural way. For example, we might have a marginal-revenue function and want to find the revenue function from it. Integral calculus also involves a concept that allows us to take the limit of a special kind of sum as the number of terms in the sum becomes infinite. This is the real power of integral calculus! With such a notion, we can find the area of a region that cannot be found by any other convenient method.

OBJECTIVE

To define the differential, interpret it geometrically, and use it in approximations. Also, to restate the reciprocal relationship between $dx/dy$ and $dy/dx$.

# 14.1 Differentials

We will soon give you a reason for using the symbol $dy/dx$ to denote the derivative of $y$ with respect to $x$. To do this, we introduce the notion of the *differential* of a function.

## DEFINITION

Let $y = f(x)$ be a differentiable function of $x$, and let $\Delta x$ denote a change in $x$, where $\Delta x$ can be any real number. Then the **differential** of $y$, denoted $dy$ or $d(f(x))$, is given by

$$dy = f'(x)\, \Delta x$$

Note that $dy$ depends on two variables, namely, $x$ and $\Delta x$. In fact, $dy$ is a function of two variables.

● **EXAMPLE 1    Computing a Differential**

*Find the differential of* $y = x^3 - 2x^2 + 3x - 4$, *and evaluate it when* $x = 1$ *and* $\Delta x = 0.04$.

**Solution:**  The differential is

$$dy = \frac{d}{dx}(x^3 - 2x^2 + 3x - 4)\, \Delta x$$
$$= (3x^2 - 4x + 3)\, \Delta x$$

When $x = 1$ and $\Delta x = 0.04$,

$$dy = [3(1)^2 - 4(1) + 3](0.04) = 0.08$$

NOW WORK PROBLEM 1 ●●

If $y = x$, then $dy = d(x) = 1\,\Delta x = \Delta x$. Hence, the differential of $x$ is $\Delta x$. We abbreviate $d(x)$ by $dx$. Thus, $dx = \Delta x$. From now on, it will be our practice to write $dx$ for $\Delta x$ when finding a differential. For example,

$$d(x^2 + 5) = \frac{d}{dx}(x^2 + 5)\, dx = 2x\, dx$$

Summarizing, we say that if $y = f(x)$ defines a differentiable function of $x$, then

$$dy = f'(x)\, dx$$

where $dx$ is any real number. Provided that $dx \neq 0$, we can divide both sides by $dx$:

$$\frac{dy}{dx} = f'(x)$$

That is, $dy/dx$ can be viewed either as the quotient of two differentials, namely, $dy$ divided by $dx$, or as one symbol for the derivative of $f$ at $x$. It is for this reason that we introduced the symbol $dy/dx$ to denote the derivative.

● **EXAMPLE 2    Finding a Differential in Terms of** $dx$

**a.** If $f(x) = \sqrt{x}$, then

$$d(\sqrt{x}) = \frac{d}{dx}(\sqrt{x})\, dx = \frac{1}{2}x^{-1/2}dx = \frac{1}{2\sqrt{x}}dx$$

**b.** If $u = (x^2 + 3)^5$, then $du = 5(x^2 + 3)^4(2x)\, dx = 10x(x^2 + 3)^4 dx$.

NOW WORK PROBLEM 3 ●●

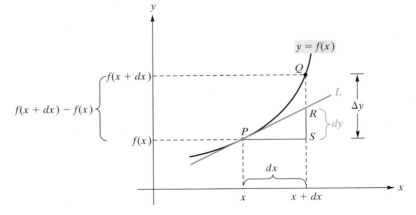

**FIGURE 14.1** Geometric interpretation of $dy$ and $\Delta x$.

The differential can be interpreted geometrically. In Figure 14.1, the point $P(x, f(x))$ is on the curve $y = f(x)$. Suppose $x$ changes by $dx$, a real number, to the new value $x + dx$. Then the new function value is $f(x + dx)$, and the corresponding point on the curve is $Q(x + dx, f(x + dx))$. Passing through $P$ and $Q$ are horizontal and vertical lines, respectively, that intersect at $S$. A line $L$ tangent to the curve at $P$ intersects segment $QS$ at $R$, forming the right triangle $PRS$. Observe that the graph of $f$ near $P$ is approximated by the tangent line at $P$. The slope of $L$ is $f'(x)$ but it is also given by $\overline{SR}/\overline{PS}$ so that

$$f'(x) = \frac{\overline{SR}}{\overline{PS}}$$

Since $dy = f'(x)\, dx$ and $dx = \overline{PS}$,

$$dy = f'(x)\, dx = \frac{\overline{SR}}{\overline{PS}} \cdot \overline{PS} = \overline{SR}$$

Thus, if $dx$ is a change in $x$ at $P$, then $dy$ is the corresponding vertical change along the **tangent line** at $P$. Note that for the same $dx$, the vertical change along the **curve** is $\Delta y = \overline{SQ} = f(x + dx) - f(x)$. Do not confuse $\Delta y$ with $dy$. However, from Figure 14.1, the following is apparent:

When $dx$ is close to 0, $dy$ is an approximation to $\Delta y$. Therefore,

$$\Delta y \approx dy$$

This fact is useful in estimating $\Delta y$, a change in $y$, as Example 3 shows.

● **EXAMPLE 3    Using the Differential to Estimate a Change in a Quantity**

*A governmental health agency examined the records of a group of individuals who were hospitalized with a particular illness. It was found that the total proportion P that are discharged at the end of t days of hospitalization is given by*

$$P = P(t) = 1 - \left( \frac{300}{300 + t} \right)^3$$

*Use differentials to approximate the change in the proportion discharged if t changes from 300 to 305.*

**Solution:** The change in $t$ from 300 to 305 is $\Delta t = dt = 305 - 300 = 5$. The change in $P$ is $\Delta P = P(305) - P(300)$. We approximate $\Delta P$ by $dP$:

$$\Delta P \approx dP = P'(t)\, dt = -3 \left( \frac{300}{300 + t} \right)^2 \left( -\frac{300}{(300 + t)^2} \right) dt = 3\frac{300^3}{(300 + t)^4}\, dt$$

When $t = 300$ and $dt = 5$,

$$dP = 3\frac{300^3}{600^4}5 = \frac{15}{2^3 600} = \frac{1}{2^3 40} = \frac{1}{320} \approx 0.0031$$

For a comparison, the true value of $\Delta P$ is

$$P(305) - P(300) = 0.87807 - 0.87500 = 0.00307$$

(to five decimal places).

NOW WORK PROBLEM 11

We said that if $y = f(x)$, then $\Delta y \approx dy$ if $dx$ is close to zero. Thus,

$$\Delta y = f(x + dx) - f(x) \approx dy$$

so that

Formula (1) is used to approximate a function value, whereas the formula $\Delta y \approx dy$ is used to approximate a change in function values.

$$f(x + dx) \approx f(x) + dy \qquad \text{(1)}$$

This formula gives us a way of estimating a function value $f(x + dx)$. For example, suppose we estimate $\ln(1.06)$. Letting $y = f(x) = \ln x$, we need to estimate $f(1.06)$. Since $d(\ln x) = (1/x)\, dx$, we have, from Formula (1),

$$f(x + dx) \approx f(x) + dy$$

$$\ln(x + dx) \approx \ln x + \frac{1}{x}\, dx$$

We know the exact value of $\ln 1$, so we will let $x = 1$ and $dx = 0.06$. Then $x + dx = 1.06$, and $dx$ is close to zero. Therefore,

$$\ln(1 + 0.06) \approx \ln(1) + \frac{1}{1}(0.06)$$

$$\ln(1.06) \approx 0 + 0.06 = 0.06$$

The true value of $\ln(1.06)$ to five decimal places is $0.05827$.

● **EXAMPLE 4    Using the Differential to Estimate a Function Value**

*The demand function for a product is given by*

$$p = f(q) = 20 - \sqrt{q}$$

*where $p$ is the price per unit in dollars for $q$ units. By using differentials, approximate the price when 99 units are demanded.*

**Solution:** We want to approximate $f(99)$. By Formula (1),

$$f(q + dq) \approx f(q) + dp$$

where

$$dp = -\frac{1}{2\sqrt{q}}\, dq \qquad \left(\frac{dp}{dq} = -\frac{1}{2}q^{-1/2}\right)$$

We choose $q = 100$ and $dq = -1$ because $q + dq = 99$, $dq$ is small, and it is easy to compute $f(100) = 20 - \sqrt{100} = 10$. We thus have

$$f(99) = f[100 + (-1)] \approx f(100) - \frac{1}{2\sqrt{100}}(-1)$$

$$f(99) \approx 10 + 0.05 = 10.05$$

Hence, the price per unit when 99 units are demanded is approximately $10.05.

NOW WORK PROBLEM 17

The equation $y = x^3 + 4x + 5$ defines $y$ as a function of $x$. We could write $f(x) = x^3 + 4x + 5$. However, the equation also defines $x$ implicitly as a function of $y$. In fact, if we restrict the domain of $f$ to some set of real numbers $x$ so that

$y = f(x)$ is a one-to-one function, then in principle we could solve for $x$ in terms of $y$ and get $x = f^{-1}(y)$. (Actually, no restriction of the domain is necessary here. Since $f'(x) = 3x^2 + 4 > 0$, for all $x$, we see that $f$ is strictly increasing on $(-\infty, \infty)$ and is thus one-to-one on $(-\infty, \infty)$.) As we did in Example 6 of Section 12.2, we can look at the derivative of $x$ with respect to $y$, $dx/dy$ and we have seen that it is given by

$$\frac{dx}{dy} = \frac{1}{\dfrac{dy}{dx}} \qquad \text{provided that } dy/dx \neq 0$$

Since $dx/dy$ can be considered a quotient of differentials, we now see that it is the reciprocal of the quotient of differentials $dy/dx$. Thus

$$\frac{dx}{dy} = \frac{1}{3x^2 + 4}$$

It is important to understand that it is not necessary to be able to solve $y = x^3 + 4x + 5$ for $x$ in terms of $y$ and the equation $\dfrac{dx}{dy} = \dfrac{1}{3x^2 + 4}$ holds for all $x$.

● EXAMPLE 5   **Finding $dp/dq$ from $dq/dp$**

*Find* $\dfrac{dp}{dq}$ *if* $q = \sqrt{2500 - p^2}$.

Solution:

**Strategy**   There are a number of ways to find $dp/dq$. One approach is to solve the given equation for $p$ explicitly in terms of $q$ and then differentiate directly. Another approach to find $dp/dq$ is to use implicit differentiation. However, since $q$ is given explicitly as a function of $p$, we can easily find $dq/dp$ and then use the preceding reciprocal relation to find $dp/dq$. We will take this approach.

We have

$$\frac{dq}{dp} = \frac{1}{2}(2500 - p^2)^{-1/2}(-2p) = -\frac{p}{\sqrt{2500 - p^2}}$$

Hence,

$$\frac{dp}{dq} = \frac{1}{\dfrac{dq}{dp}} = -\frac{\sqrt{2500 - p^2}}{p}$$

NOW WORK PROBLEM 27   ●●●

## Problems 14.1

*In Problems 1–10, find the differential of the function in terms of $x$ and $dx$.*

*1. $y = 5x - 7$

2. $y = 2$

*3. $f(x) = \sqrt{x^4 - 9}$

4. $f(x) = (4x^2 - 5x + 2)^3$

5. $u = \dfrac{1}{x^2}$

6. $u = \dfrac{1}{\sqrt{x}}$

7. $p = \ln(x^2 + 7)$

8. $p = e^{x^3 + 2x - 5}$

9. $y = (9x + 3)e^{2x^2 + 3}$

10. $y = \ln\sqrt{x^2 + 12}$

*In Problems 11–16, find $\Delta y$ and $dy$ for the given values of $x$ and $dx$.*

*11. $y = 4 - 7x$; $x = 3$, $dx = 0.02$

12. $y = 5x^2$; $x = -1$, $dx = -0.02$

13. $y = 2x^2 + 5x - 7$; $x = -2$, $dx = 0.1$

14. $y = (3x + 2)^2$; $x = -1$, $dx = -0.03$

15. $y = \sqrt{32 - x^2}$; $x = 4$, $dx = -0.05$   Round your answer to three decimal places.

16. $y = \ln(-x)$; $x = -5$, $dx = 0.1$

*17. Let $f(x) = \dfrac{x + 5}{x + 1}$

   (a) Evaluate $f'(1)$.
   (b) Use differentials to estimate the value of $f(1.1)$.

18. Let $f(x) = x^{3x}$

   (a) Evaluate $f'(1)$.
   (b) Use differentials to estimate the value of $f(0.98)$.

*In Problems 19–26, approximate each expression by using differentials.*

**19.** $\sqrt{288}$   (*Hint:* $17^2 = 289$.)   **20.** $\sqrt{122}$

**21.** $\sqrt[3]{65.5}$   **22.** $\sqrt[4]{16.3}$

**23.** $\ln 0.97$   **24.** $\ln 1.01$

**25.** $e^{0.001}$   **26.** $e^{-0.01}$

*In Problems 27–32, find $dx/dy$ or $dp/dq$.*

**\*27.** $y = 2x - 1$   **28.** $y = 5x^2 + 3x + 2$

**29.** $q = (p^2 + 5)^3$   **30.** $q = \sqrt{p + 5}$

**31.** $q = \dfrac{1}{p}$   **32.** $q = e^{4-2p}$

**33.** If $y = 7x^2 - 6x + 3$, find the value of $dx/dy$ when $x = 3$.

**34.** If $y = \ln x^2$, find the value of $dx/dy$ when $x = 3$.

*In Problems 35 and 36, find the rate of change of q with respect to p for the indicated value of q.*

**35.** $p = \dfrac{500}{q + 2}$; $q = 18$   **36.** $p = 50 - \sqrt{q}$; $q = 100$

**37. Profit**   Suppose that the profit (in dollars) of producing $q$ units of a product is
$$P = 397q - 2.3q^2 - 400$$
Using differentials, find the approximate change in profit if the level of production changes from $q = 90$ to $q = 91$. Find the true change.

**38. Revenue**   Given the revenue function
$$r = 250q + 45q^2 - q^3$$
use differentials to find the approximate change in revenue if the number of units increases from $q = 40$ to $q = 41$. Find the true change.

**39. Demand**   The demand equation for a product is
$$p = \frac{10}{\sqrt{q}}$$
Using differentials, approximate the price when 24 units are demanded.

**40. Demand**   Given the demand function
$$p = \frac{200}{\sqrt{q + 8}}$$
use differentials to estimate the price per unit when 40 units are demanded.

**41.** If $y = f(x)$, then the *proportional change in y* is defined to be $\Delta y/y$, which can be approximated with differentials

by $dy/y$. Use this last form to approximate the proportional change in the cost function
$$c = f(q) = \frac{q^4}{2} + 3q + 400$$
when $q = 10$ and $dq = 2$. Round your answer to one decimal place.

**42. Status/Income**   Suppose that $S$ is a numerical value of status based on a person's annual income $I$ (in thousands of dollars). For a certain population, suppose $S = 20\sqrt{I}$. Use differentials to approximate the change in $S$ if annual income decreases from $45,000 to $44,500.

**43. Biology**   The volume of a spherical cell is given by $V = \frac{4}{3}\pi r^3$, where $r$ is the radius. Estimate the change in volume when the radius changes from $6.5 \times 10^{-4}$ cm to $6.6 \times 10^{-4}$ cm.

**44. Muscle Contraction**   The equation
$$(P + a)(v + b) = k$$
is called the "fundamental equation of muscle contraction."[1] Here $P$ is the load imposed on the muscle, $v$ is the velocity of the shortening of the muscle fibers, and $a$, $b$, and $k$ are positive constants. Find $P$ in terms of $v$, and then use the differential to approximate the change in $P$ due to a small change in $v$.

**45. Demand**   The demand, $q$, for a monopolist's product is related to the price per unit, $p$, according to the equation
$$2 + \frac{q^2}{200} = \frac{4000}{p^2}$$

**(a)** Verify that 40 units will be demanded when the price per unit is $20.

**(b)** Show that $\dfrac{dq}{dp} = -2.5$ when the price per unit is $20.

**(c)** Use differentials and the results of parts (a) and (b) to approximate the number of units that will be demanded if the price per unit is reduced to $19.20.

**46. Profit**   The demand equation for a monopolist's product is
$$p = \frac{1}{2}q^2 - 66q + 7000$$
and the average-cost function is
$$\bar{c} = 500 - q + \frac{80,000}{2q}$$

**(a)** Find the profit when 100 units are demanded.

**(b)** Use differentials and the result of part (a) to estimate the profit when 98 units are demanded.

---

OBJECTIVE

To define the antiderivative and the indefinite integral and to apply basic integration formulas.

# 14.2 The Indefinite Integral

Given a function $f$, if $F$ is a function such that
$$F'(x) = f(x) \tag{1}$$
then $F$ is called an *antiderivative* of $f$. Thus,

An antiderivative of $f$ is simply a function whose derivative is $f$.

---
[1] R. W. Stacy et al., *Essentials of Biological and Medical Physics* (New York: McGraw-Hill, 1955).

Multiplying both sides of Equation (1) by the differential $dx$ gives $F'(x)\,dx = f(x)\,dx$. However, because $F'(x)\,dx$ is the differential of $F$, we have $dF = f(x)\,dx$. Hence, we can think of an antiderivative of $f$ as a function whose differential is $f(x)\,dx$.

> **DEFINITION**
> An *antiderivative* of a function $f$ is a function $F$ such that
> $$F'(x) = f(x)$$
> Equivalently, in differential notation,
> $$dF = f(x)\,dx$$

For example, because the derivative of $x^2$ is $2x$, $x^2$ is an antiderivative of $2x$. However, it is not the only antiderivative of $2x$: Since

$$\frac{d}{dx}(x^2 + 1) = 2x \quad \text{and} \quad \frac{d}{dx}(x^2 - 5) = 2x$$

both $x^2 + 1$ and $x^2 - 5$ are also antiderivatives of $2x$. In fact, it is obvious that because the derivative of a constant is zero, $x^2 + C$ is also an antiderivative of $2x$ for *any* constant $C$. Thus, $2x$ has infinitely many antiderivatives. More importantly, *all* antiderivatives of $2x$ must be functions of the form $x^2 + C$, because of the following fact:

Any two antiderivatives of a function differ only by a constant.

Since $x^2 + C$ describes all antiderivatives of $2x$, we can refer to it as being the *most general antiderivative* of $2x$, denoted by $\int 2x\,dx$, which is read "the *indefinite integral* of $2x$ with respect to $x$." Thus, we write

$$\int 2x\,dx = x^2 + C$$

The symbol $\int$ is called the **integral sign,** $2x$ is the **integrand,** and $C$ is the **constant of integration.** The $dx$ is part of the integral notation and indicates the variable involved. Here $x$ is the **variable of integration.**

More generally, the **indefinite integral** of any function $f$ with respect to $x$ is written $\int f(x)\,dx$ and denotes the most general antiderivative of $f$. Since all antiderivatives of $f$ differ only by a constant, if $F$ is any antiderivative of $f$, then

$$\int f(x)\,dx = F(x) + C \quad \text{where } C \text{ is a constant}$$

To *integrate $f$* means to find $\int f(x)\,dx$. In summary,

$$\int f(x)\,dx = F(x) + C \quad \text{if and only if} \quad F'(x) = f(x)$$

Thus we have

$$\frac{d}{dx}\left(\int f(x)\,dx\right) = f(x) \quad \text{and} \quad \int \frac{d}{dx}(F(x))\,dx = F(x) + C$$

which shows the extent to which differentiation and indefinite integration are inverse procedures.

**CAUTION**

A common mistake is to omit $C$, the constant of integration.

**● EXAMPLE 1   Finding an Indefinite Integral**

*Find* $\int 5\,dx.$

Solution:

**Strategy**   First we must find (perhaps better words are "guess at") a function whose derivative is 5. Then we add the constant of integration.

Since we know that the derivative of $5x$ is 5, $5x$ is an antiderivative of 5. Therefore,

$$\int 5\,dx = 5x + C$$

NOW WORK PROBLEM 1 ●●●

**TABLE 14.1** Basic Integration Formulas

1. $\int k\,dx = kx + C$     $k$ is a constant

2. $\int x^n\,dx = \dfrac{x^{n+1}}{n+1} + C$     $n \neq -1$

3. $\int x^{-1}\,dx = \int \dfrac{1}{x}dx = \int \dfrac{dx}{x} = \ln x + C$     for $x > 0$

4. $\int e^x\,dx = e^x + C$

5. $\int kf(x)\,dx = k\int f(x)\,dx$     $k$ is a constant

6. $\int (f(x) \pm g(x))\,dx = \int f(x)\,dx \pm \int g(x)\,dx$

Using differentiation formulas from Chapters 11 and 12, we have compiled a list of basic integration formulas in Table 14.1. These formulas are easily verified. For example, Formula 2 is true because the derivative of $x^{n+1}/(n+1)$ is $x^n$ for $n \neq -1$. (We must have $n \neq -1$ because the denominator is 0 when $n = -1$.) Formula 2 states that the indefinite integral of a power of $x$ (except $x^{-1}$) is obtained by increasing the exponent of $x$ by 1, dividing by the new exponent, and adding on the constant of integration. The indefinite integral of $x^{-1}$ will be discussed in Section 14.4.

To verify Formula 5, we must show that the derivative of $k\int f(x)\,dx$ is $kf(x)$. Since the derivative of $k\int f(x)\,dx$ is simply $k$ times the derivative of $\int f(x)\,dx$, and the derivative of $\int f(x)\,dx$ is $f(x)$, Formula 5 is verified. You should verify the other formulas. Formula 6 can be extended to any number of sums or differences.

**● EXAMPLE 2   Indefinite Integrals of a Constant and of a Power of $x$**

**a.** *Find* $\int 1\,dx.$

Solution:   By Formula 1 with $k = 1$

$$\int 1\,dx = 1x + C = x + C$$

Usually, we write $\int 1\,dx$ as $\int dx$. Thus, $\int dx = x + C$.

**b.** Find $\displaystyle\int x^5\, dx$.

Solution: By Formula 2 with $n = 5$,

$$\int x^5\, dx = \frac{x^{5+1}}{5+1} + C = \frac{x^6}{6} + C$$

NOW WORK PROBLEM 3

---

**CAUTION**

Only a *constant* factor of the integrand can "pass through" an integral sign. Because $x$ is not a constant, one cannot find $\int 7x\, dx$ as $7x$ times $\int dx$.

**EXAMPLE 3  Indefinite Integral of a Constant Times a Function**

Find $\displaystyle\int 7x\, dx$.

Solution: By Formula 5 with $k = 7$ and $f(x) = x$,

$$\int 7x\, dx = 7 \int x\, dx$$

Since $x$ is $x^1$, by Formula 2 we have

$$\int x^1\, dx = \frac{x^{1+1}}{1+1} + C_1 = \frac{x^2}{2} + C_1$$

where $C_1$ is the constant of integration. Therefore,

$$\int 7x\, dx = 7 \int x\, dx = 7\left(\frac{x^2}{2} + C_1\right) = \frac{7}{2}x^2 + 7C_1$$

Since $7C_1$ is just an arbitrary constant, we will replace it by $C$ for simplicity. Thus,

$$\int 7x\, dx = \frac{7}{2}x^2 + C$$

It is not necessary to write all intermediate steps when integrating. More simply, we write

$$\int 7x\, dx = (7)\frac{x^2}{2} + C = \frac{7}{2}x^2 + C$$

NOW WORK PROBLEM 5

**EXAMPLE 4  Indefinite Integral of a Constant Times a Function**

Find $\displaystyle\int -\frac{3}{5}e^x\, dx$.

Solution:

$$\int -\frac{3}{5}e^x\, dx = -\frac{3}{5} \int e^x\, dx \qquad \text{(Formula 5)}$$

$$= -\frac{3}{5}e^x + C \qquad \text{(Formula 4)}$$

NOW WORK PROBLEM 21

**EXAMPLE 5  Finding Indefinite Integrals**

**a.** Find $\displaystyle\int \frac{1}{\sqrt{t}}\, dt$.

Solution: Here $t$ is the variable of integration. We rewrite the integrand so that a basic formula can be used. Since $1/\sqrt{t} = t^{-1/2}$, applying Formula 2 gives

$$\int \frac{1}{\sqrt{t}}\, dt = \int t^{-1/2}\, dt = \frac{t^{(-1/2)+1}}{-\frac{1}{2}+1} + C = \frac{t^{1/2}}{\frac{1}{2}} + C = 2\sqrt{t} + C$$

**b.** *Find* $\int \dfrac{1}{6x^3}\,dx$.

Solution:

$$\int \frac{1}{6x^3}\,dx = \frac{1}{6}\int x^{-3}\,dx = \left(\frac{1}{6}\right)\frac{x^{-3+1}}{-3+1} + C$$

$$= -\frac{x^{-2}}{12} + C = -\frac{1}{12x^2} + C$$

NOW WORK PROBLEM 9

---

**PRINCIPLES IN PRACTICE 4**

**INDEFINITE INTEGRAL OF A SUM**

The rate of growth of the population of a new city is estimated by $\dfrac{dN}{dt} = 500 + 300\sqrt{t}$, where $t$ is in years. Find

$$\int (500 + 300\sqrt{t})\,dt$$

When integrating an expression involving more than one term, only one constant of integration is needed.

● **EXAMPLE 6   Indefinite Integral of a Sum**

*Find* $\int (x^2 + 2x)\,dx$.

Solution:  By Formula 6,

$$\int (x^2 + 2x)\,dx = \int x^2\,dx + \int 2x\,dx$$

Now,

$$\int x^2\,dx = \frac{x^{2+1}}{2+1} + C_1 = \frac{x^3}{3} + C_1$$

and

$$\int 2x\,dx = 2\int x\,dx = (2)\frac{x^{1+1}}{1+1} + C_2 = x^2 + C_2$$

Thus,

$$\int (x^2 + 2x)\,dx = \frac{x^3}{3} + x^2 + C_1 + C_2$$

For convenience, we will replace the constant $C_1 + C_2$ by $C$. We then have

$$\int (x^2 + 2x)\,dx = \frac{x^3}{3} + x^2 + C$$

Omitting intermediate steps, we simply integrate term by term and write

$$\int (x^2 + 2x)\,dx = \frac{x^3}{3} + (2)\frac{x^2}{2} + C = \frac{x^3}{3} + x^2 + C$$

NOW WORK PROBLEM 11

---

**PRINCIPLES IN PRACTICE 5**

**INDEFINITE INTEGRAL OF A SUM AND DIFFERENCE**

Suppose the rate of savings in the United States is given by $\dfrac{dS}{dt} = 2.1t^2 - 65.4t + 491.6$, where $t$ is the time in years and $S$ is the amount of money saved in billions of dollars. Find the form of the equation for the amount of money saved.

● **EXAMPLE 7   Indefinite Integral of a Sum and Difference**

*Find* $\int (2\sqrt[5]{x^4} - 7x^3 + 10e^x - 1)\,dx$.

Solution:

$$\int (2\sqrt[5]{x^4} - 7x^3 + 10e^x - 1)\,dx$$

$$= 2\int x^{4/5}\,dx - 7\int x^3\,dx + 10\int e^x\,dx - \int 1\,dx \qquad \text{(Formulas 5 \& 6)}$$

$$= (2)\frac{x^{9/5}}{\frac{9}{5}} - (7)\frac{x^4}{4} + 10e^x - x + C \qquad \text{(Formulas 1, 2, \& 4)}$$

$$= \frac{10}{9}x^{9/5} - \frac{7}{4}x^4 + 10e^x - x + C$$

NOW WORK PROBLEM 15

Sometimes, in order to apply the basic integration formulas, it is necessary first to perform algebraic manipulations on the integrand, as Example 8 shows.

● EXAMPLE 8  **Using Algebraic Manipulation to Find an Indefinite Integral**

*Find* $\int y^2 \left( y + \frac{2}{3} \right) dy$.

**Solution:** The integrand does not fit a familiar integration form. However, by multiplying the integrand we get

$$\int y^2 \left( y + \frac{2}{3} \right) dy = \int \left( y^3 + \frac{2}{3} y^2 \right) dy$$

$$= \frac{y^4}{4} + \left( \frac{2}{3} \right) \frac{y^3}{3} + C = \frac{y^4}{4} + \frac{2y^3}{9} + C$$

NOW WORK PROBLEM 41 ●●●

**CAUTION**

In Example 8, we first multiplied the factors in the integrand. The answer could not have been found simply in terms of $\int y^2 \, dy$ and $\int (y + \frac{2}{3}) \, dy$. There is not a formula for the integral of a general product of functions.

● EXAMPLE 9  **Using Algebraic Manipulation to Find an Indefinite Integral**

**a.** *Find* $\int \frac{(2x-1)(x+3)}{6} dx$.

**Solution:** By factoring out the constant $\frac{1}{6}$ and multiplying the binomials, we get

$$\int \frac{(2x-1)(x+3)}{6} dx = \frac{1}{6} \int (2x^2 + 5x - 3) \, dx$$

$$= \frac{1}{6} \left( (2) \frac{x^3}{3} + (5) \frac{x^2}{2} - 3x \right) + C$$

$$= \frac{x^3}{9} + \frac{5x^2}{12} - \frac{x}{2} + C$$

Another algebraic approach to part (b) is

$$\int \frac{x^3 - 1}{x^2} dx = \int (x^3 - 1) x^{-2} \, dx$$

$$= \int (x - x^{-2}) \, dx$$

and so on.

**b.** *Find* $\int \frac{x^3 - 1}{x^2} dx$.

**Solution:** We can break up the integrand into fractions by dividing each term in the numerator by the denominator:

$$\int \frac{x^3 - 1}{x^2} dx = \int \left( \frac{x^3}{x^2} - \frac{1}{x^2} \right) dx = \int (x - x^{-2}) \, dx$$

$$= \frac{x^2}{2} - \frac{x^{-1}}{-1} + C = \frac{x^2}{2} + \frac{1}{x} + C$$

NOW WORK PROBLEM 49 ●●●

## Problems 14.2

*In Problems 1–52, find the indefinite integrals.*

*1. $\int 7 \, dx$

2. $\int \frac{1}{2x} dx$

*3. $\int x^8 \, dx$

4. $\int 5x^{24} \, dx$

*5. $\int 5x^{-7} \, dx$

6. $\int \frac{z^{-3}}{3} dz$

7. $\int \frac{2}{x^{10}} dx$

8. $\int \frac{7}{x^4 \, dx}$

*9. $\int \frac{1}{t^{7/4}} dt$

10. $\int \frac{7}{2x^{9/4}} dx$

*11. $\int (4 + t) \, dt$

12. $\int (r^3 + 2r) \, dr$

13. $\int (y^5 - 5y) \, dy$

14. $\int (5 - 2w - 6w^2) \, dw$

*15. $\int (3t^2 - 4t + 5) \, dt$

16. $\int (1 + t^2 + t^4 + t^6) \, dt$

**17.** $\int (7+e)\,dx$

**18.** $\int (5-2^{-1})\,dx$

**39.** $\int \left(-\frac{\sqrt[3]{x^2}}{5} - \frac{7}{2\sqrt{x}} + 6x\right)dx$

**19.** $\int \left(\frac{x}{7} - \frac{3}{4}x^4\right)dx$

**20.** $\int \left(\frac{2x^2}{7} - \frac{8}{3}x^4\right)dx$

**40.** $\int \left(\sqrt[3]{u} + \frac{1}{\sqrt{u}}\right)du$

**\*41.** $\int (x^2+5)(x-3)\,dx$

**\*21.** $\int \pi e^x\,dx$

**22.** $\int \left(\frac{e^x}{3} + 2x\right)dx$

**42.** $\int x^4(x^3 + 8x^2 + 7)\,dx$

**43.** $\int \sqrt{x}(x+3)\,dx$

**23.** $\int (x^{8.3} - 9x^6 + 3x^{-4} + x^{-3})\,dx$

**44.** $\int (z+2)^2\,dz$

**45.** $\int (3u+2)^3\,du$

**24.** $\int (0.7y^3 + 10 + 2y^{-3})\,dy$

**46.** $\int \left(\frac{2}{\sqrt[5]{x}} - 1\right)^2 dx$

**47.** $\int v^{-2}(2v^4 + 3v^2 - 2v^{-3})\,dv$

**25.** $\int \frac{-2\sqrt{x}}{3}\,dx$

**26.** $\int dz$

**48.** $\int (6e^u - u^3(\sqrt{u}+1))\,du$

**\*49.** $\int \frac{z^4 + 10z^3}{2z^2}\,dz$

**27.** $\int \frac{1}{4\sqrt[8]{x^2}}\,dx$

**28.** $\int \frac{-4}{(3x)^3}\,dx$

**50.** $\int \frac{x^4 - 5x^2 + 2x}{5x^2}\,dx$

**51.** $\int \frac{e^x + e^{2x}}{e^x}\,dx$

**29.** $\int \left(\frac{x^3}{3} - \frac{3}{x^3}\right)dx$

**30.** $\int \left(\frac{1}{2x^3} - \frac{1}{x^4}\right)dx$

**52.** $\int \frac{(x^3+1)^2}{x^2}\,dx$

**31.** $\int \left(\frac{3w^2}{2} - \frac{2}{3w^2}\right)dw$

**32.** $\int \frac{4}{e^{-s}}\,ds$

**53.** If $F(x)$ and $G(x)$ are such that $F'(x) = G'(x)$, is it true that $F(x) - G(x)$ must be zero?

**33.** $\int \frac{3u-4}{5}\,du$

**34.** $\int \frac{1}{12}\left(\frac{1}{3}e^x\right)dx$

**54.** **(a)** Find a function $F$ such that $\int F(x)\,dx = xe^x + C$.
**(b)** Is there only one function $F$ satisfying the equation given in part (a), or are there many such functions?

**35.** $\int (u^e + e^u)\,du$

**36.** $\int \left(3y^3 - 2y^2 + \frac{e^y}{6}\right)dy$

**55.** Find $\int \frac{d}{dx}\left(\frac{1}{\sqrt{x^2+1}}\right)dx$.

**37.** $\int (2\sqrt{x} - 3\sqrt[4]{x})\,dx$

**38.** $\int 0\,dt$

---

OBJECTIVE

To find a particular antiderivative of a function that satisfies certain conditions. This involves evaluating constants of integration.

# 14.3 Integration with Initial Conditions

If we know the rate of change, $f'$, of the function $f$, then the function $f$ itself is an antiderivative of $f'$ (since the derivative of $f$ is $f'$). Of course, there are many antiderivatives of $f'$, and the most general one is denoted by the indefinite integral. For example, if

$$f'(x) = 2x$$

then

$$f(x) = \int f'(x)\,dx = \int 2x\,dx = x^2 + C. \tag{1}$$

That is, *any* function of the form $f(x) = x^2 + C$ has its derivative equal to $2x$. Because of the constant of integration, notice that we do not know $f(x)$ specifically. However, if $f$ must assume a certain function value for a particular value of $x$, then we can determine the value of $C$ and thus determine $f(x)$ specifically. For instance, if $f(1) = 4$, then from Equation (1),

$$f(1) = 1^2 + C$$
$$4 = 1 + C$$
$$C = 3$$

Thus,

$$f(x) = x^2 + 3$$

That is, we now know the particular function $f(x)$ for which $f'(x) = 2x$ and $f(1) = 4$. The condition $f(1) = 4$, which gives a function value of $f$ for a specific value of $x$, is called an *initial condition*.

● **EXAMPLE 1    Initial-Condition Problem**

*If $y$ is a function of $x$ such that $y' = 8x - 4$ and $y(2) = 5$, find $y$. [Note: $y(2) = 5$ means that $y = 5$ when $x = 2$.] Also, find $y(4)$.*

**Solution:** Here $y(2) = 5$ is the initial condition. Since $y' = 8x - 4$, $y$ is an antiderivative of $8x - 4$:

$$y = \int (8x - 4)\, dx = 8 \cdot \frac{x^2}{2} - 4x + C = 4x^2 - 4x + C \tag{2}$$

We can determine the value of $C$ by using the initial condition. Because $y = 5$ when $x = 2$, from Equation (2), we have

$$5 = 4(2)^2 - 4(2) + C$$
$$5 = 16 - 8 + C$$
$$C = -3$$

Replacing $C$ by $-3$ in Equation (2) gives the function that we seek:

$$y = 4x^2 - 4x - 3 \tag{3}$$

To find $y(4)$, we let $x = 4$ in Equation (3):

$$y(4) = 4(4)^2 - 4(4) - 3 = 64 - 16 - 3 = 45$$

NOW WORK PROBLEM 1  ●●●

● **EXAMPLE 2    Initial-Condition Problem Involving $y''$**

*Given that $y'' = x^2 - 6$, $y'(0) = 2$, and $y(1) = -1$, find $y$.*

**Solution:**

**Strategy**   To go from $y''$ to $y$, two integrations are needed: the first to take us from $y''$ to $y'$ and the other to take us from $y'$ to $y$. Hence, there will be two constants of integration, which we will denote by $C_1$ and $C_2$.

Since $y'' = \frac{d}{dx}(y') = x^2 - 6$, $y'$ is an antiderivative of $x^2 - 6$. Thus,

$$y' = \int (x^2 - 6)\, dx = \frac{x^3}{3} - 6x + C_1 \tag{4}$$

Now, $y'(0) = 2$ means that $y' = 2$ when $x = 0$; therefore, from Equation (4), we have

$$2 = \frac{0^3}{3} - 6(0) + C_1$$

Hence, $C_1 = 2$, so

$$y' = \frac{x^3}{3} - 6x + 2$$

By integration, we can find $y$:

$$y = \int \left( \frac{x^3}{3} - 6x + 2 \right) dx$$

$$= \left( \frac{1}{3} \right) \frac{x^4}{4} - (6)\frac{x^2}{2} + 2x + C_2$$

so

$$y = \frac{x^4}{12} - 3x^2 + 2x + C_2 \tag{5}$$

Now, since $y = -1$ when $x = 1$, we have, from Equation (5),

$$-1 = \frac{1^4}{12} - 3(1)^2 + 2(1) + C_2$$

Thus, $C_2 = -\frac{1}{12}$, so

$$y = \frac{x^4}{12} - 3x^2 + 2x - \frac{1}{12}$$

NOW WORK PROBLEM 5 ●●●

Integration with initial conditions is applicable to many applied situations, as the next three examples illustrate.

### ● EXAMPLE 3   Income and Education

*For a particular urban group, sociologists studied the current average yearly income y (in dollars) that a person can expect to receive with x years of education before seeking regular employment. They estimated that the rate at which income changes with respect to education is given by*

$$\frac{dy}{dx} = 100x^{3/2} \quad 4 \le x \le 16$$

*where $y = 28{,}720$ when $x = 9$. Find y.*

**Solution:**  Here $y$ is an antiderivative of $100x^{3/2}$. Thus,

$$y = \int 100x^{3/2}\, dx = 100 \int x^{3/2}\, dx$$

$$= (100)\frac{x^{5/2}}{\dfrac{5}{2}} + C$$

$$y = 40x^{5/2} + C \tag{6}$$

The initial condition is that $y = 28{,}720$ when $x = 9$. By putting these values into Equation (6), we can determine the value of $C$:

$$28{,}720 = 40(9)^{5/2} + C$$

$$= 40(243) + C$$

$$28{,}720 = 9720 + C$$

Therefore, $C = 19{,}000$, and

$$y = 40x^{5/2} + 19{,}000$$

NOW WORK PROBLEM 17 ●●●

### ● EXAMPLE 4   Finding the Demand Function from Marginal Revenue

*If the marginal-revenue function for a manufacturer's product is*

$$\frac{dr}{dq} = 2000 - 20q - 3q^2$$

*find the demand function.*

**Solution:**

> **Strategy**  By integrating $dr/dq$ and using an initial condition, we can find the revenue function $r$. But revenue is also given by the general relationship $r = pq$, where $p$ is the price per unit. Thus, $p = r/q$. Replacing $r$ in this equation by the revenue function yields the demand function.

Since $dr/dq$ is the derivative of total revenue $r$,

$$r = \int (2000 - 20q - 3q^2)\, dq$$

$$= 2000q - (20)\frac{q^2}{2} - (3)\frac{q^3}{3} + C$$

so that

$$r = 2000q - 10q^2 - q^3 + C \qquad (7)$$

Revenue is 0 when $q$ is 0.

We assume that **when no units are sold, there is no revenue;** that is, $r = 0$ when $q = 0$. This is our initial condition. Putting these values into Equation (7) gives

$$0 = 2000(0) - 10(0)^2 - 0^3 + C$$

Although $q = 0$ gives $C = 0$, this is not true in general. It occurs in this section because the revenue functions are polynomials. In later sections, evaluating at $q = 0$ may produce a nonzero value for $C$.

Hence, $C = 0$, and

$$r = 2000q - 10q^2 - q^3$$

To find the demand function, we use the fact that $p = r/q$ and substitute for $r$:

$$p = \frac{r}{q} = \frac{2000q - 10q^2 - q^3}{q}$$

$$p = 2000 - 10q - q^2$$

NOW WORK PROBLEM 11 ◖●●

### ●EXAMPLE 5   Finding Cost from Marginal Cost

*In the manufacture of a product, fixed costs per week are $4000. (Fixed costs are costs, such as rent and insurance, that remain constant at all levels of production during a given time period.) If the marginal-cost function is*

$$\frac{dc}{dq} = 0.000001(0.002q^2 - 25q) + 0.2$$

*where c is the total cost (in dollars) of producing q pounds of product per week, find the cost of producing 10,000 lb in 1 week.*

**Solution:**  Since $dc/dq$ is the derivative of the total cost $c$,

$$c(q) = \int [0.000001(0.002q^2 - 25q) + 0.2]\, dq$$

$$= 0.000001 \int (0.002q^2 - 25q)\, dq + \int 0.2\, dq$$

$$c(q) = 0.000001 \left( \frac{0.002q^3}{3} - \frac{25q^2}{2} \right) + 0.2q + C$$

When $q$ is 0, total cost is equal to fixed cost.

Fixed costs are constant regardless of output. Therefore, when $q = 0, c = 4000$, which is our initial condition. Putting $c(0) = 4000$ in the last equation, we find that $C = 4000$, so

Although $q = 0$ gives $C$ a value equal to fixed costs, this is not true in general. It occurs in this section because the cost functions are polynomials. In later sections, evaluating at $q = 0$ may produce a value for $C$ that is different from fixed cost.

$$c(q) = 0.000001 \left( \frac{0.002q^3}{3} - \frac{25q^2}{2} \right) + 0.2q + 4000 \qquad (8)$$

From Equation (8), we have $c(10,000) = 5416\frac{2}{3}$. Thus, the total cost for producing 10,000 pounds of product in 1 week is $5416.67.

NOW WORK PROBLEM 15 ◖●●

# Problems 14.3

*In Problems 1 and 2, find y subject to the given conditions.*

*1. $dy/dx = 3x - 4$;  $y(-1) = \frac{13}{2}$

2. $dy/dx = x^2 - x$;  $y(3) = \frac{19}{2}$

*In Problems 3 and 4, if y satisfies the given conditions, find y(x) for the given value of x.*

3. $y' = 5/\sqrt{x}$, $y(9) = 50$;  $x = 16$

4. $y' = -x^2 + 2x$, $y(2) = 1$;  $x = 1$

*In Problems 5–8, find y subject to the given conditions.*

*5. $y'' = -3x^2 + 4x$;  $y'(1) = 2$, $y(1) = 3$

6. $y'' = x + 1$;  $y'(0) = 0$, $y(0) = 5$

7. $y''' = 2x$;  $y''(-1) = 3$, $y'(3) = 10$, $y(0) = 13$

8. $y''' = e^x + 1$;  $y''(0) = 1$, $y'(0) = 2$, $y(0) = 3$

*In Problems 9–12, dr/dq is a marginal-revenue function. Find the demand function.*

9. $dr/dq = 0.7$

10. $dr/dq = 10 - \frac{1}{16}q$

*11. $dr/dq = 275 - q - 0.3q^2$

12. $dr/dq = 5{,}000 - 3(2q + 2q^3)$

*In Problems 13–16, dc/dq is a marginal-cost function and fixed costs are indicated in braces. For Problems 13 and 14, find the total-cost function. For Problems 15 and 16, find the total cost for the indicated value of q.*

13. $dc/dq = 1.35$;  {200}

14. $dc/dq = 2q + 75$;  {2000}

*15. $dc/dq = 0.08q^2 - 1.6q + 6.5$;  {8000};  $q = 25$

16. $dc/dq = 0.000204q^2 - 0.046q + 6$;  {15,000};  $q = 200$

*17. **Diet for Rats**  A group of biologists studied the nutritional effects on rats that were fed a diet containing 10% protein.[2] The protein consisted of yeast and corn flour.

Over a period of time, the group found that the (approximate) rate of change of the average weight gain $G$ (in grams) of a rat with respect to the percentage $P$ of yeast in the protein mix was

$$\frac{dG}{dP} = -\frac{P}{25} + 2 \qquad 0 \le P \le 100$$

If $G = 38$ when $P = 10$, find $G$.

18. **Winter Moth**  A study of the winter moth was made in Nova Scotia.[3] The prepupae of the moth fall onto the ground from host trees. It was found that the (approximate) rate at which prepupal density $y$ (the number of prepupae per square foot of soil) changes with respect to distance $x$ (in feet) from the base of a host tree is

$$\frac{dy}{dx} = -1.5 - x \quad 1 \le x \le 9$$

If $y = 57.3$ when $x = 1$, find $y$.

19. **Fluid Flow**  In the study of the flow of fluid in a tube of constant radius $R$, such as blood flow in portions of the body, one can think of the tube as consisting of concentric tubes of radius $r$, where $0 \le r \le R$. The velocity $v$ of the fluid is a function of $r$ and is given by[4]

$$v = \int -\frac{(P_1 - P_2)r}{2l\eta} \, dr$$

where $P_1$ and $P_2$ are pressures at the ends of the tube, $\eta$ (a Greek letter read "eta") is fluid viscosity, and $l$ is the length of the tube. If $v = 0$ when $r = R$, show that

$$v = \frac{(P_1 - P_2)(R^2 - r^2)}{4l\eta}$$

20. **Elasticity of Demand**  The sole producer of a product has determined that the marginal-revenue function is

$$\frac{dr}{dq} = 100 - 3q^2$$

Determine the point elasticity of demand for the product when $q = 5$. (*Hint:* First find the demand function.)

21. **Average Cost**  A manufacturer has determined that the marginal-cost function is

$$\frac{dc}{dq} = 0.003q^2 - 0.4q + 40$$

where $q$ is the number of units produced. If marginal cost is $27.50 when $q = 50$ and fixed costs are $5000, what is the *average* cost of producing 100 units?

22. If $f''(x) = 30x^4 + 12x$ and $f'(1) = 10$, evaluate

$$f(965.335245) - f(-965.335245)$$

---

OBJECTIVE

To learn and apply the formulas for $\int u^n \, du$, $\int e^u \, du$, and $\int \frac{1}{u} \, du$.

# 14.4  More Integration Formulas

## Power Rule for Integration

The formula

$$\int x^n \, dx = \frac{x^{n+1}}{n+1} + C \qquad \text{if } n \ne -1$$

---

[2] Adapted from R. Bressani, "The Use of Yeast in Human Foods," in *Single-Cell Protein*, ed. R. I. Mateles and S. R. Tannenbaum (Cambridge, MA: MIT Press, 1968).

[3] Adapted from D. G. Embree, "The Population Dynamics of the Winter Moth in Nova Scotia, 1954–1962," *Memoirs of the Entomological Society of Canada*, no. 46 (1965).

[4] R. W. Stacy et al., *Essentials of Biological and Medical Physics* (New York: McGraw-Hill, 1955).

which applies to a power of $x$, can be generalized to handle a power of a *function* of $x$. Let $u$ be a differentiable function of $x$. By the power rule for differentiation, if $n \neq -1$, then

$$\frac{d}{dx}\left(\frac{(u(x))^{n+1}}{n+1}\right) = \frac{(n+1)(u(x))^n \cdot u'(x)}{n+1} = (u(x))^n \cdot u'(x)$$

Thus,

$$\int (u(x))^n \cdot u'(x)\,dx = \frac{(u(x))^{n+1}}{n+1} + C \quad n \neq -1$$

We call this the *power rule for integration*. Note that $u'(x)\,dx$ is the differential of $u$, namely $du$. In mathematical shorthand, we can replace $u(x)$ by $u$ and $u'(x)\,dx$ by $du$:

---

**Power Rule for Integration**

*If $u$ is differentiable, then*

$$\int u^n\,du = \frac{u^{n+1}}{n+1} + C \qquad \text{if } n \neq -1 \tag{1}$$

---

It is essential that you realize the difference between the power rule for integration and the formula for $\int x^n\,dx$. In the power rule, $u$ represents a function, whereas in $\int x^n\,dx$, $x$ is a variable.

● **EXAMPLE 1  Applying the Power Rule for Integration**

**a.** *Find* $\int (x+1)^{20}\,dx$.

**Solution:** Since the integrand is a power of the function $x+1$, we will set $u = x+1$. Then $du = dx$, and $\int (x+1)^{20}\,dx$ has the form $\int u^{20}\,du$. By the power rule for integration,

$$\int (x+1)^{20}\,dx = \int u^{20}\,du = \frac{u^{21}}{21} + C = \frac{(x+1)^{21}}{21} + C$$

Note that we give our answer not in terms of $u$, but explicitly in terms of $x$.

**b.** *Find* $\int 3x^2(x^3+7)^3\,dx$.

**Solution:** We observe that the integrand contains a power of the function $x^3+7$. Let $u = x^3+7$. Then $du = 3x^2\,dx$. Fortunately, $3x^2$ appears as a factor in the integrand and we have

$$\int 3x^2(x^3+7)^3\,dx = \int (x^3+7)^3[3x^2\,dx] = \int u^3\,du$$

$$= \frac{u^4}{4} + C = \frac{(x^3+7)^4}{4} + C$$

NOW WORK PROBLEM 3 ●●●

After integrating, you may wonder what happened to $3x^2$. We note again that $du = 3x^2\,dx$.

In order to apply the power rule for integration, sometimes an adjustment must be made to obtain $du$ in the integrand, as Example 2 illustrates.

● **EXAMPLE 2  Adjusting for *du***

*Find* $\int x\sqrt{x^2+5}\,dx$.

**Solution:** We can write this as $\int x(x^2+5)^{1/2}\,dx$. Notice that the integrand contains a power of the function $x^2+5$. If $u = x^2+5$, then $du = 2x\,dx$. Since the *constant* factor 2 in $du$ does *not* appear in the integrand, this integral does not have the form $\int u^n\,du$. However, from $du = 2x\,dx$ we can write $x\,dx = \dfrac{du}{2}$ so that the integral

becomes

$$\int x(x^2 + 5)^{1/2}\, dx = \int (x^2 + 5)^{1/2}[x\, dx] = \int u^{1/2}\frac{du}{2}$$

Moving the *constant* factor $\frac{1}{2}$ in front of the integral sign, we have

$$\int x(x^2 + 5)^{1/2}\, dx = \frac{1}{2}\int u^{1/2}\, du = \frac{1}{2}\left(\frac{u^{3/2}}{\frac{3}{2}}\right) + C = \frac{1}{3}u^{3/2} + C$$

which in terms of $x$ (as is required) gives

$$\int x\sqrt{x^2 + 5}\, dx = \frac{(x^2 + 5)^{3/2}}{3} + C$$

**CAUTION**

The answer to an integration problem must be expressed in terms of the original variable.

NOW WORK PROBLEM 15 ●●

In Example 2, the integrand $x\sqrt{x^2 + 5}$ missed being of the form $(u(x))^{1/2}u'(x)$ by the *constant factor* of 2. In general, if we have $\int (u(x))^n \frac{u'(x)}{k}\, dx$, for $k$ a nonzero constant, then we can write

**CAUTION**

We can adjust for constant factors, but not variable factors.

$$\int (u(x))^n \frac{u'(x)}{k}\, dx = \int u^n \frac{du}{k} = \frac{1}{k}\int u^n\, du$$

to simplify the integral, but such *adjustments* of the integrand are *not possible for variable factors*.

When using the form $\int u^n\, du$, do not neglect $du$. For example,

$$\int (4x + 1)^2\, dx \neq \frac{(4x + 1)^3}{3} + C$$

The correct way to do this problem is as follows. Let $u = 4x + 1$, from which it follows that $du = 4\, dx$. Thus $dx = \dfrac{du}{4}$ and

$$\int (4x + 1)^2\, dx = \int u^2\left[\frac{du}{4}\right] = \frac{1}{4}\int u^2\, du = \frac{1}{4}\cdot\frac{u^3}{3} + C = \frac{(4x + 1)^3}{12} + C$$

● **EXAMPLE 3    Applying the Power Rule for Integration**

**a.** *Find* $\displaystyle\int \sqrt[3]{6y}\, dy$.

**Solution:** The integrand is $(6y)^{1/3}$, a power of a function. However, in this case the obvious substitution $u = 6y$ can be avoided. More simply, we have

$$\int \sqrt[3]{6y}\, dy = \int 6^{1/3}y^{1/3}\, dy = \sqrt[3]{6}\int y^{1/3}\, dy = \sqrt[3]{6}\frac{y^{4/3}}{\frac{4}{3}} + C = \frac{3\sqrt[3]{6}}{4}y^{4/3} + C$$

**b.** *Find* $\displaystyle\int \frac{2x^3 + 3x}{(x^4 + 3x^2 + 7)^4}\, dx$.

**Solution:** We can write this as $\int (x^4 + 3x^2 + 7)^{-4}(2x^3 + 3x)\, dx$. Let us try to use the power rule for integration. If $u = x^4 + 3x^2 + 7$, then $du = (4x^3 + 6x)\, dx$, which is two times the quantity $(2x^3 + 3x)\, dx$ in the integral. Thus $(2x^3 + 3x)\, dx = \dfrac{du}{2}$ and we again illustrate the *adjustment* technique:

$$\int (x^4 + 3x^2 + 7)^{-4}[(2x^3 + 3x)\, dx] = \int u^{-4}\left[\frac{du}{2}\right] = \frac{1}{2}\int u^{-4}\, du$$

$$= \frac{1}{2}\cdot\frac{u^{-3}}{-3} + C = -\frac{1}{6u^3} + C = -\frac{1}{6(x^4 + 3x^2 + 7)^3} + C$$

NOW WORK PROBLEM 5 ●●

In using the power rule for integration, take care when making your choice for $u$. In Example 3(b), you would *not* be able to proceed very far if, for instance, you let $u = 2x^3 + 3x$. At times you may find it necessary to try many different choices. So don't just sit and look at the integral. Try something even if it is wrong, because it may give you a hint as to what might work. **Skill at integration comes only after many hours of practice and conscientious study.**

● EXAMPLE 4    An Integral to Which the Power Rule Does Not Apply

*Find* $\displaystyle\int 4x^2(x^4 + 1)^2\,dx.$

**Solution:** If we set $u = x^4 + 1$, then $du = 4x^3\,dx$. To get $du$ in the integral, we need an additional factor of the *variable x*. However, we can adjust only for **constant** factors. Thus, we cannot use the power rule. Instead, to find the integral, we will first expand $(x^4 + 1)^2$:

$$\int 4x^2(x^4+1)^2\,dx = 4\int x^2(x^8 + 2x^4 + 1)\,dx$$

$$= 4\int (x^{10} + 2x^6 + x^2)\,dx$$

$$= 4\left(\frac{x^{11}}{11} + \frac{2x^7}{7} + \frac{x^3}{3}\right) + C$$

NOW WORK PROBLEM 67 ●●

### Integrating Natural Exponential Functions

We now turn our attention to integrating exponential functions. If $u$ is a differentiable function of $x$, then

$$\frac{d}{dx}(e^u) = e^u\frac{du}{dx}$$

Corresponding to this differentiation formula is the integration formula

$$\int e^u\frac{du}{dx}\,dx = e^u + C$$

But $\dfrac{du}{dx}\,dx$ is the differential of $u$, namely, $du$. Thus,

$$\int e^u\,du = e^u + C \tag{2}$$

**PRINCIPLES IN PRACTICE 1**

INTEGRALS INVOLVING EXPONENTIAL FUNCTIONS

When an object is moved from one environment to another, its temperature $T$ changes at a rate given by $\dfrac{dT}{dt} = kCe^{kt}$, where $t$ is the time (in hours) after changing environments, $C$ is the temperature difference (original minus new) between the environments, and $k$ is a constant. If the original environment is $70°$, the new environment is $60°$, and $k = -0.5$, find the general form of $T(t)$.

● EXAMPLE 5    Integrals Involving Exponential Functions

**a.** *Find* $\displaystyle\int 2xe^{x^2}\,dx.$

**Solution:** Let $u = x^2$. Then $du = 2x\,dx$, and by Equation (2),

$$\int 2xe^{x^2}\,dx = \int e^{x^2}[2x\,dx] = \int e^u\,du$$

$$= e^u + C = e^{x^2} + C$$

**b.** *Find* $\int (x^2 + 1)e^{x^3+3x}\, dx$.

**Solution:** If $u = x^3 + 3x$, then $du = (3x^2 + 3)\, dx = 3(x^2 + 1)\, dx$. If the integrand contained a factor of 3, the integral would have the form $\int e^u\, du$. Thus, we write

$$\int (x^2 + 1)e^{x^3+3x}\, dx = \int e^{x^3+3x}[(x^2 + 1)\, dx]$$

$$= \frac{1}{3}\int e^u\, du = \frac{1}{3}e^u + C$$

$$= \frac{1}{3}e^{x^3+3x} + C$$

where in the second step we replaced $(x^2 + 1)\, dx$ by $\frac{1}{3}\, du$ but wrote $\frac{1}{3}$ outside the integral.

NOW WORK PROBLEM 41

## Integrals Involving Logarithmic Functions

As you know, the power-rule formula $\int u^n\, du = u^{n+1}/(n + 1) + C$ does not apply when $n = -1$. To handle that situation, namely, $\int u^{-1}\, du = \int \frac{1}{u}\, du$, we first recall from Section 12.1 that

$$\frac{d}{dx}(\ln |u|) = \frac{1}{u}\frac{du}{dx} \quad \text{for } u \neq 0$$

which gives us the integration formula

$$\int \frac{1}{u}\, du = \ln |u| + C \quad \text{for } u \neq 0 \tag{3}$$

In particular, if $u = x$, then $du = dx$, and

$$\int \frac{1}{x}\, dx = \ln |x| + C \quad \text{for } x \neq 0 \tag{4}$$

**PRINCIPLES IN PRACTICE 2**

INTEGRALS INVOLVING $\frac{1}{u}\, du$

If the rate of vocabulary memorization of the average student in a foreign language is given by $\frac{dv}{dt} = \frac{35}{t + 1}$, where $v$ is the number of vocabulary words memorized in $t$ hours of study, find the general form of $v(t)$.

● **EXAMPLE 6**  **Integrals Involving** $\frac{1}{u}\, du$

**a.** Find $\int \frac{7}{x}\, dx$.

**Solution:** From Equation (4),

$$\int \frac{7}{x}\, dx = 7\int \frac{1}{x}\, dx = 7\ln |x| + C$$

Using properties of logarithms, we can write this answer another way:

$$\int \frac{7}{x}\, dx = \ln |x^7| + C$$

**b.** *Find* $\int \frac{2x}{x^2 + 5}\, dx$.

**Solution:** Let $u = x^2 + 5$. Then $du = 2x\, dx$. From Equation (3),

$$\int \frac{2x}{x^2 + 5}\, dx = \int \frac{1}{x^2 + 5}[2x\, dx] = \int \frac{1}{u}\, du$$

$$= \ln |u| + C = \ln |x^2 + 5| + C$$

Since $x^2 + 5$ is always positive, we can omit the absolute-value bars:

$$\int \frac{2x}{x^2 + 5}\, dx = \ln(x^2 + 5) + C$$

NOW WORK PROBLEM 31

638 Chapter 14 Integration

● EXAMPLE 7    An Integral Involving $\dfrac{1}{u}\,du$

Find $\displaystyle\int \dfrac{(2x^3 + 3x)\,dx}{x^4 + 3x^2 + 7}$.

**Solution:** If $u = x^4 + 3x^2 + 7$, then $du = (4x^3 + 6x)\,dx$, which is two times the numerator giving $(2x^3 + 3x)\,dx = \dfrac{du}{2}$. To apply Equation (3), we write

$$\int \dfrac{2x^3 + 3x}{x^4 + 3x^2 + 7}\,dx = \dfrac{1}{2}\int \dfrac{1}{u}\,du$$

$$= \dfrac{1}{2}\ln|u| + C$$

$$= \dfrac{1}{2}\ln|x^4 + 3x^2 + 7| + C \qquad \text{(Rewrite } u \text{ in terms of } x.)$$

$$= \dfrac{1}{2}\ln(x^4 + 3x^2 + 7) + C \qquad (x^4 + 3x^2 + 7 > 0 \quad \text{for all } x)$$

NOW WORK PROBLEM 51 ●●●

● EXAMPLE 8    An Integral Involving Two Forms

Find $\displaystyle\int \left( \dfrac{1}{(1-w)^2} + \dfrac{1}{w-1} \right) dw$.

**Solution:**

$$\int \left( \dfrac{1}{(1-w)^2} + \dfrac{1}{w-1} \right) dw = \int (1-w)^{-2}\,dw + \int \dfrac{1}{w-1}\,dw$$

$$= -1\int (1-w)^{-2}[-dw] + \int \dfrac{1}{w-1}\,dw$$

The first integral has the form $\int u^{-2}\,du$, and the second has the form $\int \dfrac{1}{v}\,dv$. Thus,

$$\int \left( \dfrac{1}{(1-w)^2} + \dfrac{1}{w-1} \right) dw = -\dfrac{(1-w)^{-1}}{-1} + \ln|w-1| + C$$

$$= \dfrac{1}{1-w} + \ln|w-1| + C$$

●●●

For your convenience, we list in Table 14.2 the basic integration formulas so far discussed. We assume that $u$ is a function of $x$.

TABLE 14.2  Basic Integration Formulas

1. $\displaystyle\int k\,du = ku + C \qquad k$ a constant

2. $\displaystyle\int u^n\,du = \dfrac{u^{n+1}}{n+1} + C \qquad n \neq -1$

3. $\displaystyle\int \dfrac{1}{u}\,du = \ln|u| + C \qquad u \neq 0$

4. $\displaystyle\int e^u\,du = e^u + C$

5. $\displaystyle\int kf(x)\,dx = k\int f(x)\,dx \qquad k$ a constant

6. $\displaystyle\int [f(x) \pm g(x)]\,dx = \int f(x)\,dx \pm \int g(x)\,dx$

# Problems 14.4

*In Problems 1–80, find the indefinite integrals.*

**1.** $\int (x+5)^7 \, dx$

**2.** $\int 15(x+2)^4 \, dx$

**\*3.** $\int 2x(x^2+3)^5 \, dx$

**4.** $\int (3x^2+10x)(x^3+5x^2+6) \, dx$

**\*5.** $\int (3y^2+6y)(y^3+3y^2+1)^{2/3} \, dy$

**6.** $\int (15t^2-6t+1)(5t^3-3t^2+t)^{17} \, dt$

**7.** $\int \dfrac{5}{(3x-1)^3} \, dx$

**8.** $\int \dfrac{4x}{(2x^2-7)^{10}} \, dx$

**9.** $\int \sqrt{2x-1} \, dx$

**10.** $\int \dfrac{1}{\sqrt{x-5}} \, dx$

**11.** $\int (7x-6)^4 \, dx$

**12.** $\int x^2(3x^3+7)^3 \, dx$

**13.** $\int u(5u^2-9)^{14} \, du$

**14.** $\int 9x\sqrt{1+2x^2} \, dx$

**\*15.** $\int 4x^4(27+x^5)^{1/3} \, dx$

**16.** $\int (4-5x)^9 \, dx$

**17.** $\int 3e^{3x} \, dx$

**18.** $\int 5e^{3t+7} \, dt$

**19.** $\int (2t+1)e^{t^2+t} \, dt$

**20.** $\int -3w^2 e^{-w^3} \, dw$

**21.** $\int xe^{7x^2} \, dx$

**22.** $\int x^3 e^{4x^4} \, dx$

**23.** $\int 4e^{-3x} \, dx$

**24.** $\int x^4 e^{-6x^5} \, dx$

**25.** $\int \dfrac{1}{x+5} \, dx$

**26.** $\int \dfrac{12x^2+4x+2}{x+x^2+2x^3} \, dx$

**27.** $\int \dfrac{3x^2+4x^3}{x^3+x^4} \, dx$

**28.** $\int \dfrac{6x^2-6x}{1-3x^2+2x^3} \, dx$

**29.** $\int \dfrac{6z}{(z^2-6)^5} \, dx$

**30.** $\int \dfrac{3}{(5v-1)^4} \, dv$

**\*31.** $\int \dfrac{4}{x} \, dx$

**32.** $\int \dfrac{3}{1+2y} \, dy$

**33.** $\int \dfrac{s^2}{s^3+5} \, ds$

**34.** $\int \dfrac{2x^2}{3-4x^3} \, dx$

**35.** $\int \dfrac{5}{4-2x} \, dx$

**36.** $\int \dfrac{7t}{5t^2-6} \, dt$

**37.** $\int \sqrt{5x} \, dx$

**38.** $\int \dfrac{1}{(3x)^6} \, dx$

**39.** $\int \dfrac{x}{\sqrt{x^2-4}} \, dx$

**40.** $\int \dfrac{9}{1-3x} \, dx$

**\*41.** $\int 2y^3 e^{y^4+1} \, dx$

**42.** $\int 2\sqrt{2x-1} \, dx$

**43.** $\int v^2 e^{-2v^3+1} \, dv$

**44.** $\int \dfrac{x^2}{\sqrt[3]{2x^3+9}} \, dx$

**45.** $\int (e^{-5x}+2e^x) \, dx$

**46.** $\int 4\sqrt[3]{y+1} \, dy$

**47.** $\int (8x+10)(7-2x^2-5x)^3 \, dx$

**48.** $\int 2ye^{3y^2} \, dy$

**49.** $\int \dfrac{x^2+2}{x^3+6x} \, dx$

**50.** $\int (e^x+2e^{-3x}-e^{5x}) \, dx$

**\*51.** $\int \dfrac{16s-4}{3-2s+4s^2} \, ds$

**52.** $\int (6t^2+4t)(t^3+t^2+1)^6 \, dt$

**53.** $\int x(2x^2+1)^{-1} \, dx$

**54.** $\int (8w^5+w^2-2)(6w-w^3-4w^6)^{-4} \, dw$

**55.** $\int -(x^2-2x^5)(x^3-x^6)^{-10} \, dx$

**56.** $\int \dfrac{3}{5}(v-2)e^{2-4v+v^2} \, dv$

**57.** $\int (2x^3+x)(x^4+x^2) \, dx$

**58.** $\int (e^{3.1})^2 \, dx$

**59.** $\int \dfrac{7+14x}{(4-x-x^2)^5} \, dx$

**60.** $\int (e^x-e^{-x})^2 \, dx$

**61.** $\int x(2x+1)e^{4x^3+3x^2-4} \, dx$

**62.** $\int (u^3-ue^{6-3u^2}) \, du$

**63.** $\int x\sqrt{(8-5x^2)^3} \, dx$

**64.** $\int e^{-x/7} \, dx$

**65.** $\int \left(\sqrt{2x}-\dfrac{1}{\sqrt{2x}}\right) dx$

**66.** $\int 3\dfrac{x^4}{e^{x^5}} \, dx$

**\*67.** $\int (x^2+1)^2 \, dx$

**68.** $\int \left[x(x^2-16)^2-\dfrac{1}{2x+5}\right] dx$

**69.** $\int \left[\dfrac{x}{x^2+1}+\dfrac{x^5}{(x^6+1)^2}\right] dx$

**70.** $\int \left[\dfrac{3}{x-1}+\dfrac{1}{(x-1)^2}\right] dx$

**71.** $\int \left[\dfrac{2}{4x+1}-(4x^2-8x^5)(x^3-x^6)^{-8}\right] dx$

**72.** $\int (r^3+5)^2 \, dr$

**73.** $\int \left[\sqrt{3x+1}-\dfrac{x}{x^2+3}\right] dx$

**74.** $\int \left[\dfrac{x}{3x^2+5}-\dfrac{x^2}{(x^3+1)^3}\right] dx$

**75.** $\int \dfrac{e^{\sqrt{x}}}{\sqrt{x}} \, dx$

**76.** $\int (e^5-3^e) \, dx$

**77.** $\int \dfrac{1+e^{2x}}{4e^x} \, dx$

**78.** $\int \dfrac{2}{t^2}\sqrt{\dfrac{1}{t}+9} \, dt$

**79.** $\int \dfrac{x+1}{x^2+2x}\ln(x^2+2x) \, dx$

**80.** $\int \sqrt[3]{x}e^{\sqrt[3]{8x^4}} \, dx$

*In Problems 81–84, find y subject to the given conditions.*

**81.** $y'=(3-2x)^2;\quad y(0)=1$

**82.** $y'=\dfrac{x}{x^2+6};\quad y(1)=0$

**83.** $y'' = \dfrac{1}{x^2};\quad y'(-2) = 3,\ y(1) = 2$

**84.** $y'' = (x+1)^{3/2};\quad y'(3) = 0,\ y(3) = 0$

**85. Real Estate** The rate of change of the value of a house that cost \$350,000 to build can be modeled by $\dfrac{dV}{dt} = 8e^{0.05t}$, where $t$ is the time in years since the house was built and $V$ is the value (in thousands of dollars) of the house. Find $V(t)$.

**86. Life Span** If the rate of change of the expected life span $l$ at birth of people born in the United States can be modeled by $\dfrac{dl}{dt} = \dfrac{12}{2t + 50}$, where $t$ is the number of years after 1940 and the expected life span was 63 years in 1940, find the expected life span for people born in 1998.

**87. Oxygen in Capillary** In a discussion of the diffusion of oxygen from capillaries,[5] concentric cylinders of radius $r$ are used as a model for a capillary. The concentration $C$ of oxygen in the capillary is given by

$$C = \int \left( \dfrac{Rr}{2K} + \dfrac{B_1}{r} \right) dr$$

where $R$ is the constant rate at which oxygen diffuses from the capillary, and $K$ and $B_1$ are constants. Find $C$. (Write the constant of integration as $B_2$.)

**88.** Find $f(2)$ if $f\left(\tfrac{1}{3}\right) = 2$ and $f'(x) = e^{3x+2} - 3x$.

## 14.5 Techniques of Integration

OBJECTIVE

To discuss techniques of handling more challenging integration problems, namely, by algebraic manipulation and by fitting the integrand to a familiar form. To integrate an exponential function with a base different from $e$ and to find the consumption function, given the marginal propensity to consume.

We turn now to some more difficult integration problems.

When you are integrating fractions, sometimes a preliminary division is needed to get familiar integration forms, as the next example shows.

●**EXAMPLE 1  Preliminary Division before Integration**

**a.** Find $\displaystyle\int \dfrac{x^3 + x}{x^2}\, dx$.

**Solution:** A familiar integration form is not apparent. However, we can break up the integrand into two fractions by dividing each term in the numerator by the denominator. We then have

$$\int \dfrac{x^3 + x}{x^2}\, dx = \int \left( \dfrac{x^3}{x^2} + \dfrac{x}{x^2} \right) dx = \int \left( x + \dfrac{1}{x} \right) dx$$

$$= \dfrac{x^2}{2} + \ln|x| + C$$

Here we split up the integrand.

**b.** Find $\displaystyle\int \dfrac{2x^3 + 3x^2 + x + 1}{2x + 1}\, dx$.

**Solution:** Here the integrand is a quotient of polynomials in which the degree of the numerator is greater than or equal to that of the denominator. In such a situation we first use long division. Recall that if $f$ and $g$ are polynomials, with the degree of $f$ greater than or equal to the degree of $g$, then long division allows us to find (uniquely) polynomials $q$ and $r$, where either $r$ is the zero polynomial or the degree of $r$ is strictly less than the degree of $g$, satisfying

$$\dfrac{f}{g} = q + \dfrac{r}{g}$$

Using an obvious, abbreviated notation, we see that

$$\int \dfrac{f}{g} = \int \left( q + \dfrac{r}{g} \right) = \int q + \int \dfrac{r}{g}$$

Since integrating a polynomial is easy, we see that integrating rational functions reduces to the task of integrating *proper rational functions*—those for which the degree of the numerator is strictly less than the degree of the denominator. In

---

[5]W. Simon, *Mathematical Techniques for Physiology and Medicine* (New York: Academic Press, Inc., 1972).

Here we used long division to rewrite the integrand.

this case we obtain

$$\int \frac{2x^3 + 3x^2 + x + 1}{2x + 1}\, dx = \int \left( x^2 + x + \frac{1}{2x+1} \right) dx$$

$$= \frac{x^3}{3} + \frac{x^2}{2} + \int \frac{1}{2x+1}\, dx$$

$$= \frac{x^3}{3} + \frac{x^2}{2} + \frac{1}{2} \int \frac{1}{2x+1}\, d(2x+1)$$

$$= \frac{x^3}{3} + \frac{x^2}{2} + \frac{1}{2} \ln|2x+1| + C$$

NOW WORK PROBLEM 1 ⬤◖◗

● EXAMPLE 2   **Indefinite Integrals**

**a.** *Find* $\int \dfrac{1}{\sqrt{x}(\sqrt{x}-2)^3}\, dx.$

Solution:  We can write this integral as $\int \dfrac{(\sqrt{x}-2)^{-3}}{\sqrt{x}}\, dx.$ Let us try the power rule for integration with $u = \sqrt{x} - 2.$ Then $du = \dfrac{1}{2\sqrt{x}}\, dx,$ so that $\dfrac{dx}{\sqrt{x}} = 2\,du,$ and

Here the integral is fit to the form to which the power rule for integration applies.

$$\int \frac{(\sqrt{x}-2)^{-3}}{\sqrt{x}}\, dx = \int (\sqrt{x}-2)^{-3} \left[ \frac{dx}{\sqrt{x}} \right]$$

$$= 2 \int u^{-3}\, du = 2 \left( \frac{u^{-2}}{-2} \right) + C$$

$$= -\frac{1}{u^2} + C = -\frac{1}{(\sqrt{x}-2)^2} + C$$

**b.** *Find* $\int \dfrac{1}{x \ln x}\, dx.$

Solution:  If $u = \ln x,$ then $du = \dfrac{1}{x}\, dx,$ and

Here the integral fits the familiar form $\int \dfrac{1}{u}\, du.$

$$\int \frac{1}{x \ln x}\, dx = \int \frac{1}{\ln x} \left( \frac{1}{x}\, dx \right) = \int \frac{1}{u}\, du$$

$$= \ln|u| + C = \ln|\ln x| + C$$

**c.** *Find* $\int \dfrac{5}{w(\ln w)^{3/2}}\, dw.$

Solution:  If $u = \ln w,$ then $du = \dfrac{1}{w}\, dw.$ Applying the power rule for integration, we have

Here the integral is fit to the form to which the power rule for integration applies.

$$\int \frac{5}{w(\ln w)^{3/2}}\, dw = 5 \int (\ln w)^{-3/2} \left[ \frac{1}{w}\, dw \right]$$

$$= 5 \int u^{-3/2}\, du = 5 \cdot \frac{u^{-1/2}}{-\frac{1}{2}} + C$$

$$= \frac{-10}{u^{1/2}} + C = -\frac{10}{(\ln w)^{1/2}} + C$$

NOW WORK PROBLEM 23 ⬤◖◗

**Integrating $b^u$**

In Section 14.4, we integrated an exponential function to the base $e$:

$$\int e^u\, du = e^u + C$$

Now let us consider the integral of an exponential function with an arbitrary base, $b$.

$$\int b^u \, du$$

To find this integral, we first convert to base $e$ using

$$b^u = e^{(\ln b)u} \tag{1}$$

(as we did in many differentiation examples too). Example 3 will illustrate.

● **EXAMPLE 3**   **An Integral Involving $b^u$**

*Find* $\int 2^{3-x} \, dx$.

**Solution:**

> **Strategy**   We want to integrate an exponential function to the base 2. To do this, we will first convert from base 2 to base $e$ by using Equation (1).

$$\int 2^{3-x} \, dx = \int e^{(\ln 2)(3-x)} \, dx$$

The integrand of the second integral is of the form $e^u$, where $u = (\ln 2)(3 - x)$. Since $du = -\ln 2 \, dx$, we can solve for $dx$ and write

$$\int e^{(\ln 2)(3-x)} \, dx = -\frac{1}{\ln 2} \int e^u \, du$$

$$= -\frac{1}{\ln 2} e^u + C = -\frac{1}{\ln 2} e^{(\ln 2)(3-x)} + C = -\frac{1}{\ln 2} 2^{3-x} + C$$

Thus,

$$\int 2^{3-x} \, dx = -\frac{1}{\ln 2} 2^{3-x} + C$$

Notice that we expressed our answer in terms of an exponential function to the base 2, the base of the original integrand.

NOW WORK PROBLEM 27 ●●●

Generalizing the procedure described in Example 3, we can obtain a formula for integrating $b^u$:

$$\int b^u \, du = \int e^{(\ln b)u} \, du$$

$$= \frac{1}{\ln b} \int e^{(\ln b)u} \, d((\ln b)u) \qquad (\ln b \text{ is a constant})$$

$$= \frac{1}{\ln b} e^{(\ln b)u} + C$$

$$= \frac{1}{\ln b} b^u + C$$

Hence, we have

$$\int b^u \, du = \frac{1}{\ln b} b^u + C$$

Applying this formula to the integral in Example 3 gives

$$\int 2^{3-x} \, dx \qquad\qquad (b = 2, u = 3 - x)$$

$$= -\int 2^{3-x} \, d(3 - x) \qquad (-d(3 - x) = dx)$$

$$= -\frac{1}{\ln 2} 2^{3-x} + C$$

which is the same result that we obtained before.

## Application of Integration

We will now consider an application of integration that relates a consumption function to the marginal propensity to consume.

● EXAMPLE 4   **Finding a Consumption Function from Marginal Propensity to Consume**

*For a certain country, the marginal propensity to consume is given by*

$$\frac{dC}{dI} = \frac{3}{4} - \frac{1}{2\sqrt{3I}}$$

*where consumption C is a function of national income I. Here I is expressed in large denominations of money. Determine the consumption function for the country if it is known that consumption is 10 (C = 10) when I = 12.*

**Solution:**  Since the marginal propensity to consume is the derivative of $C$, we have

$$C = C(I) = \int \left( \frac{3}{4} - \frac{1}{2\sqrt{3I}} \right) dI = \int \frac{3}{4} dI - \frac{1}{2} \int (3I)^{-1/2} dI$$

$$= \frac{3}{4} I - \frac{1}{2} \int (3I)^{-1/2} dI$$

If we let $u = 3I$, then $du = 3\, dI = d(3I)$, and

$$C = \frac{3}{4} I - \left( \frac{1}{2} \right) \frac{1}{3} \int (3I)^{-1/2} d(3I)$$

$$= \frac{3}{4} I - \frac{1}{6} \frac{(3I)^{1/2}}{\frac{1}{2}} + K$$

$$C = \frac{3}{4} I - \frac{\sqrt{3I}}{3} + K$$

This is an example of an initial-value problem.

When $I = 12$, $C = 10$, so

$$10 = \frac{3}{4}(12) - \frac{\sqrt{3(12)}}{3} + K$$

$$10 = 9 - 2 + K$$

Thus, $K = 3$, and the consumption function is

$$C = \frac{3}{4} I - \frac{\sqrt{3I}}{3} + 3$$

NOW WORK PROBLEM 61 ●●

## Problems 14.5

*In Problems 1–56, determine the indefinite integrals.*

*1. $\int \frac{2x^6 + 8x^4 - 4x}{2x^2} dx$

2. $\int \frac{9x^2 + 5}{3x} dx$

3. $\int (3x^2 + 2)\sqrt{2x^3 + 4x + 1}\, dx$

4. $\int \frac{x}{\sqrt[4]{x^2 + 1}} dx$

5. $\int \frac{9}{\sqrt{2 - 3x}} dx$

6. $\int \frac{2xe^{x^2}\, dx}{e^{x^2} - 2}$

7. $\int 4^{7x}\, dx$

8. $\int 5^t\, dt$

9. $\int 2x(7 - e^{x^2/4})\, dx$

10. $\int \left( e^x + x^e + ex + \frac{e}{x} \right) dx$

11. $\int \frac{6x^2 - 11x + 5}{3x - 1} dx$

12. $\int \frac{(3x + 2)(x - 4)}{x - 3} dx$

13. $\int \frac{5e^{2x}}{7e^{2x} + 4} dx$

14. $\int 6(e^{4-3x})^2\, dx$

15. $\int \frac{e^{7/x}}{x^2} dx$

16. $\int \frac{2x^4 - 6x^3 + x - 2}{x - 2} dx$

17. $\int \frac{5x^3}{x^2 + 9} dx$

18. $\int \frac{5 - 4x^2}{3 + 2x} dx$

19. $\int \frac{(\sqrt{x} + 2)^2}{3\sqrt{x}} dx$

**20.** $\int \dfrac{5e^s}{1 + 3e^s} \, ds$

**21.** $\int \dfrac{5(x^{1/3} + 2)^4}{\sqrt[3]{x^2}} \, dx$

**22.** $\int \dfrac{\sqrt{1 + \sqrt{x}}}{\sqrt{x}} \, dx$

**\*23.** $\int \dfrac{\ln x}{x} \, dx$

**24.** $\int \sqrt{t}(3 - t\sqrt{t})^{0.6} \, dt$

**25.** $\int \dfrac{\ln^2(r + 1)}{r + 1} \, dr$

**26.** $\int \dfrac{9x^5 - 6x^4 - ex^3}{7x^2} \, dx$

**\*27.** $\int \dfrac{3^{\ln x}}{x} \, dx$

**28.** $\int \dfrac{4}{x \ln(2x^2)} \, dx$

**29.** $\int x^2 \sqrt{e^{x^3 + 1}} \, dx$

**30.** $\int \dfrac{x + 3}{x + 6} \, dx$

**31.** $\int \dfrac{8}{(x + 3) \ln(x + 3)} \, dx$

**32.** $\int (e^{e^2} + x^e - 2x) \, dx$

**33.** $\int \dfrac{x^3 + x^2 - x - 3}{x^2 - 3} \, dx$

**34.** $\int \dfrac{4x \ln \sqrt{1 + x^2}}{1 + x^2} \, dx$

**35.** $\int \dfrac{6x^2 \sqrt{\ln(x^3 + 1)^2}}{x^3 + 1} \, dx$

**36.** $\int 3(x^2 + 2)^{-1/2} x e^{\sqrt{x^2 + 2}} \, dx$

**37.** $\int \left( \dfrac{x^3 - 1}{\sqrt{x^4 - 4x}} - \ln 7 \right) dx$

**38.** $\int \dfrac{x - x^{-2}}{x^2 + 2x^{-1}} \, dx$

**39.** $\int \dfrac{2x^4 - 8x^3 - 6x^2 + 4}{x^3} \, dx$

**40.** $\int \dfrac{e^x + e^{-x}}{e^x - e^{-x}} \, dx$

**41.** $\int \dfrac{x}{x + 1} \, dx$

**42.** $\int \dfrac{2x}{(x^2 + 1) \ln(x^2 + 1)} \, dx$

**43.** $\int \dfrac{x e^{x^2}}{\sqrt{e^{x^2} + 2}} \, dx$

**44.** $\int \dfrac{5}{(3x + 1)[1 + \ln(3x + 1)]^2} \, dx$

**45.** $\int \dfrac{(e^{-x} + 6)^2}{e^x} \, dx$

**46.** $\int \left[ \dfrac{1}{8x + 1} - \dfrac{1}{e^x(8 + e^{-x})^2} \right] dx$

**47.** $\int (x^3 + ex) \sqrt{x^2 + e} \, dx$

**48.** $\int 3^{x \ln x}(1 + \ln x) \, dx$  (*Hint:* $\dfrac{d}{dx}(x \ln x) = 1 + \ln x$)

**49.** $\int \sqrt{x} \sqrt{(8x)^{3/2} + 3} \, dx$

**50.** $\int \dfrac{2}{x(\ln x)^{2/3}} \, dx$

**51.** $\int \dfrac{\sqrt{s}}{e^{\sqrt{s^3}}} \, ds$

**52.** $\int \dfrac{\ln^3 x}{3x} \, dx$

**53.** $\int e^{\ln(x^2 + 1)} \, dx$

**54.** $\int dx$

**55.** $\int \dfrac{\ln(x e^x)}{x} \, dx$

**56.** $\int e^{f(x) + \ln(f'(x))} \, dx$  assuming $f' > 0$

*In Problems 57 and 58, $dr/dq$ is a marginal-revenue function. Find the demand function.*

**57.** $\dfrac{dr}{dq} = \dfrac{200}{(q + 2)^2}$

**58.** $\dfrac{dr}{dq} = \dfrac{900}{(2q + 3)^3}$

*In Problems 59 and 60, $dc/dq$ is a marginal-cost function. Find the total-cost function if fixed costs in each case are 2000.*

**59.** $\dfrac{dc}{dq} = \dfrac{20}{q + 5}$

**60.** $\dfrac{dc}{dq} = 3e^{0.002q}$

*In Problems 61–63, $dC/dI$ represents the marginal propensity to consume. Find the consumption function subject to the given condition.*

**\*61.** $\dfrac{dC}{dI} = \dfrac{1}{\sqrt{I}}; \quad C(9) = 8$

**62.** $\dfrac{dC}{dI} = \dfrac{1}{2} - \dfrac{1}{2\sqrt{2I}}; \quad C(2) = \dfrac{3}{4}$

**63.** $\dfrac{dC}{dI} = \dfrac{3}{4} - \dfrac{1}{6\sqrt{I}}; \quad C(25) = 23.$

**64. Cost Function**   The marginal-cost function for a manufacturer's product is given by

$$\frac{dc}{dq} = 10 - \frac{100}{q + 10}$$

where $c$ is the total cost in dollars when $q$ units are produced. When 100 units are produced, the average cost is $50 per unit. To the nearest dollar, determine the manufacturer's fixed cost.

**65. Cost Function**   Suppose the marginal-cost function for a manufacturer's product is given by

$$\frac{dc}{dq} = \frac{100q^2 - 3998q + 60}{q^2 - 40q + 1}$$

where $c$ is the total cost in dollars when $q$ units are produced.

**(a)** Determine the marginal cost when 40 units are produced.

**(b)** If fixed costs are $10,000, find the total cost of producing 40 units.

**(c)** Use the results of parts (a) and (b) and differentials to approximate the total cost of producing 42 units.

**66. Cost Function**   The marginal-cost function for a manufacturer's product is given by

$$\frac{dc}{dq} = \frac{9}{10} \sqrt{q} \sqrt{0.04q^{3/4} + 4}$$

where $c$ is the total cost in dollars when $q$ units are produced. Fixed costs are $360.

**(a)** Determine the marginal cost when 25 units are produced.

**(b)** Find the total cost of producing 25 units.

**(c)** Use the results of parts (a) and (b) and differentials to approximate the total cost of producing 23 units.

**67. Value of Land**   It is estimated that $t$ years from now the value $V$ (in dollars) of an acre of land near the ghost town of Cherokee, California, will be increasing at the rate of

$$\frac{8t^3}{\sqrt{0.2t^4 + 8000}}$$

dollars per year. If the land is currently worth $500 per acre, how much will it be worth in 10 years? Express your answer to the nearest dollar.

**68. Revenue Function**   The marginal-revenue function for a manufacturer's product is of the form

$$\frac{dr}{dq} = \frac{a}{e^q + b}$$

for constants $a$ and $b$, where $r$ is the total revenue received (in dollars) when $q$ units are produced and sold. Find the demand function, and express it in the form $p = f(q)$. (*Hint:* Rewrite $dr/dq$ by multiplying both numerator and denominator by $e^{-q}$.)

**69. Savings**   A certain country's marginal propensity to save is given by

$$\frac{dS}{dI} = \frac{5}{(I+2)^2}$$

where $S$ and $I$ represent total national savings and income, respectively, and are measured in billions of dollars. If total national consumption is $7.5 billion when total national income is $8 billion, for what value(s) of $I$ is total national savings equal to zero?

**70. Consumption Function**   A certain country's marginal propensity to save is given by

$$\frac{dS}{dI} = \frac{1}{2} - \frac{1.8}{\sqrt[3]{3I^2}}$$

where $S$ and $I$ represent total national savings and income, respectively, and are measured in billions of dollars.

**(a)** Determine the marginal propensity to consume when total national income is $81 billion.

**(b)** Determine the consumption function, given that savings are $3 billion when total national income is $24 billion.

**(c)** Use the result in part (b) to show that consumption is $54.9 billion when total national income is $81 billion.

**(d)** Use differentials and the results in parts (a) and (c) to approximate consumption when total national income is $78 billion.

---

OBJECTIVE

To motivate, by means of the concept of area, the definite integral as a limit of a special sum; to evaluate simple definite integrals by using a limiting process.

## 14.6 The Definite Integral

Figure 14.2 shows the region $R$ bounded by the lines $y = f(x) = 2x$, $y = 0$ (the $x$-axis), and $x = 1$. The region is simply a right triangle. If $b$ and $h$ are the lengths of the base and the height, respectively, then, from geometry, the area of the triangle is $A = \frac{1}{2}bh = \frac{1}{2}(1)(2) = 1$ square unit. (Henceforth, we will treat areas as pure numbers and write *square unit* only if it seems necessary for emphasis.) We will now find this area by another method, which, as you will see later, applies to more complex regions. This method involves the summation of areas of rectangles.

Let us divide the interval $[0, 1]$ on the $x$-axis into four subintervals of equal length by means of the equally spaced points $x_0 = 0$, $x_1 = \frac{1}{4}$, $x_2 = \frac{2}{4}$, $x_3 = \frac{3}{4}$, and $x_4 = \frac{4}{4} = 1$. (See Figure 14.3.) Each subinterval has length $\Delta x = \frac{1}{4}$. These subintervals determine four subregions of $R$: $R_1$, $R_2$, $R_3$, and $R_4$, as indicated.

With each subregion, we can associate a *circumscribed* rectangle (Figure 14.4)—that is, a rectangle whose base is the corresponding subinterval and whose height is the *maximum* value of $f(x)$ on that subinterval. Since $f$ is an increasing function, the maximum value of $f(x)$ on each subinterval occurs when $x$ is the right-hand endpoint. Thus, the areas of the circumscribed rectangles associated with regions $R_1$, $R_2$, $R_3$, and $R_4$ are $\frac{1}{4}f(\frac{1}{4})$, $\frac{1}{4}f(\frac{2}{4})$, $\frac{1}{4}f(\frac{3}{4})$, and $\frac{1}{4}f(\frac{4}{4})$, respectively. The area of each rectangle is an approximation to the area of its corresponding subregion. Hence, the sum of the areas of these rectangles, denoted by $\overline{S}_4$ (read "$S$ upper bar sub 4" or "the fourth

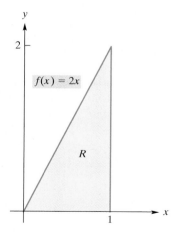

**FIGURE 14.2**   Region bounded by $f(x) = 2x$, $y = 0$, and $x = 1$.

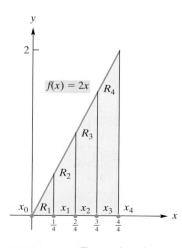

**FIGURE 14.3**   Four subregions of $R$.

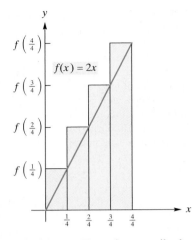

**FIGURE 14.4** Four circumscribed rectangles.

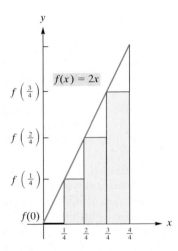

**FIGURE 14.5** Four inscribed rectangles.

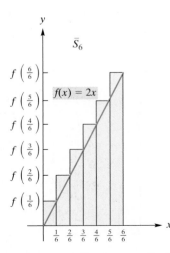

**FIGURE 14.6** Six circumscribed rectangles.

upper sum"), approximates the area $A$ of the triangle. We have

$$\overline{S}_4 = \tfrac{1}{4}f\left(\tfrac{1}{4}\right) + \tfrac{1}{4}f\left(\tfrac{2}{4}\right) + \tfrac{1}{4}f\left(\tfrac{3}{4}\right) + \tfrac{1}{4}f\left(\tfrac{4}{4}\right)$$

$$= \tfrac{1}{4}\left(2\left(\tfrac{1}{4}\right) + 2\left(\tfrac{2}{4}\right) + 2\left(\tfrac{3}{4}\right) + 2\left(\tfrac{4}{4}\right)\right) = \tfrac{5}{4}$$

You can verify that $\overline{S}_4 = \sum_{i=1}^{4} f(x_i)\Delta x$. The fact that $\overline{S}_4$ is greater than the actual area of the triangle might have been expected, since $\overline{S}_4$ includes areas of shaded regions that are not in the triangle. (See Figure 14.4.)

On the other hand, with each subregion we can also associate an *inscribed* rectangle (Figure 14.5)—that is, a rectangle whose base is the corresponding subinterval, but whose height is the *minimum* value of $f(x)$ on that subinterval. Since $f$ is an increasing function, the minimum value of $f(x)$ on each subinterval will occur when $x$ is the left-hand endpoint. Thus, the areas of the four inscribed rectangles associated with $R_1$, $R_2$, $R_3$, and $R_4$ are $\tfrac{1}{4}f(0)$, $\tfrac{1}{4}f(\tfrac{1}{4})$, $\tfrac{1}{4}f(\tfrac{2}{4})$, and $\tfrac{1}{4}f(\tfrac{3}{4})$, respectively. Their sum, denoted $\underline{S}_4$ (read "$S$ lower bar sub 4" or "the fourth lower sum"), is also an approximation to the area $A$ of the triangle. We have

$$\underline{S}_4 = \tfrac{1}{4}f(0) + \tfrac{1}{4}f\left(\tfrac{1}{4}\right) + \tfrac{1}{4}f\left(\tfrac{2}{4}\right) + \tfrac{1}{4}f\left(\tfrac{3}{4}\right)$$

$$= \tfrac{1}{4}\left(2(0) + 2\left(\tfrac{1}{4}\right) + 2\left(\tfrac{2}{4}\right) + 2\left(\tfrac{3}{4}\right)\right) = \tfrac{3}{4}$$

Using summation notation, we can write $\underline{S}_4 = \sum_{i=0}^{3} f(x_i)\Delta x$. Note that $\underline{S}_4$ is less than the area of the triangle, because the rectangles do not account for the portion of the triangle that is not shaded in Figure 14.5.

Since

$$\frac{3}{4} = \underline{S}_4 \le A \le \overline{S}_4 = \frac{5}{4}$$

we say that $\underline{S}_4$ is an approximation to $A$ from *below* and $\overline{S}_4$ is an approximation to $A$ from *above*.

If $[0, 1]$ is divided into more subintervals, we expect that better approximations to $A$ will occur. To test this, let us use six subintervals of equal length $\Delta x = \tfrac{1}{6}$. Then $\overline{S}_6$, the total area of six circumscribed rectangles (see Figure 14.6), and $\underline{S}_6$, the total area of six inscribed rectangles (see Figure 14.7), are

$$\overline{S}_6 = \tfrac{1}{6}f\left(\tfrac{1}{6}\right) + \tfrac{1}{6}f\left(\tfrac{2}{6}\right) + \tfrac{1}{6}f\left(\tfrac{3}{6}\right) + \tfrac{1}{6}f\left(\tfrac{4}{6}\right) + \tfrac{1}{6}f\left(\tfrac{5}{6}\right) + \tfrac{1}{6}f\left(\tfrac{6}{6}\right)$$

$$= \tfrac{1}{6}\left(2\left(\tfrac{1}{6}\right) + 2\left(\tfrac{2}{6}\right) + 2\left(\tfrac{3}{6}\right) + 2\left(\tfrac{4}{6}\right) + 2\left(\tfrac{5}{6}\right) + 2\left(\tfrac{6}{6}\right)\right) = \tfrac{7}{6}$$

and

$$\underline{S}_6 = \tfrac{1}{6}f(0) + \tfrac{1}{6}f\left(\tfrac{1}{6}\right) + \tfrac{1}{6}f\left(\tfrac{2}{6}\right) + \tfrac{1}{6}f\left(\tfrac{3}{6}\right) + \tfrac{1}{6}f\left(\tfrac{4}{6}\right) + \tfrac{1}{6}f\left(\tfrac{5}{6}\right)$$

$$= \tfrac{1}{6}\left(2(0) + 2\left(\tfrac{1}{6}\right) + 2\left(\tfrac{2}{6}\right) + 2\left(\tfrac{3}{6}\right) + 2\left(\tfrac{4}{6}\right) + 2\left(\tfrac{5}{6}\right)\right) = \tfrac{5}{6}$$

Note that $\underline{S}_6 \le A \le \overline{S}_6$, and, with appropriate labeling, both $\overline{S}_6$ and $\underline{S}_6$ will be of the form $\Sigma f(x)\,\Delta x$. Clearly, using six subintervals gives better approximations to the area than does four subintervals, as expected.

More generally, if we divide $[0, 1]$ into $n$ subintervals of equal length $\Delta x$, then $\Delta x = 1/n$, and the endpoints of the subintervals are $x = 0, 1/n, 2/n, \ldots,$ $(n - 1)/n$, and $n/n = 1$. (See Figure 14.8.) The endpoints of the $k$th subinterval, for $k = 1, \ldots n$, are $(k - 1)/n$ and $k/n$ and the maximum value of $f$ occurs at the right-hand endpoint $k/n$. It follows the area of the $k$th circumscribed rectangle is $1/n \cdot f(k/n) = 1/n \cdot 2(k/n) = 2k/n^2$, for $k = 1, \ldots n$. The total area of *all $n$ circumscribed* rectangles is

$$\overline{S}_n = \sum_{k=1}^{n} f(k/n)\Delta x = \sum_{k=1}^{n} \frac{2k}{n^2} \qquad (1)$$

$$= \frac{2}{n^2}\sum_{k=1}^{n} k \qquad \left(\text{by factoring } \frac{2}{n^2} \text{ from each term}\right)$$

$$= \frac{2}{n^2} \cdot \frac{n(n + 1)}{2} \qquad (\text{from Section 1.5})$$

$$= \frac{n + 1}{n}$$

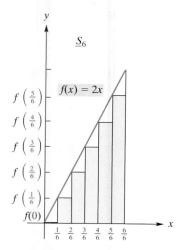

**FIGURE 14.7** Six inscribed rectangles.

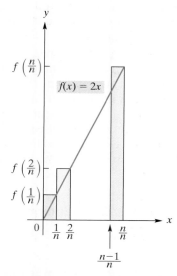

**FIGURE 14.8** $n$ circumscribed rectangles.

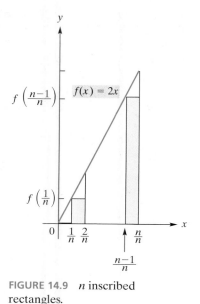

**FIGURE 14.9** $n$ inscribed rectangles.

(We recall that $\sum_{k=1}^{n} k = 1 + 2 + \cdots + n$ is the sum of the first $n$ positive integers and the formula used above was derived in Section 1.5 in anticipation of its application here.)

For *inscribed* rectangles, we note that the minimum value of $f$ occurs at the left-hand endpoint, $(k-1)/n$, of $[(k-1)/n, k/n]$ so that the area of the $k$th inscribed rectangle is $1/n \cdot f(k-1/n) = 1/n \cdot 2((k-1)/n) = 2(k-1)/n^2$, for $k = 1, \ldots n$. The total area determined of *all $n$ inscribed* rectangles (see Figure 14.9) is

$$\underline{S}_n = \sum_{k=1}^{n} f((k-1)/n)\, \Delta x = \sum_{k=1}^{n} \frac{2(k-1)}{n^2} \tag{2}$$

$$= \frac{2}{n^2} \sum_{k=1}^{n} k - 1 \qquad \left(\text{by factoring } \frac{2}{n^2} \text{ from each term}\right)$$

$$= \frac{2}{n^2} \sum_{k=0}^{n-1} k \qquad \text{(adjusting the summation)}$$

$$= \frac{2}{n^2} \cdot \frac{(n-1)n}{2} \qquad \text{(adapted from Section 1.5)}$$

$$= \frac{n-1}{n}$$

From Equations (1) and (2), we again see that both $\overline{S}_n$ and $\underline{S}_n$ are sums of the form $\sum f(x) \Delta x$, namely, $\overline{S}_n = \sum_{k=1}^{n} f\left(\dfrac{k}{n}\right) \Delta x$ and $\underline{S}_n = \sum_{k=1}^{n} f\left(\dfrac{k-1}{n}\right) \Delta x$.

From the nature of $\overline{S}_n$ and $\underline{S}_n$, it seems reasonable—and it is indeed true—that

$$\underline{S}_n \le A \le \overline{S}_n$$

As $n$ becomes larger, $\underline{S}_n$ and $\overline{S}_n$ become better approximations to $A$. In fact, let us take the limits of $\underline{S}_n$ and $\overline{S}_n$ as $n$ approaches $\infty$ through positive integral values:

$$\lim_{n \to \infty} \underline{S}_n = \lim_{n \to \infty} \frac{n-1}{n} = \lim_{n \to \infty} \left(1 - \frac{1}{n}\right) = 1$$

$$\lim_{n \to \infty} \overline{S}_n = \lim_{n \to \infty} \frac{n+1}{n} = \lim_{n \to \infty} \left(1 + \frac{1}{n}\right) = 1$$

Since $\overline{S}_n$ and $\underline{S}_n$ have the same limit, namely,

$$\lim_{n \to \infty} \overline{S}_n = \lim_{n \to \infty} \underline{S}_n = 1 \tag{3}$$

and since

$$\underline{S}_n \le A \le \overline{S}_n$$

we will take this limit to be the area of the triangle. Thus $A = 1$, which agrees with our prior finding. It is important to understand that here we developed a *definition of the notion of area* that is applicable to many different regions.

We call the common limit of $\overline{S}_n$ and $\underline{S}_n$, namely, 1, the *definite integral* of $f(x) = 2x$ on the interval from $x = 0$ to $x = 1$, and we denote this quantity by writing

$$\int_0^1 2x\, dx = 1 \tag{4}$$

The reason for using the term *definite integral* and the symbolism in Equation (4) will become apparent in the next section. The numbers 0 and 1 appearing with the integral sign $\int$ in Equation (4) are called the *limits of integration*; 0 is the *lower limit* and 1 is the *upper limit*.

In general, for a function $f$ defined on the interval from $x = a$ to $x = b$, where $a < b$, we can form the sums $\overline{S}_n$ and $\underline{S}_n$, which are obtained by considering the maximum and minimum values, respectively, on each of $n$ subintervals of equal length $\Delta x$.[6] We can now state the following:

> The common limit of $\overline{S}_n$ and $\underline{S}_n$ as $n \to \infty$, if it exists, is called the **definite integral** of $f$ over $[a, b]$ and is written
>
> $$\int_a^b f(x)\, dx$$
>
> The numbers $a$ and $b$ are called **limits of integration;** $a$ is the **lower limit** and $b$ is the **upper limit.** The symbol $x$ is called the **variable of integration** and $f(x)$ is the **integrand.**

In terms of a limiting process, we have

$$\sum f(x)\, \Delta x \to \int_a^b f(x)\, dx$$

Two points must be made about the definite integral. First, the definite integral is the limit of a sum of the form $\sum f(x)\,\Delta x$. In fact, we can think of the integral sign as an elongated "$S$," the first letter of "*Summation*." Second, for an arbitrary function $f$ defined on an interval, we may be able to calculate the sums $\overline{S}_n$ and $\underline{S}_n$ and determine their common limit if it exists. However, some terms in the sums may be negative if $f(x)$ is negative at points in the interval. These terms are not areas of rectangles (an area is never negative), so the common limit may not represent an area. Thus, **the definite integral is nothing more than a real number; it may or may not represent an area.**

As you saw in Equation (3), $\lim_{n \to \infty} \underline{S}_n$ is equal to $\lim_{n \to \infty} \overline{S}_n$. For an arbitrary function, this is not always true. However, for the functions that we will consider, these limits will be equal, and the definite integral will always exist. To save time, we will just use the **right-hand endpoint** of each subinterval in computing a sum. For the functions in this section, this sum will be denoted $S_n$.

### ● EXAMPLE 1    Computing an Area by Using Right-Hand Endpoints

*Find the area of the region in the first quadrant bounded by $f(x) = 4 - x^2$ and the lines $x = 0$ and $y = 0$.*

**Solution:** A sketch of the region appears in Figure 14.10. The interval over which $x$ varies in this region is seen to be $[0, 2]$, which we divide into $n$ subintervals of equal length $\Delta x$. Since the length of $[0, 2]$ is 2, we take $\Delta x = 2/n$. The endpoints of the subintervals are $x = 0, 2/n, 2(2/n), \ldots, (n-1)(2/n)$, and $n(2/n) = 2$, which are shown in Figure 14.11. The diagram also shows the corresponding rectangles obtained by using the right-hand endpoint of each subinterval. The area of the $k$th rectangle, for $k = 1, \ldots n$, is the product of its width, $2/n$, and its height, $f(k(2/n)) = 4 - (2k/n)^2$, which is the function value at the right-hand endpoint of its base. Summing these areas, we get

$$S_n = \sum_{k=1}^n f\left(k \cdot \left(\frac{2}{n}\right)\right)\Delta x = \sum_{k=1}^n \left(4 - \left(\frac{2k}{n}\right)^2\right)\frac{2}{n}$$

$$= \sum_{k=1}^n \left(\frac{8}{n} - \frac{8k^2}{n^3}\right) = \sum_{k=1}^n \frac{8}{n} - \sum_{k=1}^n \frac{8k^2}{n^3} = \frac{8}{n}\sum_{k=1}^n 1 - \frac{8}{n^3}\sum_{k=1}^n k^2$$

$$= \frac{8}{n}n - \frac{8}{n^3}\frac{n(n+1)(2n+1)}{6}$$

$$= 8 - \frac{4}{3}\left(\frac{(n+1)(2n+1)}{n^2}\right)$$

In general, over $[a, b]$, we have

$$\Delta x = \frac{b - a}{n}$$

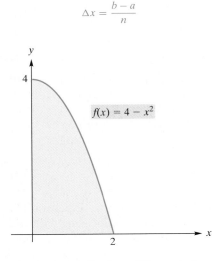

**FIGURE 14.10**   Region of Example 1.

---

[6] Here we assume that the maximum and minimum values exist.

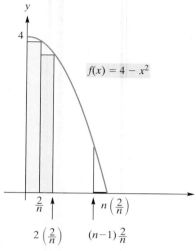

$f(x) = 4 - x^2$

$\frac{2}{n}$

$2\left(\frac{2}{n}\right)$

$(n-1)\frac{2}{n}$

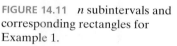

$n\left(\frac{2}{n}\right)$

**FIGURE 14.11** *n* subintervals and corresponding rectangles for Example 1.

The second line of the preceding computations uses basic summation manipulations as discussed in Section 1.5. The third line uses two specific summation formulas, also from Section 1.5: The sum of *n* copies of 1 is *n* and the sum of the first *n* squares is $\frac{n(n+1)(2n+1)}{6}$.

Finally, we take the limit of the $S_n$ as $n \to \infty$:

$$\lim_{n \to \infty} S_n = \lim_{n \to \infty} \left( 8 - \frac{4}{3}\left(\frac{(n+1)(2n+1)}{n^2}\right)\right)$$

$$= 8 - \frac{4}{3}\lim_{n \to \infty}\left(\frac{2n^2 + 3n + 1}{n^2}\right)$$

$$= 8 - \frac{4}{3}\lim_{n \to \infty}\left(2 + \frac{3}{n} + \frac{1}{n^2}\right)$$

$$= 8 - \frac{8}{3} = \frac{16}{3}$$

Hence, the area of the region is $\frac{16}{3}$.

NOW WORK PROBLEM 7

## ● EXAMPLE 2  Evaluating a Definite Integral

*Evaluate* $\int_0^2 (4 - x^2)\, dx$.

**Solution:** We want to find the definite integral of $f(x) = 4 - x^2$ over the interval $[0, 2]$. Thus, we must compute $\lim_{n \to \infty} S_n$. But this limit is precisely the limit $\frac{16}{3}$ found in Example 1, so we conclude that

No units are attached to the answer, since a definite integral is simply a number.

$$\int_0^2 (4 - x^2)\, dx = \frac{16}{3}$$

NOW WORK PROBLEM 19

$0 \quad \frac{3}{n}$

$2\left(\frac{3}{n}\right)$

$(n-1)\frac{3}{n}$

$n\left(\frac{3}{n}\right) = 3$

**FIGURE 14.12** Dividing $[0, 3]$ into *n* subintervals.

## ● EXAMPLE 3  Integrating a Function over an Interval

*Integrate* $f(x) = x - 5$ *from* $x = 0$ *to* $x = 3$; *that is, evaluate* $\int_0^3 (x - 5)\, dx$.

**Solution:** We first divide $[0, 3]$ into *n* subintervals of equal length $\Delta x = 3/n$. The endpoints are $0, 3/n, 2(3/n), \ldots, (n-1)(3/n), n(3/n) = 3$. (See Figure 14.12.) Using right-hand endpoints, we form the sum and simplify

$$S_n = \sum_{k=1}^{n} f\left(k\frac{3}{n}\right)\frac{3}{n}$$

$$= \sum_{k=1}^{n}\left(\left(k\frac{3}{n} - 5\right)\frac{3}{n}\right) = \sum_{k=1}^{n}\left(\frac{9}{n^2}k - \frac{15}{n}\right) = \frac{9}{n^2}\sum_{k=1}^{n}k - \frac{15}{n}\sum_{k=1}^{n}1$$

$$= \frac{9}{n^2}\left(\frac{n(n+1)}{2}\right) - \frac{15}{n}(n)$$

$$= \frac{9}{2}\frac{n+1}{n} - 15 = \frac{9}{2}\left(1 + \frac{1}{n}\right) - 15$$

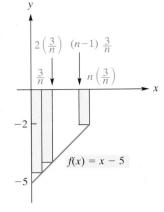

FIGURE 14.13   $f(x)$ is negative at each right-hand endpoint.

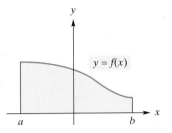

FIGURE 14.14   If $f$ is continuous and $f(x) \geq 0$ on $[a, b]$, then $\int_a^b f(x)\,dx$ represents the area under the curve.

Taking the limit, we obtain

$$\lim_{n \to \infty} S_n = \lim_{n \to \infty} \left( \frac{9}{2}\left(1 + \frac{1}{n}\right) - 15 \right) = \frac{9}{2} - 15 = -\frac{21}{2}$$

Thus,

$$\int_0^3 (x - 5)\,dx = -\frac{21}{2}$$

Note that the definite integral here is a *negative* number. The reason is clear from the graph of $f(x) = x - 5$ over the interval $[0, 3]$. (See Figure 14.13.) Since the value of $f(x)$ is negative at each right-hand endpoint, each term in $S_n$ must also be negative. Hence, $\lim_{n \to \infty} S_n$, which is the definite integral, is negative.

Geometrically, each term in $S_n$ is the negative of the area of a rectangle. (Refer again to Figure 14.13.) Although the definite integral is simply a number, here we can interpret it as representing the negative of the area of the region bounded by $f(x) = x - 5$, $x = 0$, $x = 3$, and the $x$-axis ($y = 0$).

NOW WORK PROBLEM 17

In Example 3, it was shown that *the definite integral does not have to represent an area.* In fact, there the definite integral was negative. However, if $f$ is continuous and $f(x) \geq 0$ on $[a, b]$, then $S_n \geq 0$ for all values of $n$. Therefore, $\lim_{n \to \infty} S_n \geq 0$, so $\int_a^b f(x)\,dx \geq 0$. Furthermore, this definite integral gives the area of the region bounded by $y = f(x)$, $y = 0$, $x = a$, and $x = b$. (See Figure 14.14.)

Although the approach that we took to discuss the definite integral is sufficient for our purposes, it is by no means rigorous. **The important thing to remember about the definite integral is that it is the limit of a special sum.**

## TECHNOLOGY

Here is a program for the TI-83 Plus graphing calculator that will estimate the limit of $S_n$ as $n \to \infty$ for a function $f$ defined on $[a, b]$.

PROGRAM:RIGHTSUM
Lbl 1
Input "SUBINTV",N
$(B - A)/N \to H$
$\emptyset \to S$
$A + H \to X$
$1 \to I$
Lbl 2
$Y_1 + S \to S$
$X + H \to X$
$I + 1 \to I$
If $I \leq N$
Goto 2
$H*S \to S$
Disp S
Pause
Goto 1

```
prgmRIGHTSUM
SUBINTV100
              -10.455
SUBINTV1000
              -10.4955
SUBINTV2000
              -10.49775
■
```

FIGURE 14.15   Values of $S_n$ for $f(x) = x - 5$ on $[0, 3]$.

value of $S_n$. Each time ENTER is pressed, the program repeats. In this way, a display of values of $S_n$ for various numbers of subintervals may be obtained. Figure 14.15 shows values of $S_n (n = 100, 1000, \text{and } 2000)$ for the function $f(x) = x - 5$ on the interval $[0, 3]$. As $n \to \infty$, it appears that $S_n \to -10.5$. Thus, we estimate that

$$\lim_{n \to \infty} S_n \approx -10.5$$

Equivalently,

$$\int_0^3 (x - 5)\,dx \approx -10.5$$

which agrees with our result in Example 3.

It is interesting to note that the time required for an older calculator to compute $S_{2000}$ in Figure 14.15 was in excess of 1.5 minutes. The time required on a TI-84 Plus is less than 1 minute.

RIGHTSUM will compute $S_n$ for a given number $n$ of subintervals. Before executing the program, store $f(x)$, $a$, and $b$ as $Y_1$, A, and B, respectively. Upon execution of the program, you will be prompted to enter the number of subintervals. Then the program proceeds to display the

# Problems 14.6

*In Problems 1–4, sketch the region in the first quadrant that is bounded by the given curves. Approximate the area of the region by the indicated sum. Use the right-hand endpoint of each subinterval.*

1. $f(x) = x$, $y = 0$, $x = 1$;  $S_3$

2. $f(x) = 3x$, $y = 0$, $x = 1$;  $S_5$

3. $f(x) = x^2$, $y = 0$, $x = 1$;  $S_4$

4. $f(x) = x^2 + 1$, $y = 0$, $x = 0$, $x = 1$;  $S_2$

*In Problems 5 and 6, by dividing the indicated interval into n subintervals of equal length, find $S_n$ for the given function. Use the right-hand endpoint of each subinterval. Do not find $\lim_{n\to\infty} S_n$.*

5. $f(x) = 4x$;  $[0, 1]$

6. $f(x) = 3x + 2$;  $[0, 3]$

*In Problems 7 and 8, (a) simplify $S_n$ and (b) find $\lim_{n\to\infty} S_n$.*

*7. $S_n = \dfrac{1}{n}\left[\left(\dfrac{1}{n}+1\right) + \left(\dfrac{2}{n}+1\right) + \cdots + \left(\dfrac{n}{n}+1\right)\right]$

8. $S_n = \dfrac{2}{n}\left[\left(\dfrac{2}{n}\right)^2 + \left(2\cdot\dfrac{2}{n}\right)^2 + \cdots + \left(n\cdot\dfrac{2}{n}\right)^2\right]$

*In Problems 9–14, sketch the region in the first quadrant that is bounded by the given curves. Determine the exact area of the region by considering the limit of $S_n$ as $n \to \infty$. Use the right-hand endpoint of each subinterval.*

9. Region as described in Problem 1

10. Region as described in Problem 2

11. Region as described in Problem 3

12. $y = x^2$, $y = 0$, $x = 1$, $x = 2$

13. $f(x) = 3x^2$, $y = 0$, $x = 1$

14. $f(x) = 9 - x^2$, $y = 0$, $x = 0$

*In Problems 15–20, evaluate the given definite integral by taking the limit of $S_n$. Use the right-hand endpoint of each subinterval. Sketch the graph, over the given interval, of the function to be integrated.*

15. $\displaystyle\int_1^3 5x\,dx$

16. $\displaystyle\int_0^4 9\,dx$

*17. $\displaystyle\int_0^3 -4x\,dx$

18. $\displaystyle\int_1^4 (2x+1)\,dx$

*19. $\displaystyle\int_0^1 (x^2 + x)\,dx$

20. $\displaystyle\int_1^2 (x+2)\,dx$

21. Find $D_x\left[\displaystyle\int_2^3 \sqrt{x^2+1}\,dx\right]$ without the use of limits.

22. Find $\displaystyle\int_0^3 f(x)\,dx$ without the use of limits, where

$$f(x) = \begin{cases} 2 & \text{if } 0 \le x < 1 \\ 4 - 2x & \text{if } 1 \le x < 2 \\ 5x - 10 & \text{if } 2 \le x \le 3 \end{cases}$$

23. Find $\displaystyle\int_{-1}^3 f(x)\,dx$ without the use of limits, where

$$f(x) = \begin{cases} 1 & \text{if } x \le 1 \\ 2 - x & \text{if } 1 \le x \le 2 \\ -1 + \dfrac{x}{2} & \text{if } x > 2 \end{cases}$$

*In each of Problems 24–26, use a program, such as **RIGHTSUM**, to estimate the area of the region in the first quadrant bounded by the given curves. Round your answer to one decimal place.*

24. $f(x) = x^3 + 1$, $y = 0$, $x = 2$, $x = 3.7$

25. $f(x) = 4 - \sqrt{x}$, $y = 0$, $x = 1$, $x = 9$

26. $f(x) = e^x$, $y = 0$, $x = 0$, $x = 1$

*In each of Problems 27–30, use a program, such as **RIGHTSUM**, to estimate the value of the definite integral. Round your answer to one decimal place.*

27. $\displaystyle\int_2^5 \dfrac{x+1}{x+2}\,dx$

28. $\displaystyle\int_{-3}^{-1} \dfrac{1}{x^2}\,dx$

29. $\displaystyle\int_{-1}^2 (4x^2 + x - 13)\,dx$

30. $\displaystyle\int_1^2 \ln x\,dx$

---

OBJECTIVE

To informally develop the Fundamental Theorem of Integral Calculus and to use it to compute definite integrals.

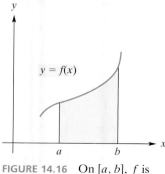

**FIGURE 14.16**  On $[a, b]$, $f$ is continuous and $f(x) \ge 0$.

# 14.7  The Fundamental Theorem of Integral Calculus

## The Fundamental Theorem

Thus far, the limiting processes of both the derivative and definite integral have been considered separately. We will now bring these fundamental ideas together and develop the important relationship that exists between them. As a result, we will be able to evaluate definite integrals more efficiently.

The graph of a function $f$ is given in Figure 14.16. Assume that $f$ is continuous on the interval $[a, b]$ and that its graph does not fall below the $x$-axis. That is, $f(x) \ge 0$. From the preceding section, the area of the region below the graph and above the $x$-axis from $x = a$ to $x = b$ is given by $\int_a^b f(x)\,dx$. We will now consider another way to determine this area.

Suppose that there is a function $A = A(x)$, which we will refer to as an area function, that gives the area of the region below the graph of $f$ and above the $x$-axis from $a$ to $x$, where $a \le x \le b$. This region is shaded in Figure 14.17. Do not confuse $A(x)$, which is an area, with $f(x)$, which is the height of the graph at $x$.

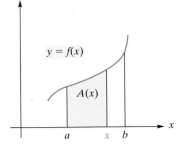

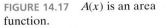

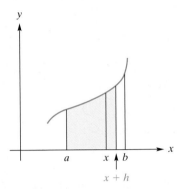

**FIGURE 14.17** $A(x)$ is an area function.

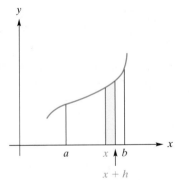

**FIGURE 14.18** $A(x + h)$ gives the area of the shaded region.

FIGURE 14.19 Area of shaded region is $A(x + h) - A(x)$.

**FIGURE 14.20** Area of rectangle is the same as area of shaded region in Figure 14.19.

From its definition, we can state two properties of $A$ immediately:

**1.** $A(a) = 0$, since there is "no area" from $a$ to $a$

**2.** $A(b)$ is the area from $a$ to $b$; that is,

$$A(b) = \int_a^b f(x)\,dx$$

If $x$ is increased by $h$ units, then $A(x + h)$ is the area of the shaded region in Figure 14.18. Hence, $A(x + h) - A(x)$ is the difference of the areas in Figure. 14.18 and 14.17, namely, the area of the shaded region in Figure 14.19. For $h$ sufficiently close to zero, the area of this region is the same as the area of a rectangle (Figure 14.20) whose base is $h$ and whose height is some value $\overline{y}$ between $f(x)$ and $f(x + h)$. Here $\overline{y}$ is a function of $h$. Thus, on the one hand, the area of the rectangle is $A(x + h) - A(x)$, and, on the other hand, it is $h\overline{y}$, so

$$A(x + h) - A(x) = h\overline{y}$$

Equivalently,

$$\frac{A(x + h) - A(x)}{h} = \overline{y} \qquad \text{(dividing by } h)$$

Since $\overline{y}$ is between $f(x)$ and $f(x + h)$, it follows that as $h \to 0$, $\overline{y}$ approaches $f(x)$, so

$$\lim_{h \to 0} \frac{A(x + h) - A(x)}{h} = f(x) \qquad \textbf{(1)}$$

But the left side is merely the derivative of $A$. Thus, Equation (1) becomes

$$A'(x) = f(x)$$

We conclude that the area function $A$ has the additional property that its derivative $A'$ is $f$. That is, $A$ is an antiderivative of $f$. Now, suppose that $F$ is *any* antiderivative of $f$. Then, since both $A$ and $F$ are antiderivatives of the same function, they differ at most by a constant $C$:

$$A(x) = F(x) + C. \qquad \textbf{(2)}$$

Recall that $A(a) = 0$. So, evaluating both sides of Equation (2) when $x = a$ gives

$$0 = F(a) + C$$

so that

$$C = -F(a)$$

Thus, Equation (2) becomes

$$A(x) = F(x) - F(a) \qquad \textbf{(3)}$$

If $x = b$, then, from Equation (3),

$$A(b) = F(b) - F(a) \qquad \textbf{(4)}$$

But recall that

$$A(b) = \int_a^b f(x)\,dx \qquad \textbf{(5)}$$

From Equations (4) and (5), we get

$$\int_a^b f(x)\,dx = F(b) - F(a)$$

A relationship between a definite integral and antidifferentiation has now become clear. To find $\int_a^b f(x)\,dx$, it suffices to find an antiderivative of $f$, say, $F$, and subtract the value of $F$ at the lower limit $a$ from its value at the upper limit $b$. We assumed here that $f$ was continuous and $f(x) \geq 0$ so that we could appeal to the concept of an area. However, our result is true for any continuous function[7] and is known as the *Fundamental Theorem of Integral Calculus*.

### Fundamental Theorem of Integral Calculus

If $f$ is continuous on the interval $[a, b]$ and $F$ is any antiderivative of $f$ on $[a, b]$, then

$$\int_a^b f(x)\, dx = F(b) - F(a)$$

It is important that you understand the difference between a definite integral and an indefinite integral. The **definite integral** $\int_a^b f(x)\, dx$ is a **number** defined to be the limit of a sum. The Fundamental Theorem states that the **indefinite integral** $\int f(x)\, dx$ (the most general antiderivative of $f$), which is a **function** of $x$ related to the differentiation process, can be used to determine this limit.

Suppose we apply the Fundamental Theorem to evaluate $\int_0^2 (4 - x^2)\, dx$. Here $f(x) = 4 - x^2$, $a = 0$, and $b = 2$. Since an antiderivative of $4 - x^2$ is $F(x) = 4x - (x^3/3)$, it follows that

$$\int_0^2 (4 - x^2)\, dx = F(2) - F(0) = \left(8 - \frac{8}{3}\right) - (0) = \frac{16}{3}$$

This confirms our result in Example 2 of Section 14.6. If we had chosen $F(x)$ to be $4x - (x^3/3) + C$, then we would have

$$F(2) - F(0) = \left[\left(8 - \frac{8}{3}\right) + C\right] - [0 + C] = \frac{16}{3}$$

as before. Since the choice of the value of $C$ is immaterial, for convenience we will always choose it to be 0, as originally done. Usually, $F(b) - F(a)$ is abbreviated by writing

$$F(b) - F(a) = F(x)\Big|_a^b$$

Since $F$ in the Fundamental Theorem of Calculus is *any* antiderivative of $f$ and $\int f(x)\, dx$ is the most general antiderivative of $f$, it showcases the notation to write

$$\int_a^b f(x)\, dx = \left(\int f(x)\, dx\right)\Bigg|_a^b$$

Using the $\Big|_a^b$ notation, we have

$$\int_0^2 (4 - x^2)\, dx = \left(4x - \frac{x^3}{3}\right)\Bigg|_0^2 = \left(8 - \frac{8}{3}\right) - 0 = \frac{16}{3}$$

### ● EXAMPLE 1   Applying the Fundamental Theorem

*Find* $\displaystyle\int_{-1}^3 (3x^2 - x + 6)\, dx$.

**Solution:**  An antiderivative of $3x^2 - x + 6$ is

$$x^3 - \frac{x^2}{2} + 6x$$

---

[7]If $f$ is continuous on $[a, b]$, it can be shown that $\int_a^b f(x)\, dx$ does indeed exist.

Thus,

$$\int_{-1}^{3} (3x^2 - x + 6)\, dx$$

$$= \left( x^3 - \frac{x^2}{2} + 6x \right) \Bigg|_{-1}^{3}$$

$$= \left[ 3^3 - \frac{3^2}{2} + 6(3) \right] - \left[ (-1)^3 - \frac{(-1)^2}{2} + 6(-1) \right]$$

$$= \left( \frac{81}{2} \right) - \left( -\frac{15}{2} \right) = 48$$

NOW WORK PROBLEM 1

### Properties of the Definite Integral

For $\int_a^b f(x)\, dx$, we have assumed that $a < b$. We now define the cases in which $a > b$ or $a = b$. First,

$$\text{If } a > b, \quad \text{then} \quad \int_a^b f(x)\, dx = -\int_b^a f(x)\, dx.$$

That is, interchanging the limits of integration changes the integral's sign. For example,

$$\int_2^0 (4 - x^2)\, dx = -\int_0^2 (4 - x^2)\, dx$$

If the limits of integration are equal, we have

$$\int_a^a f(x)\, dx = 0$$

Some properties of the definite integral deserve mention. The first of the properties that follow restates more formally our comment from the preceding section concerning area.

**Properties of the Definite Integral**

1. If $f$ is continuous and $f(x) \geq 0$ on $[a, b]$, then $\int_a^b f(x)\, dx$ can be interpreted as the area of the region bounded by the curve $y = f(x)$, the $x$-axis, and the lines $x = a$ and $x = b$.
2. $\int_a^b k f(x)\, dx = k \int_a^b f(x)\, dx$     where $k$ is a constant
3. $\int_a^b [f(x) \pm g(x)]\, dx = \int_a^b f(x)\, dx \pm \int_a^b g(x)\, dx$

Properties 2 and 3 are similar to rules for indefinite integrals because a definite integral may be evaluated by the Fundamental Theorem in terms of an antiderivative. Two more properties of definite integrals are as follows.

4. $\int_a^b f(x)\, dx = \int_a^b f(t)\, dt$

The variable of integration is a "dummy variable" in the sense that any other variable produces the same result—that is, the same number.

To illustrate property 4, you can verify, for example, that

$$\int_0^2 x^2\, dx = \int_0^2 t^2\, dt$$

**5.** If $f$ is continuous on an interval $I$ and $a$, $b$, and $c$ are in $I$, then

$$\int_a^c f(x)\,dx = \int_a^b f(x)\,dx + \int_b^c f(x)\,dx$$

Property 5 means that the definite integral over an interval can be expressed in terms of definite integrals over subintervals. Thus,

$$\int_0^2 (4-x^2)\,dx = \int_0^1 (4-x^2)\,dx + \int_1^2 (4-x^2)\,dx$$

We will look at some examples of definite integration now and compute some areas in Section 14.9.

● **EXAMPLE 2   Using the Fundamental Theorem**

*Find* $\displaystyle \int_0^1 \frac{x^3}{\sqrt{1+x^4}}\,dx$.

**Solution:** To find an antiderivative of the integrand, we will apply the power rule for integration:

$$\int_0^1 \frac{x^3}{\sqrt{1+x^4}}\,dx = \int_0^1 x^3(1+x^4)^{-1/2}\,dx$$

$$= \frac{1}{4}\int_0^1 (1+x^4)^{-1/2}\,d(1+x^4) = \left(\frac{1}{4}\right)\frac{(1+x^4)^{1/2}}{\frac{1}{2}}\Bigg|_0^1$$

$$= \frac{1}{2}(1+x^4)^{1/2}\Bigg|_0^1 = \frac{1}{2}\left((2)^{1/2} - (1)^{1/2}\right)$$

$$= \frac{1}{2}(\sqrt{2}-1)$$

NOW WORK PROBLEM 13  ●●●

> **CAUTION**
>
> In Example 2, the value of the antiderivative $\frac{1}{2}(1+x^4)^{1/2}$ at the lower limit 0 is $\frac{1}{2}(1)^{1/2}$. **Do not** assume that an evaluation at the limit zero will yield 0.

● **EXAMPLE 3   Evaluating Definite Integrals**

**a.** *Find* $\displaystyle \int_1^2 \left[4t^{1/3} + t(t^2+1)^3\right]dt$.

**Solution:**

$$\int_1^2 \left[4t^{1/3} + t(t^2+1)^3\right]dt = 4\int_1^2 t^{1/3}\,dt + \frac{1}{2}\int_1^2 (t^2+1)^3\,d(t^2+1)$$

$$= (4)\frac{t^{4/3}}{\frac{4}{3}}\Bigg|_1^2 + \left(\frac{1}{2}\right)\frac{(t^2+1)^4}{4}\Bigg|_1^2$$

$$= 3(2^{4/3}-1) + \frac{1}{8}(5^4 - 2^4)$$

$$= 3\cdot 2^{4/3} - 3 + \frac{609}{8}$$

$$= 6\sqrt[3]{2} + \frac{585}{8}$$

**b.** *Find* $\displaystyle \int_0^1 e^{3t}\,dt$.

**Solution:**

$$\int_0^1 e^{3t}\,dt = \frac{1}{3}\int_0^1 e^{3t}\,d(3t)$$

$$= \left(\frac{1}{3}\right)e^{3t}\Bigg|_0^1 = \frac{1}{3}(e^3 - e^0) = \frac{1}{3}(e^3 - 1)$$

NOW WORK PROBLEM 15  ●●●

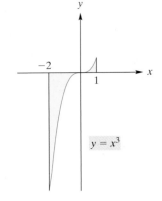

**FIGURE 14.21** Graph of $y = x^3$ on the interval $[-2, 1]$.

   CAUTION

Remember that $\int_a^b f(x)\,dx$ is a limit of a sum. In some cases this limit represents an area. In others it does not. When $f(x) \geq 0$ on $[a, b]$ the integral represents the area between the graph of $f$ and the $x$-axis from $x = a$ to $x = b$.

● **EXAMPLE 4** Finding and Interpreting a Definite Integral

*Evaluate* $\displaystyle\int_{-2}^{1} x^3\,dx$.

Solution:

$$\int_{-2}^{1} x^3\,dx = \frac{x^4}{4}\bigg|_{-2}^{1} = \frac{1^4}{4} - \frac{(-2)^4}{4} = \frac{1}{4} - \frac{16}{4} = -\frac{15}{4}$$

The reason the result is negative is clear from the graph of $y = x^3$ on the interval $[-2, 1]$. (See Figure 14.21.) For $-2 \leq x < 0$, $f(x)$ is negative. Since a definite integral is a limit of a sum of the form $\Sigma f(x)\,\Delta x$, it follows that $\int_{-2}^{0} x^3\,dx$ is not only a negative number, but also the negative of the area of the shaded region in the third quadrant. On the other hand, $\int_0^1 x^3\,dx$ is the area of the shaded region in the first quadrant, since $f(x) \geq 0$ on $[0, 1]$. The definite integral over the entire interval $[-2, 1]$ is the *algebraic* sum of these numbers, because, from property 5,

$$\int_{-2}^{1} x^3\,dx = \int_{-2}^{0} x^3\,dx + \int_0^1 x^3\,dx$$

Thus, $\int_{-2}^{1} x^3\,dx$ does not represent the area between the curve and the $x$-axis. However, if area is desired, it can be given by

$$\left|\int_{-2}^{0} x^3\,dx\right| + \int_0^1 x^3\,dx$$

NOW WORK PROBLEM 25 ●●●

### The Definite Integral of a Derivative

Since a function $f$ is an antiderivative of $f'$, by the Fundamental Theorem we have

$$\int_a^b f'(x)\,dx = f(b) - f(a) \qquad (6)$$

But $f'(x)$ is the rate of change of $f$ with respect to $x$. Hence, if we know the rate of change of $f$ and want to find the difference in function values $f(b) - f(a)$, it suffices to evaluate $\int_a^b f'(x)\,dx$.

● **EXAMPLE 5** Finding a Change in Function Values by Definite Integration

*A manufacturer's marginal-cost function is*

$$\frac{dc}{dq} = 0.6q + 2$$

*If production is presently set at $q = 80$ units per week, how much more would it cost to increase production to 100 units per week?*

Solution: The total-cost function is $c = c(q)$, and we want to find the difference $c(100) - c(80)$. The rate of change of $c$ is $dc/dq$, so by Equation (6),

$$c(100) - c(80) = \int_{80}^{100} \frac{dc}{dq}\,dq = \int_{80}^{100} (0.6q + 2)\,dq$$

$$= \left[\frac{0.6q^2}{2} + 2q\right]\bigg|_{80}^{100} = [0.3q^2 + 2q]\bigg|_{80}^{100}$$

$$= [0.3(100)^2 + 2(100)] - [0.3(80)^2 + 2(80)]$$

$$= 3200 - 2080 = 1120$$

If $c$ is in dollars, then the cost of increasing production from 80 units to 100 units is $1120.

NOW WORK PROBLEM 59 ●●●

# TECHNOLOGY

Many graphing calculators have the capability to estimate the value of a definite integral. On a TI-83 Plus, to estimate

$$\int_{80}^{100} (0.6q + 2)\, dq$$

we use the "fnInt(" command, as indicated in Figure 14.22. The four parameters that must be entered with this command are

| function to | variable of | lower | upper |
| be integrated | integration | limit | limit |

We see that the value of the definite integral is approximately 1120, which agrees with the result in Example 5.
   Similarly, to estimate

$$\int_{-2}^{1} x^3\, dx$$

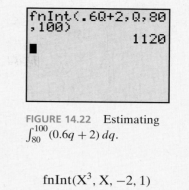

**FIGURE 14.22** Estimating $\int_{80}^{100}(0.6q + 2)\, dq$.

we enter

$$\text{fnInt}(X^3, X, -2, 1)$$

or, alternatively, if we first store $x^3$ as $Y_1$, we can enter

$$\text{fnInt}(Y_1, X, -2, 1)$$

In each case we obtain $-3.75$, which agrees with the result in Example 4.

## Problems 14.7

*In Problems 1–43, evaluate the definite integral.*

**\*1.** $\displaystyle\int_0^3 5\, dx$

**2.** $\displaystyle\int_2^4 (1 - e)\, dx$

**3.** $\displaystyle\int_1^2 5x\, dx$

**4.** $\displaystyle\int_2^8 -5x\, dx$

**5.** $\displaystyle\int_{-3}^1 (2x - 3)\, dx$

**6.** $\displaystyle\int_{-1}^1 (4 - 9y)\, dy$

**7.** $\displaystyle\int_2^3 (y^2 - 2y + 1)\, dy$

**8.** $\displaystyle\int_4^1 (2t - 3t^2)\, dt$

**9.** $\displaystyle\int_{-2}^{-1} (3w^2 - w - 1)\, dw$

**10.** $\displaystyle\int_8^9 dt$

**11.** $\displaystyle\int_1^3 3t^{-3}\, dt$

**12.** $\displaystyle\int_1^2 \frac{x^{-2}}{2}\, dx$

**\*13.** $\displaystyle\int_{-8}^8 \sqrt[3]{x^4}\, dx$

**14.** $\displaystyle\int_{1/2}^{3/2} (x^2 + x + 1)\, dx$

**\*15.** $\displaystyle\int_{1/2}^3 \frac{1}{x^2}\, dx$

**16.** $\displaystyle\int_9^{36} (\sqrt{x} - 2)\, dx$

**17.** $\displaystyle\int_{-1}^1 (z + 1)^5\, dz$

**18.** $\displaystyle\int_1^8 (x^{1/3} - x^{-1/3})\, dx$

**19.** $\displaystyle\int_0^1 2x^2(x^3 - 1)^3\, dx$

**20.** $\displaystyle\int_2^3 (x + 2)^3\, dx$

**21.** $\displaystyle\int_1^8 \frac{4}{y}\, dy$

**22.** $\displaystyle\int_{-(e^e)}^{-1} \frac{6}{x}\, dx$

**23.** $\displaystyle\int_0^1 e^5\, dx$

**24.** $\displaystyle\int_2^{e+1} \frac{1}{x - 1}\, dx$

**\*25.** $\displaystyle\int_0^1 5x^2 e^{x^3}\, dx$

**26.** $\displaystyle\int_0^1 (3x^2 + 4x)(x^3 + 2x^2)^4\, dx$

**27.** $\displaystyle\int_4^5 \frac{2}{(x - 3)^3}\, dx$

**28.** $\displaystyle\int_{-1/3}^{20/3} \sqrt{3x + 5}\, dx$

**29.** $\displaystyle\int_{1/3}^2 \sqrt{10 - 3p}\, dp$

**30.** $\displaystyle\int_{-1}^1 q\sqrt{q^2 + 3}\, dq$

**31.** $\displaystyle\int_0^1 x^2 \sqrt[3]{7x^3 + 1}\, dx$

**32.** $\displaystyle\int_0^{\sqrt{7}} \left(3x - \frac{x}{(x^2 + 2)^{4/3}}\right) dx$

**33.** $\displaystyle\int_0^1 \frac{2x^3 + x}{x^2 + x^4 + 1}\, dx$

**34.** $\displaystyle\int_a^b (m + ny)\, dy$

**35.** $\displaystyle\int_0^1 \frac{e^x - e^{-x}}{2}\, dx$

**36.** $\displaystyle\int_{-2}^1 8|x|\, dx$

**37.** $\displaystyle\int_\pi^e 3(x^{-2} + x^{-3} - x^{-4})\, dx$

**38.** $\displaystyle\int_1^2 \left(6\sqrt{x} - \frac{1}{\sqrt{2x}}\right) dx$

**39.** $\displaystyle\int_1^3 (x + 1)e^{x^2 + 2x}\, dx$

**40.** $\displaystyle\int_1^{95} \frac{x}{\ln e^x}\, dx$

**41.** $\displaystyle\int_0^2 \frac{x^6 + 6x^4 + x^3 + 8x^2 + x + 5}{x^3 + 5x + 1}\, dx$

**42.** $\displaystyle\int_{-1}^1 \frac{2}{1 + e^x}\, dx$ (*Hint:* Multiply the integrand by $\frac{e^{-x}}{e^{-x}}$.)

**43.** $\displaystyle\int_0^2 f(x)\, dx$  where $f(x) = \begin{cases} 4x^2 & \text{if } 0 \le x < \frac{1}{2} \\ 2x & \text{if } \frac{1}{2} \le x \le 2 \end{cases}$

**44.** Evaluate $\displaystyle\left(\int_1^3 x\, dx\right)^3 - \int_1^3 x^3\, dx$.

**45.** Suppose $\displaystyle f(x) = \int_1^x 3\frac{1}{t^2}\, dt$. Evaluate $\displaystyle\int_e^1 f(x)\, dx$.

**46.** Evaluate $\displaystyle\int_{7}^{7} e^{x^2}\,dx + \int_{0}^{\sqrt{2}} \frac{1}{3\sqrt{2}}\,dx$

**47.** If $\displaystyle\int_{1}^{3} f(x)\,dx = 4$ and $\displaystyle\int_{3}^{2} f(x)\,dx = 3$, find $\displaystyle\int_{1}^{2} f(x)\,dx$.

**48.** If $\displaystyle\int_{1}^{4} f(x)\,dx = 6$, $\displaystyle\int_{2}^{4} f(x)\,dx = 5$, and $\displaystyle\int_{1}^{3} f(x)\,dx = 2$, find $\displaystyle\int_{2}^{3} f(x)\,dx$.

**49.** Evaluate $\displaystyle\int_{2}^{3} \left( \frac{d}{dx} \int_{2}^{3} e^{x^3}\,dx \right) dx$

(*Hint:* It is not necessary to find $\int_{2}^{3} e^{x^3}\,dx$.)

**50.** Suppose that $f(x) = \displaystyle\int_{e}^{x} \frac{e^t - e^{-t}}{e^t + e^{-t}}\,dt$   where $x > e$. Find $f'(x)$.

**51. Severity Index**   In discussing traffic safety, Shonle[8] considers how much acceleration a person can tolerate in a crash so that there is no major injury. The *severity index* is defined as

$$\text{S.I.} = \int_{0}^{T} \alpha^{5/2}\,dt$$

where $\alpha$ (a Greek letter read "alpha") is considered a constant involved with a weighted average acceleration, and $T$ is the duration of the crash. Find the severity index.

**52. Statistics**   In statistics, the mean $\mu$ (a Greek letter read "mu") of the continuous probability density function $f$ defined on the interval $[a, b]$ is given by

$$\mu = \int_{a}^{b} [x \cdot f(x)]\,dx$$

and the variance $\sigma^2$ ($\sigma$ is a Greek letter read "sigma") is given by

$$\sigma^2 = \int_{a}^{b} (x - \mu)^2 f(x)\,dx$$

Compute $\mu$ and then $\sigma^2$ if $a = 0$, $b = 1$, and $f(x) = 1$.

**53. Distribution of Incomes**   The economist Pareto[9] has stated an empirical law of distribution of higher incomes that gives the number $N$ of persons receiving $x$ or more dollars. If

$$\frac{dN}{dx} = -Ax^{-B}$$

where $A$ and $B$ are constants, set up a definite integral that gives the total number of persons with incomes between $a$ and $b$, where $a < b$.

**54. Biology**   In a discussion of gene mutation,[10] the following integral occurs:

$$\int_{0}^{10^{-4}} x^{-1/2}\,dx$$

Evaluate this integral.

**55. Continuous Income Flow**   The present value (in dollars) of a continuous flow of income of $2000 a year for five years at 6% compounded continuously is given by

$$\int_{0}^{5} 2000 e^{-0.06t}\,dt$$

Evaluate the present value to the nearest dollar.

**56. Biology**   In biology, problems frequently arise involving the transfer of a substance between compartments. An example is a transfer from the bloodstream to tissue. Evaluate the following integral, which occurs in a two-compartment diffusion problem:[11]

$$\int_{0}^{t} (e^{-a\tau} - e^{-b\tau})\,d\tau$$

Here, $\tau$ (read "tau") is a Greek letter; $a$ and $b$ are constants.

**57. Demography**   For a certain population, suppose $l$ is a function such that $l(x)$ is the number of persons who reach the age of $x$ in any year of time. This function is called a *life table function*. Under appropriate conditions, the integral

$$\int_{x}^{x+n} l(t)\,dt$$

gives the expected number of people in the population between the exact ages of $x$ and $x + n$, inclusive. If

$$l(x) = 10{,}000\sqrt{100 - x}$$

determine the number of people between the exact ages of 36 and 64, inclusive. Give your answer to the nearest integer, since fractional answers make no sense.

**58. Mineral Consumption**   If $C$ is the yearly consumption of a mineral at time $t = 0$, then, under continuous consumption, the total amount of the mineral used in the interval $[0, t]$ is

$$\int_{0}^{t} Ce^{k\tau}\,d\tau$$

where $k$ is the rate of consumption. For a rare-earth mineral, it has been determined that $C = 3000$ units and $k = 0.05$. Evaluate the integral for these data.

**\*59. Marginal Cost**   A manufacturer's marginal-cost function is

$$\frac{dc}{dq} = 0.2q + 8$$

If $c$ is in dollars, determine the cost involved to increase production from 65 to 75 units.

**60. Marginal Cost**   Repeat Problem 59 if

$$\frac{dc}{dq} = 0.004q^2 - 0.5q + 50$$

and production increases from 90 to 180 units.

[8]J. I. Shonle, *Environmental Applications of General Physics* (Reading, MA: Addison-Wesley Publishing Company, Inc., 1975).

[9]G. Tintner, *Methodology of Mathematical Economics and Econometrics* (Chicago: University of Chicago Press, 1967), p. 16.

[10]W. J. Ewens, *Population Genetics* (London: Methuen & Company Ltd., 1969).

[11]W. Simon, *Mathematical Techniques for Physiology and Medicine* (New York: Academic Press, Inc., 1972).

**61. Marginal Revenue** A manufacturer's marginal-revenue function is

$$\frac{dr}{dq} = \frac{2000}{\sqrt{300q}}$$

If $r$ is in dollars, find the change in the manufacturer's total revenue if production is increased from 500 to 800 units.

**62. Marginal Revenue** Repeat Problem 61 if

$$\frac{dr}{dq} = 250 + 90q - 3q^2$$

and production is increased from 10 to 20 units.

**63. Crime Rate** A sociologist is studying the crime rate in a certain city. She estimates that $t$ months after the beginning of next year, the total number of crimes committed will increase at the rate of $8t + 10$ crimes per month. Determine the total number of crimes that can be expected to be committed next year. How many crimes can be expected to be committed during the last six months of that year?

**64. Hospital Discharges** For a group of hospitalized individuals, suppose the discharge rate is given by

$$f(t) = \frac{81 \times 10^6}{(300 + t)^4}$$

where $f(t)$ is the proportion of the group discharged per day at the end of $t$ days. What proportion has been discharged by the end of 700 days?

**65. Production** Imagine a one-dimensional country of length $2R$. (See Figure 14.23.[12]) Suppose the production of goods for this country is continuously distributed from border to border. If the amount produced each year per unit of distance is $f(x)$, then the country's total yearly production is given by

$$G = \int_{-R}^{R} f(x)\,dx$$

Evaluate $G$ if $f(x) = i$, where $i$ is constant.

One-dimensional country

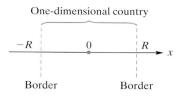

**FIGURE 14.23** Diagram for Problem 65.

**66. Exports** For the one-dimensional country of Problem 65, under certain conditions the amount of the country's exports is given by

$$E = \int_{-R}^{R} \frac{i}{2} \left[ e^{-k(R-x)} + e^{-k(R+x)} \right] dx$$

where $i$ and $k$ are constants ($k \neq 0$). Evaluate $E$.

**67. Average Delivered Price** In a discussion of a delivered price of a good from a mill to a customer, DeCanio[13] claims that the average delivered price paid by consumers is given by

$$A = \frac{\int_0^R (m + x)[1 - (m + x)]\,dx}{\int_0^R [1 - (m + x)]\,dx}$$

where $m$ is mill price, and $x$ is the maximum distance to the point of sale. DeCanio determines that

$$A = \frac{m + \dfrac{R}{2} - m^2 - mR - \dfrac{R^2}{3}}{1 - m - \dfrac{R}{2}}$$

Verify this.

*In Problems 68–70, use the Fundamental Theorem of Integral Calculus to determine the value of the definite integral. Confirm your result with your calculator.*

**68.** $\displaystyle\int_{2.5}^{3.5} (1 + 2x + 3x^2)\,dx$

**69.** $\displaystyle\int_{0}^{4} \frac{1}{(4x + 4)^2}\,dx$

**70.** $\displaystyle\int_{0}^{1} e^{3t}\,dt$   Round your answer to two decimal places.

*In Problems 71–74, estimate the value of the definite integral. Round your answer to two decimal places.*

**71.** $\displaystyle\int_{-1}^{5} \frac{x^2 + 1}{x^2 + 4}\,dx$        **72.** $\displaystyle\int_{3}^{4} \frac{1}{x \ln x}\,dx$

**73.** $\displaystyle\int_{0}^{3} 2\sqrt{t^2 + 3}\,dt$

**74.** $\displaystyle\int_{-1}^{1} \frac{6\sqrt{q + 1}}{q + 3}\,dq$

# 14.8 Approximate Integration

## Trapezoidal Rule

Any function $f$ constructed from polynomials, exponentials, and logarithms using algebraic operations and composition can be differentiated and the resulting function $f'$ is again of the same kind—one that can be constructed from polynomials, exponentials, and logarithms using algebraic operations and composition. Let us call such

---

[12]R. Taagepera, "Why the Trade/GNP Ratio Decreases with Country Size," *Social Science Research*, 5 (1976), 385–404.

[13]S. J. DeCanio, "Delivered Pricing and Multiple Basing Point Equationilibria: A Reevaluation," *The Quarterly Journal of Economics*, XCIX, no. 2 (1984), 329–49.

functions *elementary* (although the term usually has a slightly different meaning). In this terminology, the derivative of an elementary function is also elementary. Integration is more complicated. If an elementary function $f$ has $F$ as an antiderivative, then $F$ may fail to be elementary. Said otherwise, even for a fairly simple-looking function $f$ it is sometimes impossible to find $\int f(x)\,dx$ in terms of the functions that we consider in this book. For example, there is no elementary function whose derivative is $e^{x^2}$ so that you cannot expect to "do" the integral $\int e^{x^2}\,dx$.

On the other hand, consider a function $f$ that is continuous on a closed interval $[a, b]$ with $f(x) \geq 0$ for all $x$ in $[a, b]$. Then $\int_a^b f(x)\,dx$ is simply the *number* that gives the area of the region bounded by the curves $y = f(x)$, $y = 0$, $x = a$, and $x = b$. It is unsatisfying, and perhaps impractical, to not say anything about the number $\int_a^b f(x)\,dx$ because of an inability to "do" the integral $\int f(x)\,dx$. This also applies when the integral $\int f(x)\,dx$ is merely too difficult for the person who needs to find the number $\int_a^b f(x)\,dx$.

Since $\int_a^b f(x)\,dx$ is defined as a limit of sums of the form $\sum f(x)\,\Delta x$, any particular well-formed sum of the form $\sum f(x)\,\Delta x$ can be regarded as an approximation of $\int_a^b f(x)\,dx$. At least for nonnegative $f$ such sums can be regarded as sums of areas of thin rectagles. Consider for example Figure 14.11 in Section 14.6, in which two rectangles are explicitly shown. It is clear that the error that arises from such rectangles is associated with the small side at the top. The error would be reduced if we replaced the rectangles by shapes that have a top side that is closer to the shape of the curve. We will consider two possibilities: using thin trapezoids rather than thin rectangles, the *trapezoidal rule;* and using thin regions surmounted by parabolic arcs, *Simpson's rule.* In each case only a finite number of numerical values of $f(x)$ need be known and the calculations involved are especially suitable for computers or calculators. In both cases, we assume that $f$ is continuous on $[a, b]$.

In developing the trapezoidal rule, for convenience we will also assume that $f(x) \geq 0$ on $[a, b]$, so that we can think in terms of area. Basically, this rule involves approximating the graph of $f$ by straight-line segments.

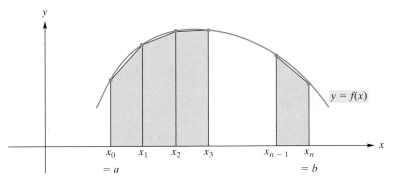

**FIGURE 14.24**   Approximating an area by using trapezoids.

In Figure 14.24, the interval $[a, b]$ is divided into $n$ subintervals of equal length by the points $a = x_0, x_1, x_2, \ldots$, and $x_n = b$. Since the length of $[a, b]$ is $b - a$, the length of each subinterval is $(b - a)/n$, which we will call $h$.

Clearly,

$$x_1 = a + h, x_2 = a + 2h, \ldots, x_n = a + nh = b$$

With each subinterval, we can associate a trapezoid (a four-sided figure with two parallel sides). The area $A$ of the region bounded by the curve, the $x$-axis, and the lines $x = a$ and $x = b$ is $\int_a^b f(x)\,dx$ and can be approximated by the sum of the areas of the trapezoids determined by the subintervals.

Consider the first trapezoid, which is redrawn in Figure 14.25. Since the area of a trapezoid is equal to one-half the base times the sum of the lengths of the parallel sides, this trapezoid has area

$$\tfrac{1}{2}h[\,f(a) + f(a + h)]$$

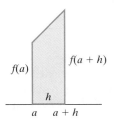

**FIGURE 14.25**   First trapezoid.

Similarly, the second trapezoid has area

$$\tfrac{1}{2}h[f(a+h)+f(a+2h)]$$

The area $A$ under the curve is approximated by the sum of the areas of $n$ trapezoids:

$$A \approx \tfrac{1}{2}h[f(a)+f(a+h)] + \tfrac{1}{2}h[f(a+h)+f(a+2h)]$$
$$+ \tfrac{1}{2}h[f(a+2h)+f(a+3h)] + \cdots + \tfrac{1}{2}h[f(a+(n-1)h)+f(b)]$$

Since $A = \int_a^b f(x)\,dx$, by simplifying the preceding formula we have the trapezoidal rule:

**The Trapezoidal Rule**

$$\int_a^b f(x)\,dx \approx \frac{h}{2}[f(a)+2f(a+h)+2f(a+2h)$$
$$+ \cdots + 2f(a+(n-1)h)+f(b)]$$

where $h = (b-a)/n$.

The pattern of the coefficients inside the braces is 1, 2, 2, ... , 2, 1. Usually, the more subintervals, the better is the approximation. In our development, we assumed for convenience that $f(x) \geq 0$ on $[a, b]$. However, the trapezoidal rule is valid without this restriction.

**PRINCIPLES IN PRACTICE 1**

**TRAPEZOIDAL RULE**

An oil tanker is losing oil at a rate of $R'(t) = \dfrac{60}{\sqrt{t^2+9}}$, where $t$ is the time in minutes and $R(t)$ is the radius of the oil slick in feet. Use the trapezoidal rule with $n=5$ to approximate $\displaystyle\int_0^5 \dfrac{60}{\sqrt{t^2+9}}\,dt$, the size of the radius after five seconds.

● **EXAMPLE 1 Trapezoidal Rule**

*Use the trapezoidal rule to estimate the value of*

$$\int_0^1 \frac{1}{1+x^2}\,dx$$

*for $n = 5$. Compute each term to four decimal places, and round the answer to three decimal places.*

**Solution:** Here $f(x) = 1/(1+x^2)$, $n = 5$, $a = 0$, and $b = 1$. Thus,

$$h = \frac{b-a}{n} = \frac{1-0}{5} = \frac{1}{5} = 0.2$$

The terms to be added are

$$
\begin{aligned}
f(a) &= f(0) &&= 1.0000 \\
2f(a+h) &= 2f(0.2) &&= 1.9231 \\
2f(a+2h) &= 2f(0.4) &&= 1.7241 \\
2f(a+3h) &= 2f(0.6) &&= 1.4706 \\
2f(a+4h) &= 2f(0.8) &&= 1.2195 \\
f(b) &= f(1) &&= \underline{0.5000} \qquad (a+nh=b)\\
& && \;\,7.8373 = \text{sum}
\end{aligned}
$$

Hence, our estimate for the integral is

$$\int_0^1 \frac{1}{1+x^2}\,dx \approx \frac{0.2}{2}(7.8373) \approx 0.784$$

The actual value of the integral is approximately 0.785.

NOW WORK PROBLEM 1 ●●

## Simpson's Rule

Another method for estimating $\int_a^b f(x)\,dx$ is given by Simpson's rule, which involves approximating the graph of $f$ by parabolic segments. We will omit the derivation.

### Simpson's Rule

$$\int_a^b f(x)\, dx \approx \frac{h}{3}[f(a) + 4f(a+h) + 2f(a+2h)$$
$$+ \cdots + 4f(a + (n-1)h) + f(b)]$$

where $h = (b-a)/n$ and $n$ is even.

The pattern of coefficients inside the braces is $1, 4, 2, 4, 2, \ldots, 2, 4, 1$, which requires that **$n$ be even.** Let us use this rule for the integral in Example 1.

**SIMPSON'S RULE**

A yeast culture is growing at the rate of $A'(t) = 0.3e^{0.2t^2}$, where $t$ is the time in hours and $A(t)$ is the amount in grams. Use Simpson's rule with $n = 8$ to approximate $\int_0^4 0.3e^{0.2t^2}\, dt$, the amount the culture grew over the first four hours.

### ● EXAMPLE 2  Simpson's Rule

*Use Simpson's rule to estimate the value of* $\displaystyle\int_0^1 \frac{1}{1+x^2}\, dx$ *for* $n = 4$. *Compute each term to four decimal places, and round the answer to three decimal places.*

**Solution:** Here $f(x) = 1/(1 + x^2)$, $n = 4$, $a = 0$, and $b = 1$. Thus, $h = (b-a)/n = 1/4 = 0.25$. The terms to be added are

$$
\begin{aligned}
f(a) = \quad f(0) \quad &= 1.0000 \\
4f(a+h) = 4f(0.25) &= 3.7647 \\
2f(a+2h) = \;2f(0.5) \;\; &= 1.6000 \\
4f(a+3h) = 4f(0.75) &= 2.5600 \\
f(b) = \quad f(1) \quad &= \underline{0.5000} \\
& \;\;\; 9.4247 = \text{sum}
\end{aligned}
$$

Therefore, by Simpson's rule,

$$\int_0^1 \frac{1}{1+x^2}\, dx \approx \frac{0.25}{3}(9.4247) \approx 0.785$$

This is a better approximation than that which we obtained in Example 1 by using the trapezoidal rule.

NOW WORK PROBLEM 5 ●●●

Both Simpson's rule and the trapezoidal rule can be used if we know only $f(a)$, $f(a+h)$, and so on; we do not need to know $f(x)$ for all $x$ in $[a, b]$. Example 3 will illustrate.

In Example 3, a definite integral is estimated from data points; the function itself is not known.

### ● EXAMPLE 3  Demography

*A function often used in demography (the study of births, marriages, mortality, etc., in a population) is the **life-table function**, denoted l. In a population having 100,000 births in any year of time, l(x) represents the number of persons who reach the age of x in any year of time. For example, if l(20) = 98,857, then the number of persons who attain age 20 in any year of time is 98,857. Suppose that the function l applies to all people born over an extended period of time. It can be shown that, at any time, the expected number of persons in the population between the exact ages of x and x + m, inclusive, is given by*

$$\int_x^{x+m} l(t)\, dt$$

*The following table gives values of l(x) for males and females in the United States[14] Approximate the number of women in the 20–35 age group by using the trapezoidal rule with $n = 3$.*

---

[14]*National Vital Statistics Report*, Vol. 48, No. 18, February 7, 2001.

Life Table

| Age = x | l(x) Males | l(x) Females | Age = x | l(x) Males | l(x) Females |
|---|---|---|---|---|---|
| 0 | 100,000 | 100,000 | 45 | 93,717 | 96,582 |
| 5 | 99,066 | 99,220 | 50 | 91,616 | 95,392 |
| 10 | 98,967 | 99,144 | 55 | 88,646 | 93,562 |
| 15 | 98,834 | 99,059 | 60 | 84,188 | 90,700 |
| 20 | 98,346 | 98,857 | 65 | 77,547 | 86,288 |
| 25 | 97,648 | 98,627 | 70 | 68,375 | 79,926 |
| 30 | 96,970 | 98,350 | 75 | 56,288 | 70,761 |
| 35 | 96,184 | 97,964 | 80 | 42,127 | 58,573 |
| 40 | 95,163 | 97,398 | | | |

**Solution:** We want to estimate

$$\int_{20}^{35} l(t)\, dt$$

We have $h = \dfrac{b-a}{n} = \dfrac{35-20}{3} = 5$. The terms to be added under the trapezoidal rule are

$$l(20) = 98,857$$
$$2l(25) = 2(98,627) = 197,254$$
$$2l(30) = 2(98,350) = 196,700$$
$$l(35) = \underline{97,964}$$
$$590,775 = \text{sum}$$

By the trapezoidal rule,

$$\int_{20}^{35} l(t)\, dt \approx \frac{5}{2}(590,775) = 1,476,937.5$$

NOW WORK PROBLEM 17

Formulas used to determine the accuracy of answers obtained with the trapezoidal or Simpson's rule can be found in standard texts on numerical analysis.

## Problems 14.8

In Problems 1 and 2, use the trapezoidal rule or Simpson's rule (as indicated) and the given value of n to estimate the integral.

*1. $\int_{-2}^{4} \dfrac{170}{1+x^2}\, dx$;   trapezoidal rule, $n = 6$

2. $\int_{-2}^{4} \dfrac{170}{1+x^2}\, dx$;   Simpson's rule, $n = 6$

In Problems 3–8, use the trapezoidal rule or Simpson's rule (as indicated) and the given value of n to estimate the integral. Compute each term to four decimal places, and round the answer to three decimal places. In Problems 3–6, also evaluate the integral by antidifferentiation (the Fundamental Theorem of Integral Calculus).

3. $\int_{0}^{1} x^2\, dx$;   trapezoidal rule, $n = 5$

4. $\int_{0}^{1} x^2\, dx$;   Simpson's rule, $n = 4$

*5. $\int_{1}^{4} \dfrac{dx}{x^2}$;   Simpson's rule, $n = 4$

6. $\int_{1}^{4} \dfrac{dx}{x}$;   trapezoidal rule, $n = 6$

7. $\int_{0}^{2} \dfrac{x\, dx}{x+1}$;   trapezoidal rule, $n = 4$

8. $\int_{2}^{4} \dfrac{dx}{x+x^2}$;   Simpson's rule, $n = 4$

*In Problems 9 and 10, use the life table in Example 3 to estimate the given integrals by the trapezoidal rule.*

**9.** $\int_{45}^{70} l(t)\, dt$, males, $n = 5$

**10.** $\int_{35}^{55} l(t)\, dt$, females, $n = 4$

*In Problems 11 and 12, suppose the graph of a continuous function f, where $f(x) \geq 0$, contains the given points. Use Simpson's rule and all of the points to approximate the area between the graph and the x-axis on the given interval. Round the answer to one decimal place.*

**11.** $(1, 0.4), (2, 0.6), (3, 1.2), (4, 0.8), (5, 0.5);$ [1,5]

**12.** $(2, 0), (2.5, 6), (3, 10), (3.5, 11), (4, 14), (4.5, 15), (5, 16);$ [2,5]

**13.** Using all the information given in Figure 14.26, estimate $\int_{1}^{3} f(x)\, dx$ by using Simpson's rule. Give your answer in fractional form.

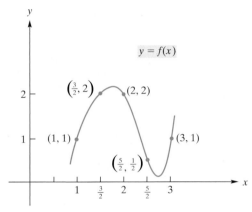

**FIGURE 14.26** Graph of $f$ for Problem 13.

*In Problems 14 and 15, use Simpson's rule and the given value of n to estimate the integral. Compute each term to four decimal places, and round the answer to three decimal places.*

**14.** $\int_{1}^{3} \dfrac{2}{\sqrt{1+x}}\, dx;\ n = 4$ Also, evaluate the integral by the Fundamental Theorem of Integral Calculus.

**15.** $\int_{0}^{1} \sqrt{1 - x^2}\, dx;\ n = 4$

**16. Revenue** Use Simpson's rule to approximate the total revenue received from the production and sale of 80 units of a product if the values of the marginal-revenue function $dr/dq$ are as follows:

| q (units) | 0 | 10 | 20 | 30 | 40 | 50 | 60 | 70 | 80 |
|---|---|---|---|---|---|---|---|---|---|
| $\dfrac{dr}{dq}$ (\$ per unit) | 10 | 9 | 8.5 | 8 | 8.5 | 7.5 | 7 | 6.5 | 7 |

*17. **Area of Lake** A straight stretch of highway runs alongside a lake. A surveyor who wishes to know the approximate area of the lake measures the distance from various points along the road to the near and far shores of the lake according to the following table:

| Distance along highway (km) | 0.0 | 0.5 | 1.0 | 1.5 | 2.0 | 2.5 | 3.0 | 3.5 | 4.0 |
|---|---|---|---|---|---|---|---|---|---|
| Distance to near shore (km) | 0.5 | 0.3 | 0.7 | 1.0 | 0.5 | 0.2 | 0.5 | 0.8 | 1.0 |
| Distance to far shore (km) | 0.5 | 2.3 | 2.2 | 3.0 | 2.5 | 2.2 | 1.5 | 1.3 | 1.0 |

Draw a rough sketch of the geographical situation. Then use Simpson's rule to give the best estimate of the lake's area. Give your answer in fractional form.

**18. Manufacturing** A manufacturer estimated both marginal cost (MC) and marginal revenue (MR) at various levels of output ($q$). These estimates are given in the following table:

| q (units) | 0 | 20 | 40 | 60 | 80 | 100 |
|---|---|---|---|---|---|---|
| MC (\$ per unit) | 260 | 250 | 240 | 200 | 240 | 250 |
| MR (\$ per unit) | 410 | 350 | 300 | 250 | 270 | 250 |

**(a)** Using the trapezoidal rule, estimate the total variable costs of production for 100 units.
**(b)** Using the trapezoidal rule, estimate the total revenue from the sale of 100 units.
**(c)** If we assume that maximum profit occurs when MR = MC (that is, when $q = 100$), estimate the maximum profit if fixed costs are \$2000.

OBJECTIVE

To use vertical strips and the definite integral to find the area of the region between a curve and the $x$-axis.

# 14.9 Area

In Section 14.7 we saw that the area of a region could be found by evaluating the limit of a sum of the form $\Sigma f(x)\, \Delta x$, where $f(x)\, \Delta x$ represents the area of a rectangle. This limit is a special case of a definite integral, so it can easily be found by using the Fundamental Theorem.

When using the definite integral to determine area, you should make a rough sketch of the region involved. Let us consider the area of the region bounded by $y = f(x)$ and the x-axis from $x = a$ to $x = b$, where $f(x) \geq 0$ on $[a, b]$. (See Figure 14.27.) To set up the integral, a sample rectangle should be included in the sketch because the area of the region is a limit of sums of areas of rectangles. This will not only help you understand the integration process, but it will also help you find areas of more complicated regions. Such a rectangle (see Figure 14.27) is called a

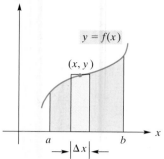

FIGURE 14.27  Region with vertical element.

**vertical element of area** (or a **vertical strip**). In the diagram, the width of the vertical element is $\Delta x$. The height is the $y$-value of the curve. Hence, the rectangle has area $y \, \Delta x$ or $f(x) \, \Delta x$. The area of the entire region is found by summing the areas of all such elements between $x = a$ and $x = b$ and finding the limit of this sum, which is the definite integral. Symbolically, we have

$$\Sigma f(x) \, \Delta x \rightarrow \int_a^b f(x) \, dx = \text{area}$$

Example 1 will illustrate.

● **EXAMPLE 1  Using the Definite Integral to Find Area**

*Find the area of the region bounded by the curve*

$$y = 6 - x - x^2$$

*and the x-axis.*

**Solution:**  First we must sketch the curve so that we can visualize the region. Since

$$y = -(x^2 + x - 6) = -(x - 2)(x + 3)$$

the $x$-intercepts are $(2, 0)$ and $(-3, 0)$. Using techniques of graphing that were previously discussed, we obtain the graph and region shown in Figure 14.28. *With this region, it is crucial that the x-intercepts of the curve be found, because they determine the interval over which the areas of the elements must be summed. That is, these x-values are the limits of integration.* The vertical element shown has width $\Delta x$ and height $y$. Hence, the area of the element is $y \, \Delta x$. Summing the areas of all such elements from $x = -3$ to $x = 2$ and taking the limit via the definite integral gives the area:

$$\sum y \, \Delta x \rightarrow \int_{-3}^{2} y \, dx = \text{area}$$

To evaluate the integral, we must express the integrand in terms of the variable of integration, $x$. Since $y = 6 - x - x^2$,

$$\text{area} = \int_{-3}^{2} (6 - x - x^2) \, dx = \left( 6x - \frac{x^2}{2} - \frac{x^3}{3} \right) \Bigg|_{-3}^{2}$$

$$= \left( 12 - \frac{4}{2} - \frac{8}{3} \right) - \left( -18 - \frac{9}{2} - \frac{-27}{3} \right) = \frac{125}{6}$$

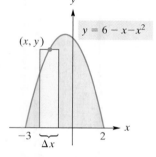

FIGURE 14.28  Region of Example 1 with vertical element.

NOW WORK PROBLEM 1 ●●●

● **EXAMPLE 2  Finding the Area of a Region**

*Find the area of the region bounded by the curve $y = x^2 + 2x + 2$, the x-axis, and the lines $x = -2$ and $x = 1$.*

**Solution:**  A sketch of the region is given in Figure 14.29. We have

$$\text{area} = \int_{-2}^{1} y \, dx = \int_{-2}^{1} (x^2 + 2x + 2) \, dx$$

$$= \left( \frac{x^3}{3} + x^2 + 2x \right) \Bigg|_{-2}^{1} = \left( \frac{1}{3} + 1 + 2 \right) - \left( -\frac{8}{3} + 4 - 4 \right)$$

$$= 6$$

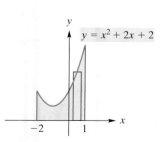

FIGURE 14.29  Diagram for Example 2.

NOW WORK PROBLEM 7 ●●●

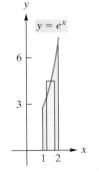

**FIGURE 14.30**
Diagram for
Example 3.

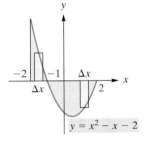

**FIGURE 14.31** Diagram for
Example 4.

**CAUTION**

It is wrong to write hastily that the area is $\int_{-2}^{2} y \, dx$, for the following reason: For the left rectangle, the height is $y$. However, for the rectangle on the right, $y$ is negative, so its height is the positive number $-y$. This points out the importance of sketching the region.

● **EXAMPLE 3   Finding the Area of a Region**

*Find the area of the region between the curve $y = e^x$ and the x-axis from $x = 1$ to $x = 2$.*

**Solution:** A sketch of the region is given in Figure 14.30. We write

$$\text{area} = \int_{1}^{2} y \, dx = \int_{1}^{2} e^x \, dx = e^x \Big|_{1}^{2}$$

$$= e^2 - e = e(e - 1)$$

NOW WORK PROBLEM 27 ●●

● **EXAMPLE 4   An Area Requiring Two Definite Integrals**

*Find the area of the region bounded by the curve*

$$y = x^2 - x - 2$$

*and the line $y = 0$ (the x-axis) from $x = -2$ to $x = 2$.*

**Solution:** A sketch of the region is given in Figure 14.31. Notice that the $x$-intercepts are $(-1, 0)$ and $(2, 0)$.
  On the interval $[-2, -1]$, the area of the element is

$$y \, \Delta x = (x^2 - x - 2) \, \Delta x$$

On $[-1, 2]$ the area is

$$-y \, \Delta x = -(x^2 - x - 2) \, \Delta x$$

Thus,

$$\text{area} = \int_{-2}^{-1} (x^2 - x - 2) \, dx + \int_{-1}^{2} -(x^2 - x - 2) \, dx$$

$$= \left( \frac{x^3}{3} - \frac{x^2}{2} - 2x \right) \Big|_{-2}^{-1} - \left( \frac{x^3}{3} - \frac{x^2}{2} - 2x \right) \Big|_{-1}^{2}$$

$$= \left[ \left( -\frac{1}{3} - \frac{1}{2} + 2 \right) - \left( -\frac{8}{3} - \frac{4}{2} + 4 \right) \right]$$

$$\quad - \left[ \left( \frac{8}{3} - \frac{4}{2} - 4 \right) - \left( -\frac{1}{3} - \frac{1}{2} + 2 \right) \right]$$

$$= \frac{19}{3}$$

NOW WORK PROBLEM 31 ●●

The next example shows the use of area as a probability in statistics.

● **EXAMPLE 5   Statistics Application**

*In statistics, a (probability) **density function** $f$ of a variable $x$, where $x$ assumes all values in the interval $[a, b]$, has the following properties:*

**(i)** $f(x) \geq 0$
**(ii)** $\int_{a}^{b} f(x) \, dx = 1$

*The probability that $x$ assumes a value between $c$ and $d$, which is written $P(c \leq x \leq d)$, where $a \leq c \leq d \leq b$, is represented by the area of the region bounded by the graph of $f$ and the x-axis between $x = c$ and $x = d$. Hence (see Figure 14.32),*

$$P(c \leq x \leq d) = \int_{c}^{d} f(x) \, dx$$

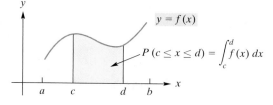

**FIGURE 14.32**   Probability as an area.

*For the density function* $f(x) = 6(x - x^2)$, *where* $0 \le x \le 1$, *find each of the following probabilities.*

**a.** $P(0 \le x \le \frac{1}{4})$

**Solution:** Here $[a, b]$ is $[0, 1]$, $c$ is $0$, and $d$ is $\frac{1}{4}$. We have

$$P\left(0 \le x \le \tfrac{1}{4}\right) = \int_0^{1/4} 6(x - x^2)\, dx = 6\int_0^{1/4} (x - x^2)\, dx$$

$$= 6\left(\frac{x^2}{2} - \frac{x^3}{3}\right)\bigg|_0^{1/4} = (3x^2 - 2x^3)\bigg|_0^{1/4}$$

$$= \left(3\left(\frac{1}{4}\right)^2 - 2\left(\frac{1}{4}\right)^3\right) - 0 = \frac{5}{32}$$

**b.** $P\left(x \ge \frac{1}{2}\right)$

**Solution:** Since the domain of $f$ is $0 \le x \le 1$, to say that $x \ge \frac{1}{2}$ means that $\frac{1}{2} \le x \le 1$. Thus,

$$P\left(x \ge \frac{1}{2}\right) = \int_{1/2}^1 6(x - x^2)\, dx = 6\int_{1/2}^1 (x - x^2)\, dx$$

$$= 6\left(\frac{x^2}{2} - \frac{x^3}{3}\right)\bigg|_{1/2}^1 = (3x^2 - 2x^3)\bigg|_{1/2}^1 = \frac{1}{2}$$

NOW WORK PROBLEM 37 ●●

## Problems 14.9

*In Problems 1–34, use a definite integral to find the area of the region bounded by the given curve, the x-axis, and the given lines. In each case, first sketch the region. Watch out for areas of regions that are below the x-axis.*

*1. $y = 4x$,   $x = 2$

2. $y = \frac{3}{4}x + 1$,   $x = 0$,   $x = 16$

3. $y = 5x + 2$,   $x = 1$,   $x = 4$

4. $y = x + 5$,   $x = 2$,   $x = 4$

5. $y = x - 1$,   $x = 5$

6. $y = 3x^2$,   $x = 1$,   $x = 3$

*7. $y = x^2$,   $x = 2$,   $x = 3$

8. $y = 2x^2 - x$,   $x = -2$,   $x = -1$

9. $y = x^2 + 2$,   $x = -1$,   $x = 2$

10. $y = x + x^2 + x^3$,   $x = 1$

11. $y = x^2 - 2x$,   $x = -3$,   $x = -1$

12. $y = 3x^2 - 4x$,   $x = -2$,   $x = -1$

13. $y = 2 - x - x^2$

14. $y = \frac{4}{x}$,   $x = 1$,   $x = 2$

15. $y = 2 - x - x^3$,   $x = -3$,   $x = 0$

16. $y = e^x$,   $x = 1$,   $x = 3$

17. $y = 3 + 2x - x^2$

18. $y = \frac{1}{(x - 1)^2}$,   $x = 2$,   $x = 3$

19. $y = \frac{1}{x}$,   $x = 1$,   $x = e$

20. $y = \frac{1}{x}$,   $x = 1$,   $x = e^2$

21. $y = \sqrt{x + 9}$,   $x = -9$,   $x = 0$

22. $y = x^2 - 4x$,   $x = 2$,   $x = 6$

23. $y = \sqrt{2x - 1}$,   $x = 1$,   $x = 5$

24. $y = x^3 + 3x^2$,   $x = -2$,   $x = 2$

25. $y = \sqrt[3]{x}$,   $x = 2$

26. $y = x^2 + 4x - 5$,   $x = -5$,   $x = 1$

*27. $y = e^x + 1$,   $x = 0$,   $x = 1$

28. $y = |x|$,   $x = -2$,   $x = 2$

29. $y = x + \frac{2}{x}$,   $x = 1$,   $x = 2$

30. $y = 4 + 3x - x^2$

*31. $y = x^3$, $x = -2$, $x = 4$

32. $y = \sqrt{x - 2}$, $x = 2$, $x = 6$

33. $y = 2x - x^2$, $x = 1$, $x = 3$

34. $y = x^2 + 1$, $x = 0$, $x = 4$

35. Given that

$$f(x) = \begin{cases} 3x^2 & \text{if } 0 \le x < 2 \\ 16 - 2x & \text{if } x \ge 2 \end{cases}$$

determine the area of the region bounded by the graph of $y = f(x)$, the $x$-axis, and the line $x = 3$. Include a sketch of the region.

36. Under conditions of a continuous uniform distribution (a topic in statistics) the proportion of persons with incomes between $a$ and $t$, where $a \le t \le b$, is the area of the region between the curve $y = 1/(b - a)$ and the $x$-axis from $x = a$ to $x = t$. Sketch the graph of the curve and determine the area of the given region.

*37. Suppose $f(x) = x/8$, where $0 \le x \le 4$. If $f$ is a density function (refer to Example 5), find each of the following.

(a) $P(0 \le x \le 1)$

(b) $P(2 \le x \le 4)$

(c) $P(x \ge 3)$

38. Suppose $f(x) = \frac{1}{3}(1 - x)^2$, where $0 \le x \le 3$. If $f$ is a density function (refer to Example 5), find each of the following.

(a) $P(1 \le x \le 2)$

(b) $P\left(1 \le x \le \frac{5}{2}\right)$

(c) $P(x \le 1)$

(d) $P(x \ge 1)$ using your result from part (c)

39. Suppose $f(x) = 1/x$, where $e \le x \le e^2$. If $f$ is a density function (refer to Example 5), find each of the following.

(a) $P(3 \le x \le 7)$

(b) $P(x \le 5)$

(c) $P(x \ge 4)$

(d) Verify that $P(e \le x \le e^2) = 1$

40. (a) Let $r$ be a real number, where $r > 1$. Evaluate

$$\int_1^r \frac{1}{x^2}\, dx$$

(b) Your answer to part (a) can be interpreted as the area of a certain region of the plane. Sketch this region.

(c) Evaluate $\lim_{r \to \infty} \left( \int_1^r \frac{1}{x^2}\, dx \right)$.

(d) Your answer to part (c) can be interpreted as the area of a certain region of the plane. Sketch this region.

*In Problems 41–44, use definite integration to estimate the area of the region bounded by the given curve, the x-axis, and the given lines. Round your answer to two decimal places.*

41. $y = \dfrac{1}{x^2 + 1}$, $x = -2$, $x = 1$

42. $y = \dfrac{x}{\sqrt{x + 5}}$, $x = 2$, $x = 7$

43. $y = x^4 - 2x^3 - 2$, $x = 1$, $x = 3$

44. $y = 1 + 3x - x^4$

## 14.10 Area between Curves

OBJECTIVE

To find the area of a region bounded by two or more curves by using either vertical or horizontal strips.

### Vertical Elements

We will now find the area of a region enclosed by several curves. As before, our procedure will be to draw a sample element of area and use the definite integral to "add together" the areas of all such elements.

For example, consider the area of the region in Figure 14.33 that is bounded on the top and bottom by the curves $y = f(x)$ and $y = g(x)$ and on the sides by the lines $x = a$ and $x = b$. The width of the indicated vertical element is $\Delta x$, and the height is the $y$-value of the upper curve minus the $y$-value of the lower curve, which we will write as $y_{\text{upper}} - y_{\text{lower}}$. Thus, the area of the element is

$$[y_{\text{upper}} - y_{\text{lower}}]\, \Delta x$$

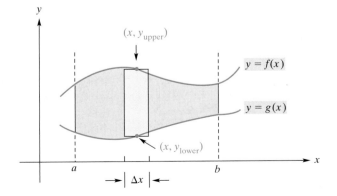

FIGURE 14.33  Region between curves.

which is

$$[f(x) - g(x)] \Delta x$$

Summing the areas of all such elements from $x = a$ to $x = b$ by the definite integral gives the area of the region:

$$\sum [f(x) - g(x)] \Delta x \rightarrow \int_a^b [f(x) - g(x)] \, dx = \text{area}$$

● EXAMPLE 1  **Finding an Area between Two Curves**

*Find the area of the region bounded by the curves $y = \sqrt{x}$ and $y = x$.*

**Solution:** A sketch of the region appears in Figure 14.34. To determine where the curves intersect, we solve the system formed by the equations $y = \sqrt{x}$ and $y = x$. Eliminating $y$ by substitution, we obtain

$$\sqrt{x} = x$$
$$x = x^2 \qquad\qquad \text{(squaring both sides)}$$
$$0 = x^2 - x = x(x - 1)$$
$$x = 0 \quad \text{or} \quad x = 1$$

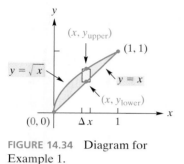

**FIGURE 14.34** Diagram for Example 1.

It should be obvious to you that knowing the points of intersection is important in determining the limits of integration.

Since we squared both sides, we must check the solutions found with respect to the *original* equation. It is easily determined that both $x = 0$ and $x = 1$ are solutions of $\sqrt{x} = x$. If $x = 0$, then $y = 0$; if $x = 1$, then $y = 1$. Thus, the curves intersect at $(0, 0)$ and $(1, 1)$. The width of the indicated element of area is $\Delta x$. The height is the $y$-value on the upper curve minus the $y$-value on the lower curve:

$$y_{\text{upper}} - y_{\text{lower}} = \sqrt{x} - x$$

Hence, the area of the element is $(\sqrt{x} - x) \Delta x$. Summing the areas of all such elements from $x = 0$ to $x = 1$ by the definite integral, we get the area of the entire region:

$$\text{area} = \int_0^1 (\sqrt{x} - x) \, dx$$

$$= \int_0^1 (x^{1/2} - x) \, dx = \left( \frac{x^{3/2}}{\frac{3}{2}} - \frac{x^2}{2} \right) \Bigg|_0^1$$

$$= \left( \frac{2}{3} - \frac{1}{2} \right) - (0 - 0) = \frac{1}{6}$$

NOW WORK PROBLEM 9 ●●

● EXAMPLE 2  **Finding an Area between Two Curves**

*Find the area of the region bounded by the curves $y = 4x - x^2 + 8$ and $y = x^2 - 2x$.*

**Solution:** A sketch of the region appears in Figure 14.35. To find where the curves intersect, we solve the system of equations $y = 4x - x^2 + 8$ and $y = x^2 - 2x$:

$$4x - x^2 + 8 = x^2 - 2x,$$
$$-2x^2 + 6x + 8 = 0,$$
$$x^2 - 3x - 4 = 0,$$
$$(x + 1)(x - 4) = 0 \qquad \text{(factoring)}$$
$$x = -1 \quad \text{or} \quad x = 4$$

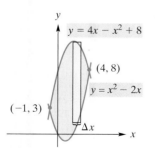

**FIGURE 14.35** Diagram for Example 2.

When $x = -1$, then $y = 3$; when $x = 4$, then $y = 8$. Thus, the curves intersect at $(-1, 3)$ and $(4, 8)$. The width of the indicated element is $\Delta x$. The height is the $y$-value on the upper curve minus the $y$-value on the lower curve:

$$y_{\text{upper}} - y_{\text{lower}} = (4x - x^2 + 8) - (x^2 - 2x)$$

Therefore, the area of the element is

$$[(4x - x^2 + 8) - (x^2 - 2x)]\,\Delta x = (-2x^2 + 6x + 8)\,\Delta x$$

Summing all such areas from $x = -1$ to $x = 4$, we have

$$\text{area} = \int_{-1}^{4} (-2x^2 + 6x + 8)\,dx = 41\tfrac{2}{3}$$

NOW WORK PROBLEM 25

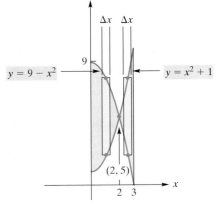

FIGURE 14.36   $y_{\text{upper}}$ is $9 - x^2$ on $[0, 2]$ and is $x^2 + 1$ on $[2, 3]$.

### ● EXAMPLE 3   Area of a Region Having Two Different Upper Curves

*Find the area of the region between the curves $y = 9 - x^2$ and $y = x^2 + 1$ from $x = 0$ to $x = 3$.*

**Solution:**  The region is sketched in Figure 14.36. The curves intersect when

$$9 - x^2 = x^2 + 1$$
$$8 = 2x^2$$
$$4 = x^2$$
$$x = \pm 2 \qquad \text{(two solutions)}$$

When $x = \pm 2$, then $y = 5$, so the points of intersection are $(\pm 2, 5)$. Because we are interested in the region from $x = 0$ to $x = 3$, the intersection point that is of concern to us is $(2, 5)$. Notice in Figure 14.36 that in the region to the *left* of the intersection point $(2, 5)$, an element has

$$y_{\text{upper}} = 9 - x^2 \quad \text{and} \quad y_{\text{lower}} = x^2 + 1$$

but for an element to the *right* of $(2, 5)$ the reverse is true, namely,

$$y_{\text{upper}} = x^2 + 1 \quad \text{and} \quad y_{\text{lower}} = 9 - x^2$$

Thus, from $x = 0$ to $x = 2$, the area of an element is

$$(y_{\text{upper}} - y_{\text{lower}})\,\Delta x = [(9 - x^2) - (x^2 + 1)]\,\Delta x$$
$$= (8 - 2x^2)\,\Delta x$$

but from $x = 2$ to $x = 3$, it is

$$(y_{\text{upper}} - y_{\text{lower}})\,\Delta x = [(x^2 + 1) - (9 - x^2)]\,\Delta x$$
$$= (2x^2 - 8)\,\Delta x$$

Therefore, to find the area of the entire region, we need *two* integrals:

$$\text{area} = \int_{0}^{2} (8 - 2x^2)\,dx + \int_{2}^{3} (2x^2 - 8)\,dx$$

$$= \left(8x - \frac{2x^3}{3}\right)\Bigg|_{0}^{2} + \left(\frac{2x^3}{3} - 8x\right)\Bigg|_{2}^{3}$$

$$= \left[\left(16 - \frac{16}{3}\right) - 0\right] + \left[(18 - 24) - \left(\frac{16}{3} - 16\right)\right]$$

$$= \frac{46}{3}$$

NOW WORK PROBLEM 33

## Horizontal Elements

Sometimes area can more easily be determined by summing areas of horizontal elements rather than vertical elements. In the following example, an area will be found by both methods. In each case, the element of area determines the form of the integral.

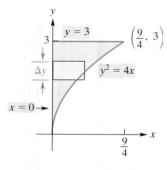

**FIGURE 14.37**   Vertical element of area.

● **EXAMPLE 4   The Methods of Vertical Elements and Horizontal Elements**

*Find the area of the region bounded by the curve $y^2 = 4x$ and the lines $y = 3$ and $x = 0$ (the y-axis).*

**Solution:**   The region is sketched in Figure 14.37. When the curves $y = 3$ and $y^2 = 4x$ intersect, $9 = 4x$, so $x = \frac{9}{4}$. Thus, the intersection point is $(\frac{9}{4}, 3)$. Since the width of the vertical strip is $\Delta x$, we integrate with respect to the variable $x$. Accordingly, $y_{\text{upper}}$ and $y_{\text{lower}}$ must be expressed as functions of $x$. For the lower curve, $y^2 = 4x$, we have $y = \pm 2\sqrt{x}$. But $y \geq 0$ for the portion of this curve that bounds the region, so we use $y = 2\sqrt{x}$. The upper curve is $y = 3$. Hence, the height of the strip is

$$y_{\text{upper}} - y_{\text{lower}} = 3 - 2\sqrt{x}$$

Therefore, the strip has an area of $(3 - 2\sqrt{x}) \, \Delta x$, and we wish to sum all such areas from $x = 0$ to $x = \frac{9}{4}$. We have

$$\text{area} = \int_0^{9/4} (3 - 2\sqrt{x}) \, dx = \left( 3x - \frac{4x^{3/2}}{3} \right) \Bigg|_0^{9/4}$$

$$= \left[ 3 \left( \frac{9}{4} \right) - \frac{4}{3} \left( \frac{9}{4} \right)^{3/2} \right] - (0)$$

$$= \frac{27}{4} - \frac{4}{3} \left[ \left( \frac{9}{4} \right)^{1/2} \right]^3 = \frac{27}{4} - \frac{4}{3} \left( \frac{3}{2} \right)^3 = \frac{9}{4}$$

**CAUTION**

With horizontal elements, the width is $\Delta y$, not $\Delta x$.

   Let us now approach this problem from the point of view of a **horizontal element of area** (or **horizontal strip**) as shown in Figure 14.38. The width of the element is $\Delta y$. The length of the element is *the x-value on the rightmost curve minus the x-value on the leftmost curve*. Thus, the area of the element is

$$(x_{\text{right}} - x_{\text{left}}) \, \Delta y$$

We wish to sum all such areas from $y = 0$ to $y = 3$:

$$\sum (x_{\text{right}} - x_{\text{left}}) \, \Delta y \rightarrow \int_0^3 (x_{\text{right}} - x_{\text{left}}) \, dy$$

**FIGURE 14.38**   Horizontal element of area.

Since the variable of integration is $y$, we must express $x_{\text{right}}$ and $x_{\text{left}}$ as functions of $y$. The rightmost curve is $y^2 = 4x$ so that $x = y^2/4$. The left curve is $x = 0$. Thus,

$$\text{area} = \int_0^3 (x_{\text{right}} - x_{\text{left}}) \, dy$$

$$= \int_0^3 \left( \frac{y^2}{4} - 0 \right) dy = \frac{y^3}{12} \Bigg|_0^3 = \frac{9}{4}$$

Note that for this region, horizontal strips make the definite integral easier to evaluate (and set up) than an integral with vertical strips. In any case, remember that **the limits of integration are those limits for the variable of integration.**

NOW WORK PROBLEM 23 ●●●

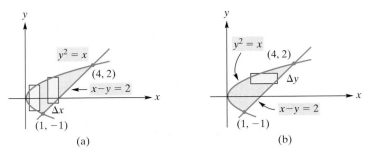

FIGURE 14.39   Region of Example 5 with vertical and horizontal elements.

●EXAMPLE 5   **Advantage of Horizontal Elements**

*Find the area of the region bounded by the graphs of $y^2 = x$ and $x - y = 2$.*

Solution: The region is sketched in Figure 14.39. The curves intersect when $y^2 - y = 2$. Thus, $y^2 - y - 2 = 0$; equivalently, $(y + 1)(y - 2) = 0$, from which it follows that $y = -1$ or $y = 2$. This gives the intersection points $(1, -1)$ and $(4, 2)$. Let us try vertical elements of area. (See Figure 14.39(a).) Solving $y^2 = x$ for $y$ gives $y = \pm\sqrt{x}$. As seen in Figure 14.39(a), to the *left* of $x = 1$, the upper end of the element lies on $y = \sqrt{x}$ and the lower end lies on $y = -\sqrt{x}$. To the *right* of $x = 1$, the upper curve is $y = \sqrt{x}$ and the lower curve is $x - y = 2$ (or $y = x - 2$). Thus, with vertical strips, *two* integrals are needed to evaluate the area:

$$\text{area} = \int_0^1 (\sqrt{x} - (-\sqrt{x}))\, dx + \int_1^4 (\sqrt{x} - (x - 2))\, dx$$

Perhaps the use of horizontal strips can simplify our work. In Figure 14.39(b), the width of the strip is $\Delta y$. The rightmost curve is *always* $x - y = 2$ (or $x = y + 2$), and the leftmost curve is always $y^2 = x$ (or $x = y^2$). Therefore, the area of the horizontal strip is $[(y + 2) - y^2]\,\Delta y$, so the total area is

$$\text{area} = \int_{-1}^2 (y + 2 - y^2)\, dy = \frac{9}{2}$$

Clearly, the use of horizontal strips is the most desirable approach to solving the problem. Only a single integral is needed, and it is much simpler to compute.

NOW WORK PROBLEM 19   ●●●

## TECHNOLOGY

**Problem:** Estimate the area of the region bounded by the graphs of

$$y = x^4 - 2x^3 - 2 \quad \text{and} \quad y = 1 + 2x - 2x^2$$

**Solution:** With a TI-83 Plus, we enter $x^4 - 2x^3 - 2$ as $Y_1$ and $1 + 2x - 2x^2$ as $Y_2$ and display their graphs. The region in question is shaded in Figure 14.40; $y_{\text{upper}}$ corresponds to $Y_2$ and $y_{\text{lower}}$ corresponds to $Y_1$. Using vertical strips, we have

$$\text{area} = \int_A^B (Y_2 - Y_1)\, dx$$

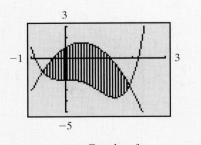

FIGURE 14.40   Graphs of $Y_1 (y_{\text{lower}})$ and $Y_2 (y_{\text{upper}})$.

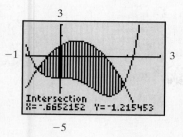

FIGURE 14.41   Intersection point in Quadrant III.

where A and B are the *x*-values of the intersection points in Quadrants III and IV, respectively. With the intersection feature we find A, as indicated in Figure 14.41. This value of *x* is then stored from the home screen as A. (See

Figure 14.42.) Similarly, we find the *x*-value of the intersection point in Quadrant IV, which we store as B. Using the "fnInt(" command (Figure 14.42), we estimate the area of the region to be 7.54 square units.

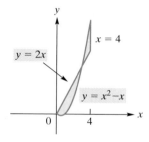

FIGURE 14.42   Storing *x*-values of intersection points and estimating area.

# Problems 14.10

*In Problems 1–6, express the area of the shaded region in terms of an integral (or integrals). Do not evaluate your expression.*

**1.** See Figure 14.43.

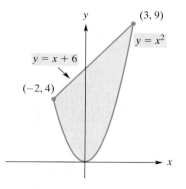

FIGURE 14.43   Region for Problem 1.

**2.** See Figure 14.44.

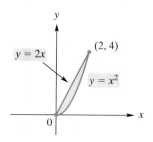

FIGURE 14.44   Region for Problem 2.

**3.** See Figure 14.45.

FIGURE 14.45   Region for Problem 3.

**4.** See Figure 14.46.

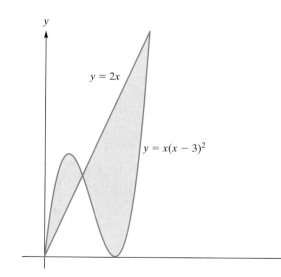

FIGURE 14.46   Region for Problem 4.

**5.** See Figure 14.47.

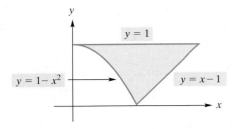

**FIGURE 14.47** Region for Problem 5.

**6.** See Figure 14.48.

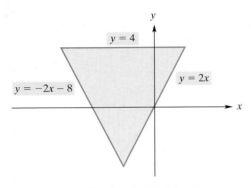

**FIGURE 14.48** Region for Problem 6.

**7.** Express, in terms of a single integral, the total area of the region to the right of the line $x = 1$ that is between the curves $y = x^2 - 5$ and $y = 7 - 2x^2$. Do *not* evaluate the integral.

**8.** Express, in terms of a single integral, the total area of the region in the first quadrant bounded by the $x$-axis and the graphs of $y^2 = x$ and $2y = 3 - x$. Do *not* evaluate the integral.

*In Problems 9–32, find the area of the region bounded by the graphs of the given equations. Be sure to find any needed points of intersection. Consider whether the use of horizontal strips makes the integral simpler than when vertical strips are used.*

**\*9.** $y = x^2$, $\quad y = 2x$

**10.** $y = x$, $\quad y = -x + 3$, $\quad y = 0$

**11.** $y = x^2 + 1$, $\quad x \geq 0$, $\quad x = 0$, $\quad y = 3$

**12.** $y = x^2 + 1$, $\quad y = x + 3$

**13.** $y = 10 - x^2$, $\quad y = 4$

**14.** $y^2 = x + 1$, $\quad x = 1$

**15.** $x = 8 + 2y$, $\quad x = 0$, $\quad y = -1$, $\quad y = 3$

**16.** $y = x - 6$, $\quad y^2 = x$

**17.** $y = 4 - x^2$, $\quad y = -3x$

**18.** $x = y^2 + 2$, $\quad x = 6$

**\*19.** $y^2 = 4x$, $\quad y = 2x - 4$

**20.** $y = x^3$, $\quad y = x + 6$, $\quad x = 0$.
(*Hint:* The only real root of $x^3 - x - 6 = 0$ is 2.)

**21.** $2y = 4x - x^2$, $\quad 2y = x - 4$

**22.** $y = \sqrt{x}$, $\quad y = x^2$

**\*23.** $y^2 = 3x$, $\quad 3x - 2y = 15$

**24.** $y = 2 - x^2$, $\quad y = x$

**\*25.** $y = 8 - x^2$, $\quad y = x^2$, $\quad x = -1$, $\quad x = 1$

**26.** $y^2 = 6 - x$, $\quad 3y = x + 12$

**27.** $y = x^2$, $\quad y = 2$, $\quad y = 5$

**28.** $y = x^3 + x$, $y = 0$, $x = -1$, $x = 2$

**29.** $y = x^3 - 1$, $\quad y = x - 1$

**30.** $y = x^3$, $\quad y = \sqrt{x}$

**31.** $4x + 4y + 17 = 0$, $\quad y = \dfrac{1}{x}$

**32.** $y^2 = -x - 2$, $\quad x - y = 5$, $\quad y = -1$, $\quad y = 1$

**\*33.** Find the area of the region that is between the curves

$$y = x - 1 \quad \text{and} \quad y = 5 - 2x$$

from $x = 0$ to $x = 4$.

**34.** Find the area of the region that is between the curves

$$y = x^2 - 4x + 4 \quad \text{and} \quad y = 10 - x^2$$

from $x = 2$ to $x = 4$.

**35. Lorenz Curve** A *Lorenz curve* is used in studying income distributions. If $x$ is the cumulative percentage of income recipients, ranked from poorest to richest, and $y$ is the cumulative percentage of income, then equality of income distribution is given by the line $y = x$ in Figure 14.49, where $x$ and $y$ are expressed as decimals. For example, 10% of the people receive 10% of total income, 20% of the people receive 20% of the income, and so on. Suppose the actual distribution is given by the Lorenz curve defined by

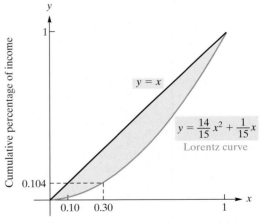

**FIGURE 14.49** Diagram for Problem 35.

$$y = \frac{14}{15}x^2 + \frac{1}{15}x$$

Note, for example, that 30% of the people receive only 10.4% of total income. The degree of deviation from equality is measured by the *coefficient of inequality*[15] for a Lorenz curve. This coefficient is defined to be the area

[15]G. Stigler, *The Theory of Price*, 3rd ed. (New York: The Macmillan Company, 1966), pp. 293–94.

between the curve and the diagonal, divided by the area under the diagonal:

$$\frac{\text{area between curve and diagonal}}{\text{area under diagonal}}$$

For example, when all incomes are equal, the coefficient of inequality is zero. Find the coefficient of inequality for the Lorenz curve just defined.

**36. Lorenz curve**  Find the coefficient of inequality as in Problem 35 for the Lorenz curve defined by $y = \frac{11}{12}x^2 + \frac{1}{12}x$.

**37.** Find the area of the region bounded by the graphs of the equations $y^2 = 3x$ and $y = mx$, where $m$ is a positive constant.

**38. (a)** Find the area of the region bounded by the graphs of $y = x^2 - 1$ and $y = 2x + 2$.

**(b)** What percentage of the area in part (a) lies above the $x$-axis?

**39.** The region bounded by the curve $y = x^2$ and the line $y = 4$ is divided into two parts of equal area by the line $y = k$, where $k$ is a constant. Find the value of $k$.

*In Problems 40–44, estimate the area of the region bounded by the graphs of the given equations. Round your answer to two decimal places.*

**40.** $y = x^2 - 4x + 1$,  $y = -\dfrac{6}{x}$

**41.** $y = \sqrt{25 - x^2}$,  $y = 7 - 2x - x^4$

**42.** $y = x^3 - 8x + 1$,  $y = x^2 - 5$

**43.** $y = x^5 - 3x^3 + 2x$,  $y = 3x^2 - 4$

**44.** $y = x^4 - 3x^3 - 15x^2 + 19x + 30$,  $y = x^3 + x^2 - 20x$

## 14.11  Consumers' and Producers' Surplus

**OBJECTIVE**

To develop the economic concepts of consumers' surplus and producers' surplus, which are represented by areas.

Determining the area of a region has applications in economics. Figure 14.50 shows a supply curve for a product. The curve indicates the price $p$ per unit at which the manufacturer will sell (or supply) $q$ units. The diagram also shows a demand curve for the product. This curve indicates the price $p$ per unit at which consumers will purchase (or demand) $q$ units. The point $(q_0, p_0)$ where the two curves intersect is called the *point of equilibrium*. Here $p_0$ is the price per unit at which consumers will purchase the same quantity $q_0$ of a product that producers wish to sell at that price. In short, $p_0$ is the price at which stability in the producer–consumer relationship occurs.

Let us assume that the market is at equilibrium and the price per unit of the product is $p_0$. According to the demand curve, there are consumers who would be willing to pay *more* than $p_0$. For example, at the price per unit of $p_1$, consumers would buy $q_1$ units. These consumers are benefiting from the lower equilibrium price $p_0$.

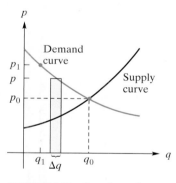

**FIGURE 14.50**  Supply and demand curves.

The vertical strip in Figure 14.50 has area $p \, \Delta q$. This expression can also be thought of as the total amount of money that consumers would spend by buying $\Delta q$ units of the product if the price per unit were $p$. Since the price is actually $p_0$, these consumers spend only $p_0 \, \Delta q$ for the $\Delta q$ units and thus benefit by the amount $p\Delta q - p_0 \, \Delta q$. This expression can be written $(p - p_0) \, \Delta q$, which is the area of a rectangle of width $\Delta q$ and height $p - p_0$. (See Figure 14.51.) Summing the areas of all such rectangles from $q = 0$ to $q = q_0$ by definite integration, we have

$$\int_0^{q_0} (p - p_0) \, dq$$

This integral, under certain conditions, represents the total gain to consumers who are willing to pay more than the equilibrium price. This total gain is called **consumers' surplus**, abbreviated CS. If the demand function is given by $p = f(q)$, then

$$\text{CS} = \int_0^{q_0} [f(q) - p_0] \, dq$$

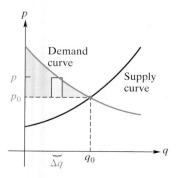

**FIGURE 14.51**  Benefit to consumers for $\Delta q$ units.

Geometrically (see Figure 14.52), consumers' surplus is represented by the area between the line $p = p_0$ and the demand curve $p = f(q)$ from $q = 0$ to $q = q_0$.

Some of the producers also benefit from the equilibrium price, since they are willing to supply the product at prices *less* than $p_0$. Under certain conditions, the

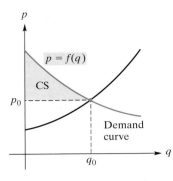

FIGURE 14.52 Consumers' surplus.

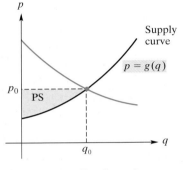

FIGURE 14.53 Producers' surplus.

total gain to the producers is represented geometrically in Figure 14.53 by the area between the line $p = p_0$ and the supply curve $p = g(q)$ from $q = 0$ to $q = q_0$. This gain, called **producers' surplus** and abbreviated PS, is given by

$$\text{PS} = \int_0^{q_0} [p_0 - g(q)] \, dq$$

● EXAMPLE 1   **Finding Consumers' Surplus and Producers' Surplus**

*The demand function for a product is*

$$p = f(q) = 100 - 0.05q$$

*where p is the price per unit (in dollars) for q units. The supply function is*

$$p = g(q) = 10 + 0.1q$$

*Determine consumers' surplus and producers' surplus under market equilibrium.*

**Solution:** First we must find the equilibrium point $(p_0, q_0)$ by solving the system formed by the functions $p = 100 - 0.05q$ and $p = 10 + 0.1q$. We thus equate the two expressions for $p$ and solve:

$$10 + 0.1q = 100 - 0.05q$$
$$0.15q = 90$$
$$q = 600$$

When $q = 600$ then $p = 10 + 0.1(600) = 70$. Hence, $q_0 = 600$ and $p_0 = 70$. Consumers' surplus is

$$\text{CS} = \int_0^{q_0} [f(q) - p_0] \, dq = \int_0^{600} (100 - 0.05q - 70) \, dq$$

$$= \left( 30q - 0.05\frac{q^2}{2} \right)\Bigg|_0^{600} = 9000$$

Producers' surplus is

$$\text{PS} = \int_0^{q_0} [p_0 - g(q)] \, dq = \int_0^{600} [70 - (10 + 0.1q)] \, dq$$

$$= \left( 60q - 0.1\frac{q^2}{2} \right)\Bigg|_0^{600} = 18{,}000$$

Therefore, consumers' surplus is $9000 and producers' surplus is $18,000.

NOW WORK PROBLEM 1 ●●

● EXAMPLE 2   **Using Horizontal Strips to Find Consumers' Surplus and Producers' Surplus**

*The demand equation for a product is*

$$q = f(p) = \frac{90}{p} - 2$$

*and the supply equation is $q = g(p) = p - 1$. Determine consumers' surplus and producers' surplus when market equilibrium has been established.*

**Solution:** Determining the equilibrium point, we have

$$p - 1 = \frac{90}{p} - 2$$
$$p^2 + p - 90 = 0$$
$$(p + 10)(p - 9) = 0$$

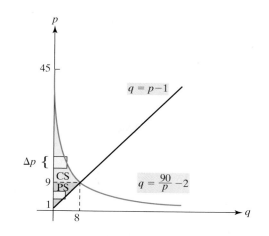

**FIGURE 14.54**    Diagram for Example 2.

Thus, $p_0 = 9$, so $q_0 = 9 - 1 = 8$. (See Figure 14.54.) Note that the demand equation expresses $q$ as a function of $p$. Since consumers' surplus can be considered an area, this area can be determined by means of horizontal strips of width $\Delta p$ and length $q = f(p)$. The areas of these strips are summed from $p = 9$ to $p = 45$ by integrating with respect to $p$:

$$\text{CS} = \int_9^{45} \left( \frac{90}{p} - 2 \right) dp = (90 \ln |p| - 2p) \Big|_9^{45}$$
$$= 90 \ln 5 - 72 \approx 72.85$$

Using horizontal strips for producers' surplus, we have

$$\text{PS} = \int_1^9 (p - 1)\, dp = \frac{(p-1)^2}{2} \Big|_1^9 = 32$$

NOW WORK PROBLEM 5  ●●

# Problems 14.11

*In Problems 1–6, the first equation is a demand equation and the second is a supply equation of a product. In each case, determine consumers' surplus and producers' surplus under market equilibrium.*

**\*1.**  $p = 22 - 0.8q$
$p = 6 + 1.2q$

**2.**  $p = 2200 - q^2$
$p = 400 + q^2$

**3.**  $p = \dfrac{50}{q + 5}$
$p = \dfrac{q}{10} + 4.5$

**4.**  $p = 400 - q^2$
$p = 20q + 100$

**\*5.**  $q = 100(10 - 2p)$
$q = 50(2p - 1)$

**6.**  $q = \sqrt{100 - p}$
$q = \dfrac{p}{2} - 10$

**7.** The demand equation for a product is

$$q = 10\sqrt{100 - p}$$

Calculate consumers' surplus under market equilibrium, which occurs at a price of $84.

**8.** The demand equation for a product is

$$q = 400 - p^2$$

and the supply equation is

$$p = \frac{q}{60} + 5$$

Find producers' surplus and consumers' surplus under market equilibrium.

**9.** The demand equation for a product is $p = 2^{11-q}$, and the supply equation is $p = 2^{q+1}$, where $p$ is the price per unit (in hundreds of dollars) when $q$ units are demanded or supplied. Determine, to the nearest thousand dollars, consumers' surplus under market equilibrium.

**10.** The demand equation for a product is

$$(p + 10)(q + 20) = 1000$$

and the supply equation is

$$q - 4p + 10 = 0$$

**(a)** Verify, by substitution, that market equilibrium occurs when $p = 10$ and $q = 30$.

**(b)** Determine consumers' surplus under market equilibrium.

**11.** The demand equation for a product is

$$p = 60 - \frac{50q}{\sqrt{q^2 + 3600}}$$

and the supply equation is

$$p = 10\ln(q + 20) - 26$$

Determine consumers' surplus and producers' surplus under market equilibrium. Round your answers to the nearest integer.

**12. Producers' Surplus**  The supply function for a product is given by the following table, where $p$ is the price per unit (in dollars) at which $q$ units are supplied to the market:

| $q$ | 0 | 10 | 20 | 30 | 40 | 50 |
|---|---|---|---|---|---|---|
| $p$ | 25 | 49 | 59 | 71 | 80 | 94 |

Use the trapezoidal rule to estimate the producers' surplus if the selling price is $80.

# 14.12 Review

## Important Terms and Symbols

**Examples**

| | | |
|---|---|---|
| Section 14.1 | **Differentials**<br>differential, $dy$, $dx$ | Ex. 1, p. 619 |
| Section 14.2 | **The Indefinite Integral**<br>antiderivative    indefinite integral    $\int f(x)\,dx$    integral sign<br>integrand    variable of integration    constant of integration | Ex. 1, p. 625<br>Ex. 2, p. 625 |
| Section 14.3 | **Integration with Initial Conditions**<br>initial condition | Ex. 1, p. 630 |
| Section 14.4 | **More integration Formulas**<br>power rule for integration | Ex. 1, p. 634 |
| Section 14.5 | **Techniques of Integration**<br>preliminary division | Ex. 1, p. 640 |
| Section 14.6 | **The Definite Integral**<br>definite integral    $\int_a^b f(x)\,dx$    limits of integration | Ex. 2, p. 649 |
| Section 14.7 | **The Fundamental Theorem of Integral Calculus**<br>Fundamental Theorem of Integral Calculus    $F(x)\vert_a^b$ | Ex. 1, p. 653 |
| Section 14.8 | **Approximate Integration**<br>trapezoidal rule    Simpson's rule | Ex. 2, p. 662 |
| Section 14.9 | **Area**<br>vertical element of area (vertical strip) | Ex. 1, p. 665 |
| Section 14.10 | **Area between Curves**<br>horizontal element of area (horizontal strip) | Ex. 5, p. 672 |
| Section 14.11 | **Consumers' and Producers' Surplus**<br>consumers' surplus    producers' surplus | Ex. 1, p. 676 |

## Summary

If $y = f(x)$ is a differentiable function of $x$, we define the differential $dy$ by

$$dy = f'(x)\,dx$$

where $dx = \Delta x$ is a change in $x$ and can be any real number. (Thus $dy$ is a function of two variables, namely $x$ and $dx$.) If $dx$ is close to zero, then $dy$ is an approximation to $\Delta y = f(x + \Delta x) - f(x)$.

$$\Delta y \approx dy$$

Moreover, $dy$ can be used to approximate a function value using

$$f(x + \Delta x) \approx f(x) + dy$$

An antiderivative of a function $f$ is a function $F$ such that $F'(x) = f(x)$. Any two antiderivatives of $f$ differ at most by a constant. The most general antiderivative of $f$ is called the indefinite integral of $f$ and is denoted $\int f(x)\,dx$. Thus,

$$\int f(x)\,dx = F(x) + C$$

where $C$ is called the constant of integration, if and only if $F' = f$.

Some basic integration formulas are as follows:

$$\int k\,dx = kx + C \qquad k \text{ a constant}$$

$$\int x^n\,dx = \frac{x^{n+1}}{n+1} + C \qquad n \neq -1$$

$$\int \frac{1}{x}\,dx = \ln x + C \qquad \text{for } x > 0$$

$$\int e^x\,dx = e^x + C$$

$$\int kf(x)\,dx = k\int f(x)\,dx \qquad k \text{ a constant}$$

and $$\int [f(x) \pm g(x)]\,dx = \int f(x)\,dx \pm \int g(x)\,dx$$

Another formula is the power rule for integration:

$$\int u^n\,du = \frac{u^{n+1}}{n+1} + C, \quad \text{if } n \neq -1$$

Here $u$ represents a differentiable function of $x$, and $du$ is its differential. In applying the power rule to a given integral, it is important that the integral be written in a form that precisely matches the power rule. Other integration formulas are

$$\int e^u\,du = e^u + C$$

and $$\int \frac{1}{u}\,du = \ln |u| + C \qquad u \neq 0$$

If the rate of change of a function $f$ is known—that is, if $f'$ is known—then $f$ is an antiderivative of $f'$. In addition, if we know that $f$ satisfies an initial condition, then we can find the particular antiderivative. For example, if a marginal-cost function $dc/dq$ is given to us, then by integration, we can find the most general form of $c$. That form involves a constant of integration. However, if we are also given fixed costs (that is, costs involved when $q = 0$), then we can determine the value of the constant of integration and thus find the particular cost function $c$. Similarly, if we are given a marginal-revenue function $dr/dq$, then by integration and by using the fact that $r = 0$ when $q = 0$, we can determine the particular revenue function $r$. Once $r$ is known, the corresponding demand equation can be found by using the equation $p = r/q$.

It is helpful at this point to review summation notation from Section 1.5. This notation is especially useful in determining areas. To find the area of the region bounded by $y = f(x)$ [where $f(x) \geq 0$ and $f$ is continuous] and the $x$-axis from $x = a$ to $x = b$, we divide the interval $[a, b]$ into $n$ subintervals of equal length $\Delta x$. If $x_i$ is the right-hand endpoint of an arbitrary subinterval, then the product $f(x_i)\,\Delta x$ is the area of a rectangle. Denoting the sum of all such areas of rectangles for the $n$ subintervals by $S_n$, we define the limit of $S_n$ as $n \to \infty$ as the area of the entire region:

$$\lim_{n \to \infty} S_n = \lim_{n \to \infty} \sum_{i=1}^{n} f(x_i)\,\Delta x = \text{area}$$

If the restriction that $f(x) \geq 0$ is omitted, this limit is defined as the definite integral of $f$ over $[a,b]$:

$$\lim_{n \to \infty} \sum_{i=1}^{n} f(x_i)\,\Delta x = \int_a^b f(x)\,dx$$

Instead of evaluating definite integrals by using limits, we may be able to employ the Fundamental Theorem of Integral Calculus. Mathematically,

$$\int_a^b f(x)\,dx = F(x)\Big|_a^b = F(b) - F(a)$$

where $F$ is any antiderivative of $f$.

Some properties of the definite integral are

$$\int_a^b kf(x)\,dx = k\int_a^b f(x)\,dx \qquad k \text{ a constant}$$

$$\int_a^b [f(x) \pm g(x)]\,dx = \int_a^b f(x)\,dx \pm \int_a^b g(x)\,dx$$

and

$$\int_a^c f(x)\,dx = \int_a^b f(x)\,dx + \int_b^c f(x)\,dx$$

If $f(x) \geq 0$ and is continuous on $[a, b]$, then the definite integral can be used to find the area of the region bounded by $y = f(x)$, the $x$-axis, $x = a$, and $x = b$. The definite integral can also be used to find areas of more complicated regions. In these situations, an element of area should be drawn in the region. This will allow you to set up the proper definite integral. In some situations vertical elements should be considered, whereas in others horizontal elements are more advantageous.

One application of finding areas involves consumers' surplus and producers' surplus. Suppose the market for a product is at equilibrium and $(q_0, p_0)$ is the equilibrium point (the point of intersection of the supply and demand curves for the product). Then consumers' surplus, CS, corresponds to the area from $q = 0$ to $q = q_0$, bounded above by the demand curve and below by the line $p = p_0$. Thus,

$$\text{CS} = \int_0^{q_0} [f(q) - p_0]\,dq$$

where $f$ is the demand function. Producers' surplus, PS, corresponds to the area from $q = 0$ to $q = q_0$, bounded above by the line $p = p_0$ and below by the supply curve. Therefore,

$$\text{PS} = \int_0^{q_0} [p_0 - g(q)]\,dq$$

where $g$ is the supply function.

# Review Problems

*Problem numbers shown in color indicate problems suggested for use as a practice chapter test.*

In Problems 1–40, determine the integrals.

1. $\int (x^3 + 2x - 7)\, dx$

2. $\int dx$

3. $\int_0^8 (\sqrt{2x} + 2x)\, dx$

4. $\int \frac{4}{5 - 3x}\, dx$

5. $\int \frac{6}{(x+5)^3}\, dx$

6. $\int_3^9 (y - 6)^{301}\, dy$

7. $\int \frac{6x^2 - 12}{x^3 - 6x + 1}\, dx$

8. $\int_0^2 xe^{4 - x^2}\, dx$

9. $\int_0^1 \sqrt[3]{3t + 8}\, dt$

10. $\int \frac{4 - 2x}{7}\, dx$

11. $\int y(y + 1)^2\, dy$

12. $\int_0^1 10^{-8}\, dx$

13. $\int \frac{\sqrt[5]{t} - \sqrt[3]{t}}{\sqrt{t}}\, dt$

14. $\int \frac{(0.5x - 0.1)^4}{0.4}\, dx$

15. $\int_1^3 \frac{2t^2}{3 + 2t^3}\, dt$

16. $\int \frac{4x^2 - x}{x}\, dx$

17. $\int x^2\sqrt{3x^3 + 2}\, dx$

18. $\int (8x^3 + 4x)(x^4 + x^2)^{5/2}\, dx$

19. $\int (e^{2y} - e^{-2y})\, dy$

20. $\int \frac{8x}{3\sqrt[3]{7 - 2x^2}}\, dx$

21. $\int \left(\frac{1}{x} + \frac{2}{x^2}\right) dx$

22. $\int_0^2 \frac{3e^{3x}}{1 + e^{3x}}\, dx$

23. $\int_{-2}^1 10(y^4 - y + 1)\, dy$

24. $\int_7^{70} dx$

25. $\int_1^2 5x\sqrt{5 - x^2}\, dx$

26. $\int_0^1 (2x + 1)(x^2 + x)^4\, dx$

27. $\int_0^1 \left[2x - \frac{1}{(x+1)^{2/3}}\right] dx$

28. $\int_3^{27} 3(\sqrt{3x} - 2x + 1)\, dx$

29. $\int \frac{\sqrt{t} - 3}{t^2}\, dt$

30. $\int \frac{3z^3}{z - 1}\, dz$

31. $\int_{-1}^0 \frac{x^2 + 4x - 1}{x + 2}\, dx$

32. $\int \frac{(x^2 + 4)^2}{x^2}\, dx$

33. $\int 9\sqrt{x}\sqrt{x^{3/2} + 1}\, dx$

34. $\int \frac{e^{\sqrt{5x}}}{\sqrt{3x}}\, dx$

35. $\int_1^e \frac{e^{\ln x}}{x^2}\, dx$

36. $\int \frac{6x^2 + 4}{e^{x^3 + 2x}}\, dx$

37. $\int \frac{(1 + e^{2x})^3}{e^{-2x}}\, dx$

38. $\int \frac{3}{e^{3x}(6 + e^{-3x})^2}\, dx$

39. $\int 3\sqrt{10^{3x}}\, dx$

40. $\int \frac{5x^3 + 15x^2 + 37x + 3}{x^2 + 3x + 7}\, dx$

In Problems 41 and 42, find y, subject to the given condition.

41. $y' = e^{2x} + 3, \quad y(0) = -\frac{1}{2}$

42. $y' = \frac{x + 5}{x}, \quad y(1) = 3$

In Problems 43–50, determine the area of the region bounded by the given curve, the x-axis, and the given lines.

43. $y = x^2 - 1, \quad x = 2$

44. $y = 4e^x, \quad x = 0, x = 3$

45. $y = \sqrt{x + 4}, \quad x = 0$

46. $y = x^2 - x - 6, \quad x = -4, \quad x = 3$

47. $y = 5x - x^2$

48. $y = \sqrt[4]{x}, \quad x = 1, \quad x = 16$

49. $y = \frac{1}{x} + 2, \quad x = 1, \quad x = 4$

50. $y = x^3 - 1, \quad x = -1$

In Problems 51–58, find the area of the region bounded by the given curves.

51. $y^2 = 4x, \quad x = 0, \quad y = 2$

52. $y = 3x^2 - 5, \quad x = 0, \quad y = 4$

53. $y = x^2 + 4x - 5, \quad y = 0$

54. $y = 2x^2, \quad y = x^2 + 9$

55. $y = x^2 - x, \quad y = 10 - x^2$

56. $y = \sqrt{x}, \quad x = 0, \quad y = 3$

57. $y = \ln x, \quad x = 0, \quad y = 0, \quad y = 1$

58. $y = 2 - x, \quad y = x - 3, \quad y = 0, \quad y = 2$

59. **Marginal Revenue** If marginal revenue is given by
$$\frac{dr}{dq} = 100 - \frac{3}{2}\sqrt{2q}$$
determine the corresponding demand equation.

60. **Marginal Cost** If marginal cost is given by
$$\frac{dc}{dq} = q^2 + 7q + 6$$
and fixed costs are 2500, determine the total cost of producing six units. Assume that costs are in dollars.

61. **Marginal Revenue** A manufacturer's marginal-revenue function is
$$\frac{dr}{dq} = 250 - q - 0.2q^2$$
If r is in dollars, find the increase in the manufacturer's total revenue if production is increased from 15 to 25 units.

62. **Marginal Cost** A manufacturer's marginal-cost function is
$$\frac{dc}{dq} = \frac{1000}{\sqrt{3q + 70}}$$
If c is in dollars, determine the cost involved to increase production from 10 to 33 units.

63. **Hospital Discharges** For a group of hospitalized individuals, suppose the discharge rate is given by
$$f(t) = 0.008e^{-0.008t}$$
where $f(t)$ is the proportion discharged per day at the end of t days of hospitalization. What proportion of the group is discharged at the end of 100 days?

**64. Business Expenses**   The total expenditures (in dollars) of a business over the next five years are given by

$$\int_0^5 4000e^{0.05t} \, dt$$

Evaluate the expenditures.

**65.** Find the area of the region between the curves $y = 9 - 2x$ and $y = x$ from $x = 0$ to $x = 4$.

**66.** Find the area of the region between the curves $y = 2x^2$ and $y = 2 - 5x$ from $x = -1$ to $x = \frac{1}{3}$.

**67. Consumers' and Producers' Surplus**   The demand equation for a product is

$$p = 0.01q^2 - 1.1q + 30$$

and the supply equation is

$$p = 0.01q^2 + 8$$

Determine consumers' surplus and producers' surplus when market equilibrium has been established.

**68. Consumers' Surplus**   The demand equation for a product is

$$p = (q - 5)^2$$

and the supply equation is

$$p = q^2 + q + 3$$

where $p$ (in thousands of dollars) is the price per 100 units when $q$ hundred units are demanded or supplied. Determine consumers' surplus under market equilibrium.

**69. Biology**   In a discussion of gene mutation,[16] the equation

$$\int_{q_0}^{q_n} \frac{dq}{q - \widehat{q}} = -(u + v) \int_0^n dt$$

occurs, where $u$ and $v$ are gene mutation rates, the $q$'s are gene frequencies, and $n$ is the number of generations. Assume that all letters represent constants, except $q$ and $t$. Integrate both sides and then use your result to show that

$$n = \frac{1}{u + v} \ln \left| \frac{q_0 - \widehat{q}}{q_n - \widehat{q}} \right|$$

**70. Fluid Flow**   In studying the flow of a fluid in a tube of constant radius $R$, such as blood flow in portions of the body, we can think of the tube as consisting of concentric tubes of radius $r$, where $0 \le r \le R$. The velocity $v$ of the fluid is a function of $r$ and is given by[17]

$$v = \frac{(P_1 - P_2)(R^2 - r^2)}{4\eta l}$$

where $P_1$ and $P_2$ are pressures at the ends of the tube, $\eta$ (a Greek letter read "eta") is the fluid viscosity, and $l$ is the length of the tube. The volume rate of flow through the tube, $Q$, is given by

$$Q = \int_0^R 2\pi r v \, dr$$

Show that $Q = \dfrac{\pi R^4 (P_1 - P_2)}{8\eta l}$. Note that $R$ occurs as a factor to the fourth power. Thus, doubling the radius of the tube has the effect of increasing the flow by a factor of 16. The formula that you derived for the volume rate of flow is called *Poiseuille's law*, after the French physiologist Jean Poiseuille.

**71. Inventory**   In a discussion of inventory, Barbosa and Friedman[18] refer to the function

$$g(x) = \frac{1}{k} \int_1^{1/x} ku^r \, du$$

where $k$ and $r$ are constants, $k > 0$ and $r > -2$, and $x > 0$. Verify the claim that

$$g'(x) = -\frac{1}{x^{r+2}}$$

(*Hint:* Consider two cases: when $r \ne -1$ and when $r = -1$.)

*In Problems 72–74, estimate the area of the region bounded by the given curves. Round your answer to two decimal places.*

**72.** $y = x^3 + 9x^2 + 14x - 24$, $y = 0$

**73.** $y = x^3 - 3x - 2$, $y = 3 + x - 2x^2$

**74.** $y = x^3 + x^2 - 5x - 3$, $y = x^2 + 2x + 3$

**75.** The demand equation for a product is

$$p = \frac{200}{\sqrt{q + 20}}$$

and the supply equation is

$$p = 2\ln(q + 10) + 5$$

Determine consumers' surplus and producers' surplus under market equilibrium. Round your answers to the nearest integer.

---

[16]W. B. Mather, *Principles of Quantitative Genetics* (Minneapolis: Burgess Publishing Company, 1964).

[17]R. W. Stacy et al., *Essentials of Biological and Medical Physics* (New York: McGraw-Hill, 1955).

[18]L. C. Barbosa and M. Friedman, "Deterministic Inventory Lot Size Models—a General Root Law," *Management Science,* 24, no. 8 (1978), 819–26.

# Mathematical Snapshot

## Delivered Price

Suppose that you are a manufacturer of a product whose sales occur within $R$ miles of your mill. Assume that you charge customers for shipping at the rate $s$, in dollars per mile, for each unit of product sold. If $m$ is the unit price (in dollars) at the mill, then the delivered unit price $p$ to a customer $x$ miles from the mill is the mill price plus the shipping charge $sx$:

$$p = m + sx \qquad 0 \le x \le R \qquad \text{(1)}$$

The problem is to determine the average delivered price of the units sold.

Suppose that there is a function $f$ such that $f(t) \ge 0$ on the interval $[0, R]$ and such that the area under the graph of $f$ and above the $t$-axis from $t = 0$ to $t = x$ represents the total number of units $Q$ sold to customers within $x$ miles of the mill. [See Figure 14.55(a).] You can refer to $f$ as the distribution of demand. Because $Q$ is a function of $x$ and is represented by area,

$$Q(x) = \int_0^x f(t)\,dt$$

In particular, the total number of units sold within the market area is

$$Q(R) = \int_0^R f(t)\,dt$$

[see Figure 14.55(b)]. For example, if $f(t) = 10$ and $R = 100$, then the total number of units sold within the market area is

$$Q(100) = \int_0^{100} 10\,dt = 10t \Big|_0^{100} = 1000 - 0 = 1000$$

The average delivered price $A$ is given by

$$A = \frac{\text{total revenue}}{\text{total number of units sold}}$$

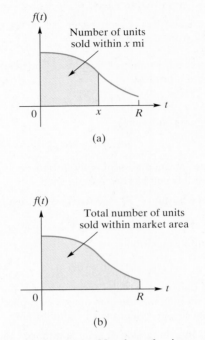

(a)

(b)

**FIGURE 14.55** Number of units sold as an area.

Because the denominator is $Q(R)$, $A$ can be determined once the total revenue is found.

To find the total revenue, first consider the number of units sold over an interval. If $t_1 < t_2$ [see Figure 14.56(a)], then the area under the graph of $f$ and above the $t$-axis from $t = 0$ to $t = t_1$ represents the number of units sold within $t_1$ miles of the mill. Similarly, the area under the graph of $f$ and above the $t$-axis from $t = 0$ to $t = t_2$ represents the number of units sold within $t_2$ miles of the mill. Thus the difference in these areas is geometrically the area of the shaded region in Figure 14.56(a) and represents the number of units sold between $t_1$ and $t_2$ miles of the mill, which is $Q(t_2) - Q(t_1)$. Thus

$$Q(t_2) - Q(t_1) = \int_{t_1}^{t_2} f(t)\,dt$$

For example, if $f(t) = 10$, then the number of units sold to customers located between 4 and 6 miles of the mill is

$$Q(6) - Q(4) = \int_4^6 10\,dt = 10t \Big|_4^6 = 60 - 40 = 20$$

The area of the shaded region in Figure 14.56(a) can be approximated by the area of a rectangle [see Figure 14.56(b)] whose height is $f(t)$ and whose width is $\Delta t$, where $\Delta t = t_2 - t_1$. Thus the number of units sold over the interval

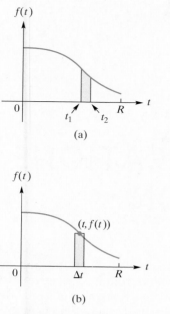

(a)

(b)

FIGURE 14.56   Number of units sold over an interval.

of length $\Delta t$ is approximately $f(t)\,\Delta t$. Because the price of each of these units is [from Equation (1)] approximately $m + st$, the revenue received is approximately

$$(m + st)\, f(t)\, \Delta t$$

The sum of all such products from $t = 0$ to $t = R$ approximates the total revenue. Definite integration gives

$$\sum (m + st)\, f(t)\, \Delta t \to \int_0^R (m + st)\, f(t)\, dt$$

Thus,

$$\text{total revenue} = \int_0^R (m + st)\, f(t)\, dt$$

Consequently, the average delivered price $A$ is given by

$$A = \frac{\displaystyle\int_0^R (m + st)\, f(t)\, dt}{Q(R)}$$

Equivalently,

$$A = \frac{\displaystyle\int_0^R (m + st)\, f(t)\, dt}{\displaystyle\int_0^R f(t)\, dt}$$

For example, if $f(t) = 10, m = 200, s = 0.25$, and $R = 100$, then

$$\int_0^R (m + st)\, f(t)\, dt = \int_0^{100} (200 + 0.25t) \cdot 10 \, dt$$

$$= 10 \int_0^{100} (200 + 0.25t) \, dt$$

$$= 10 \left( 200t + \frac{t^2}{8} \right)\Big|_0^{100}$$

$$= 10 \left[ \left( 20{,}000 + \frac{10{,}000}{8} \right) - 0 \right]$$

$$= 212{,}500$$

From before,

$$\int_0^R f(t)\, dt = \int_0^{100} 10 \, dt = 1000$$

Thus, the average delivered price is $212{,}500 / 1000 = \$212.50$.

## Problems

1. If $f(t) = 100 - 2t$, determine the number of units sold to customers located (a) within 5 miles of the mill, and (b) between 20 and 25 miles of the mill.

2. If $f(t) = 40 - 0.5t, m = 50, s = 0.20$, and $R = 80$, determine (a) the total revenue, (b) the total number of units sold, and (c) the average delivered price.

3. If $f(t) = 900 - t^2, m = 100, s = 1$, and $R = 30$, determine (a) the total revenue, (b) the total number of units sold, and (c) the average delivered price. Use a graphing calculator if you like.

4. How do real-world sellers of such things as books and clothing generally determine shipping charges for an order? (Visit an online retailer to find out.) How would you calculate average delivered price for their products? Is the procedure fundamentally different from the one in the Snapshot?

# 15

# METHODS AND APPLICATIONS OF INTEGRATION

**Mathematical Snapshot**   Dieting

We now know how to find the derivative of a function, and in some cases we know how to find a function from its derivative through integration. However, the integration process is not always straightforward.

Suppose we model the gradual disappearance of a chemical substance using the equations $M' = -0.004t$ and $M(0) = 3000$, where the amount $M$, in grams, is a function of time $t$ in days. This initial-condition problem is easily solved by integration with respect to $t$: $M = -0.002t^2 + 3000$. But what if, instead, the disappearance of the substance were modeled by the equations $M' = -0.004M$ and $M(0) = 3000$? The simple replacement of $t$ in the first equation with $M$ changes the character of the problem. We have not yet learned how to find a function when its derivative is described in terms of the function itself.

If you worked through the Mathematical Snapshot in Chapter 13, you may remember a similar situation, involving an equation with $P$ on one side and the derivative of $P$ on the other. There, we used an approximation to solve the problem. In this chapter, we will learn a method that yields an exact solution for many problems of this type.

Equations of the form $y' = ky$, where $k$ is a constant, are especially common. When $y$ represents the amount of a radioactive substance, $y' = ky$ can represent the rate of its disappearance through radioactive decay. And if $y$ is the temperature of a chicken just taken out of the oven or just put into a freezer, then a related formula, called Newton's law of cooling, can be used to describe the change in the chicken's internal temperature over time. Newton's law, which is discussed in this chapter, might be used to write procedures for a restaurant kitchen, so that food prone to contamination through bacterial growth does not spend too much time in the temperature danger zone (40°F to 140°F). (Bacterial growth, for that matter, also follows a $y' = ky$ law!)

# 15.1 Integration by Parts[1]

Many integrals cannot be found by our previous methods. However, there are ways of changing certain integrals to forms that are easier to integrate. Of these methods, we will discuss two: *integration by parts* and (in Section 15.2) *integration using partial fractions.*

If $u$ and $v$ are differentiable functions of $x$, we have, by the product rule,

$$(uv)' = uv' + vu'$$

Rearranging gives

$$uv' = (uv)' - vu'$$

Integrating both sides with respect to $x$, we get

$$\int uv' \, dx = \int (uv)' \, dx - \int vu' \, dx \qquad (1)$$

For $\int (uv)' \, dx$, we must find a function whose derivative with respect to $x$ is $(uv)'$. Clearly, $uv$ is such a function. Hence $\int (uv)' \, dx = uv + C_1$, and Equation (1) becomes

$$\int uv' \, dx = uv + C_1 - \int vu' \, dx$$

Absorbing $C_1$ into the constant of integration for $\int vu' \, dx$ and replacing $v' \, dx$ by $dv$ and $u' \, dx$ by $du$, we have the *formula for integration by parts:*

**Formula for Integration by Parts**

$$\int u \, dv = uv - \int v \, du \qquad (2)$$

This formula expresses an integral, $\int u \, dv$, in terms of another integral, $\int v \, du$, that may be easier to find.

To apply the formula to a given integral $\int f(x) \, dx$, we must write $f(x) \, dx$ as the product of two factors (or *parts*) by choosing a function $u$ and a differential $dv$ such that $f(x) \, dx = u \, dv$. However, for the formula to be useful, we must be able to integrate the part chosen for $dv$. To illustrate, consider

$$\int xe^x \, dx$$

This integral cannot be determined by previous integration formulas. One way to write $xe^x \, dx$ in the form $u \, dv$ is by letting

$$u = x \quad \text{and} \quad dv = e^x \, dx$$

To apply the formula for integration by parts, we must find $du$ and $v$:

$$du = dx \quad \text{and} \quad v = \int e^x \, dx = e^x + C_1$$

Thus,

$$\int xe^x \, dx = \int u \, dv$$

$$= uv - \int v \, du$$

$$= x(e^x + C_1) - \int (e^x + C_1) \, dx$$

$$= xe^x + C_1 x - e^x - C_1 x + C$$

$$= xe^x - e^x + C$$

$$= e^x(x - 1) + C$$

---

[1]This section may be omitted without loss of continuity.

The first constant, $C_1$, does not appear in the final answer. It is easy to prove that the constant involved in finding $v$ from $dv$ will always drop out, so from now on we will not write it when we find $v$.

When you are using the formula for integration by parts, sometimes the "best choice" for $u$ and $dv$ may not be obvious. In some cases, one choice may be as good as another; in other cases, only one choice may be suitable. Insight into making a good choice (if any exists) will come only with practice and, of course, trial and error.

**INTEGRATION BY PARTS**

The monthly sales of a computer keyboard are estimated to decline at the rate of $S'(t) = -4te^{0.1t}$ keyboards per month, where $t$ is time in months and $S(t)$ is the number of keyboards sold each month. If 5000 keyboards are sold now ($S(0) = 5000$), find $S(t)$.

● **EXAMPLE 1    Integration by Parts**

*Find* $\displaystyle\int \frac{\ln x}{\sqrt{x}}\, dx$ *by integration by parts.*

**Solution:** We try

$$u = \ln x \quad \text{and} \quad dv = \frac{1}{\sqrt{x}}\, dx$$

Then

$$du = \frac{1}{x}\, dx \quad \text{and} \quad v = \int x^{-1/2}\, dx = 2x^{1/2}$$

Thus,

$$\int \ln x \left( \frac{1}{\sqrt{x}}\, dx \right) = \int u\, dv = uv - \int v\, du$$

$$= (\ln x)(2\sqrt{x}) - \int (2x^{1/2}) \left( \frac{1}{x}\, dx \right)$$

$$= 2\sqrt{x}\, \ln x - 2 \int x^{-1/2}\, dx$$

$$= 2\sqrt{x}\, \ln x - 2(2\sqrt{x}) + C \qquad (x^{1/2} = \sqrt{x})$$

$$= 2\sqrt{x}[\ln(x) - 2] + C$$

NOW WORK PROBLEM 3 ●●●

Example 2 shows how a poor choice for $u$ and $dv$ can be made. If you make a choice that does not work, do not become frustrated. Rather, make other choices until one that works is found (if such a choice exists).

● **EXAMPLE 2    Integration by Parts**

*Evaluate* $\displaystyle\int_1^2 x \ln x\, dx.$

**Solution:** Since the integral does not fit a familiar form, we will try integration by parts. Let $u = x$ and $dv = \ln x\, dx$. Then $du = dx$, but $v = \int \ln x\, dx$ is not apparent by inspection. So we will make a different choice for $u$ and $dv$. Let

$$u = \ln x \quad \text{and} \quad dv = x\, dx$$

Then

$$du = \frac{1}{x}\, dx \quad \text{and} \quad v = \int x\, dx = \frac{x^2}{2}$$

Therefore,

$$\int_1^2 x \ln x\, dx = (\ln x) \left( \frac{x^2}{2} \right) \Big|_1^2 - \int_1^2 \left( \frac{x^2}{2} \right) \frac{1}{x}\, dx$$

$$= (\ln x) \left( \frac{x^2}{2} \right) \Big|_1^2 - \frac{1}{2} \int_1^2 x\, dx$$

$$= \frac{x^2 \ln x}{2} \Big|_1^2 - \frac{1}{2} \left( \frac{x^2}{2} \right) \Big|_1^2$$

$$= (2 \ln 2 - 0) - \left( 1 - \tfrac{1}{4} \right) = 2 \ln 2 - \tfrac{3}{4}$$

NOW WORK PROBLEM 5 ●●●

● EXAMPLE 3   **Integration by Parts where $u$ Is the Entire Integrand**

*Determine* $\int \ln y\, dy$.

**Solution:** We cannot integrate $\ln y$ by previous methods, so we will try integration by parts. Let $u = \ln y$ and $dv = dy$. Then $du = (1/y)\, dy$ and $v = y$. So we have

$$\int \ln y\, dy = (\ln y)(y) - \int y\left(\frac{1}{y}\, dy\right)$$

$$= y \ln y - \int dy = y \ln y - y + C$$

$$= y[\ln(y) - 1] + C$$

NOW WORK PROBLEM 37  ●●●

   Before trying integration by parts, see whether the technique is really needed. Sometimes the integral can be handled by a basic technique, as Example 4 shows.

● EXAMPLE 4   **Basic Integration Form**

*Determine* $\int xe^{x^2}\, dx$.

**Solution:** This integral can be fit to the form $\int e^u\, du$.

$$\int xe^{x^2}\, dx = \frac{1}{2}\int e^{x^2}(2x\, dx)$$

$$= \frac{1}{2}\int e^u\, du \qquad (\text{where } u = x^2)$$

$$= \frac{1}{2}e^u + C = \frac{1}{2}e^{x^2} + C$$

**CAUTION**

Do not forget about basic integration forms. Integration by parts is not needed here!

NOW WORK PROBLEM 17  ●●●

   Sometimes integration by parts must be used more than once, as shown in the following example.

---

**PRINCIPLES IN PRACTICE 2**

**APPLYING INTEGRATION BY PARTS TWICE**

Suppose a population of bacteria grows at a rate of

$$P'(t) = 0.1t(\ln t)^2$$

Find the general form of $P(t)$.

---

● EXAMPLE 5   **Applying Integration by Parts Twice**

*Determine* $\int x^2 e^{2x+1}\, dx$.

**Solution:** Let $u = x^2$ and $dv = e^{2x+1}\, dx$. Then $du = 2x\, dx$ and $v = e^{2x+1}/2$.

$$\int x^2 e^{2x+1}\, dx = \frac{x^2 e^{2x+1}}{2} - \int \frac{e^{2x+1}}{2}(2x\, dx)$$

$$= \frac{x^2 e^{2x+1}}{2} - \int xe^{2x+1}\, dx$$

To find $\int xe^{2x+1}\, dx$, we will again use integration by parts. Here, let $u = x$ and $dv = e^{2x+1}\, dx$. Then $du = dx$ and $v = e^{2x+1}/2$, and we have

$$\int xe^{2x+1}\, dx = \frac{xe^{2x+1}}{2} - \int \frac{e^{2x+1}}{2}\, dx$$

$$= \frac{xe^{2x+1}}{2} - \frac{e^{2x+1}}{4} + C_1$$

Thus,

$$\int x^2 e^{2x+1} \, dx = \frac{x^2 e^{2x+1}}{2} - \frac{x e^{2x+1}}{2} + \frac{e^{2x+1}}{4} + C \qquad \text{(where } C = -C_1\text{)}$$

$$= \frac{e^{2x+1}}{2} \left( x^2 - x + \frac{1}{2} \right) + C$$

NOW WORK PROBLEM 23

## Problems 15.1

1. In applying integration by parts to

$$\int f(x) \, dx$$

a student found that $u = x$, $du = dx$, $dv = (x+5)^{1/2}$, and $v = \frac{2}{3}(x+5)^{3/2}$. Use this information to find $\int f(x) \, dx$.

2. Use integration by parts to find

$$\int x e^{3x+1} \, dx$$

by choosing $u = x$ and $dv = e^{3x+1} \, dx$.

*In Problems 3–29, find the integrals.*

*3. $\displaystyle\int x e^{-x} \, dx$

4. $\displaystyle\int x e^{-5x} \, dx$

*5. $\displaystyle\int y^3 \ln y \, dy$

6. $\displaystyle\int x^2 \ln x \, dx$

7. $\displaystyle\int \ln(4x) \, dx$

8. $\displaystyle\int \frac{t}{e^t} \, dt$

9. $\displaystyle\int 3x \sqrt{2x+3} \, dx$

10. $\displaystyle\int \frac{12x}{\sqrt{1+4x}} \, dx$

11. $\displaystyle\int \frac{x}{(5x+2)^3} \, dx$

12. $\displaystyle\int \frac{\ln(x+1)}{2(x+1)} \, dx$

13. $\displaystyle\int \frac{\ln x}{x^2} \, dx$

14. $\displaystyle\int \frac{3x+5}{e^{2x}} \, dx$

15. $\displaystyle\int_1^2 4x e^{2x} \, dx$

16. $\displaystyle\int_1^2 2x e^{-3x} \, dx$

*17. $\displaystyle\int_0^1 x e^{-x^2} \, dx$

18. $\displaystyle\int \frac{3x^3}{\sqrt{4-x^2}} \, dx$

19. $\displaystyle\int_1^2 \frac{3x}{\sqrt{4-x}} \, dx$

20. $\displaystyle\int (\ln x)^2 \, dx$

21. $\displaystyle\int 3(2x-2) \ln(x-2) \, dx$

22. $\displaystyle\int \frac{x e^x}{(x+1)^2} \, dx$

*23. $\displaystyle\int x^2 e^x \, dx$

24. $\displaystyle\int_e^3 \sqrt[3]{x} \ln(x^5) \, dx$

25. $\displaystyle\int (x - e^{-x})^2 \, dx$

26. $\displaystyle\int x^2 e^{3x} \, dx$

27. $\displaystyle\int x^3 e^{x^2} \, dx$

28. $\displaystyle\int x^5 e^{x^2} \, dx$

29. $\displaystyle\int (2^x + x)^2 \, dx$

30. Find $\int \ln(x + \sqrt{x^2+1}) \, dx$. *Hint:* Show that

$$\frac{d}{dx} [\ln(x + \sqrt{x^2+1})] = \frac{1}{\sqrt{x^2+1}}$$

31. Find the area of the region bounded by the $x$-axis, the curve $y = \ln x$, and the line $x = e^3$.

32. Find the area of the region bounded by the $x$-axis and the curve $y = x^2 e^x$ between $x = 0$ and $x = 1$.

33. Find the area of the region bounded by the $x$-axis and the curve $y = x^2 \ln x$ between $x = 1$ and $x = 2$.

34. **Consumers' Surplus**    Suppose the demand equation for a manufacturer's product is given by

$$p = 10(q + 10)e^{-(0.1q+1)}$$

where $p$ is the price per unit (in dollars) when $q$ units are demanded. Assume that market equilibrium occurs when $q = 20$. Determine consumers' surplus at market equilibrium.

35. **Revenue**    Suppose total revenue $r$ and price per unit $p$ are differentiable functions of output $q$.

(a) Use integration by parts to show that

$$\int p \, dq = r - \int q \frac{dp}{dq} \, dq$$

(b) Using part (a), show that

$$r = \int \left( p + q \frac{dp}{dq} \right) dq$$

(c) Using part (b), prove that

$$r(q_0) = \int_0^{q_0} \left( p + q \frac{dp}{dq} \right) dq$$

(*Hint:* Refer to Section 14.7.)

36. Suppose $f$ is a differentiable function. Apply integration by parts to $\int f(x) e^x \, dx$ to prove that

$$\int f(x) e^x \, dx + \int f'(x) e^x \, dx = f(x) e^x + C$$

$$\left( \text{Hence, } \int [f(x) + f'(x)] e^x \, dx = f(x) e^x + C \right)$$

*37. Suppose that $f$ has an inverse and that $F' = f$. Use integration by parts to develop a useful formula for $\int f^{-1}(x) \, dx$ in terms of $F$ and $f^{-1}$. (*Hint:* Review Example 3. It used the idea required here, for the special case of $f(x) = e^x$.)

OBJECTIVE

To show how to integrate a proper rational function by first expressing it as a sum of its partial fractions.

# 15.2  Integration by Partial Fractions[2]

Recall that a *rational function* is a quotient of polynomials $N(x)/D(x)$ and that it is *proper* if $N$ and $D$ have no common polynomial factor and the degree of the numerator $N$ is less than the degree of the denominator $D$. If $N/D$ is not proper, then we can use long division to divide $N(x)$ by $D(x)$:

$$D(x)\overline{)N(x)}\ \ \ \begin{array}{c}Q(x)\\ \vdots\\ \overline{R(x)}\end{array} \quad \text{thus} \quad \frac{N(x)}{D(x)} = Q(x) + \frac{R(x)}{D(x)}$$

Here the quotient $Q(x)$ and the remainder $R(x)$ are also polynomials and either $R(x)$ is the constant 0-polynomial or the degree of $R(x)$ is less than that of $D(x)$. Thus $R/D$ is a proper rational function. Since

$$\int \frac{N(x)}{D(x)}\,dx = \int \left(Q(x) + \frac{R(x)}{D(x)}\right)\,dx = \int Q(x)\,dx + \int \frac{R(x)}{D(x)}\,dx$$

and we already know how to integrate a polynomial, it follows that the task of integrating rational functions reduces to that of integrating *proper* rational functions. We emphasize that the technique we are about to explain requires that a rational function be proper so that the long division step is not optional. For example,

$$\int \frac{2x^4 - 3x^3 - 4x^2 - 17x - 6}{x^3 - 2x^2 - 3x}\,dx = \int \left(2x + 1 + \frac{4x^2 - 14x - 6}{x^3 - 2x^2 - 3x}\right)\,dx$$

$$= x^2 + x + \int \frac{4x^2 - 14x - 6}{x^3 - 2x^2 - 3x}\,dx$$

**Distinct Linear Factors**

Therefore, we will consider

$$\int \frac{4x^2 - 14x - 6}{x^3 - 2x^2 - 3x}\,dx$$

It is essential that the denominator be expressed in factored form:

$$\int \frac{4x^2 - 14x - 6}{x(x+1)(x-3)}\,dx$$

Observe that in this example the denominator consists only of **linear factors** and that each factor occurs exactly once. It can be shown that, to each such factor $x - a$, there corresponds a *partial fraction* of the form

$$\frac{A}{x-a} \qquad (A \text{ a constant})$$

such that the integrand is the sum of the partial fractions. If there are $n$ such *distinct* linear factors, there will be $n$ such partial fractions, each of which is easily integrated. Applying these facts, we can write

$$\frac{4x^2 - 14x - 6}{x(x+1)(x-3)} = \frac{A}{x} + \frac{B}{x+1} + \frac{C}{x-3} \qquad (1)$$

To determine the constants $A$, $B$, and $C$, we first combine the terms on the right side:

$$\frac{4x^2 - 14x - 6}{x(x+1)(x-3)} = \frac{A(x+1)(x-3) + Bx(x-3) + Cx(x+1)}{x(x+1)(x-3)}$$

---

[2]This section may be omitted without loss of continuity.

Since the denominators of both sides are equal, we can equate their numerators:

$$4x^2 - 14x - 6 = A(x+1)(x-3) + Bx(x-3) + Cx(x+1) \qquad (2)$$

Although Equation (1) is not defined for $x = 0$, $x = -1$, and $x = 3$, we want to find values for $A$, $B$, and $C$ that will make Equation (2) true for all values of $x$, so that the two sides of the equality provide equal functions. By successively setting $x$ in Equation (2) equal to any three different numbers, we can obtain a system of equations that can be solved for $A$, $B$, and $C$. In particular, the work can be simplified by letting $x$ be the roots of $D(x) = 0$; in our case, $x = 0$, $x = -1$, and $x = 3$. Using Equation (2), we have, for $x = 0$,

$$-6 = A(1)(-3) + B(0) + C(0) = -3A, \quad \text{so } A = 2$$

If $x = -1$,

$$12 = A(0) + B(-1)(-4) + C(0) = 4B, \quad \text{so } B = 3$$

If $x = 3$,

$$-12 = A(0) + B(0) + C(3)(4) = 12C, \quad \text{so } C = -1$$

Thus Equation (1) becomes

$$\frac{4x^2 - 14x - 6}{x(x+1)(x-3)} = \frac{2}{x} + \frac{3}{x+1} - \frac{1}{x-3}$$

Hence,

$$\int \frac{4x^2 - 14x - 6}{x(x+1)(x-3)}\,dx$$
$$= \int \left(\frac{2}{x} + \frac{3}{x+1} - \frac{1}{x-3}\right)dx$$
$$= 2\int \frac{dx}{x} + 3\int \frac{dx}{x+1} - \int \frac{dx}{x-3}$$
$$= 2\ln|x| + 3\ln|x+1| - \ln|x-3| + C$$

For the *original* integral, we can now state that

$$\int \frac{2x^4 - 3x^3 - 4x^2 - 17x - 6}{x^3 - 2x^2 - 3x}\,dx = x^2 + x + 2\ln|x| + 3\ln|x+1| - \ln|x-3| + C$$

An alternative method of determining $A$, $B$, and $C$ involves expanding the right side of Equation (2) and combining like terms:

$$4x^2 - 14x - 6 = A(x^2 - 2x - 3) + B(x^2 - 3x) + C(x^2 + x)$$
$$= Ax^2 - 2Ax - 3A + Bx^2 - 3Bx + Cx^2 + Cx$$
$$4x^2 - 14x - 6 = (A + B + C)x^2 + (-2A - 3B + C)x + (-3A)$$

For this last equation to express an equality of functions, the coefficients of corresponding powers of $x$ on the left and right sides must be equal:

$$\begin{cases} 4 = A + B + C \\ -14 = -2A - 3B + C \\ -6 = -3A \end{cases}$$

Solving gives $A = 2$, $B = 3$, and $C = -1$ as before.

**DISTINCT LINEAR FACTORS**

The marginal revenue for a company manufacturing $q$ radios per week is given by $r'(q) = \dfrac{5(q+4)}{q^2 + 4q + 3}$, where $r(q)$ is the revenue in thousands of dollars. Find the equation for $r(q)$.

**EXAMPLE 1  Distinct Linear Factors**

*Determine* $\displaystyle\int \frac{2x+1}{3x^2 - 27}\, dx$ *by using partial fractions.*

**Solution:** Since the degree of the numerator is less than the degree of the denominator, no long division is necessary. The integral can be written as

$$\frac{1}{3}\int \frac{2x+1}{x^2 - 9}\, dx$$

Expressing $(2x+1)/(x^2 - 9)$ as a sum of partial fractions, we have

$$\frac{2x+1}{x^2 - 9} = \frac{2x+1}{(x+3)(x-3)} = \frac{A}{x+3} + \frac{B}{x-3}$$

Combining terms and equating numerators gives

$$2x+1 = A(x-3) + B(x+3)$$

If $x = 3$, then

$$7 = 6B, \quad \text{so } B = \frac{7}{6}$$

If $x = -3$, then

$$-5 = -6A, \quad \text{so } A = \frac{5}{6}$$

Thus,

$$\int \frac{2x+1}{3x^2 - 27}\, dx = \frac{1}{3}\left( \int \frac{\frac{5}{6}\, dx}{x+3} + \int \frac{\frac{7}{6}\, dx}{x-3} \right)$$

$$= \frac{1}{3}\left( \frac{5}{6}\ln|x+3| + \frac{7}{6}\ln|x-3| \right) + C$$

NOW WORK PROBLEM 1

### Repeated Linear Factors

If the denominator of $N(x)/D(x)$ contains only linear factors, some of which are repeated, then, for each factor $(x-a)^k$, where $k$ is the maximum number of times $x - a$ occurs as a factor, there will correspond the sum of $k$ partial fractions:

$$\frac{A}{x-a} + \frac{B}{(x-a)^2} + \cdots + \frac{K}{(x-a)^k}$$

**EXAMPLE 2  Repeated Linear Factors**

*Determine* $\displaystyle\int \frac{6x^2 + 13x + 6}{(x+2)(x+1)^2}\, dx$ *by using partial fractions.*

**Solution:** Since the degree of the numerator, namely 2, is less than that of the denominator, namely 3, no long division is necessary. In the denominator, the linear factor $x+2$ occurs once and the linear factor $x+1$ occurs twice. There will thus be three partial fractions and three constants to determine, and we have

$$\frac{6x^2 + 13x + 6}{(x+2)(x+1)^2} = \frac{A}{x+2} + \frac{B}{x+1} + \frac{C}{(x+1)^2}$$

$$6x^2 + 13x + 6 = A(x+1)^2 + B(x+2)(x+1) + C(x+2)$$

Let us choose $x = -2$, $x = -1$, and, for convenience, $x = 0$. For $x = -2$, we have

$$4 = A$$

If $x = -1$, then

$$-1 = C$$

If $x = 0$, then

$$6 = A + 2B + 2C = 4 + 2B - 2 = 2 + 2B$$

$$4 = 2B$$

$$2 = B$$

Therefore,

$$\int \frac{6x^2 + 13x + 6}{(x + 2)(x + 1)^2}\, dx = 4 \int \frac{dx}{x + 2} + 2 \int \frac{dx}{x + 1} - \int \frac{dx}{(x + 1)^2}$$

$$= 4 \ln |x + 2| + 2 \ln |x + 1| + \frac{1}{x + 1} + C$$

$$= \ln[(x + 2)^4 (x + 1)^2] + \frac{1}{x + 1} + C$$

The last line above is somewhat optional (depending on what you need the integral for). It merely illustrates that in problems of this kind the logarithms that arise can often be combined.

NOW WORK PROBLEM 5

### Distinct Irreducible Quadratic Factors

Suppose a quadratic factor $x^2 + bx + c$ occurs in $D(x)$ and it cannot be expressed as a product of two linear factors with real coefficients. Such a factor is said to be an *irreducible quadratic factor over the real numbers*. To each distinct irreducible quadratic factor that occurs exactly once in $D(x)$, there will correspond a partial fraction of the form

$$\frac{Ax + B}{x^2 + bx + c}$$

Note that even after you have expressed a rational function in terms of partial fractions, you may still find it impossible to integrate using only the calculus you have been taught so far. For example, a very simple irreducible quadratic factor is $x^2 + 1$ and yet

$$\int \frac{1}{x^2 + 1}\, dx = \int \frac{dx}{x^2 + 1} = \tan^{-1} x + C$$

where $\tan^{-1}$ is the inverse of the trigonometric function tan when tan is restricted to $(-\pi/2, \pi/2)$. We do not discuss trigonometric functions in this book, but note that any good calculator has a $\tan^{-1}$ key.

### EXAMPLE 3 An Integral with a Distinct Irreducible Quadratic Factor

*Determine* $\int \dfrac{-2x - 4}{x^3 + x^2 + x}\, dx$ *by using partial fractions.*

**Solution:** Since $x^3 + x^2 + x = x(x^2 + x + 1)$, we have the linear factor $x$ and the quadratic factor $x^2 + x + 1$, which does not seem factorable on inspection. If it were factorable as $(x - r_1)(x - r_2)$, with $r_1$ and $r_2$ real, then $r_1$ and $r_2$ would be roots of the equation $x^2 + x + 1 = 0$. By the quadratic formula, the roots are

$$x = \frac{-1 \pm \sqrt{1 - 4}}{2}$$

Since there are no real roots, we conclude that $x^2 + x + 1$ is irreducible. Thus there will be two partial fractions and *three* constants to determine. We have

$$\frac{-2x - 4}{x(x^2 + x + 1)} = \frac{A}{x} + \frac{Bx + C}{x^2 + x + 1}$$

$$-2x - 4 = A(x^2 + x + 1) + (Bx + C)x$$

$$= Ax^2 + Ax + A + Bx^2 + Cx$$

$$0x^2 - 2x - 4 = (A + B)x^2 + (A + C)x + A$$

Equating coefficients of like powers of $x$, we obtain

$$\begin{cases} 0 = A + B \\ -2 = A + C \\ -4 = A \end{cases}$$

Solving gives $A = -4$, $B = 4$, and $C = 2$. Hence,

$$\int \frac{-2x - 4}{x(x^2 + x + 1)}\, dx = \int \left( \frac{-4}{x} + \frac{4x + 2}{x^2 + x + 1} \right) dx$$

$$= -4 \int \frac{dx}{x} + 2 \int \frac{2x + 1}{x^2 + x + 1}\, dx$$

Both integrals have the form $\int \frac{du}{u}$, so

$$\int \frac{-2x - 4}{x(x^2 + x + 1)}\, dx = -4 \ln |x| + 2 \ln |x^2 + x + 1| + C$$

$$= \ln \left[ \frac{(x^2 + x + 1)^2}{x^4} \right] + C$$

NOW WORK PROBLEM 7

### Repeated Irreducible Quadratic Factors

Suppose $D(x)$ contains factors of the form $(x^2 + bx + c)^k$, where $k$ is the maximum number of times the irreducible factor $x^2 + bx + c$ occurs. Then, to each such factor there will correspond a sum of $k$ partial fractions of the form

$$\frac{A + Bx}{x^2 + bx + c} + \frac{C + Dx}{(x^2 + bx + c)^2} + \cdots + \frac{M + Nx}{(x^2 + bx + c)^k}$$

### EXAMPLE 4   Repeated Irreducible Quadratic Factors

*Determine* $\int \frac{x^5}{(x^2 + 4)^2}\, dx$ *by using partial fractions.*

**Solution:** Since the numerator has degree 5 and the denominator has degree 4, we first use long division, which gives

$$\frac{x^5}{x^4 + 8x^2 + 16} = x - \frac{8x^3 + 16x}{(x^2 + 4)^2}$$

The quadratic factor $x^2 + 4$ in the denominator of $(8x^3 + 16x)/(x^2 + 4)^2$ is irreducible and occurs as a factor twice. Thus, to $(x^2 + 4)^2$ there correspond two partial fractions and *four* coefficients to be determined. Accordingly, we set

$$\frac{8x^3 + 16x}{(x^2 + 4)^2} = \frac{Ax + B}{x^2 + 4} + \frac{Cx + D}{(x^2 + 4)^2}$$

and obtain

$$8x^3 + 16x = (Ax + B)(x^2 + 4) + Cx + D$$
$$8x^3 + 0x^2 + 16x + 0 = Ax^3 + Bx^2 + (4A + C)x + 4B + D$$

Equating like powers of $x$ yields

$$\begin{cases} 8 = A \\ 0 = B \\ 16 = 4A + C \\ 0 = 4B + D \end{cases}$$

Solving gives $A = 8$, $B = 0$, $C = -16$, and $D = 0$. Therefore,

$$\int \frac{x^5}{(x^2+4)^2}\, dx = \int \left( x - \left( \frac{8x}{x^2+4} - \frac{16x}{(x^2+4)^2} \right) \right) dx$$

$$= \int x\, dx - 4 \int \frac{2x}{x^2+4}\, dx + 8 \int \frac{2x}{(x^2+4)^2}\, dx$$

The second integral on the preceding line has the form $\int \frac{du}{u}$, and the third integral has the form $\int \frac{du}{u^2}$. So

$$\int \frac{x^5}{(x^2+4)^2} = \frac{x^2}{2} - 4\ln(x^2+4) - \frac{8}{x^2+4} + C$$

NOW WORK PROBLEM 27 ●●●

From our examples, you may have deduced that the number of constants needed to express $N(x)/D(x)$ by partial fractions is equal to the degree of $D(x)$, if it is assumed that $N(x)/D(x)$ defines a proper rational function. This is indeed the case. Note also that the representation of a proper rational function by partial fractions is unique; that is, there is only one choice of constants that can be made. Furthermore, regardless of the complexity of the polynomial $D(x)$, it can always (theoretically) be expressed as a product of linear and irreducible quadratic factors with real coefficients.

**CAUTION**

Do not forget about basic integration forms.

**PRINCIPLES IN PRACTICE 2**

**AN INTEGRAL NOT REQUIRING PARTIAL FRACTIONS**

The rate of change of the voting population of a city with respect to time $t$ (in years) is estimated to be $V'(t) = \dfrac{300t^3}{t^2+6}$. Find the general form of $V(t)$.

● **EXAMPLE 5** **An Integral Not Requiring Partial Fractions**

*Find* $\int \dfrac{2x+3}{x^2+3x+1}\, dx$.

**Solution:** This integral has the form $\int \dfrac{1}{u}\, du$. Thus,

$$\int \frac{2x+3}{x^2+3x+1}\, dx = \ln|x^2+3x+1| + C$$

NOW WORK PROBLEM 17 ●●●

## Problems 15.2

*In Problems 1–8, express the given rational function in terms of partial fractions. Watch out for any preliminary divisions.*

**\*1.** $f(x) = \dfrac{10x}{x^2+7x+6}$

**2.** $f(x) = \dfrac{x+5}{x^2-1}$

**3.** $f(x) = \dfrac{2x^2}{x^2+5x+6}$

**4.** $f(x) = \dfrac{2x^2-15}{x^2+5x}$

**\*5.** $f(x) = \dfrac{x+4}{x^2+4x+4}$

**6.** $f(x) = \dfrac{2x+3}{x^2(x-1)}$

**\*7.** $f(x) = \dfrac{x^2+3}{x^3+x}$

**8.** $f(x) = \dfrac{3x^2+5}{(x^2+4)^2}$

*In Problems 9–30, determine the integrals.*

**9.** $\displaystyle\int \frac{5x-2}{x^2-x}\, dx$

**10.** $\displaystyle\int \frac{7x+6}{x^2+3x}\, dx$

**11.** $\displaystyle\int \frac{x+10}{x^2-x-2}\, dx$

**12.** $\displaystyle\int \frac{2x-1}{x^2-x-12}\, dx$

**13.** $\displaystyle\int \frac{3x^3-3x+4}{4x^2-4}\, dx$

**14.** $\displaystyle\int \frac{7(4-x^2)}{(x-4)(x-2)(x+3)}\, dx$

**15.** $\displaystyle\int \frac{3x-4}{x^3-x^2-2x}\, dx$

**16.** $\displaystyle\int \frac{4-x}{x^4-x^2}\, dx$

**\*17.** $\displaystyle\int \frac{2(3x^5+4x^3-x)}{x^6+2x^4-x^2-2}\, dx$

**18.** $\displaystyle\int \frac{x^4-2x^3+6x^2-11x+2}{x^3-3x^2+2x}\, dx$

**19.** $\displaystyle\int \frac{2x^2-5x-2}{(x-2)^2(x-1)}\, dx$

**20.** $\displaystyle\int \frac{-3x^3+2x-3}{x^2(x^2-1)}\, dx$

**21.** $\displaystyle\int \frac{2(x^2+8)}{x^3+4x}\, dx$

**22.** $\displaystyle\int \frac{4x^3-3x^2+2x-3}{(x^2+3)(x+1)(x-2)}\, dx$

**23.** $\displaystyle\int \frac{-x^3+8x^2-9x+2}{(x^2+1)(x-3)^2}\, dx$

**24.** $\displaystyle\int \frac{5x^4+9x^2+3}{x(x^2+1)^2}\, dx$

**25.** $\displaystyle\int \frac{14x^3+24x}{(x^2+1)(x^2+2)}\, dx$

**26.** $\displaystyle\int \frac{12x^3+20x^2+28x+4}{3(x^2+2x+3)(x^2+1)}\, dx$

**\*27.** $\displaystyle\int \frac{3x^3+8x}{(x^2+2)^2}\, dx$

**28.** $\displaystyle\int \frac{3x^2-8x+4}{x^3-4x^2+4x-6}\, dx$

**29.** $\displaystyle\int_0^1 \frac{2-2x}{x^2+7x+12}\,dx$     **30.** $\displaystyle\int_1^2 \frac{3x^2+15x+13}{x^2+4x+3}\,dx$

**31.** Find the area of the region bounded by the graph of

$$y = \frac{6(x^2+1)}{(x+2)^2}$$

and the $x$-axis from $x = 0$ to $x = 1$.

**32. Consumers' Surplus**   Suppose the demand equation for a manufacturer's product is given by

$$p = \frac{200(q+3)}{q^2+7q+6}$$

where $p$ is the price per unit (in dollars) when $q$ units are demanded. Assume that market equilibrium occurs at the point $(q, p) = (10, 325/22)$. Determine consumers' surplus at market equilibrium.

OBJECTIVE

To illustrate the use of the table of integrals in Appendix B.

## 15.3 Integration by Tables

Certain forms of integrals that occur frequently may be found in standard tables of integration formulas.[3] A short table appears in Appendix B, and its use will be illustrated in this section.

A given integral may have to be replaced by an equivalent form before it will fit a formula in the table. The equivalent form must match the formula *exactly*. Consequently, the steps that you perform should *not* be done mentally. *Write them down!* Failure to do this can easily lead to incorrect results. Before proceeding with the exercises, be sure you understand the examples *thoroughly*.

In the following examples, the formula numbers refer to the Table of Selected Integrals given in Appendix B.

● **EXAMPLE 1   Integration by Tables**

*Find* $\displaystyle\int \frac{x\,dx}{(2+3x)^2}$.

**Solution:**  Scanning the table, we identify the integrand with Formula 7:

$$\int \frac{u\,du}{(a+bu)^2} = \frac{1}{b^2}\left(\ln|a+bu| + \frac{a}{a+bu}\right) + C$$

Now we see if we can exactly match the given integrand with that in the formula. If we replace $x$ by $u$, 2 by $a$, and 3 by $b$, then $du = dx$, and by substitution we have

$$\int \frac{x\,dx}{(2+3x)^2} = \int \frac{u\,du}{(a+bu)^2} = \frac{1}{b^2}\left(\ln|a+bu| + \frac{a}{a+bu}\right) + C$$

Returning to the variable $x$ and replacing $a$ by 2 and $b$ by 3, we obtain

$$\int \frac{x\,dx}{(2+3x)^2} = \frac{1}{9}\left(\ln|2+3x| + \frac{2}{2+3x}\right) + C$$

Note that the answer must be given in terms of $x$, the *original* variable of integration.

NOW WORK PROBLEM 5 ●●●

● **EXAMPLE 2   Integration by Tables**

*Find* $\displaystyle\int x^2\sqrt{x^2-1}\,dx$.

**Solution:**  This integral is identified with Formula 24:

$$\int u^2\sqrt{u^2\pm a^2}\,du = \frac{u}{8}(2u^2\pm a^2)\sqrt{u^2\pm a^2} - \frac{a^4}{8}\ln|u+\sqrt{u^2\pm a^2}| + C$$

In the preceding formula, if the bottommost sign in the dual symbol "±" on the left side is used, then the bottommost sign in the dual symbols on the right side must also be used. In the original integral, we let $u = x$ and $a = 1$. Then $du = dx$, and by

---

[3]See, for example, W. H. Beyer (ed.), *CRC Standard Mathematical Tables and Formulae,* 30th ed. (Boca Raton, FL: CRC Press, 1996).

substitution the integral becomes

$$\int x^2 \sqrt{x^2 - 1}\, dx = \int u^2 \sqrt{u^2 - a^2}\, du$$

$$= \frac{u}{8}(2u^2 - a^2)\sqrt{u^2 - a^2} - \frac{a^4}{8}\ln|u + \sqrt{u^2 - a^2}| + C$$

Since $u = x$ and $a = 1$,

$$\int x^2 \sqrt{x^2 - 1}\, dx = \frac{x}{8}(2x^2 - 1)\sqrt{x^2 - 1} - \frac{1}{8}\ln|x + \sqrt{x^2 - 1}| + C$$

NOW WORK PROBLEM 17 ◖●●

This example, as well as Examples 4, 5, and 7, shows how to adjust an integral so that it conforms to one in the table.

● **EXAMPLE 3   Integration by Tables**

*Find* $\displaystyle\int \frac{dx}{x\sqrt{16x^2 + 3}}$.

**Solution:** The integrand can be identified with Formula 28:

$$\int \frac{du}{u\sqrt{u^2 + a^2}} = \frac{1}{a}\ln\left|\frac{\sqrt{u^2 + a^2} - a}{u}\right| + C$$

If we let $u = 4x$ and $a = \sqrt{3}$, then $du = 4\, dx$. Watch closely how, by inserting 4's in the numerator and denominator, we transform the given integral into an equivalent form that matches Formula 28:

$$\int \frac{dx}{x\sqrt{16x^2 + 3}} = \int \frac{(4\, dx)}{(4x)\sqrt{(4x)^2 + (\sqrt{3})^2}} = \int \frac{du}{u\sqrt{u^2 + a^2}}$$

$$= \frac{1}{a}\ln\left|\frac{\sqrt{u^2 + a^2} - a}{u}\right| + C$$

$$= \frac{1}{\sqrt{3}}\ln\left|\frac{\sqrt{16x^2 + 3} - \sqrt{3}}{4x}\right| + C$$

NOW WORK PROBLEM 7 ◖●●

● **EXAMPLE 4   Integration by Tables**

*Find* $\displaystyle\int \frac{dx}{x^2(2 - 3x^2)^{1/2}}$.

**Solution:** The integrand is identified with Formula 21:

$$\int \frac{du}{u^2\sqrt{a^2 - u^2}} = -\frac{\sqrt{a^2 - u^2}}{a^2 u} + C$$

Letting $u = \sqrt{3}x$ and $a^2 = 2$, we have $du = \sqrt{3}\, dx$. Hence, by inserting two factors of $\sqrt{3}$ in both the numerator and denominator of the original integral, we have

$$\int \frac{dx}{x^2(2 - 3x^2)^{1/2}} = \sqrt{3}\int \frac{(\sqrt{3}\, dx)}{(\sqrt{3}x)^2[2 - (\sqrt{3}x)^2]^{1/2}} = \sqrt{3}\int \frac{du}{u^2(a^2 - u^2)^{1/2}}$$

$$= \sqrt{3}\left[-\frac{\sqrt{a^2 - u^2}}{a^2 u}\right] + C = \sqrt{3}\left[-\frac{\sqrt{2 - 3x^2}}{2(\sqrt{3}x)}\right] + C$$

$$= -\frac{\sqrt{2 - 3x^2}}{2x} + C$$

NOW WORK PROBLEM 35 ◖●●

● EXAMPLE 5   **Integration by Tables**

*Find* $\int 7x^2 \ln(4x)\, dx$.

**Solution:** This is similar to Formula 42 with $n = 2$:

$$\int u^n \ln u\, du = \frac{u^{n+1}\ln u}{n+1} - \frac{u^{n+1}}{(n+1)^2} + C$$

If we let $u = 4x$, then $du = 4\, dx$. Hence,

$$\int 7x^2 \ln(4x)\, dx = \frac{7}{4^3} \int (4x)^2 \ln(4x)(4\, dx)$$

$$= \frac{7}{64} \int u^2 \ln u\, du = \frac{7}{64} \left( \frac{u^3 \ln u}{3} - \frac{u^3}{9} \right) + C$$

$$= \frac{7}{64} \left( \frac{(4x)^3 \ln(4x)}{3} - \frac{(4x)^3}{9} \right) + C$$

$$= 7x^3 \left( \frac{\ln(4x)}{3} - \frac{1}{9} \right) + C$$

$$= \frac{7x^3}{9} (3\ln(4x) - 1) + C$$

NOW WORK PROBLEM 45   ◖◖●

● EXAMPLE 6   **Integral Table Not Needed**

*Find* $\int \frac{e^{2x}\, dx}{7 + e^{2x}}$.

**Solution:** At first glance, we do not identify the integrand with any form in the table. Perhaps rewriting the integral will help. Let $u = 7 + e^{2x}$, then $du = 2e^{2x}\, dx$. So

$$\int \frac{e^{2x}\, dx}{7 + e^{2x}} = \frac{1}{2} \int \frac{(2e^{2x}\, dx)}{7 + e^{2x}} = \frac{1}{2} \int \frac{du}{u} = \frac{1}{2} \ln |u| + C$$

$$= \frac{1}{2} \ln |7 + e^{2x}| + C = \frac{1}{2} \ln(7 + e^{2x}) + C$$

Thus, we had only to use our knowledge of basic integration forms. Actually, this form appears as Formula 2 in the table.

NOW WORK PROBLEM 39   ◖◖●

● EXAMPLE 7   **Finding a Definite Integral by Using Tables**

*Evaluate* $\int_1^4 \frac{dx}{(4x^2 + 2)^{3/2}}$.

**Solution:** We will use Formula 32 to get the indefinite integral first:

$$\int \frac{du}{(u^2 \pm a^2)^{3/2}} = \frac{\pm u}{a^2 \sqrt{u^2 \pm a^2}} + C$$

Letting $u = 2x$ and $a^2 = 2$, we have $du = 2\, dx$. Thus,

$$\int \frac{dx}{(4x^2 + 2)^{3/2}} = \frac{1}{2} \int \frac{(2\, dx)}{((2x)^2 + 2)^{3/2}} = \frac{1}{2} \int \frac{du}{(u^2 + 2)^{3/2}}$$

$$= \frac{1}{2} \left( \frac{u}{2\sqrt{u^2 + 2}} \right) + C$$

Here we determine the limits of integration with respect to $u$.

Instead of substituting back to $x$ and evaluating from $x = 1$ to $x = 4$, we can determine the corresponding limits of integration with respect to $u$ and then evaluate the last expression between those limits. Since $u = 2x$, when $x = 1$ we have $u = 2$; when

**CAUTION**

When changing the variable of integration $x$ to the variable of integration $u$, be sure to change the limits of integration so that they agree with $u$.

$x = 4$ we have $u = 8$. Hence,

$$\int_1^4 \frac{dx}{(4x^2 + 2)^{3/2}} = \frac{1}{2} \int_2^8 \frac{du}{(u^2 + 2)^{3/2}}$$

$$= \frac{1}{2} \left( \frac{u}{2\sqrt{u^2 + 2}} \right) \Bigg|_2^8 = \frac{2}{\sqrt{66}} - \frac{1}{2\sqrt{6}}$$

NOW WORK PROBLEM 15 ●●●

### Integration Applied to Annuities

Tables of integrals are useful when we deal with integrals associated with annuities. Suppose that you must pay out $100 at the end of each year for the next two years. Recall from Chapter 5 that a series of payments over a period of time, such as this, is called an *annuity*. If you were to pay off the debt now instead, you would pay the present value of the $100 that is due at the end of the first year, plus the present value of the $100 that is due at the end of the second year. The sum of these present values is the present value of the annuity. (The present value of an annuity is discussed in Section 5.4.) We will now consider the present value of payments made continuously over the time interval from $t = 0$ to $t = T$, with $t$ in years, when interest is compounded continuously at an annual rate of $r$.

Suppose a payment is made at time $t$ such that on an annual basis this payment is $f(t)$. If we divide the interval $[0, T]$ into subintervals $[t_{i-1}, t_i]$ of length $\Delta t$ (where $\Delta t$ is small), then the total amount of all payments over such a subinterval is approximately $f(t_i)\,\Delta t$. (For example, if $f(t) = 2000$ and $\Delta t$ were one day, the total amount of the payments would be $2000(\frac{1}{365})$.) The present value of these payments is approximately $e^{-rt_i} f(t_i)\,\Delta t$. (See Section 5.3.) Over the interval $[0, T]$, the total of all such present values is

$$\sum e^{-rt_i} f(t_i)\,\Delta t$$

This sum approximates the present value $A$ of the annuity. The smaller $\Delta t$ is, the better the approximation. That is, as $\Delta t \to 0$, the limit of the sum is the present value. However, this limit is also a definite integral. That is,

$$A = \int_0^T f(t)e^{-rt}\,dt \tag{1}$$

where $A$ is the **present value of a continuous annuity** at an annual rate $r$ (compounded continuously) for $T$ years if a payment at time $t$ is at the rate of $f(t)$ per year.

We say that Equation (1) gives the **present value of a continuous income stream.** Equation (1) can also be used to find the present value of future profits of a business. In this situation, $f(t)$ is the annual rate of profit at time $t$.

We can also consider the *future* value of an annuity rather than its present value. If a payment is made at time $t$, then it has a certain value at the *end* of the period of the annuity—that is, $T - t$ years later. This value is

$$\left( \begin{array}{c} \text{amount of} \\ \text{payment} \end{array} \right) + \left( \begin{array}{c} \text{interest on this} \\ \text{payment for } T - t \text{ years} \end{array} \right)$$

If $S$ is the total of such values for all payments, then $S$ is called the *accumulated amount of a continuous annuity* and is given by the formula

$$S = \int_0^T f(t)e^{r(T-t)}\,dt$$

where $S$ is the **accumulated amount of a continuous annuity** at the end of $T$ years at an annual rate $r$ (compounded continuously) when a payment at time $t$ is at the rate of $f(t)$ per year.

● EXAMPLE 8    **Present Value of a Continuous Annuity**

*Find the present value (to the nearest dollar) of a continuous annuity at an annual rate of 8% for 10 years if the payment at time t is at the rate of $t^2$ dollars per year.*

**Solution:** The present value is given by

$$A = \int_0^T f(t)e^{-rt}\, dt = \int_0^{10} t^2 e^{-0.08t}\, dt$$

We will use Formula 39,

$$\int u^n e^{au}\, du = \frac{u^n e^{au}}{a} - \frac{n}{a} \int u^{n-1} e^{au}\, du$$

This is called a *reduction formula,* since it reduces one integral to an expression that involves another integral that is easier to determine. If $u = t$, $n = 2$, and $a = -0.08$, then $du = dt$, and we have

$$A = \frac{t^2 e^{-0.08t}}{-0.08}\Big|_0^{10} - \frac{2}{-0.08}\int_0^{10} t e^{-0.08t}\, dt$$

In the new integral, the exponent of $t$ has been reduced to 1. We can match this integral with Formula 38,

$$\int u e^{au}\, du = \frac{e^{au}}{a^2}(au - 1) + C$$

by letting $u = t$ and $a = -0.08$. Then $du = dt$, and

$$A = \int_0^{10} t^2 e^{-0.08t}\, dt = \frac{t^2 e^{-0.08t}}{-0.08}\Big|_0^{10} - \frac{2}{-0.08}\left(\frac{e^{-0.08t}}{(-0.08)^2}(-0.08t - 1)\right)\Big|_0^{10}$$

$$= \frac{100 e^{-0.8}}{-0.08} - \frac{2}{-0.08}\left(\frac{e^{-0.8}}{(-0.08)^2}(-0.8 - 1) - \frac{1}{(-0.08)^2}(-1)\right)$$

$$\approx 185$$

The present value is $185.

NOW WORK PROBLEM 59 ●●

# Problems 15.3

*In Problems 1 and 2, use Formula 19 in Appendix B to determine the integrals.*

**1.** $\displaystyle\int \frac{dx}{(9 - x^2)^{3/2}}$

**2.** $\displaystyle\int \frac{dx}{(25 - 4x^2)^{3/2}}$

*In Problems 3 and 4, use Formula 30 in Appendix B to determine the integrals.*

**3.** $\displaystyle\int \frac{dx}{x^2\sqrt{16x^2 + 3}}$

**4.** $\displaystyle\int \frac{3\, dx}{x^3\sqrt{x^4 - 9}}$

*In Problems 5–38, find the integrals by using the table in Appendix B*

**\*5.** $\displaystyle\int \frac{dx}{x(6 + 7x)}$

**6.** $\displaystyle\int \frac{3x^2\, dx}{(2 + 5x)^2}$

**\*7.** $\displaystyle\int \frac{dx}{x\sqrt{x^2 + 9}}$

**8.** $\displaystyle\int \frac{dx}{(x^2 + 7)^{3/2}}$

**9.** $\displaystyle\int \frac{x\, dx}{(2 + 3x)(4 + 5x)}$

**10.** $\displaystyle\int 2^{5x}\, dx$

**11.** $\displaystyle\int \frac{dx}{5 + 2e^{3x}}$

**12.** $\displaystyle\int x^2\sqrt{1 + x}\, dx$

**13.** $\displaystyle\int \frac{7\, dx}{x(5 + 2x)^2}$

**14.** $\displaystyle\int \frac{dx}{x\sqrt{5 - 11x^2}}$

**\*15.** $\displaystyle\int_0^1 \frac{x\, dx}{2 + x}$

**16.** $\displaystyle\int \frac{2x^2\, dx}{3 + 7x}$

**\*17.** $\displaystyle\int \sqrt{x^2 - 3}\, dx$

**18.** $\displaystyle\int \frac{dx}{(1 + 5x)(2x + 3)}$

**19.** $\displaystyle\int_0^{1/12} x e^{12x}\, dx$

**20.** $\displaystyle\int \sqrt{\frac{2 + 3x}{5 + 3x}}\, dx$

**21.** $\displaystyle\int x^2 e^x\, dx$

**22.** $\displaystyle\int_1^2 \frac{4\, dx}{x^2(1 + x)}$

**23.** $\displaystyle\int \frac{\sqrt{5x^2 + 1}}{2x^2}\, dx$

**24.** $\displaystyle\int \frac{dx}{x\sqrt{2 - x}}$

**25.** $\displaystyle\int \frac{x\, dx}{(1 + 3x)^2}$

**26.** $\displaystyle\int \frac{3\, dx}{\sqrt{(5 + 3x)(6 + 3x)}}$

**27.** $\displaystyle\int \frac{dx}{7 - 5x^2}$

**28.** $\displaystyle\int 7x^2\sqrt{3x^2 - 6}\, dx$

**29.** $\displaystyle\int 36x^5 \ln(3x)\, dx$

**30.** $\displaystyle\int \frac{5\, dx}{x^2(3 + 2x)^2}$

**31.** $\int 270x\sqrt{1+3x}\,dx$

**32.** $\int 9x^2 \ln x\,dx$

**33.** $\int \dfrac{dx}{\sqrt{4x^2-13}}$

**34.** $\int \dfrac{dx}{x\ln(2x)}$

***35.** $\int \dfrac{2\,dx}{x^2\sqrt{16-9x^2}}$

**36.** $\int \dfrac{\sqrt{2-3x^2}}{x}\,dx$

**37.** $\int \dfrac{dx}{\sqrt{x}(\pi+7e^{4\sqrt{x}})}$

**38.** $\int_0^1 \dfrac{3x^2\,dx}{1+2x^3}$

*In Problems 39–56, find the integrals by any method.*

***39.** $\int \dfrac{x\,dx}{x^2+1}$

**40.** $\int 3x\sqrt{x}e^{x^{5/2}}\,dx$

**41.** $\int 6x\sqrt{2x^2+1}\,dx$

**42.** $\int \dfrac{5x^3-\sqrt{x}}{2x}\,dx$

**43.** $\int \dfrac{dx}{x^2-5x+6}$

**44.** $\int \dfrac{e^{2x}}{\sqrt{e^{2x}+3}}\,dx$

***45.** $\int x^3 \ln x\,dx$

**46.** $\int_0^3 xe^{-x}\,dx$

**47.** $\int 4x^3 e^{3x^2}\,dx$

**48.** $\int_1^2 35x^2\sqrt{3+2x}\,dx$

**49.** $\int \ln^2 x\,dx$

**50.** $\int_1^e 3x\ln x^2\,dx$

**51.** $\int_1^2 \dfrac{x\,dx}{\sqrt{4-x}}$

**52.** $\int_2^3 x\sqrt{2+3x}\,dx$

**53.** $\int_0^1 \dfrac{2x\,dx}{\sqrt{8-x^2}}$

**54.** $\int_0^{\ln 2} x^2 e^{3x}\,dx$

**55.** $\int_1^2 x\ln(2x)\,dx$

**56.** $\int_1^2 dx$

**57. Biology**    In a discussion about gene frequency,[4] the integral

$$\int_{q_0}^{q_n} \dfrac{dq}{q(1-q)}$$

occurs, where the $q$'s represent gene frequencies. Evaluate this integral.

**58. Biology**    Under certain conditions, the number $n$ of generations required to change the frequency of a gene from 0.3 to 0.1 is given by[5]

$$n = -\dfrac{1}{0.4}\int_{0.3}^{0.1} \dfrac{dq}{q^2(1-q)}$$

Find $n$ (to the nearest integer).

***59. Continuous Annuity**    Find the present value, to the nearest dollar, of a continuous annuity at an annual rate of $r$ for $T$ years if the payment at time $t$ is at the annual rate of $f(t)$ dollars, given that

**(a)** $r = 0.04$    $T = 9$    $f(t) = 1000$
**(b)** $r = 0.06$    $T = 10$    $f(t) = 500t$

**60.** If $f(t) = k$, where $k$ is a positive constant, show that the value of the integral in Equation (1) of this section is

$$k\left(\dfrac{1-e^{-rT}}{r}\right)$$

**61. Continuous Annuity**    Find the accumulated amount, to the nearest dollar, of a continuous annuity at an annual rate of $r$ for $T$ years if the payment at time $t$ is at an annual rate of $f(t)$ dollars, given that

**(a)** $r = 0.06$    $T = 10$    $f(t) = 400$
**(b)** $r = 0.04$    $T = 5$    $f(t) = 40t$

**62. Value of Business**    Over the next five years, the profits of a business at time $t$ are estimated to be 50,000$t$ dollars per year. The business is to be sold at a price equal to the present value of these future profits. To the nearest 10 dollars, at what price should the business be sold if interest is compounded continuously at the annual rate of 7%?

[4]W. B. Mather, *Principles of Quantitative Genetics* (Minneapolis: Burgess Publishing Company, 1964).
[5]E. O. Wilson and W. H. Bossert, *A Primer of Population Biology* (Stamford, CT: Sinauer Associates, Inc., 1971).

OBJECTIVE

## 15.4  Average Value of a Function

To develop the concept of the average value of a function.

If we are given the three numbers 1, 2, and 9, then their average value, or *mean*, is their sum divided by 3. Denoting this average by $\bar{y}$, we have

$$\bar{y} = \dfrac{1+2+9}{3} = 4$$

Similarly, suppose we are given a function $f$ defined on the interval $[a,b]$, and the points $x_1, x_2, \ldots, x_n$ are in the interval. Then the average value of the $n$ corresponding function values $f(x_1), f(x_2), \ldots, f(x_n)$ is

$$\bar{y} = \dfrac{f(x_1)+f(x_2)+\cdots+f(x_n)}{n} = \dfrac{\displaystyle\sum_{i=1}^{n} f(x_i)}{n} \qquad (1)$$

We can go a step further. Let us divide the interval $[a,b]$ into $n$ subintervals of equal length. We will choose $x_i$ to be the right-hand endpoint of the $i$th subinterval. Because

$[a, b]$ has length $b - a$, each subinterval has length $\dfrac{b-a}{n}$, which we will call $\Delta x$. Thus, Equation (1) can be written

$$\overline{y} = \frac{\displaystyle\sum_{i=1}^{n} f(x_i)\left(\dfrac{\Delta x}{\Delta x}\right)}{n} = \frac{\dfrac{1}{\Delta x}\displaystyle\sum_{i=1}^{n} f(x_i)\,\Delta x}{n} = \frac{1}{n\,\Delta x}\sum_{i=1}^{n} f(x_i)\,\Delta x \qquad (2)$$

Since $\Delta x = \dfrac{b-a}{n}$, it follows that $n\,\Delta x = b - a$. So the expression $\dfrac{1}{n\,\Delta x}$ in Equation (2) can be replaced by $\dfrac{1}{b-a}$. Moreover, as $n \to \infty$, the number of function values used in computing $\overline{y}$ increases, and we get the so-called *average value of the function f*, denoted by $\overline{f}$:

$$\overline{f} = \lim_{n\to\infty}\left[\frac{1}{b-a}\sum_{i=1}^{n} f(x_i)\,\Delta x\right] = \frac{1}{b-a}\lim_{n\to\infty}\sum_{i=1}^{n} f(x_i)\,\Delta x$$

But the limit on the right is just the definite integral $\int_a^b f(x)\,dx$. This motivates the following definition:

> **DEFINITION**
> The ***average value of a function*** $f(x)$ over the interval $[a, b]$ is denoted $\overline{f}$ and is given by
> $$\overline{f} = \frac{1}{b-a}\int_a^b f(x)\,dx$$

● **EXAMPLE 1   Average Value of a Function**

*Find the average value of the function* $f(x) = x^2$ *over the interval* $[1, 2]$.

**Solution:**

$$\overline{f} = \frac{1}{b-a}\int_a^b f(x)\,dx$$

$$= \frac{1}{2-1}\int_1^2 x^2\,dx = \left.\frac{x^3}{3}\right|_1^2 = \frac{7}{3}$$

NOW WORK PROBLEM 1 ●●●

In Example 1, we found that the average value of $y = f(x) = x^2$ over the interval $[1, 2]$ is $\frac{7}{3}$. We can interpret this value geometrically. Since

$$\frac{1}{2-1}\int_1^2 x^2\,dx = \frac{7}{3}$$

by solving for the integral we have

$$\int_1^2 x^2\,dx = \frac{7}{3}(2-1)$$

However, this integral gives the area of the region bounded by $f(x) = x^2$ and the $x$-axis from $x = 1$ to $x = 2$. (See Figure 15.1.) From the preceding equation, this area is $\left(\frac{7}{3}\right)(2-1)$, which is the area of a rectangle whose height is the average value $\overline{f} = \frac{7}{3}$ and whose width is $b - a = 2 - 1 = 1$.

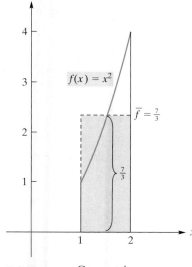

**FIGURE 15.1** Geometric interpretation of the average value of a function.

● **EXAMPLE 2   Average Flow of Blood**

*Suppose the flow of blood at time t in a system is given by*

$$F(t) = \frac{F_1}{(1+\alpha t)^2} \qquad 0 \le t \le T$$

where $F_1$ and $\alpha$ (a Greek letter read "alpha") are constants.[6] Find the average flow $\overline{F}$ on the interval $[0, T]$.

**Solution:**

$$\overline{F} = \frac{1}{T - 0} \int_0^T F(t)\, dt$$

$$= \frac{1}{T} \int_0^T \frac{F_1}{(1 + \alpha t)^2}\, dt = \frac{F_1}{\alpha T} \int_0^T (1 + \alpha t)^{-2}(\alpha\, dt)$$

$$= \frac{F_1}{\alpha T}\left(\frac{(1 + \alpha t)^{-1}}{-1}\right)\Bigg|_0^T = \frac{F_1}{\alpha T}\left(-\frac{1}{1 + \alpha T} + 1\right)$$

$$= \frac{F_1}{\alpha T}\left(\frac{-1 + 1 + \alpha T}{1 + \alpha T}\right) = \frac{F_1}{\alpha T}\left(\frac{\alpha T}{1 + \alpha T}\right) = \frac{F_1}{1 + \alpha T}$$

NOW WORK PROBLEM 11

## Problems 15.4

*In Problems 1–8, find the average value of the function over the given interval.*

*1. $f(x) = x^2$;  $[-1, 3]$

2. $f(x) = 3x - 1$;  $[1, 2]$

3. $f(x) = 2 - 3x^2$;  $[-1, 2]$

4. $f(x) = x^2 + x + 1$;  $[1, 3]$

5. $f(t) = 2t^5$;  $[-3, 3]$

6. $f(t) = t\sqrt{t^2 + 9}$;  $[0, 4]$

7. $f(x) = 6\sqrt{x}$;  $[1, 9]$

8. $f(x) = 5/x^2$;  $[1, 3]$

9. **Profit**    The profit (in dollars) of a business is given by

$$P = P(q) = 369q - 2.1q^2 - 400$$

where $q$ is the number of units of the product sold. Find the average profit on the interval from $q = 0$ to $q = 100$.

10. **Cost**    Suppose the cost (in dollars) of producing $q$ units of a product is given by

$$c = 4000 + 10q + 0.1q^2$$

Find the average cost on the interval from $q = 100$ to $q = 500$.

*11. **Investment**    An investment of \$3000 earns interest at an annual rate of 5% compounded continuously. After $t$ years,

its value $S$ (in dollars) is given by $S = 3000e^{0.05t}$. Find the average value of a two-year investment.

12. **Medicine**    Suppose that colored dye is injected into the bloodstream at a constant rate $R$. At time $t$, let

$$C(t) = \frac{R}{F(t)}$$

be the concentration of dye at a location distant (distal) from the point of injection, where $F(t)$ is as given in Example 2. Show that the average concentration on $[0, T]$ is

$$\overline{C} = \frac{R\left(1 + \alpha T + \frac{1}{3}\alpha^2 T^2\right)}{F_1}$$

13. **Revenue**    Suppose a manufacturer receives revenue $r$ from the sale of $q$ units of a product. Show that the average value of the marginal-revenue function over the interval $[0, q_0]$ is the price per unit when $q_0$ units are sold.

14. Find the average value of $f(x) = \dfrac{1}{x^2 - 4x + 5}$ over the interval $[0, 1]$ using an approximate integration tewchnique. Round your answer to two decimal places.

---

OBJECTIVE

To solve a differential equation by using the method of separation of variables. To discuss particular solutions and general solutions. To develop interest compounded continuously in terms of a differential equation. To discuss exponential growth and decay.

## 15.5 Differential Equations

Occasionally, you may have to solve an equation that involves the derivative of an unknown function. Such an equation is called a **differential equation.** An example is

$$y' = xy^2 \tag{1}$$

More precisely, Equation (1) is called a **first-order differential equation,** since it involves a derivative of the first order and none of higher order. A solution of Equation (1) is any function $y = f(x)$ that is defined on an interval and satisfies the equation for all $x$ in the interval.

---

[6]W. Simon, *Mathematical Techniques for Physiology and Medicine* (New York: Academic Press, Inc., 1972).

To solve $y' = xy^2$, equivalently,

$$\frac{dy}{dx} = xy^2 \tag{2}$$

we think of $dy/dx$ as a quotient of differentials and algebraically "separate variables" by rewriting the equation so that each side contains only one variable and a differential is not in a denominator:

$$\frac{dy}{y^2} = x\,dx$$

Integrating both sides and combining the constants of integration, we obtain

$$\int \frac{1}{y^2}\,dy = \int x\,dx$$

$$-\frac{1}{y} = \frac{x^2}{2} + C_1$$

$$-\frac{1}{y} = \frac{x^2 + 2C_1}{2}$$

Since $2C_1$ is an arbitrary constant, we can replace it by $C$.

$$-\frac{1}{y} = \frac{x^2 + C}{2} \tag{3}$$

Solving Equation (3) for $y$, we have

$$y = -\frac{2}{x^2 + C} \tag{4}$$

We can verify that $y$ is a solution to the differential equation (2):
    For if $y$ is given by Equation (4), then

$$\frac{dy}{dx} = \frac{4x}{(x^2 + C)^2}$$

while also

$$xy^2 = x\left[-\frac{2}{x^2 + C}\right]^2 = \frac{4x}{(x^2 + C)^2}$$

showing that our $y$ satisfies (2). Note in Equation (4) that, for *each* value of $C$, a different solution is obtained. We call Equation (4) the **general solution** of the differential equation. The method that we used to find it is called **separation of variables.**

In the foregoing example, suppose we are given the condition that $y = -\frac{2}{3}$ when $x = 1$, that is, $y(1) = -\frac{2}{3}$. Then the *particular* function that satisfies both Equation (2) and this condition can be found by substituting the values $x = 1$ and $y = -\frac{2}{3}$ into Equation (4) and solving for $C$:

$$-\frac{2}{3} = -\frac{2}{1^2 + C}$$

$$C = 2$$

Therefore, the solution of $dy/dx = xy^2$ such that $y(1) = -\frac{2}{3}$ is

$$y = -\frac{2}{x^2 + 2} \tag{5}$$

We call Equation (5) a **particular solution** of the differential equation.

● **EXAMPLE 1    Separation of Variables**

*Solve* $y' = -\dfrac{y}{x}$ *if* $x, y > 0$.

**Solution:** Writing $y'$ as $dy/dx$, separating variables, and integrating, we have

$$\frac{dy}{dx} = -\frac{y}{x}$$

$$\frac{dy}{y} = -\frac{dx}{x}$$

$$\int \frac{1}{y}\,dy = -\int \frac{1}{x}\,dx$$

$$\ln|y| = C_1 - \ln|x|$$

Since $x, y > 0$, we can omit the absolute-value bars:

$$\ln y = C_1 - \ln x \tag{6}$$

To solve for $y$, we convert Equation (6) to exponential form:

$$y = e^{C_1 - \ln x}$$

So

$$y = e^{C_1} e^{-\ln x} = \frac{e^{C_1}}{e^{\ln x}}$$

Replacing $e^{C_1}$ by $C$, where $C > 0$, and rewriting $e^{\ln x}$ as $x$ gives

$$y = \frac{C}{x} \qquad C, x > 0$$

NOW WORK PROBLEM 1 ●●●

In Example 1, note that Equation (6) expresses the solution implicitly, whereas the final equation ($y = C/x$) states the solution $y$ explicitly in terms of $x$. You will find that the solutions of certain differential equations are often expressed in implicit form for convenience (or necessity because of the difficulty involved in obtaining an explicit form).

## Exponential Growth and Decay

In Section 5.3, the notion of interest compounded continuously was developed. Let us now take a different approach to this topic that involves a differential equation. Suppose $P$ dollars are invested at an annual rate $r$ compounded $n$ times a year. Let the function $S = S(t)$ give the compound amount $S$ (or total amount present) after $t$ years from the date of the initial investment. Then the initial principal is $S(0) = P$. Furthermore, since there are $n$ interest periods per year, each period has length $1/n$ years, which we will denote by $\Delta t$. At the end of the first period, the accrued interest for that period is added to the principal, and the sum acts as the principal for the second period, and so on. Hence, if the beginning of an interest period occurs at time $t$, then the increase in the amount present at the end of a period $\Delta t$ is $S(t + \Delta t) - S(t)$, which we write as $\Delta S$. This increase, $\Delta S$, is also the interest earned for the period. Equivalently, the interest earned is principal times rate times time:

$$\Delta S = S \cdot r \cdot \Delta t$$

Dividing both sides by $\Delta t$, we obtain

$$\frac{\Delta S}{\Delta t} = rS \tag{7}$$

As $\Delta t \to 0$, then $n = \dfrac{1}{\Delta t} \to \infty$, and consequently interest is being *compounded continuously;* that is, the principal is subject to continuous growth at every instant. However, as $\Delta t \to 0$, then $\Delta S/\Delta t \to dS/dt$, and Equation (7) takes the form

$$\frac{dS}{dt} = rS \tag{8}$$

This differential equation means that *when interest is compounded continuously, the rate of change of the amount of money present at time t is proportional to the amount present at time t*. The constant of proportionality is $r$.

To determine the actual function $S$, we solve the differential equation (8) by the method of separation of variables:

$$\frac{dS}{dt} = rS$$

$$\frac{dS}{S} = r\,dt$$

$$\int \frac{1}{S}\,dS = \int r\,dt$$

$$\ln |S| = rt + C_1$$

We assume that $S > 0$, so $\ln |S| = \ln S$. Thus,

$$\ln S = rt + C_1$$

To get an explicit form, we can solve for $S$ by converting to exponential form.

$$S = e^{rt+C_1} = e^{C_1}e^{rt}$$

For simplicity, $e^{C_1}$ can be replaced by $C$ to obtain the general solution

$$S = Ce^{rt}$$

The condition $S(0) = P$ allows us to find the value of $C$:

$$P = Ce^{r(0)} = C \cdot 1$$

Hence $C = P$, so

$$S = Pe^{rt} \tag{9}$$

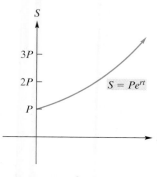

**FIGURE 15.2**   Compounding continuously.

Equation (9) gives the total value after $t$ years of an initial investment of $P$ dollars compounded continuously at an annual rate $r$. (See Figure 15.2.)

In our discussion of compound interest, we saw from Equation (8) that the rate of change in the amount present was proportional to the amount present. There are many natural quantities, such as population, whose rate of growth or decay at any time is considered proportional to the amount of that quantity present. If $N$ denotes the amount of such a quantity at time $t$, then this rate of growth means that

$$\frac{dN}{dt} = kN$$

where $k$ is a constant. If we separate variables and solve for $N$ as we did for Equation (8), we get

$$N = N_0 e^{kt} \tag{10}$$

where $N_0$ is a constant. In particular, if $t = 0$, then $N = N_0 e^0 = N_0 \cdot 1 = N_0$. Thus, the constant $N_0$ is simply $N(0)$. Due to the form of Equation (10), we say that the quantity follows an **exponential law of growth** if $k$ is positive and an **exponential law of decay** if $k$ is negative.

### ● EXAMPLE 2   Population Growth

*In a certain city, the rate at which the population grows at any time is proportional to the size of the population. If the population was 125,000 in 1970 and 140,000 in 1990, what is the expected population in 2010?*

**Solution:**  Let $N$ be the size of the population at time $t$. Since the exponential law of growth applies,

$$N = N_0 e^{kt}$$

To find the population in 2010, we must first find the particular law of growth involved by determining the values of $N_0$ and $k$. Let the year 1970 correspond to $t = 0$. Then $t = 20$ in 1990 and $t = 40$ in 2010. We have

$$N_0 = N(0) = 125{,}000$$

Thus,

$$N = 125{,}000e^{kt}$$

To find $k$, we use the fact that $N = 140{,}000$ when $t = 20$:

$$140{,}000 = 125{,}000e^{20k}$$

Hence,

$$e^{20k} = \frac{140{,}000}{125{,}000} = 1.12$$

Therefore, the law of growth is

$$
\begin{aligned}
N &= 125{,}0000e^{kt} \\
&= 125{,}000(e^{20k})^{t/20} \\
&= 125{,}000(1.12)^{t/20}
\end{aligned}
\tag{11}
$$

Setting $t = 40$ gives the expected population in 2010:

$$N = N(40) = 125{,}000(1.12)^2 = 156{,}800$$

We remark that from $e^{20k} = 1.12$ we have $20k = \ln(1.12)$ and hence $k = \dfrac{\ln(1.12)}{20} \approx 0.0057$, which can be placed in $N = 125{,}000e^{kt}$ to give

$$N \approx 125{,}000e^{0.0057t} \tag{12}$$

NOW WORK PROBLEM 23 ●●●

In Chapter 4, radioactive decay was discussed. Here we will consider this topic from the perspective of a differential equation. The rate at which a radioactive element decays at any time is found to be proportional to the amount of that element present. If $N$ is the amount of a radioactive substance at time $t$, then the rate of decay is given by

$$\frac{dN}{dt} = -\lambda N. \tag{13}$$

The positive constant $\lambda$ (a Greek letter read "lambda") is called the **decay constant,** and the minus sign indicates that $N$ is decreasing as $t$ increases. Thus, we have exponential decay. From Equation (10), the solution of this differential equation is

$$N = N_0 e^{-\lambda t} \tag{14}$$

If $t = 0$, then $N = N_0 \cdot 1 = N_0$, so $N_0$ represents the amount of the radioactive substance present when $t = 0$.

The time for one-half of the substance to decay is called the **half-life** of the substance. In Section 4.2, it was shown that the half-life is given by

$$\text{half-life} = \frac{\ln 2}{\lambda} \approx \frac{0.69315}{\lambda} \tag{15}$$

Note that the half-life depends on $\lambda$. In Chapter 4, Figure 4.13 shows the graph of radioactive decay.

● EXAMPLE 3    **Finding the Decay Constant and Half-Life**

*If 60% of a radioactive substance remains after 50 days, find the decay constant and the half-life of the element.*

**Solution:** From Equation (14),

$$N = N_0 e^{-\lambda t}$$

where $N_0$ is the amount of the element present at $t = 0$. When $t = 50$, then $N = 0.6 N_0$, and we have

$$0.6 N_0 = N_0 e^{-50\lambda}$$

$$0.6 = e^{-50\lambda}$$

$$-50\lambda = \ln(0.6) \qquad \text{(logarithmic form)}$$

$$\lambda = -\frac{\ln(0.6)}{50} \approx 0.01022$$

Thus, $N \approx N_0 e^{-0.01022t}$. The half-life, from Equation (15), is

$$\frac{\ln 2}{\lambda} \approx 67.82 \text{ days}$$

NOW WORK PROBLEM 27

Radioactivity is useful in dating such things as fossil plant remains and archaeological remains made from organic material. Plants and other living organisms contain a small amount of radioactive carbon 14($^{14}$C) in addition to ordinary carbon ($^{12}$C). The $^{12}$C atoms are stable, but the $^{14}$C atoms are decaying exponentially. However, $^{14}$C is formed in the atmosphere due to the effect of cosmic rays. This $^{14}$C is taken up by plants during photosynthesis and replaces what has decayed. As a result, the ratio of $^{14}$C atoms to $^{12}$C atoms is considered constant in living tissues over a long period of time. When a plant dies, it stops absorbing $^{14}$C, and the remaining $^{14}$C atoms decay. By comparing the proportion of $^{14}$C to $^{12}$C in a fossil plant to that of plants found today, we can estimate the age of the fossil. The half-life of $^{14}$C is approximately 5730 years. Thus, if a fossil is found to have a $^{14}$C-to-$^{12}$C ratio that is half that of a similar substance found today, we would estimate the fossil to be 5730 years old.

## EXAMPLE 4   Estimating the Age of an Ancient Tool

*A wood tool found in a Middle East excavation site is found to have a $^{14}$C-to-$^{12}$C ratio that is 0.6 of the corresponding ratio in a present-day tree. Estimate the age of the tool to the nearest hundred years.*

**Solution:** Let $N$ be the amount of $^{14}$C present in the wood $t$ years after the tool was made. Then $N = N_0 e^{-\lambda t}$, where $N_0$ is the amount of $^{14}$C when $t = 0$. Since the ratio of $^{14}$C to $^{12}$C is 0.6 of the corresponding ratio in a present-day tree, this means that we want to find the value of $t$ for which $N = 0.6 N_0$. Thus, we have

$$0.6 N_0 = N_0 e^{-\lambda t}$$

$$0.6 = e^{-\lambda t}$$

$$-\lambda t = \ln(0.6) \qquad \text{(logarithmic form)}$$

$$t = -\frac{1}{\lambda} \ln(0.6)$$

From Equation (15), the half-life is $(\ln 2)/\lambda$, which equals 5730, so $\lambda = (\ln 2)/5730$. Consequently,

$$t = -\frac{1}{(\ln 2)/5730} \ln(0.6)$$

$$= -\frac{5730 \ln(0.6)}{\ln 2}$$

$$\approx 4223 \text{ years}$$

NOW WORK PROBLEM 29

# Problems 15.5

*In Problems 1–8, solve the differential equations.*

*1. $y' = 2xy^2$

2. $y' = x^2 y^2$

3. $\dfrac{dy}{dx} - 3x\sqrt{x^2 + 1} = 0$

4. $\dfrac{dy}{dx} = \dfrac{x}{y}$

5. $\dfrac{dy}{dx} = y, \ y > 0$

6. $y' = e^x y^3$

7. $y' = \dfrac{y}{x}, \ x, y > 0$

8. $\dfrac{dy}{dx} + xe^x = 0$

*In Problems 9–18, solve each of the differential equations, subject to the given conditions.*

9. $y' = \dfrac{1}{y^2}; \ y(1) = 1$

10. $y' = e^{x-y}; \ y(0) = 0$   (*Hint:* $e^{x-y} = e^x/e^y$.)

11. $e^y y' - x^2 = 0; \quad y = 0$ when $x = 0$

12. $x^2 y' + \dfrac{1}{y^2} = 0; \quad y(1) = 2$

13. $(3x^2 + 2)^3 y' - xy^2 = 0; \quad y(0) = \dfrac{3}{2}$

14. $y' + x^3 y = 0; \quad y = e$ when $x = 0$

15. $\dfrac{dy}{dx} = \dfrac{3x\sqrt{1 + y^2}}{y}; \quad y > 0, y(1) = \sqrt{8}$

16. $2y(x^3 + 2x + 1)\dfrac{dy}{dx} = \dfrac{3x^2 + 2}{\sqrt{y^2 + 9}}; \quad y(0) = 0$

17. $2\dfrac{dy}{dx} = \dfrac{xe^{-y}}{\sqrt{x^2 + 3}}; \quad y(1) = 0$

18. $x(y^2 + 1)^{3/2}\,dx = e^{x^2} y\,dy; \quad y(0) = 0$

19. **Cost**   Find the manufacturer's cost function $c = f(q)$ given that

$$(q + 1)^2 \dfrac{dc}{dq} = cq$$

and fixed cost is $e$.

20. Find $f(2)$, given that $f(1) = 0$ and that $y = f(x)$ satisfies the differential equation

$$\dfrac{dy}{dx} = xe^{x-y}$$

21. **Circulation of Money**   A country has 1.00 billion dollars of paper money in circulation. Each week 25 million dollars is brought into the banks for deposit, and the same amount is paid out. The government decides to issue new paper money; whenever the old money comes into the banks, it is destroyed and replaced by new money. Let $y$ be the amount of old money (in millions of dollars) in circulation at time $t$ (in weeks). Then $y$ satisfies the differential equation

$$\dfrac{dy}{dt} = -0.025y$$

How long will it take for 95% of the paper money in circulation to be new? Round your answer to the nearest week. (*Hint:* If money is 95% new, then $y$ is 5% of 1000.)

22. **Marginal Revenue and Demand**   Suppose that a monopolist's marginal-revenue function is given by the differential equation

$$\dfrac{dr}{dq} = (50 - 4q)e^{-r/5}$$

Find the demand equation for the monopolist's product.

*23. **Population Growth**   In a certain town, the population at any time changes at a rate proportional to the population. If the population in 1985 was 40,000 and in 1995 was 48,000, find an equation for the population at time $t$, where $t$ is the number of years past 1985. Write your answer in two forms, one involving $e$. You may assume that $\ln 1.2 = 0.18$. What is the expected population in 2005?

24. **Population Growth**   The population of a town increases by natural growth at a rate proportional to the number $N$ of persons present. If the population at time $t = 0$ is 50,000, find two expressions for the population $N$, $t$ years later, if the population doubles in 50 years. Assume that $\ln 2 = 0.69$. Also, find $N$ for $t = 100$.

25. **Population Growth**   Suppose that the population of the world in 1930 was 2 billion and in 1960 was 3 billion. If the exponential law of growth is assumed, what is the expected population in 2015? Give your answer in terms of $e$.

26. **Population Growth**   If exponential growth is assumed, in approximately how many years will a population double if it triples in 100 years? (*Hint:* Let the population at $t = 0$ be $N_0$.)

*27. **Radioactivity**   If 30% of the initial amount of a radioactive sample remains after 100 seconds, find the decay constant and the half-life of the element.

28. **Radioactivity**   If 30% of the initial amount of a radioactive sample has *decayed* after 100 seconds, find the decay constant and the half-life of the element.

*29. **Carbon Dating**   An Egyptian scroll was found to have a $^{14}$C-to-$^{12}$C ratio 0.7 of the corresponding ratio in similar present-day material. Estimate the age of the scroll, to the nearest hundred years.

30. **Carbon Dating**   A recently discovered archaeological specimen has a $^{14}$C-to-$^{12}$C ratio 0.1 of the corresponding ratio found in present-day organic material. Estimate the age of the specimen, to the nearest hundred years.

31. **Population Growth**   Suppose that a population follows exponential growth given by $dN/dt = kN$ for $t \geq t_0$. Suppose also that $N = N_0$ when $t = t_0$. Find $N$, the population size at time $t$.

32. **Radioactivity**   Polonium-210 has a half-life of about 140 days. (a) Find the decay constant in terms of $\ln 2$. (b) What fraction of the original amount of a sample of polonium-210 remains after one year?

33. **Radioactivity**   Radioactive isotopes are used in medical diagnoses as tracers to determine abnormalities that may exist in an organ. For example, if radioactive iodine is swallowed, after some time it is taken up by the thyroid gland. With the use of a detector, the rate at which it is taken up can be measured, and a determination can be made as to whether the uptake is normal. Suppose radioactive technetium-99m, which has a half-life of six hours, is to be used in a brain scan two hours from now. What should be its activity now if the activity when it is used is to be 10 units? Give your answer to one decimal place. (*Hint:* In Equation (14), let $N$ = activity $t$ hours from now and $N_0$ = activity now.)

**34. Radioactivity**    A radioactive substance that has a half-life of eight days is to be temporarily implanted in a hospital patient until three-fifths of the amount originally present remains. How long should the implant remain in the patient?

**35. Ecology**    In a forest, natural litter occurs, such as fallen leaves and branches, dead animals, and so on.[7] Let $A = A(t)$ denote the amount of litter present at time $t$, where $A(t)$ is expressed in grams per square meter and $t$ is in years. Suppose that there is no litter at $t = 0$. Thus, $A(0) = 0$. Assume that

(a) Litter falls to the ground continuously at a constant rate of 200 grams per square meter per year.

(b) The accumulated litter decomposes continuously at the rate of 50% of the amount present per year (which is $0.50A$).

The difference of the two rates is the rate of change of the amount of litter present with respect to time:

$$\begin{pmatrix} \text{rate of change} \\ \text{of litter present} \end{pmatrix} = \begin{pmatrix} \text{rate of falling} \\ \text{to ground} \end{pmatrix} - \begin{pmatrix} \text{rate of} \\ \text{decomposition} \end{pmatrix}$$

Therefore,

$$\frac{dA}{dt} = 200 - 0.50A$$

Solve for $A$. To the nearest gram, determine the amount of litter per square meter after one year.

**36. Profit and Advertising**    A certain company determines that the rate of change of monthly net profit $P$, as a function of monthly advertising expenditure $x$, is proportional to the difference between a fixed amount, $150,000, and $2P$; that is, $dP/dx$ is proportional to $150,000 - 2P$. Furthermore, if no money is spent on monthly advertising, the monthly net profit is $15,000; if $1000 is spent on monthly advertising, the monthly net profit is $70,000. What would the monthly net profit be if $2000 were spent on advertising each month?

**37. Value of a Machine**    The value of a certain machine depreciates 25% in the first year after the machine is purchased. The rate at which the machine subsequently depreciates is proportional to its value. Suppose that such a machine was purchased new on July 1, 1995, for $80,000 and was valued at $38,900 on January 1, 2006.

(a) Determine a formula that expresses the value $V$ of the machine in terms of $t$, the number of years after July 1, 1996.

(b) Use the formula in part (a) to determine the year and month in which the machine has a value of exactly $14,000.

To develop the logistic function as a solution of a differential equation. To model the spread of a rumor. To discuss and apply Newton's law of cooling.

# 15.6  More Applications of Differential Equations

## Logistic Growth

In the previous section, we found that if the number $N$ of individuals in a population at time $t$ follows an exponential law of growth, then $N = N_0 e^{kt}$, where $k > 0$ and $N_0$ is the population when $t = 0$. This law assumes that at time $t$ the rate of growth, $dN/dt$, of the population is proportional to the number of individuals in the population. That is, $dN/dt = kN$.

Under exponential growth, a population would get infinitely large as time goes on. In reality, however, when the population gets large enough, environmental factors slow down the rate of growth. Examples are food supply, predators, overcrowding, and so on. These factors cause $dN/dt$ to decrease eventually. It is reasonable to assume that the size of a population is limited to some maximum number $M$, where $0 < N < M$, and as $N \to M$, $dN/dt \to 0$, and the population size tends to be stable.

In summary, we want a population model that has exponential growth initially but that also includes the effects of environmental resistance to large population growth. Such a model is obtained by multiplying the right side of $dN/dt = kN$ by the factor $(M - N)/M$:

$$\frac{dN}{dt} = kN\left(\frac{M - N}{M}\right)$$

Notice that if $N$ is small, then $(M - N)/M$ is close to 1, and we have growth that is approximately exponential. As $N \to M$, then $M - N \to 0$ and $dN/dt \to 0$, as we wanted in our model. Because $k/M$ is a constant, we can replace it by $K$. Thus,

$$\frac{dN}{dt} = KN(M - N) \tag{1}$$

This states that the rate of growth is proportional to the product of the size of the population and the difference between the maximum size and the actual size of the population. We can solve for $N$ in the differential equation (1) by the method of

[7]R. W. Poole, *An Introduction to Quantitative Ecology* (New York: McGraw-Hill Book Company, 1974).

separation of variables:

$$\frac{dN}{N(M-N)} = K\,dt$$

$$\int \frac{1}{N(M-N)}\,dN = \int K\,dt \qquad (2)$$

The integral on the left side can be found by using Formula 5 in the table of integrals in Appendix B. Thus, Equation (2) becomes

$$\frac{1}{M}\ln\left|\frac{N}{M-N}\right| = Kt + C$$

so

$$\ln\left|\frac{N}{M-N}\right| = MKt + MC$$

Since $N > 0$ and $M - N > 0$, we can write

$$\ln\frac{N}{M-N} = MKt + MC$$

In exponential form, we have

$$\frac{N}{M-N} = e^{MKt+MC} = e^{MKt}\,e^{MC}$$

Replacing the positive constant $e^{MC}$ by $A$ and solving for $N$ gives

$$\frac{N}{M-N} = Ae^{MKt}$$

$$N = (M-N)Ae^{MKt}$$

$$N = MAe^{MKt} - NAe^{MKt}$$

$$NAe^{MKt} + N = MAe^{MKt}$$

$$N(Ae^{MKt} + 1) = MAe^{MKt},$$

$$N = \frac{MAe^{MKt}}{Ae^{MKt} + 1}$$

Dividing numerator and denominator by $Ae^{MKt}$, we have

$$N = \frac{M}{1 + \dfrac{1}{Ae^{MKt}}} = \frac{M}{1 + \dfrac{1}{A}e^{-MKt}}$$

Replacing $1/A$ by $b$ and $MK$ by $c$ yields the so-called *logistic function:*

**Logistic Function**

The function defined by

$$N = \frac{M}{1 + be^{-ct}} \qquad (3)$$

is called the **logistic function** or the **Verhulst–Pearl logistic function.**

The graph of Equation (3), called a *logistic curve,* is S-shaped and appears in Figure 15.3. Notice that the line $N = M$ is a horizontal asymptote; that is,

$$\lim_{t \to \infty} \frac{M}{1 + be^{-ct}} = \frac{M}{1 + b(0)} = M$$

Moreover, from Equation (1), the rate of growth is

$$KN(M-N)$$

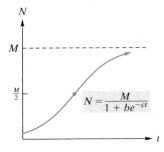

**FIGURE 15.3**   Logistic curve.

which can be considered a function of $N$. To find when the maximum rate of growth occurs, we solve $\dfrac{d}{dN}[KN(M-N)] = 0$ for $N$:

$$\frac{d}{dN}[KN(M-N)] = \frac{d}{dN}[K(MN - N^2)]$$
$$= K[M - 2N] = 0$$

Thus, $N = M/2$. In other words, the rate of growth increases until the population size is $M/2$ and decreases thereafter. The maximum rate of growth occurs when $N = M/2$ and corresponds to a point of inflection in the graph of $N$. To find the value of $t$ for which this occurs, we substitute $M/2$ for $N$ in Equation (3) and solve for $t$:

$$\frac{M}{2} = \frac{M}{1 + be^{-ct}}$$
$$1 + be^{-ct} = 2$$
$$e^{-ct} = \frac{1}{b}$$
$$e^{ct} = b$$
$$ct = \ln b \qquad \text{(logarithmic form)}$$
$$t = \frac{\ln b}{c}$$

Therefore, the maximum rate of growth occurs at the point $((\ln b)/c, \ M/2)$.

We remark that in Equation (3) we can replace $e^{-c}$ by $C$, and then the logistic function has the following form:

### Alternative Form of Logistic Function

$$N = \frac{M}{1 + bC^t}$$

### ● EXAMPLE 1    Logistic Growth of Club Membership

*Suppose the membership in a new country club is to be a maximum of 800 persons, due to limitations of the physical plant. One year ago the initial membership was 50 persons, and now there are 200. Provided that enrollment follows a logistic function, how many members will there be three years from now?*

**Solution:** Let $N$ be the number of members enrolled $t$ years after the formation of the club. Then, from Equation (3),

$$N = \frac{M}{1 + be^{-ct}}$$

Here $M = 800$, and when $t = 0$, we have $N = 50$. So

$$50 = \frac{800}{1 + b}$$
$$1 + b = \frac{800}{50} = 16$$
$$b = 15$$

Thus,

$$N = \frac{800}{1 + 15e^{-ct}} \qquad (4)$$

When $t = 1$, then $N = 200$, so we have

$$200 = \frac{800}{1 + 15e^{-c}}$$

$$1 + 15e^{-c} = \frac{800}{200} = 4$$

$$e^{-c} = \frac{3}{15} = \frac{1}{5}$$

Hence, $c = -\ln\frac{1}{5} = \ln 5$. Rather than substituting this value of $c$ into Equation (4), it is more convenient to substitute the value of $e^{-c}$ there:

$$N = \frac{800}{1 + 15\left(\frac{1}{5}\right)^t}$$

Three years from now, $t$ will be 4. Therefore,

$$N = \frac{800}{1 + 15\left(\frac{1}{5}\right)^4} \approx 781$$

NOW WORK PROBLEM 5 ◖●●

### Modeling the Spread of a Rumor

Let us now consider a simplified model[8] of how a rumor spreads in a population of size $M$. A similar situation would be the spread of an epidemic or new fad.

Let $N = N(t)$ be the number of persons who know the rumor at time $t$. We will assume that those who know the rumor spread it randomly in the population and that those who are told the rumor become spreaders of the rumor. Furthermore, we will assume that each knower tells the rumor to $k$ individuals per unit of time. (Some of these $k$ individuals may already know the rumor.) We want an expression for the rate of increase of the knowers of the rumor. Over a unit of time, each of approximately $N$ persons will tell the rumor to $k$ persons. Thus, the total number of persons who are told the rumor over the unit of time is (approximately) $Nk$. However, we are interested only in *new* knowers. The proportion of the population that does not know the rumor is $(M - N)/M$. Hence, the total number of new knowers of the rumor is

$$Nk\left(\frac{M - N}{M}\right)$$

which can be written $(k/M)N(M - N)$. Therefore,

$$\frac{dN}{dt} = \frac{k}{M}N(M - N)$$

$$= KN(M - N) \qquad \text{where } K = \frac{k}{M}$$

This differential equation has the form of Equation (1), so its solution, from Equation (3), is a *logistic function*:

$$N = \frac{M}{1 + be^{-ct}}$$

### ●EXAMPLE 2   Campus Rumor

*In a large university of 45,000 students, a sociology major is researching the spread of a new campus rumor. When she begins her research, she determines that 300 students know the rumor. After one week, she finds that 900 know it. Estimate the number of students who know it four weeks after the research begins by assuming logistic growth. Give the answer to the nearest thousand.*

**Solution:** Let $N$ be the number of students who know the rumor $t$ weeks after the research begins. Then

$$N = \frac{M}{1 + be^{-ct}}$$

---

[8]More simplified, that is, than the model described in the Mathematical Snapshot for Chapter 8.

Here $M$, the size of the population, is 45,000, and when $t = 0$, $N = 300$. So we have

$$300 = \frac{45,000}{1 + b}$$

$$1 + b = \frac{45,000}{300} = 150$$

$$b = 149$$

Thus,

$$N = \frac{45,000}{1 + 149e^{-ct}}$$

When $t = 1$, then $N = 900$. Hence,

$$900 = \frac{45,000}{1 + 149e^{-c}}$$

$$1 + 149e^{-c} = \frac{45,000}{900} = 50$$

Therefore, $e^{-c} = \frac{49}{149}$, so

$$N = \frac{45,000}{1 + 149\left(\frac{49}{149}\right)^t}$$

When $t = 4$,

$$N = \frac{45,000}{1 + 149\left(\frac{49}{149}\right)^4} \approx 16,000$$

After four weeks, approximately 16,000 students know the rumor.

NOW WORK PROBLEM 3

## Newton's Law of Cooling

We conclude this section with an interesting application of a differential equation. If a homicide is committed, the temperature of the victim's body will gradually decrease from $37°C$ (normal body temperature) to the temperature of the surroundings (ambient temperature). In general, the temperature of the cooling body changes at a rate proportional to the difference between the temperature of the body and the ambient temperature. This statement is known as **Newton's law of cooling.** Thus, if $T(t)$ is the temperature of the body at time $t$ and the ambient temperature is $a$, then

$$\frac{dT}{dt} = k(T - a)$$

where $k$ is the constant of proportionality. Therefore, Newton's law of cooling is a differential equation. It can be applied to determine the time at which a homicide was committed, as the next example illustrates.

### EXAMPLE 3  Time of Murder

*A wealthy industrialist was found murdered in his home. Police arrived on the scene at 11:00 P.M. The temperature of the body at that time was $31°C$, and one hour later it was $30°C$. The temperature of the room in which the body was found was $22°C$. Estimate the time at which the murder occurred.*

Solution: Let $t$ be the number of hours after the body was discovered and $T(t)$ be the temperature (in degrees Celsius) of the body at time $t$. We want to find the value of $t$ for which $T = 37$ (normal body temperature). This value of $t$ will, of course, be negative. By Newton's law of cooling,

$$\frac{dT}{dt} = k(T - a)$$

where $k$ is a constant and $a$ (the ambient temperature) is 22. Thus,

$$\frac{dT}{dt} = k(T - 22)$$

Separating variables, we have

$$\frac{dT}{T - 22} = k\,dt$$

$$\int \frac{dT}{T - 22} = \int k\,dt$$

$$\ln|T - 22| = kt + C$$

Because $T - 22 > 0$,

$$\ln(T - 22) = kt + C$$

When $t = 0$, then $T = 31$. Therefore,

$$\ln(31 - 22) = k \cdot 0 + C$$

$$C = \ln 9$$

Hence,

$$\ln(T - 22) = kt + \ln 9$$

$$\ln(T - 22) - \ln 9 = kt$$

$$\ln \frac{T - 22}{9} = kt \qquad \left(\ln a - \ln b = \ln \frac{a}{b}\right)$$

When $t = 1$, then $T = 30$, so

$$\ln \frac{30 - 22}{9} = k \cdot 1$$

$$k = \ln \frac{8}{9}$$

Thus,

$$\ln \frac{T - 22}{9} = t \ln \frac{8}{9}$$

Now we find $t$ when $T = 37$:

$$\ln \frac{37 - 22}{9} = t \ln \frac{8}{9}$$

$$t = \frac{\ln(15/9)}{\ln(8/9)} \approx -4.34$$

Accordingly, the murder occurred about 4.34 hours *before* the time of discovery of the body (11:00 P.M.). Since 4.34 hours is (approximately) 4 hours and 20 minutes, the industrialist was murdered about 6:40 P.M.

NOW WORK PROBLEM 9 ●●

## Problems 15.6

1. **Population**   The population of a city follows logistic growth and is limited to 100,000. If the population in 1995 was 50,000 and in 2000 was 60,000, what will the population be in 2005? Give your answer to the nearest hundred.

2. **Production**   A company believes that the production of its product in present facilities will follow logistic growth. Presently, 200 units per day are produced, and production will increase to 300 units per day in one year. If production is limited to 500 units per day, what is the anticipated daily production in two years? Give your answer to the nearest unit.

*3. **Spread of Rumor**   In a university of 40,000 students, the administration holds meetings to discuss the idea of bringing in a major rock band for homecoming weekend. Before the plans are officially announced, students representatives on the administrative council spread information about the event as a rumor. At the end of one week, 100 people know the rumor. Assuming logistic growth, how many people know the rumor after two weeks? Give your answer to the nearest hundred.

4. **Spread of Fad**   A new fad is sweeping a college campus of 30,000 students. The college newspaper feels that its readers would be interested in a series on the fad. It assigns a reporter when the number of faddists is 400. One week later, there are 1200 faddists. Assuming logistic growth, find a formula for the number $N$ of faddists $t$ weeks after the assignment of the reporter.

*5. **Flu Outbreak**   In a city whose population is 100,000, an outbreak of flu occurs. When the city health department begins its record keeping, there are 500 infected persons.

One week later, there are 1000 infected persons. Assuming logistic growth, estimate the number of infected persons two weeks after record keeping begins.

**6. Sigmoid Function** A very special case of the logistic function defined by Equation (3) is the *sigmoid function,* obtained by taking $M = b = c = 1$ so that we have

$$N(t) = \frac{1}{1 + e^{-t}}$$

(a) Show directly that the sigmoid function is the solution of the differential equation

$$\frac{dN}{dt} = N(1 - N)$$

and the initial condition $N(0) = 1/2$.

(b) Show that $(0, 1/2)$ is an inflection point on the graph of the sigmoid function.

(c) Show that the function

$$f(t) = \frac{1}{1 + e^{-t}} - \frac{1}{2}$$

is symmetric about the origin.

(d) Explain how (c) above shows that the sigmoid function is *symmetric about the point* $(0, 1/2)$, explaining at the same time what this means.

(e) Sketch the graph of the sigmoid function.

**7. Biology** In an experiment,[9] five *Paramecia* were placed in a test tube containing a nutritive medium. The number $N$ of *Paramecia* in the tube at the end of $t$ days is given approximately by

$$N = \frac{375}{1 + e^{5.2 - 2.3t}}$$

(a) Show that this equation can be written as

$$N = \frac{375}{1 + 181.27e^{-2.3t}}$$

and hence is a logistic function.

(b) Find $\lim_{t \to \infty} N$.

**8. Biology** In a study of the growth of a colony of unicellular organisms,[10] the equation

$$N = \frac{0.2524}{e^{-2.128x} + 0.005125} \qquad 0 \le x \le 5$$

was obtained, where $N$ is the estimated area of the growth in square centimeters and $x$ is the age of the colony in days after being first observed.

(a) Put this equation in the form of a logistic function.

(b) Find the area when the age of the colony is 0.

**\*9. Time of Murder** A waterfront murder was committed, and the victim's body was discovered at 4:15 A.M. by police. At that time, the temperature of the body was 28°C. One hour later, the body temperature was 20°C. After checking with the weather bureau, it was determined that the temperature

at the waterfront was −10°C from 11:00 P.M. to 6:00 A.M. About what time did the murder occur?

**10. Enzyme Formation** An enzyme is a protein that acts as a catalyst for increasing the rate of a chemical reaction that occurs in cells. In a certain reaction, an enzyme A is converted to another enzyme B. Enzyme B acts as a catalyst for its own formation. Let $p$ be the amount of enzyme B at time $t$ and $I$ be the total amount of both enzymes when $t = 0$. Suppose the rate of formation of B is proportional to $p(I - p)$. Without directly using calculus, find the value of $p$ for which the rate of formation will be a maximum.

**11. Fund-Raising** A small town decides to conduct a fund-raising drive for a fire engine whose cost is $200,000. The initial amount in the fund is $50,000. On the basis of past drives, it is determined that $t$ months after the beginning of the drive, the rate $dx/dt$ at which money is contributed to such a fund is proportional to the difference between the desired goal of $200,000 and the total amount $x$ in the fund at that time. After one month, a total of $100,000 is in the fund. How much will be in the fund after three months?

**12. Birthrate** In a discussion of unexpected properties of mathematical models of population, Bailey[11] considers the case in which the birthrate per *individual* is proportional to the population size $N$ at time $t$. Since the growth rate per individual is $\frac{1}{N}\frac{dN}{dt}$, this means that

$$\frac{1}{N}\frac{dN}{dt} = kN$$

so that

$$\frac{dN}{dt} = kN^2 \qquad \text{(subject to } N = N_0 \text{ at } t = 0)$$

where $k > 0$. Show that

$$N = \frac{N_0}{1 - kN_0 t}$$

Use this result to show that

$$\lim N = \infty \quad \text{as} \quad t \to \left(\frac{1}{kN_0}\right)^-$$

This means that over a finite interval of time, there is an infinite amount of growth. Such a model might be useful only for rapid growth over a short interval of time.

**13. Population** Suppose that the rate of growth of a population is proportional to the difference between some maximum size $M$ and the number $N$ of individuals in the population at time $t$. Suppose that when $t = 0$, the size of the population is $N_0$. Find a formula for $N$.

[9] G. F. Gause, *The Struggle for Existence* (New York: Hafner Publishing Co., 1964).

[10] A. J. Lotka, *Elements of Mathematical Biology* (New York: Dover Publications, Inc., 1956).

[11] N. T. J. Bailey, *The Mathematical Approach to Biology and Medicine* (New York: John Wiley & Sons, Inc., 1967).

OBJECTIVE

To define and evaluate improper integrals.

# 15.7 Improper Integrals[12]

Suppose $f(x)$ is continuous and nonnegative for $a \leq x < \infty$. (See Figure 15.4.) We know that the integral $\int_a^r f(x)\,dx$ is the area of the region between the curve $y = f(x)$ and the $x$-axis from $x = a$ to $x = r$. As $r \to \infty$, we can think of

$$\lim_{r \to \infty} \int_a^r f(x)\,dx$$

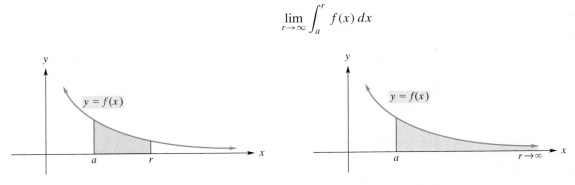

FIGURE 15.4    Area from $a$ to $r$.          FIGURE 15.5    Area from a to r as $r \to \infty$.

as the area of the unbounded region that is shaded in Figure 15.5. This limit is abbreviated by

$$\int_a^\infty f(x)\,dx \qquad (1)$$

and called an **improper integral.** If the limit exists, $\int_a^\infty f(x)\,dx$ is said to be **convergent** and the improper integral *converges* to that limit. In this case the unbounded region is considered to have a finite area, and this area is represented by $\int_a^\infty f(x)\,dx$. If the limit does not exist, the improper integral is said to be **divergent,** and the region does not have a finite area.

We can remove the restriction that $f(x) \geq 0$. In general, the improper integral $\int_a^\infty f(x)\,dx$ is defined by

$$\int_a^\infty f(x)\,dx = \lim_{r \to \infty} \int_a^r f(x)\,dx$$

Other types of improper integrals are

$$\int_{-\infty}^b f(x)\,dx \qquad (2)$$

and

$$\int_{-\infty}^\infty f(x)\,dx \qquad (3)$$

In each of the three types of improper integrals [(1), (2), and (3)], the interval over which the integral is evaluated has infinite length. The improper integral in (2) is defined by

$$\int_{-\infty}^b f(x)\,dx = \lim_{r \to -\infty} \int_r^b f(x)\,dx$$

If this limit exists, $\int_{-\infty}^b f(x)\,dx$ is said to be convergent. Otherwise, it is divergent. We will define the improper integral in (3) after the following example.

## PRINCIPLES IN PRACTICE 1

**IMPROPER INTEGRALS OF THE FORM** $\int_a^\infty f(x)\,dx$ **AND** $\int_{-\infty}^b f(x)\,dx$

The rate at which the human body eliminates a certain drug from its system may be approximated by $R(t) = 3e^{-0.1t} - 3e^{-0.3t}$, where $R(t)$ is in milliliters per minute and $t$ is the time in minutes since the drug was taken. Find $\int_0^\infty (3e^{-0.1t} - 3e^{-0.3t})\,dt$, the total amount of the drug that is eliminated.

● **EXAMPLE 1    Improper Integrals of the Form** $\int_a^\infty f(x)\,dx$ **and** $\int_{-\infty}^b f(x)\,dx$

*Determine whether the following improper integrals are convergent or divergent. For any convergent integral, determine its value.*

---

[12]This section can be omitted if Chapter 16 will not be covered.

**a.** $\displaystyle\int_1^\infty \frac{1}{x^3}\,dx$

Solution:

$$\int_1^\infty \frac{1}{x^3}\,dx = \lim_{r\to\infty}\int_1^r x^{-3}\,dx = \lim_{r\to\infty} \left.-\frac{x^{-2}}{2}\right|_1^r$$

$$= \lim_{r\to\infty}\left[-\frac{1}{2r^2}+\frac{1}{2}\right] = -0 + \frac{1}{2} = \frac{1}{2}$$

Therefore, $\displaystyle\int_1^\infty \frac{1}{x^3}\,dx$ converges to $\dfrac{1}{2}$.

**b.** $\displaystyle\int_{-\infty}^0 e^x\,dx$

Solution:

$$\int_{-\infty}^0 e^x\,dx = \lim_{r\to-\infty}\int_r^0 e^x\,dx = \lim_{r\to-\infty}\left. e^x\right|_r^0$$

$$= \lim_{r\to-\infty}(1-e^r) = 1-0 = 1 \qquad (e^0=1)$$

(Here we used the fact that as $r\to-\infty$, the graph of $y=e^r$ approaches the $r$-axis, so $e^r \to 0$.) Therefore, $\int_{-\infty}^0 e^x\,dx$ converges to 1.

**c.** $\displaystyle\int_1^\infty \frac{1}{\sqrt{x}}\,dx$

Solution:

$$\int_1^\infty \frac{1}{\sqrt{x}}\,dx = \lim_{r\to\infty}\int_1^r x^{-1/2}\,dx = \lim_{r\to\infty}\left. 2x^{1/2}\right|_1^r$$

$$= \lim_{r\to\infty} 2(\sqrt{r}-1) = \infty$$

Therefore, the improper integral diverges.

NOW WORK PROBLEM 3

The improper integral $\int_{-\infty}^\infty f(x)\,dx$ is defined in terms of improper integrals of the forms (1) and (2):

$$\int_{-\infty}^\infty f(x)\,dx = \int_{-\infty}^0 f(x)\,dx + \int_0^\infty f(x)\,dx \qquad (4)$$

If *both* integrals on the right side of Equation (4) are convergent, then $\int_{-\infty}^\infty f(x)\,dx$ is said to be convergent; otherwise, it is divergent.

● **EXAMPLE 2   An Improper Integral of the Form** $\int_{-\infty}^\infty f(x)\,dx$

*Determine whether* $\displaystyle\int_{-\infty}^\infty e^x\,dx$ *is convergent or divergent.*

Solution:

$$\int_{-\infty}^\infty e^x\,dx = \int_{-\infty}^0 e^x\,dx + \int_0^\infty e^x\,dx$$

By Example 1(b), $\int_{-\infty}^0 e^x\,dx = 1$. On the other hand,

$$\int_0^\infty e^x\,dx = \lim_{r\to\infty}\int_0^r e^x\,dx = \lim_{r\to\infty}\left. e^x\right|_0^r = \lim_{r\to\infty}(e^r-1) = \infty$$

Since $\int_0^\infty e^x\,dx$ is divergent, $\int_{-\infty}^\infty e^x\,dx$ is also divergent.

NOW WORK PROBLEM 11

### ● EXAMPLE 3 Density Function

*In statistics, a function f is called a density function if $f(x) \geq 0$ and*

$$\int_{-\infty}^{\infty} f(x)\,dx = 1$$

*Suppose*

$$f(x) = \begin{cases} ke^{-x} & \text{for } x \geq 0 \\ 0 & \text{elsewhere} \end{cases}$$

*is a density function. Find k.*

**Solution:** We write the equation $\int_{-\infty}^{\infty} f(x)\,dx = 1$ as

$$\int_{-\infty}^{0} f(x)\,dx + \int_{0}^{\infty} f(x)\,dx = 1$$

Since $f(x) = 0$ for $x < 0$, $\int_{-\infty}^{0} f(x)\,dx = 0$. Thus,

$$\int_{0}^{\infty} ke^{-x}\,dx = 1$$

$$\lim_{r \to \infty} \int_{0}^{r} ke^{-x}\,dx = 1$$

$$\lim_{r \to \infty} -ke^{-x}\Big|_{0}^{r} = 1$$

$$\lim_{r \to \infty} (-ke^{-r} + k) = 1$$

$$0 + k = 1 \qquad (\lim_{r \to \infty} e^{-r} = 0)$$

$$k = 1$$

NOW WORK PROBLEM 13 ●●

## Problems 15.7

*In Problems 1–12, determine the integrals if they exist. Indicate those that are divergent.*

**1.** $\int_{3}^{\infty} \dfrac{1}{x^3}\,dx$

**2.** $\int_{1}^{\infty} \dfrac{1}{(3x-1)^2}\,dx$

**\*3.** $\int_{1}^{\infty} \dfrac{1}{x}\,dx$

**4.** $\int_{2}^{\infty} \dfrac{1}{\sqrt[3]{(x+2)^2}}\,dx$

**5.** $\int_{1}^{\infty} e^{-x}\,dx$

**6.** $\int_{0}^{\infty} (5+e^{-x})\,dx$

**7.** $\int_{1}^{\infty} \dfrac{1}{\sqrt{x}}\,dx$

**8.** $\int_{4}^{\infty} \dfrac{x\,dx}{\sqrt{(x^2+9)^3}}$

**9.** $\int_{-\infty}^{-3} \dfrac{1}{(x+1)^2}\,dx$

**10.** $\int_{-\infty}^{3} \dfrac{1}{\sqrt{7-x}}\,dx$

**\*11.** $\int_{-\infty}^{\infty} 2xe^{-x^2}\,dx$

**12.** $\int_{-\infty}^{\infty} (5-3x)\,dx$

**\*13. Density Function** The density function for the life $x$, in hours, of an electronic component in a radiation meter is given by

$$f(x) = \begin{cases} \dfrac{k}{x^2} & \text{for } x \geq 800 \\ 0 & \text{for } x < 800 \end{cases}$$

**(a)** If $k$ satisfies the condition that $\int_{800}^{\infty} f(x)\,dx = 1$, find $k$.

**(b)** The probability that the component will last at least 1200 hours is given by $\int_{1200}^{\infty} f(x)\,dx$. Evaluate this integral.

**14. Density Function** Given the density function

$$f(x) = \begin{cases} ke^{-2x} & \text{for } x \geq 1 \\ 0 & \text{elsewhere} \end{cases}$$

find $k$. (*Hint:* See Example 3.)

**15. Future Profits** For a business, the present value of all future profits at an annual interest rate $r$ compounded continuously is given by

$$\int_{0}^{\infty} p(t)e^{-rt}\,dt$$

where $p(t)$ is the profit per year in dollars at time $t$. If $p(t) = 240,000$ and $r = 0.06$, evaluate this integral.

**16. Psychology** In a psychological model for signal detection,[13] the probability $\alpha$ (a Greek letter read "alpha") of reporting a signal when no signal is present is given by

$$\alpha = \int_{x_c}^{\infty} e^{-x}\,dx \quad x \geq 0$$

[13]D. Laming, *Mathematical Psychology* (New York: Academic Press, Inc., 1973).

The probability $\beta$ (a Greek letter read "beta") of detecting a signal when it is present is

$$\beta = \int_{x_c}^{\infty} ke^{-kx}\,dx \quad x \geq 0$$

In both integrals, $x_c$ is a constant (called a criterion value in this model). Find $\alpha$ and $\beta$ if $k = \frac{1}{8}$.

**17.** Find the area of the region in the third quadrant bounded by the curve $y = e^{3x}$ and the x-axis.

**18. Economics**   In discussing entrance of a firm into an industry, Stigler[14] uses the equation

$$V = \pi_0 \int_0^{\infty} e^{\theta t} e^{-\rho t}\,dt$$

where $\pi_0, \theta$ (a Greek letter read "theta"), and $\rho$ (a Greek letter read "rho") are constants. Show that $V = \pi_0/(\rho - \theta)$ if $\theta < \rho$.

**19. Population**   The predicted rate of growth per year of the population of a certain small city is given by

$$\frac{40{,}000}{(t+2)^2}$$

where $t$ is the number of years from now. In the long run (that is, as $t \to \infty$), what is the expected change in population from today's level?

# 15.8 Review

## Important Terms and Symbols

## Summary

Sometimes we can easily determine an integral whose form is $\int u\,dv$, where $u$ and $v$ are functions of the same variable, by applying the formula for integration by parts:

$$\int u\,dv = uv - \int v\,du$$

A proper rational function can be integrated by applying the technique of partial fractions (although *some* of the partial fractions that may result have integrals that are beyond the scope of this book). Here we express the rational function as a sum of fractions, each of which is easier to integrate than the original function.

To determine an integral that does not have a familiar form, you may be able to match it with a formula in a table of integrals.

However, it may be necessary to transform the given integral into an equivalent form before the matching can occur.

An annuity is a series of payments over a period of time. Suppose payments are made continuously for $T$ years such that a payment at time $t$ is at the rate of $f(t)$ per year. If the annual rate of interest is $r$ compounded continuously then the present value of the continuous annuity is given by

$$A = \int_0^T f(t)e^{-rt}\,dt$$

and the accumulated amount is given by

$$S = \int_0^T f(t)e^{r(T-t)}\,dt$$

---

[14]G. Stigler, *The Theory of Price*, 3rd ed. (New York: Macmillan Publishing Company, 1966), p. 344.

The average value $\overline{f}$ of a function $f$ over the interval $[a, b]$ is given by

$$\overline{f} = \frac{1}{b-a} \int_a^b f(x)\, dx$$

An equation that involves the derivative of an unknown function is called a differential equation. If the highest-order derivative that occurs is the first, the equation is called a first-order differential equation. Some first-order differential equations can be solved by the method of separation of variables. In that method, by considering the derivative to be a quotient of differentials, we rewrite the equation so that each side contains only one variable and a single differential in the numerator. Integrating both sides of the resulting equation gives the solution. This solution involves a constant of integration and is called the general solution of the differential equation. If the unknown function must satisfy the condition that it has a specific function value for a given value of the independent variable, then a particular solution can be found.

Differential equations arise when we know a relation involving the rate of change of a function. For example, if a quantity $N$ at time $t$ is such that it changes at a rate proportional to the amount present, then

$$\frac{dN}{dt} = kN \qquad \text{where } k \text{ is a constant}$$

The solution of this differential equation is

$$N = N_0 e^{kt}$$

where $N_0$ is the quantity present at $t = 0$. The value of $k$ may be determined when the value of $N$ is known for a given value of $t$ other than $t = 0$. If $k$ is positive, then $N$ follows an exponential law of growth; if $k$ is negative, $N$ follows an exponential law of decay. If $N$ represents a quantity of a radioactive element, then

$$\frac{dN}{dt} = -\lambda N \qquad \text{where } \lambda \text{ is a positive constant}$$

Thus, $N$ follows an exponential law of decay, and hence

$$N = N_0 e^{-\lambda t}$$

The constant $\lambda$ is called the decay constant. The time for one half of the element to decay is the half-life of the element:

$$\text{half-life} = \frac{\ln 2}{\lambda} \approx \frac{0.69315}{\lambda}$$

A quantity $N$ may follow a rate of growth given by

$$\frac{dN}{dt} = KN(M - N) \qquad \text{where } K, M \text{ are constants}$$

Solving this differential equation gives a function of the form

$$N = \frac{M}{1 + be^{-ct}} \qquad \text{where } b, c \text{ are constants}$$

which is called a logistic function. Many population sizes can be described by a logistic function. In this case, $M$ represents the limit of the size of the population. A logistic function is also used in analyzing the spread of a rumor.

Newton's law of cooling states that the temperature $T$ of a cooling body at time $t$ changes at a rate proportional to the difference $T - a$, where $a$ is the ambient temperature. Thus,

$$\frac{dT}{dt} = k(T - a) \qquad \text{where } k \text{ is a constant}$$

The solution of this differential equation can be used to determine, for example, the time at which a homicide was committed.

An integral of the form

$$\int_a^\infty f(x)\, dx \qquad \int_{-\infty}^b f(x)\, dx \qquad \text{or} \qquad \int_{-\infty}^\infty f(x)\, dx$$

is called an improper integral. The first two integrals are defined as follows:

$$\int_a^\infty f(x)\, dx = \lim_{r \to \infty} \int_a^r f(x)\, dx$$

and

$$\int_{-\infty}^b f(x)\, dx = \lim_{r \to -\infty} \int_r^b f(x)\, dx$$

If $\int_a^\infty f(x)\, dx$ (or $\int_{-\infty}^b f(x)\, dx$) is a finite number, we say that the integral is convergent; otherwise, it is divergent. The improper integral $\int_{-\infty}^\infty f(x)\, dx$ is defined by

$$\int_{-\infty}^\infty f(x)\, dx = \int_{-\infty}^0 f(x)\, dx + \int_0^\infty f(x)\, dx$$

If both integrals on the right side are convergent, $\int_{-\infty}^\infty f(x)\, dx$ is said to be convergent; otherwise, it is divergent.

## Review Problems

*Problem numbers shown in color indicate problems suggested for use as a practice chapter test.*

*In Problems 1–22, determine the integrals.*

**1.** $\displaystyle\int x \ln x\, dx$

**2.** $\displaystyle\int \frac{1}{\sqrt{4x^2 + 1}}\, dx$

**3.** $\displaystyle\int_0^2 \sqrt{9x^2 + 16}\, dx$

**4.** $\displaystyle\int \frac{16x}{3 - 4x}\, dx$

**5.** $\displaystyle\int \frac{15x - 2}{(3x + 1)(x - 2)}\, dx$

**6.** $\displaystyle\int_e^{e^2} \frac{1}{x \ln x}\, dx$

**7.** $\displaystyle\int \frac{dx}{x(x + 2)^2}$

**8.** $\displaystyle\int \frac{dx}{x^2 - 1}$

**9.** $\displaystyle\int \frac{dx}{x^2 \sqrt{9 - 16x^2}}$

**10.** $\displaystyle\int x^3 \ln x^2\, dx$

**11.** $\displaystyle\int \frac{9\, dx}{x^2 - 9}$

**12.** $\displaystyle\int \frac{x}{\sqrt{2 + 5x}}\, dx$

**13.** $\displaystyle\int 49xe^{7x}\, dx$

**14.** $\displaystyle\int \frac{dx}{2 + 3e^{4x}}$

**15.** $\displaystyle\int \frac{dx}{2x \ln x^2}$

**16.** $\displaystyle\int \frac{dx}{x(2 + x)}$

**17.** $\displaystyle\int \frac{2x}{3 + 2x}\, dx$

**18.** $\displaystyle\int \frac{dx}{x^2 \sqrt{4x^2 - 9}}$

[15]**19.** $\displaystyle\int \frac{5x^2 + 2}{x^3 + x}\, dx$

[15]**20.** $\displaystyle\int \frac{3x^3 + 5x^2 + 4x + 3}{x^4 + x^3 + x^2}\, dx$

[16]**21.** $\displaystyle\int \frac{\ln(x + 1)}{\sqrt{x + 1}}\, dx$

[16]**22.** $\displaystyle\int x^2 e^x\, dx$

---

[15]Problems 19 and 20 refer to Section 15.2.

[16]Problems 21 and 22 refer to Section 15.1.

**23.** Find the average value of $f(x) = 3x^2 + 2x$ over the interval $[2, 4]$.

**24.** Find the average value of $f(t) = t^2 e^t$ over the interval $[0, 1]$.

*In Problems 25 and 26, solve the differential equations.*

**25.** $y' = 3x^2 y + 2xy$      $y > 0$

**26.** $y' - 2xe^{x^2 - y + 3} = 0$      $y(0) = 3$

*In Problems 27–30, determine the improper integrals if they exist.[17] Indicate those that are divergent.*

**27.** $\displaystyle\int_{1}^{\infty} \frac{1}{x^{2.5}}\, dx$

**28.** $\displaystyle\int_{-\infty}^{0} e^{2x}\, dx$

**29.** $\displaystyle\int_{1}^{\infty} \frac{1}{2x}\, dx$

**30.** $\displaystyle\int_{-\infty}^{\infty} xe^{1-x^2}\, dx$

**31. Population**   The population of a city in 1985 was 100,000 and in 2000 was 120,000. Assuming exponential growth, project the population in 2015.

**32. Population**   The population of a city doubles every 10 years due to exponential growth. At a certain time, the population is 40,000. Find an expression for the number of people $N$ at time $t$ years later. Give your answer in terms of $\ln 2$.

**33. Radioactive**   If 95% of a radioactive substance remains after 100 years, find the decay constant, and, to the nearest percent, give the percentage of the original amount present after 200 years.

**34. Medicine**   Suppose $q$ is the amount of penicillin in the body at time $t$, and let $q_0$ be the amount at $t = 0$. Assume that the rate of change of $q$ with respect to $t$ is proportional to $q$ and that $q$ decreases as $t$ increases. Then we have $dq/dt = -kq$, where $k > 0$. Solve for $q$. What percentage of the original amount present is there when $t = 7/k$?

**35. Biology**   Two organisms are initially placed in a medium and begin to multiply. The number $N$ of organisms that are present after $t$ days is recorded on a graph with the horizontal axis labeled $t$ and the vertical axis labeled $N$. It is observed that the points lie on a logistic curve. The number of organisms present after 6 days is 300, and beyond 10 days the number approaches a limit of 450. Find the logistic equation.

**36. College Enrollment**   A college believes that enrollment follows logistic growth. Last year enrollment was 1000, and this year it is 1100. If the college can accommodate a maximum of 2000 students, what is the anticipated enrollment next year? Give your answer to the nearest hundred.

**37. Time of Murder**   A coroner is called in on a murder case. He arrives at 6:00 P.M. and finds that the victim's temperature is 35°C. One hour later the body temperature is 34°C. The temperature of the room is 25°C. About what time was the murder committed? (Assume that normal body temperature is 37°C.)

**38. Annuity**   Find the present value, to the nearest dollar, of a continuous annuity at an annual rate of 6% for 12 years if the payment at time $t$ is at the annual rate of $f(t) = 10t$ dollars.

**[18]39. Hospital Discharges**   For a group of hospitalized individuals, suppose the proportion that has been discharged at the end of $t$ days is given by

$$\int_{0}^{t} f(x)\, dx$$

where $f(x) = 0.007e^{-0.01x} + 0.00005e^{-0.0002x}$. Evaluate

$$\int_{0}^{\infty} f(x)\, dx$$

**[18]40. Product Consumption**   Suppose that $A(t)$ is the amount of a product that is consumed at time $t$ and that $A$ follows an exponential law of growth. If $t_1 < t_2$ and at time $t_2$ the amount consumed, $A(t_2)$, is double the amount consumed at time $t_1$, $A(t_1)$, then $t_2 - t_1$ is called a doubling period. In a discussion of exponential growth, Shonle[19] states that under exponential growth, "the amount of a product consumed during one doubling period is equal to the total used for all time up to the beginning of the doubling period in question." To justify this statement, reproduce his argument as follows. The amount of the product used up to time $t_1$ is given by

$$\int_{-\infty}^{t_1} A_0 e^{kt}\, dt \quad k > 0$$

where $A_0$ is the amount when $t = 0$. Show that this is equal to $(A_0/k)e^{kt_1}$. Next, the amount used during the time interval from $t_1$ to $t_2$ is

$$\int_{t_1}^{t_2} A_0 e^{kt}\, dt$$

Show that this is equal to

$$\frac{A_0}{k} e^{kt_1} [e^{k(t_2 - t_1)} - 1] \tag{1}$$

If the interval $[t_1, t_2]$ is a doubling period, then

$$A_0 e^{kt_2} = 2A_0 e^{kt_1}$$

Show that this relationship implies that $e^{k(t_2 - t_1)} = 2$. Substitute this value into Equation (1); your result should be the same as the total used during all time up to $t_1$, namely, $(A_0/k)e^{kt_1}$.

**41. Revenue, Cost, and Profit**   The following table gives values of a company's marginal-revenue (MR) and marginal-cost (MC) functions:

| $q$  | 0  | 3  | 6  | 9  | 12 | 15 | 18 |
|------|----|----|----|----|----|----|----|
| MR   | 25 | 22 | 18 | 13 | 7  | 3  | 0  |
| MC   | 15 | 14 | 12 | 10 | 7  | 4  | 2  |

The company's fixed cost is 25. Assume that profit is a maximum when MR = MC and that this occurs when $q = 12$. Moreover, assume that the output of the company is chosen to maximize the profit. Use the trapezoidal rule and Simpson's rule for each of the following parts.

**(a)** Estimate the total revenue by using as many data values as possible.

**(b)** Estimate the total cost by using as few data values as possible.

**(c)** Determine how the maximum profit is related to the area enclosed by the line $q = 0$ and the MR and MC curves, and use this relation to estimate the maximum profit as accurately as possible.

---

[17]Problems 27–30 refer to Section 15.7.

[18]Problems 39 and 40 refer to Section 15.7.

---

[19]J. I. Shonle, *Environmental Applications of General Physics* (Reading, MA: Addison-Wesley Publishing Company, Inc., 1975).

# Mathematical Snapshot

## Dieting

Today there is great concern about diet and weight loss. Some people want to lose weight in order to "look good." Others lose weight for physical fitness or for health reasons. In fact, some lose weight because of peer pressure. Advertisements for weight control programs frequently appear on television and in newspapers and magazines. In many bookstores, entire sections are devoted to diet and weight control.

Suppose you want to determine a mathematical model of the weight of a person on a restricted caloric diet.[20] A person's weight depends both on the daily rate of energy intake, say $C$ calories per day, and on the daily rate of energy consumption, which is typically between 15 and 20 calories per day for each pound of body weight. Consumption depends on age, sex, metabolic rate, and so on. For an average value of 17.5 calories per pound per day, a person weighing $w$ pounds expends $17.5w$ calories per day. If $C = 17.5w$, then his or her weight remains constant; otherwise weight gain or loss occurs according to whether $C$ is greater or less than $17.5w$.

How fast will weight gain or loss occur? The most plausible physiological assumption is that $dw/dt$ is proportional to the net excess (or deficit) $C - 17.5w$ in the number of calories per day. That is,

$$\frac{dw}{dt} = K(C - 17.5w) \qquad (1)$$

where $K$ is a constant. The left side of the equation has units of pounds per day, and $C - 17.5w$ has units of calories per day. Hence the units of $K$ are pounds per calorie. Therefore, you need to know how many pounds each excess or deficit calorie puts on or takes off. The commonly used dietetic conversion factor is that 3500 calories is equivalent to one pound. Thus $K = 1/3500$ lb per calorie.

Now, the differential equation modeling weight gain or loss is

$$\frac{dw}{dt} = \frac{1}{3500}(C - 17.5w) \qquad (2)$$

If $C$ is constant, the equation is separable and its solution is

$$w(t) = \frac{C}{17.5} + \left(w_0 - \frac{C}{17.5}\right)e^{-0.005t} \qquad (3)$$

where $w_0$ is the initial weight and $t$ is in days. In the long run, note that the equilibrium weight (that is, the weight as $t \to \infty$) is $w_{eq} = C/17.5$.

For example, if someone initially weighing 180 lb adopts a diet of 2500 calories per day, then we have $w_{eq} = 2500/17.5 \approx 143$ lb and the weight function is

$$w(t) \approx 143 + (180 - 143)e^{-0.005t}$$
$$= 143 + 37e^{-0.005t}$$

Figure 15.6 shows the graph of $w(t)$. Notice how long it takes to get close to the equilibrium weight of 143 lb. The half-life for the process is $(\ln 2)/0.005 \approx 138.6$ days, about 20 weeks. (It would take about 584 days, or 83 weeks, to get to 145 lb.) This may be why so many dieters give up in frustration.

---

[20]Adapted from A. C. Segal, "A Linear Diet Model," *The College Mathematics Journal*, 18, no. 1 (1987), 44–45. By permission of the Mathematical Association of America.

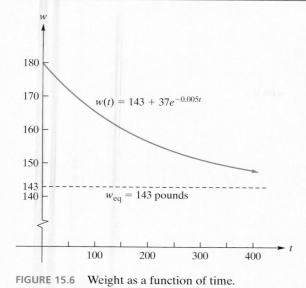

$$w(t) = 143 + 37e^{-0.005t}$$

$w_{eq} = 143$ pounds

**FIGURE 15.6** Weight as a function of time.

## Problems

1. If a person weighing 200 lb adopts a 2000-calorie-per-day diet, determine, to the nearest pound, the equilibrium weight $w_{eq}$. To the nearest day, after how many days will the person reach a weight of 175 lb? Obtain the answer either algebraically or using a graphing calculator.

2. Show that the solution of Equation (2) is given by Equation (3).

3. The weight of a person on a restricted caloric diet at time $t$ is given by $w(t)$. [See Equation (3).] The difference between this weight and the equilibrium weight $w_{eq}$ is $w(t) - w_{eq}$. Suppose it takes $d$ days for the person to lose half of the weight difference. Then

$$w(t + d) = w(t) - \tfrac{1}{2}[w(t) - w_{eq}]$$

By solving this equation for $d$, show that $d = \dfrac{\ln 2}{0.005}$.

4. Ideally, weight loss goals should be set in consultation with a physician. In general, however, one's ideal weight is related to one's height by the body mass index (BMI), which equals weight in kilograms divided by height in meters squared. The optimal BMI range is 18.5 to 24.9.

   How many pounds would a 5'8"-tall, 190-pound woman need to lose to be within the ideal BMI range? (Be mindful of units as you calculate the answer.) To the nearest day, how long would it take for her to lose this much weight on a 2200-calorie-per-day diet?

   Further information on weight and dieting can be found at

   www.consumer.gov/weightloss/setgoals.htm.

5. What are the pros and cons of a "crash" diet, one based on drastic changes in eating habits to achieve rapid weight loss?

# CONTINUOUS RANDOM VARIABLES

**Mathematical Snapshot**  Cumulative Distribution from Data

Suppose you are designing a cellular phone network for a large urban area. Ideally, the system would always have enough capacity to meet demand. However, you know that demand fluctuates. Some periods of increased demand can be foreseen, such as holidays, when many people call their families. But other times are not predictable, such as after an earthquake or some other natural disaster, when many people may be calling emergency services or checking in with friends and relatives. Building and operating a phone system with enough capacity to handle any sudden rise in demand, no matter how great, would be hugely expensive. How do you strike a balance between the goal of serving customers and the need to limit costs?

A sensible approach would be to design a system capable of handling the load of phone traffic under normally busy conditions, and to accept the fact that on rare occasions, heavy traffic will lead to overloads. You cannot always predict when overloads will occur, since disasters such as earthquakes are unforeseen occurrences. But some good *probabilistic* predictions of future traffic volume would suffice. You could build a system that would meet demand 99.4% of the time, for example. The remaining 0.6% of the time, customers would simply have to put up with intermittent delays in service.

A probabilistic description of traffic on a phone network is an example of a probability density function. Such functions are the focus of this chapter. They have a wide range of applications—not only calculating how often a system will be overloaded, for example, but also calculating its average load. This allows prediction of such things as average power consumption and average volume of system maintenance activity.

OBJECTIVE

To introduce continuous random variables; to discuss density functions, including uniform and exponential distributions; to discuss cumulative distribution functions; and to compute the mean, variance, and standard deviation for a continuous random variable.

# 16.1  Continuous Random Variables

## Density Functions

In Chapter 9, the random variables that we considered were primarily discrete. Now we will concern ourselves with ***continuous* random variables.** A random variable is continuous if it can assume any value in some interval or intervals. A continuous random variable usually represents data that are *measured,* such as heights, weights, distances, and periods of time. By contrast, the discrete random variables of Chapter 9 usually represent data that are *counted.*

For example, the number of hours of life of a calculator battery is a continuous random variable $X$. If the maximum possible life is 1000 hours, then $X$ can assume any value in the interval [0, 1000]. In a practical sense, the likelihood that $X$ will assume a single specified value, such as 764.1238, is extremely remote. It is more meaningful to consider the likelihood of $X$ lying within an *interval,* such as that between 764 and 765. Thus, $764 < X < 765$. (For that matter, the nature of measurement of physical quantities, like time, tells us that a statement such as $X = 764.1238$ is really one of the form $764.123750 < X < 764.123849$.) In general, *with a continuous random variable, our concern is the likelihood that it falls within an interval and not that it assumes a particular value.*

As another example, consider an experiment in which a number $X$ is randomly selected from the interval [0, 2]. Then $X$ is a continuous random variable. What is the probability that $X$ lies in the interval [0, 1]? Because we can loosely think of [0, 1] as being "half" the interval [0, 2], a reasonable (and correct) answer is $\frac{1}{2}$. Similarly, if we think of the interval $[0, \frac{1}{2}]$ as being one-fourth of [0, 2], then $P(0 \le X \le \frac{1}{2}) = \frac{1}{4}$. Actually, each one of these probabilities is simply the length of the given interval divided by the length of [0, 2]. For example,

$$P\left(0 \le X \le \frac{1}{2}\right) = \frac{\text{length of } [0, \frac{1}{2}]}{\text{length of } [0, 2]} = \frac{\frac{1}{2}}{2} = \frac{1}{4}$$

Let us now consider a similar experiment in which $X$ denotes a number chosen at random from the interval [0, 1]. As you might expect, the probability that $X$ will assume a value in any given interval within [0, 1] is equal to the length of the given interval divided by the length of [0, 1]. Because [0, 1] has length 1, we can simply say that the probability of $X$ falling in an interval is the length of the interval. For example,

$$P(0.2 \le X \le 0.5) = 0.5 - 0.2 = 0.3$$

and $P(0.2 \le X \le 0.2001) = 0.0001$. Clearly, as the length of an interval approaches 0, the probability that $X$ assumes a value in that interval approaches 0. Keeping this in mind, we can think of a single number such as 0.2 as the limiting case of an interval as the length of the interval approaches 0. (Think of $[0.2, 0.2 + x]$ as $x \to 0$.) Thus, $P(X = 0.2) = 0$. In general, *the probability that a continuous random variable $X$ assumes a particular value is 0.* As a result, **the probability that $X$ lies in some interval is not affected by whether or not either of the endpoints of the interval is included or excluded.** For example,

$$P(X \le 0.4) = P(X < 0.4) + P(X = 0.4)$$
$$= P(X < 0.4) + 0$$
$$= P(X < 0.4)$$

Similarly, $P(0.2 \le X \le 0.5) = P(0.2 < X < 0.5)$.

We can geometrically represent the probabilities associated with a continuous random variable $X$. This is done by means of the graph of a function $y = f(x)$ such that the area under this graph (and above the $x$-axis) between the lines $x = a$

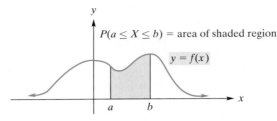

**FIGURE 16.1** Probability density function.

and $x = b$ represents the probability that $X$ assumes a value between $a$ and $b$. (See Figure 16.1.) Since this area is given by the definite integral $\int_a^b f(x)\,dx$, we have

$$P(a \le X \le b) = \int_a^b f(x)\,dx$$

We call the function $f$ the *probability density function* for $X$ (or simply the *density function* for $X$) and say that it defines the *distribution of X*. Because probabilities are always nonnegative, it is always true that $f(x) \ge 0$. Also, because the event $-\infty < X < \infty$ must occur, the total area under the density function curve must be 1. That is, $\int_{-\infty}^{\infty} f(x)\,dx = 1$. In summary, we have the following definition.

**DEFINITION**

If $X$ is a continuous random variable, then a function $y = f(x)$ is called a (*probability*) *density function* for $X$ if and only if it has the following properties:

**1.** $f(x) \ge 0$
**2.** $\int_{-\infty}^{\infty} f(x)\,dx = 1$

We then define

**3.** $P(a \le X \le b) = \int_a^b f(x)\,dx$

To illustrate a density function, we return to the previous experiment in which a number $X$ is chosen at random from the interval $[0, 1]$. Recall that

$$P(a \le X \le b) = \text{length of } [a, b] = b - a \tag{1}$$

where $a$ and $b$ are in $[0, 1]$. We will show that the function

$$f(x) = \begin{cases} 1 & \text{if } 0 \le x \le 1 \\ 0 & \text{otherwise} \end{cases} \tag{2}$$

whose graph appears in Figure 16.2(a), is a density function for $X$. To do this, we must verify that $f(x)$ satisfies the three conditions stated in the definition of a density

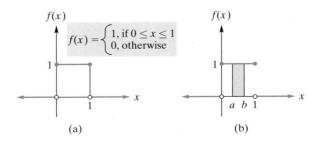

**FIGURE 16.2** Probability density function.

function. First, $f(x)$ is either 0 or 1, so $f(x) \geq 0$. Next, since $f(x) = 0$ for $x$ outside $[0, 1]$,

$$\int_{-\infty}^{\infty} f(x)\, dx = \int_0^1 1\, dx = x \Big|_0^1 = 1$$

Finally, to verify that $P(a \leq X \leq b) = \int_a^b f(x)\, dx$, we compute the area under the graph between $x = a$ and $x = b$ [Figure 16.2(b)]. We have

$$\int_a^b f(x)\, dx = \int_a^b 1\, dx = x \Big|_a^b = b - a$$

which, as stated in Equation (1), is $P(a \leq X \leq b)$.

The function in Equation (2) is called the **uniform density function** over $[0, 1]$, and $X$ is said to have a **uniform distribution.** The word *uniform* is meaningful in the sense that the graph of the density function is horizontal, or "flat," over $[0, 1]$. As a result, $X$ is just as likely to assume a value in one interval within $[0, 1]$ as in another of equal length. A more general uniform distribution is given in Example 1.

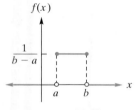

$f(x)$

$\dfrac{1}{b-a}$

$a$    $b$    $x$

**FIGURE 16.3** Uniform density function over $[a, b]$.

### ● EXAMPLE 1    Uniform Density Function

The uniform density function over $[a, b]$ for the random variable $X$ is given by

$$f(x) = \begin{cases} \dfrac{1}{b-a} & \text{if } a \leq x \leq b \\ 0 & \text{otherwise} \end{cases}$$

(See Figure 16.3.) Note that over $[a, b]$, the region under the graph is a rectangle with height $1/(b-a)$ and width $b-a$. Thus, its area is given by $(1/(b-a))(b-a) = 1$ so $\int_{-\infty}^{\infty} f(x)\, dx = 1$, as must be the case for a density function. If $[c, d]$ is any interval within $[a, b]$ then

$$P(c \leq X \leq d) = \int_c^d f(x)\, dx = \int_c^d \frac{1}{b-a}\, dx$$

$$= \frac{x}{b-a} \Big|_c^d = \frac{d-c}{b-a}$$

For example, suppose $X$ is uniformly distributed over the interval $[1, 4]$ and we need to find $P(2 < X < 3)$. Then $a = 1$, $b = 4$, $c = 2$, and $d = 3$. Therefore,

$$P(2 < X < 3) = \frac{3-2}{4-1} = \frac{1}{3}$$

NOW WORK PROBLEM 3(a)–(g) ●●●

### ● EXAMPLE 2    Density Function

*The density function for a random variable $X$ is given by*

$$f(x) = \begin{cases} kx & \text{if } 0 \leq x \leq 2 \\ 0 & \text{otherwise} \end{cases}$$

*where $k$ is a constant.*

**a.** *Find $k$.*

**Solution:** Since $\int_{-\infty}^{\infty} f(x)\, dx$ must be 1 and $f(x) = 0$ outside $[0, 2]$, we have

$$\int_{-\infty}^{\infty} f(x)\, dx = \int_0^2 kx\, dx = \frac{kx^2}{2} \Big|_0^2 = 2k = 1$$

Thus, $k = \frac{1}{2}$, so $f(x) = \frac{1}{2}x$ on $[0, 2]$.

**b.** *Find* $P(\frac{1}{2} < X < 1)$.

Solution:
$$P\left(\frac{1}{2} < X < 1\right) = \int_{1/2}^{1} \frac{1}{2}x\, dx = \left.\frac{x^2}{4}\right|_{1/2}^{1} = \frac{1}{4} - \frac{1}{16} = \frac{3}{16}$$

**c.** *Find* $P(X < 1)$.

Solution: Since $f(x) = 0$ for $x < 0$, we need only compute the area under the density function between 0 and 1. Thus,
$$P(x < 1) = \int_{0}^{1} \frac{1}{2}x\, dx = \left.\frac{x^2}{4}\right|_{0}^{1} = \frac{1}{4}$$

NOW WORK PROBLEM 9(a)–(d), (g), (h)

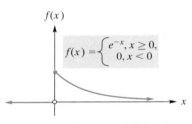

**FIGURE 16.4** Exponential density function.

● **EXAMPLE 3  Exponential Density Function**

*The **exponential density function** is defined by*
$$f(x) = \begin{cases} ke^{-kx} & \text{if } x \geq 0 \\ 0 & \text{if } x < 0 \end{cases}$$

*where k is a positive constant, called a **parameter**, whose value depends on the experiment under consideration. If X is a random variable with this density function, then X is said to have an **exponential distribution**. Let $k = 1$. Then $f(x) = e^{-x}$ for $x \geq 0$, and $f(x) = 0$ for $x < 0$ (Figure 16.4).*

**a.** *Find* $P(2 < X < 3)$.

Solution:
$$P(2 < X < 3) = \int_{2}^{3} e^{-x}\, dx = \left.-e^{-x}\right|_{2}^{3}$$
$$= -e^{-3} - (-e^{-2}) = e^{-2} - e^{-3} \approx 0.086$$

**b.** *Find* $P(X > 4)$.

Solution:
$$P(X > 4) = \int_{4}^{\infty} e^{-x}\, dx = \lim_{r \to \infty} \int_{4}^{r} e^{-x}\, dx$$
$$= \lim_{r \to \infty} \left.-e^{-x}\right|_{4}^{r} = \lim_{r \to \infty}(-e^{-r} + e^{-4})$$
$$= \lim_{r \to \infty}\left(-\frac{1}{e^r} + e^{-4}\right) = 0 + e^{-4}$$
$$\approx 0.018$$

Alternatively, we can avoid an improper integral because
$$P(X > 4) = 1 - P(X \leq 4) = 1 - \int_{0}^{4} e^{-x}\, dx$$

NOW WORK PROBLEM 7(a)–(c), (e)

The **cumulative distribution function** $F$ for the continuous random variable $X$ with density function $f$ is defined by
$$F(x) = P(X \leq x) = \int_{-\infty}^{x} f(t)\, dt$$

For example, $F(2)$ represents the entire area under the density curve that is to the left of the line $x = 2$ (Figure 16.5). Where $f(x)$ is continuous, it can be shown that
$$F'(x) = f(x)$$

That is, the derivative of the cumulative distribution function is the density function. Thus, $F$ is an antiderivative of $f$, and by the Fundamental Theorem of Integral

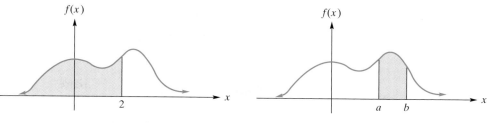

FIGURE 16.5   $F(2) = P(X \le 2) =$ area of shaded region.

FIGURE 16.6   $P(a < X < b)$.

Calculus,

$$P(a < X < b) = \int_a^b f(x)\, dx = F(b) - F(a) \qquad (3)$$

This means that the area under the density curve between $a$ and $b$ (Figure 16.6) is simply the area to the left of $b$ minus the area to the left of $a$.

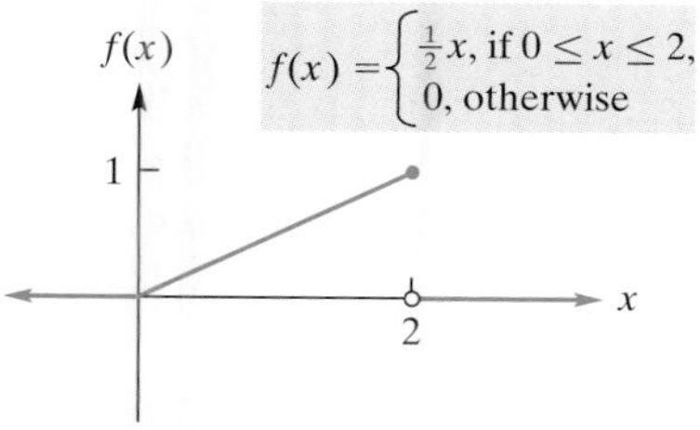

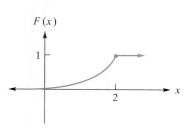

FIGURE 16.7   Density function for Example 4.

● **EXAMPLE 4   Finding and Applying the Cumulative Distribution Function**

*Suppose X is a random variable with density function given by*

$$f(x) = \begin{cases} \frac{1}{2}x & \text{if } 0 \le x \le 2 \\ 0 & \text{otherwise} \end{cases}$$

*as shown in Figure 16.7.*

**a.** *Find and sketch the cumulative distribution function.*

**Solution:** Because $f(x) = 0$ if $x < 0$, the area under the density curve to the left of $x = 0$ is 0. Hence, $F(x) = 0$ if $x < 0$. If $0 \le x \le 2$, then

$$F(x) = \int_{-\infty}^x f(t)\, dt = \int_0^x \frac{1}{2}t\, dt = \left.\frac{t^2}{4}\right|_0^x = \frac{x^2}{4}$$

Since $f$ is a density function and $f(x) = 0$ for $x < 0$ and also for $x > 2$, the area under the density curve from $x = 0$ to $x = 2$ is 1. Thus, if $x > 2$, the area to the left of $x$ is 1, so $F(x) = 1$. Hence, the cumulative distribution function is

$$F(x) = \begin{cases} 0 & \text{if } x < 0 \\ \dfrac{x^2}{4} & \text{if } 0 \le x \le 2 \\ 1 & \text{if } x > 2 \end{cases}$$

which is shown in Figure 16.8.

FIGURE 16.8   Cumulative distribution function for Example 4.

**b.** *Find $P(X < 1)$ and $P(1 < X < 1.1)$.*

**Solution:** Using the results of part (a), we have

$$P(X < 1) = F(1) = \frac{1^2}{4} = \frac{1}{4}$$

From Equation (3),

$$P(1 < X < 1.1) = F(1.1) - F(1) = \frac{1.1^2}{4} - \frac{1}{4} = 0.0525$$

NOW WORK PROBLEM 1   ●●●

## Mean, Variance, and Standard Deviation

For a random variable $X$ with density function $f$, the **mean** $\mu$ (also called the **expectation** of $X$, $E(X)$) is given by

$$\mu = E(X) = \int_{-\infty}^{\infty} x f(x)\, dx$$

if the integral is convergent, and can be thought of as the average value of $X$ in the long run. The **variance** $\sigma^2$ (also written $\mathrm{Var}(X)$) is given by

$$\sigma^2 = \mathrm{Var}(X) = \int_{-\infty}^{\infty} (x - \mu)^2 f(x)\, dx$$

if the integral is convergent. You may have noticed that these formulas are similar to the corresponding ones in Chapter 9 for a discrete random variable. It is easy to show that an alternative formula for the variance is

$$\sigma^2 = \mathrm{Var}(X) = \int_{-\infty}^{\infty} x^2 f(x)\, dx - \mu^2$$

The **standard deviation** is

$$\sigma = \sqrt{\mathrm{Var}(X)}$$

For example, it can be shown that if $X$ is exponentially distributed (see Example 3), then $\mu = 1/k$ and $\sigma = 1/k$. As with a discrete random variable, the standard deviation of a continuous random variable $X$ is small if $X$ is likely to assume values close to the mean but unlikely to assume values far from the mean. The standard deviation is large if the opposite is true.

**PRINCIPLES IN PRACTICE 3**

**FINDING THE MEAN AND STANDARD DEVIATION**

The life expectancy (in years) of patients after they have contracted a certain disease is exponentially distributed with $k = 0.2$. Use the information in the paragraph that precedes Example 5 to find the mean life expectancy and the standard deviation.

### ● EXAMPLE 5 Finding the Mean and Standard Deviation

*If $X$ is a random variable with density function given by*

$$f(x) = \begin{cases} \frac{1}{2}x & \text{if } 0 \le x \le 2 \\ 0 & \text{otherwise} \end{cases}$$

*find its mean and standard deviation.*

**Solution:** The mean is simply given by

$$\mu = \int_{-\infty}^{\infty} x f(x)\, dx = \int_{0}^{2} x \cdot \frac{1}{2} x\, dx = \left. \frac{x^3}{6} \right|_0^2 = \frac{4}{3}$$

By the alternative formula for variance, we have

$$\sigma^2 = \int_{-\infty}^{\infty} x^2 f(x)\, dx - \mu^2 = \int_{0}^{2} x^2 \cdot \frac{1}{2} x\, dx - \left(\frac{4}{3}\right)^2$$

$$= \left. \frac{x^4}{8} \right|_0^2 - \frac{16}{9} = 2 - \frac{16}{9} = \frac{2}{9}$$

Thus, the standard deviation is

$$\sigma = \sqrt{\frac{2}{9}} = \frac{\sqrt{2}}{3}$$

NOW WORK PROBLEM 5 ●●

We conclude this section by emphasizing that a density function for a continuous random variable must not be confused with a probability distribution function for a discrete random variable. Evaluating such a probability distribution function at a *point* gives a probability. But evaluating a density function at a point does not. Instead, the *area* under the density function curve over an *interval* is interpreted as a probability. That is, probabilities associated with a continuous random variable are given by integrals.

# Problems 16.1

*1. Suppose $X$ is a continuous random variable with density function given by

$$f(x) = \begin{cases} \frac{1}{6}(x+1) & \text{if } 1 < x < 3 \\ 0 & \text{otherwise} \end{cases}$$

(a) Find $P(1 < X < 2)$.   (b) Find $P(X < 2.5)$.
(c) Find $P(X \geq \frac{3}{2})$.
(d) Find $c$ such that $P(X < c) = \frac{1}{2}$. Give your answer in radical form.

2. Suppose $X$ is a continuous random variable with density function given by

$$f(x) = \begin{cases} \dfrac{1000}{x^2} & \text{if } x > 1000 \\ 0 & \text{otherwise} \end{cases}$$

(a) Find $P(3000 < X < 4000)$.
(b) Find $P(X > 2000)$.

*3. Suppose $X$ is a continuous random variable that is uniformly distributed on $[1, 4]$.

(a) What is the formula of the density function for $X$? Sketch its graph.
(b) Find $P\left(\frac{3}{2} < X < \frac{7}{2}\right)$.
(c) Find $P(0 < X < 1)$.
(d) Find $P(X \leq 3.5)$.
(e) Find $P(X > 3)$.
(f) Find $P(X = 2)$.
(g) Find $P(X < 5)$.
(h) Find $\mu$.
(i) Find $\sigma$.
(j) Find the cumulative distribution function $F$ and sketch its graph. Use $F$ to find $P(X < 2)$ and $P(1 < X < 3)$.

4. Suppose $X$ is a continuous random variable that is uniformly distributed on $[0, 5]$.

(a) What is the formula of the density function for $X$? Sketch its graph.
(b) Find $P(1 < X < 3)$.
(c) Find $P(4.5 \leq X < 5)$.
(d) Find $P(X = 4)$.
(e) Find $P(X > 2)$.
(f) Find $P(X < 5)$.
(g) Find $P(X > 5)$.
(h) Find $\mu$.
(i) Find $\sigma$.
(j) Find the cumulative distribution function $F$ and sketch its graph. Use $F$ to find $P(1 < X < 3.5)$.

*5. Suppose $X$ is uniformly distributed on $[a, b]$.

(a) What is the density function for $X$?
(b) Find $\mu$.
(c) Find $\sigma^2$ and $\sigma$.

6. Suppose $X$ is a continuous random variable with density function given by

$$f(x) = \begin{cases} k & \text{if } a \leq x \leq b \\ 0 & \text{otherwise} \end{cases}$$

(a) Show that $k = \dfrac{1}{b-a}$ and thus $X$ is uniformly distributed.
(b) Find the cumulative distribution function $F$.

*7. Suppose the random variable $X$ is exponentially distributed with $k = 3$.

(a) Find $P(1 < X < 4)$.
(b) Find $P(X < 4)$.
(c) Find $P(X > 6)$.
(d) Find $P(\mu - 2\sigma < X < \mu + 2\sigma)$.
(e) Verify that the density function in question satisfies the requirement that the area under the curve is 1.
(f) Find the cumulative distribution function $F$.

8. Suppose the random variable $X$ is exponentially distributed with $k = 0.5$.

(a) Find $P(X > 4)$.
(b) Find $P(0.5 < X < 2.6)$.
(c) Find $P(X < 5)$.
(d) Find $P(X = 4)$.
(e) Find $c$ such that $P(0 < X < c) = \frac{1}{2}$.

*9. The density function for a random variable $X$ is given by

$$f(x) = \begin{cases} kx & \text{if } 0 \leq x \leq 4 \\ 0 & \text{otherwise} \end{cases}$$

(a) Find $k$.
(b) Find $P(2 < X < 3)$.
(c) Find $P(X > 2.5)$.
(d) Find $P(X > 0)$.
(e) Find $\mu$.
(f) Find $\sigma$.
(g) Find $c$ such that $P(X < c) = \frac{1}{2}$.
(h) Find $P(3 < X < 5)$.

10. The density function for a random variable $X$ is given by

$$f(x) = \begin{cases} \frac{1}{2}x + k & \text{if } 2 \leq x \leq 4 \\ 0 & \text{otherwise} \end{cases}$$

(a) Find $k$.   (b) Find $P(X \geq 2.5)$.
(c) Find $\mu$.   (d) Find $P(2 < X < \mu)$.

11. **Waiting Time** At a bus stop, the time $X$ (in minutes) that a randomly arriving person must wait for a bus is uniformly distributed with density function $f(x) = \frac{1}{10}$, where $0 \leq x \leq 10$ and $f(x) = 0$ otherwise. What is the probability that a person must wait at most seven minutes? What is the average time that a person must wait?

12. **Soft-Drink Dispensing** An automatic soft-drink dispenser at a fast-food restaurant dispenses $X$ ounces of cola in a 12-ounce drink. If $X$ is uniformly distributed over $[11.93, 12.07]$, what is the probability that less than 12 ounces will be dispensed? What is the probability that exactly 12 ounces will be dispensed? What is the average amount dispensed?

13. **Emergency Room Arrivals** At a particular hospital, the length of time $X$ (in hours) between successive arrivals at the emergency room is exponentially distributed with $k = 3$. What is the probability that more than one hour passes without an arrival?

14. **Electronic Component Life** The length of life $X$ (in years) of a computer component has an exponential distribution with $k = \frac{2}{5}$. What is the probability that such a component will fail within three years of use? What is the probability that it will last more than five years?

OBJECTIVE

To discuss the normal distribution, standard units, and the table of areas under the standard normal curve (Appendix C).

## 16.2 The Normal Distribution

Quite often, measured data in nature—such as heights of individuals in a population—are represented by a random variable whose density function may be approximated by the bell-shaped curve in Figure 16.9. The curve extends indefinitely to the right and left and never touches the $x$-axis. This curve, called the **normal curve**, is the graph of the most important of all density functions, the *normal density function*.

> **DEFINITION**
>
> A continuous random variable $X$ is a ***normal random variable,*** equivalently has a ***normal*** (also called Gaussian[1]) ***distribution,*** if its density function is given by
>
> $$f(x) = \frac{1}{\sigma\sqrt{2\pi}} e^{-(1/2)[(x-\mu)/\sigma]^2} \qquad -\infty < x < \infty$$
>
> called the ***normal density function.*** The parameters $\mu$ and $\sigma$ are the mean and standard deviation of $X$, respectively.

Observe in Figure 16.9 that $f(x) \to 0$ as $x \to \pm\infty$. That is, the normal curve has the $x$-axis as a horizontal asymptote. Also note that the normal curve is symmetric about the vertical line $x = \mu$. That is, the height of a point on the curve $d$ units to the right of $x = \mu$ is the same as the height of the point on the curve that is $d$ units to the left of $x = \mu$. Because of this symmetry and the fact that the area under the normal curve is 1, the area to the right (or left) of the mean must be $\frac{1}{2}$.

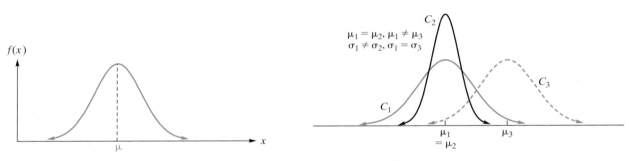

FIGURE 16.9   Normal curve.

FIGURE 16.10   Normal curves.

Each choice of values for $\mu$ and $\sigma$ determines a different normal curve. The value of $\mu$ determines where the curve is "centered," and $\sigma$ determines how "spread out" the curve is. The smaller the value of $\sigma$, the less spread out is the area near $\mu$. For example, Figure 16.10 shows normal curves $C_1$, $C_2$, and $C_3$, where $C_1$ has mean $\mu_1$ and standard deviation $\sigma_1$, $C_2$ has mean $\mu_2$, and so on. Here $C_1$ and $C_2$ have the same mean but different standard deviations: $\sigma_1 > \sigma_2$. $C_1$ and $C_3$ have the same standard deviation but different means: $\mu_1 < \mu_3$. Curves $C_2$ and $C_3$ have different means and different standard deviations.

The standard deviation plays a significant role in describing probabilities associated with a normal random variable $X$. More precisely, the probability that $X$ will lie within one standard deviation of the mean is approximately 0.68:

$$P(\mu - \sigma < X < \mu + \sigma) = 0.68$$

In other words, approximately 68% of the area under a normal curve is within one standard deviation of the mean (Figure 16.11). Between $\mu \pm 2\sigma$ is about 95% of the area, and between $\mu \pm 3\sigma$ is about 99.7%:

$$P(\mu - 2\sigma < X < \mu + 2\sigma) = 0.95$$

$$P(\mu - 3\sigma < X < \mu + 3\sigma) = 0.997$$

You are encouraged to become familiar with the percentages in Figure 16.11.

Thus, it is highly likely that $X$ will lie within three standard deviations of the mean.

---

[1] After the German mathematician Carl Friedrich Gauss (1777–1855).

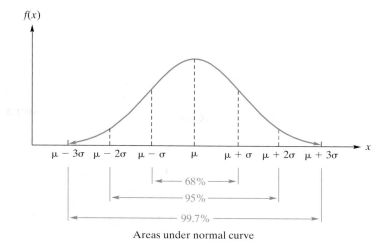

Areas under normal curve

**FIGURE 16.11**   Probability and number of standard deviations from $\mu$.

## EXAMPLE 1   Analysis of Test Scores

Let $X$ be a random variable whose values are the scores obtained on a nationwide test given to high school seniors. Suppose, for modeling purposes, that $X$ is normally distributed with mean 600 and standard deviation 90. Then the probability that $X$ lies within $2\sigma = 2(90) = 180$ points of 600 is 0.95. In other words, 95% of the scores lie between 420 and 780. Similarly, 99.7% of the scores are within $3\sigma = 3(90) = 270$ points of 600—that is, between 330 and 870.

NOW WORK PROBLEM 17

If $Z$ is a normally distributed random variable with $\mu = 0$ and $\sigma = 1$, we obtain the normal curve of Figure 16.12, called the **standard normal curve.**

### DEFINITION
A continuous random variable $Z$ is a ***standard normal random variable*** (or has a ***standard normal distribution***) if its density function is given by

$$f(z) = \frac{1}{\sqrt{2\pi}}e^{-z^2/2}$$

called the ***standard normal density function.*** The variable $Z$ has mean 0 and standard deviation 1.

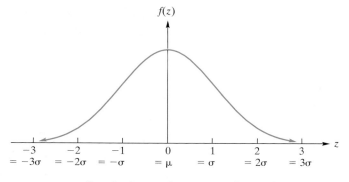

**FIGURE 16.12**   Standard normal curve: $\mu = 0, \sigma = 1$.

Because a standard normal random variable $Z$ has mean 0 and standard deviation 1, its values are in units of standard deviations from the mean, which are called **standard units.** For example, if $0 < Z < 2.54$, then $Z$ lies within 2.54 standard deviations to the right of 0, the mean. That is, $0 < Z < 2.54\sigma$. To find the probability $P(0 < Z < 2.54)$, we have

$$P(0 < Z < 2.54) = \int_0^{2.54} \frac{e^{-z^2/2}}{\sqrt{2\pi}}\, dz$$

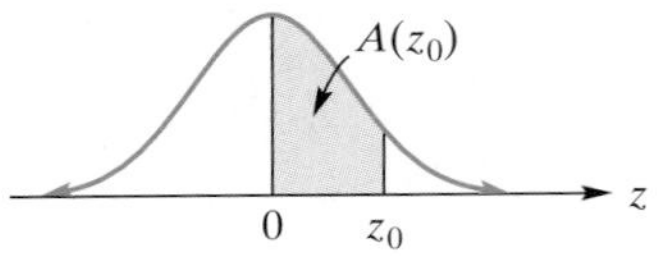

The integral on the right cannot be evaluated by elementary functions. However, values for integrals of this kind have been approximated and put in tabular form.

One such table is given in Appendix C. The table there gives the area under a standard normal curve between $z = 0$ and $z = z_0$, where $z_0 \geq 0$. This area is shaded in Figure 16.13 and is denoted by $A(z_0)$. In the left-hand columns of the table are $z$-values to the nearest tenth. The numbers across the top are the hundredths' values. For example, the entry in the row for 2.5 and column under 0.04 corresponds to $z = 2.54$ and is 0.4945. Thus, the area under a standard normal curve between $z = 0$ and $z = 2.54$ is (approximately) 0.4945:

$$P(0 < Z < 2.54) = A(2.54) \approx 0.4945$$

The numbers in the table are necessarily approximate, but for the balance of this chapter we will write $A(2.54) = 0.4945$ and the like in the interests of improved readbility. Similarly, you should verify that $A(2) = 0.4772$ and $A(0.33) = 0.1293$.

Using symmetry, we compute an area to the left of $z = 0$ by computing the corresponding area to the right of $z = 0$. For example,

$$P(-z_0 < Z < 0) = P(0 < Z < z_0) = A(z_0)$$

as shown in Figure 16.14. Hence, $P(-2.54 < Z < 0) = A(2.54) = 0.4945$.

When computing probabilities for a standard normal variable, you may have to add or subtract areas. A useful aid for doing this properly is a rough sketch of a standard normal curve in which you have shaded the entire area that you want to find, as Example 2 shows.

### ● EXAMPLE 2  Probabilities for Standard Normal Variable $Z$

**a.** *Find* $P(Z > 1.5)$.

**Solution:** This probability is the area to the right of $z = 1.5$ (Figure 16.15). That area is equal to the difference between the total area to the right of $z = 0$, which is 0.5, and the area between $z = 0$ and $z = 1.5$, which is $A(1.5)$. Thus,

$$P(Z > 1.5) = 0.5 - A(1.5)$$
$$= 0.5 - 0.4332 = 0.0668 \qquad \text{(from Appendix C)}$$

**b.** *Find* $P(0.5 < Z < 2)$.

**Solution:** This probability is the area between $z = 0.5$ and $z = 2$ (Figure 16.16). That area is the difference of two areas. It is the area between $z = 0$ and $z = 2$, which is $A(2)$, minus the area between $z = 0$ and $z = 0.5$, which is $A(0.5)$. Thus,

$$P(0.5 < Z < 2) = A(2) - A(0.5)$$
$$= 0.4772 - 0.1915 = 0.2857$$

**c.** *Find* $P(Z \leq 2)$.

**Solution:** This probability is the area to the left of $z = 2$ (Figure 16.17). That area is equal to the sum of the area to the left of $z = 0$, which is 0.5, and the area between $z = 0$ and $z = 2$, which is $A(2)$. Thus,

$$P(Z \leq 2) = 0.5 + A(2)$$
$$= 0.5 + 0.4772 = 0.9772$$

NOW WORK PROBLEM 1

**FIGURE 16.13**
$A(z_0) = P(0 < Z < z_0)$.

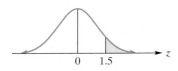

**FIGURE 16.14**
$P(-z_0 < Z < 0) =$
$P(0 < Z < z_0)$.

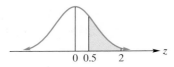

**FIGURE 16.15**  $P(Z > 1.5)$.

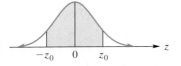

**FIGURE 16.16**
$P(0.5 < Z < 2)$.

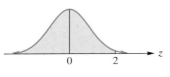

**FIGURE 16.17**  $P(Z \leq 2)$.

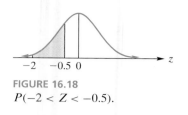

**FIGURE 16.18**
$P(-2 < Z < -0.5)$.

### ●EXAMPLE 3  Probabilities for Standard Normal Variable $Z$

**a.** *Find* $P(-2 < Z < -0.5)$.

**Solution:** This probability is the area between $z = -2$ and $z = -0.5$ (Figure 16.18). By symmetry, that area is equal to the area between $z = 0.5$ and $z = 2$, which was computed in Example 2(b). We have

$$P(-2 < Z < -0.5) = P(0.5 < Z < 2)$$
$$= A(2) - A(0.5) = 0.2857$$

**b.** *Find* $z_0$ *such that* $P(-z_0 < Z < z_0) = 0.9642$.

**Solution:** Figure 16.19 shows the corresponding area. Because the total area is 0.9642, by symmetry the area between $z = 0$ and $z = z_0$ is $\frac{1}{2}(0.9642) = 0.4821$, which is $A(z_0)$. Looking at the body of the table in Appendix C, we see that 0.4821 corresponds to a $Z$-value of 2.1. Thus, $z_0 = 2.1$.

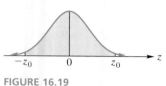

**FIGURE 16.19**
$P(-z_0 < Z < z_0) = 0.9642$.

NOW WORK PROBLEM 3 ●●●

### Transforming to a Standard Normal Variable $Z$

If $X$ is normally distributed with mean $\mu$ and standard deviation $\sigma$, you might think that a table of areas is needed for each pair of values of $\mu$ and $\sigma$. Fortunately, this is not the case. Appendix C is still used. But you must first express the area of a given region as an equal area under a standard normal curve. This involves transforming $X$ into a standard variable $Z$ (with mean 0 and standard deviation 1) by using the following change-of-variable formula:

$$Z = \frac{X - \mu}{\sigma} \tag{1}$$

*Here we convert a normal variable to a standard normal variable.*

On the right side, subtracting $\mu$ from $X$ gives the distance from $\mu$ to $X$. Dividing by $\sigma$ expresses this distance in terms of units of standard deviation. Thus, $Z$ is the number of standard deviations that $X$ is from $\mu$. That is, formula (1) converts units of $X$ into standard units ($Z$-values). For example, if $X = \mu$, then using formula (1) gives $Z = 0$. Hence, $\mu$ is zero standard deviations from $\mu$.

Suppose $X$ is normally distributed with $\mu = 4$ and $\sigma = 2$. Then to find—for example—$P(0 < X < 6)$, we first use formula (1) to convert the $X$-values 0 and 6 to $Z$-values (standard units):

$$z_1 = \frac{x_1 - \mu}{\sigma} = \frac{0 - 4}{2} = -2$$
$$z_2 = \frac{x_2 - \mu}{\sigma} = \frac{6 - 4}{2} = 1$$

It can be shown that

$$P(0 < X < 6) = P(-2 < Z < 1)$$

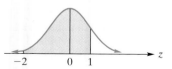

**FIGURE 16.20**  $P(-2 < Z < 1)$.

This means that the area under a normal curve with $\mu = 4$ and $\sigma = 2$ between $x = 0$ and $x = 6$ is equal to the area under a standard normal curve between $z = -2$ and $z = 1$ (Figure 16.20). This area is the sum of the area $A_1$ between $z = -2$ and $z = 0$ and the area $A_2$ between $z = 0$ and $z = 1$. Using symmetry for $A_1$, we have

$$P(-2 < Z < 1) = A_1 + A_2 = A(2) + A(1)$$
$$= 0.4772 + 0.3413 = 0.8185$$

FIGURE 16.21 Diagram for Example 4.

● **EXAMPLE 4** Employees' Salaries

*The weekly salaries of 5000 employees of a large corporation are assumed to be normally distributed with mean $640 and standard deviation $56. How many employees earn less than $570 per week?*

Solution: Converting to standard units, we have

$$P(X < 570) = P\left(Z < \frac{570 - 640}{56}\right) = P(Z < -1.25)$$

This probability is the area shown in Figure 16.21(a). By symmetry, that area is equal to the area in Figure 16.21(b) that corresponds to $P(Z > 1.25)$. This area is the difference between the total area to the right of $z = 0$, which is 0.5, and the area between $z = 0$ and $z = 1.25$, which is $A(1.25)$. Thus,

$$P(X < 570) = P(Z < -1.25) = P(Z > 1.25)$$

$$= 0.5 - A(1.25) = 0.5 - 0.3944 = 0.1056$$

That is, 10.56% of the employees have salaries less than $570. This corresponds to $0.1056(5000) = 528$ employees.

NOW WORK PROBLEM 21 ●●

## Problems 16.2

*1. If $Z$ is a standard normal random variable, find each of the following probabilities.

(a) $P(0 < Z < 1.7)$    (b) $P(0.43 < Z < 2.89)$
(c) $P(Z > -1.23)$    (d) $P(Z \leq 2.91)$
(e) $P(-2.51 < Z \leq 1.3)$    (f) $P(Z > 0.03)$

2. If $Z$ is a standard normal random variable, find each of the following.

(a) $P(-1.96 < Z < 1.96)$    (b) $P(-2.11 < Z < -1.35)$
(c) $P(Z < -1.05)$    (d) $P(Z > 3\sigma)$
(e) $P(|Z| > 2)$    (f) $P(|Z| < \frac{1}{2})$

*In Problems 3–8, find $z_0$ such that the given statement is true. Assume that $Z$ is a standard normal random variable.*

*3. $P(Z < z_0) = 0.5517$    4. $P(Z < z_0) = 0.0668$
5. $P(Z > z_0) = 0.8599$    6. $P(Z > z_0) = 0.4129$
7. $P(-z_0 < Z < z_0) = 0.2662$    8. $P(|Z| > z_0) = 0.3174$

9. If $X$ is normally distributed with $\mu = 16$ and $\sigma = 4$, find each of the following probabilities.

(a) $P(X < 27)$    (b) $P(X < 10)$
(c) $P(10.8 < X < 12.4)$

10. If $X$ is normally distributed with $\mu = 200$ and $\sigma = 40$, find each of the following probabilities.

(a) $P(X > 150)$    (b) $P(210 < X < 250)$

11. If $X$ is normally distributed with $\mu = -3$ and $\sigma = 2$, find $P(X > -2)$.

12. If $X$ is normally distributed with $\mu = 0$ and $\sigma = 1.5$, find $P(X < 3)$.

13. If $X$ is normally distributed with $\mu = 65$ and $\sigma^2 = 100$, find $P(35 < X \leq 95)$.

14. If $X$ is normally distributed with $\mu = 8$ and $\sigma = 1$, find $P(X > \mu - \sigma)$.

15. If $X$ is normally distributed such that $\mu = 40$ and $P(X > 54) = 0.0401$, find $\sigma$.

16. If $X$ is normally distributed with $\mu = 16$ and $\sigma = 2.25$, find $x_0$ such that the probability that $X$ is between $x_0$ and 16 is 0.4641.

*17. **Test Scores** The scores on a national achievement test are normally distributed with mean 500 and standard deviation 100. What percentage of those who took the test had a score between 300 and 700?

18. **Test Scores** In a test given to a large group of people, the scores were normally distributed with mean 65 and standard deviation 10. What is the least whole-number score that a person could get and yet score in about the top 20%?

19. **Adult Heights** The heights (in inches) of adults in a large population are normally distributed with $\mu = 68$ and $\sigma = 3$. What percentage of the group is under 6 feet tall?

20. **Income** The yearly income for a group of 10,000 professional people is normally distributed with $\mu = \$60,000$ and $\sigma = \$5000$.

(a) What is the probability that a person from this group has a yearly income less than $46,000?
(b) How many of these people have yearly incomes over $75,000?

*21. **IQ**   The IQs of a large population of children are normally distributed with mean 100.4 and standard deviation 11.6.

    **(a)** What percentage of the children have IQs greater than 125?

    **(b)** About 90% of the children have IQs greater than what value?

22. Suppose $X$ is a random variable with $\mu = 10$ and $\sigma = 2$. If $P(4 < X < 16) = 0.25$, can $X$ be normally distributed?

## 16.3 The Normal Approximation to the Binomial Distribution

OBJECTIVE

To show the technique of estimating the binomial distribution by using the normal distribution.

We conclude this chapter by bringing together the notions of a discrete random variable and a continuous random variable. Recall from Chapter 9 that if $X$ is a binomial random variable (which is discrete), and if the probability of success on any trial is $p$, then for $n$ independent trials, the probability of $x$ successes is given by

$$P(X = x) = {}_nC_x\, p^x q^{n-x}$$

where $q = 1 - p$. You would no doubt agree that calculating probabilities for a binomial random variable can be quite tedious when the number of trials is large. For example, just imagine trying to compute ${}_{100}C_{40}(0.3)^{40}(0.7)^{60}$. To handle expressions like this, we can approximate a binomial distribution by a normal distribution and then use a table of areas.

To show how this is done, let us take a simple example. Figure 16.22 gives a probability histogram for a binomial experiment with $n = 10$ and $p = 0.5$. The rectangles centered at $x = 0$ and $x = 10$ are not shown because their heights are very close to 0. Superimposed on the histogram is a normal curve, which approximates it. The approximation would be even better if $n$ were larger. That is, as $n$ gets larger, the width of each unit interval appears to get smaller, and the outline of the histogram tends to take on the appearance of a smooth curve. In fact, *it is not unusual to think of a density curve as the limiting case of a probability histogram.* In spite of the fact that in our case $n$ is only 10, the approximation shown does not seem too bad. The question that now arises is, "Which normal distribution approximates the binomial distribution?" Since the mean and standard deviation are measures of central tendency and dispersion of a random variable, we choose the approximating normal distribution to have the same mean and standard deviation as that of the binomial distribution. For this choice, we can estimate the areas of rectangles in the histogram (that is, the binomial probabilities) by finding the corresponding area under the normal curve. In summary, we have the following:

If $X$ is a binomial random variable and $n$ is sufficiently large, then the distribution of $X$ can be approximated by a normal random variable whose mean and standard deviation are the same as for $X$, which are $np$ and $\sqrt{npq}$, respectively.

Perhaps a word of explanation is appropriate concerning the phrase "$n$ is sufficiently large." Generally speaking, a normal approximation to a binomial distribution is not good if $n$ is small and $p$ is near 0 or 1, because much of the area in the binomial histogram would be concentrated at one end of the distribution (that is, at 0 or $n$). Thus, the distribution would not be fairly symmetric, and a normal curve would not "fit" well. A general rule you can follow is that the normal approximation to the binomial distribution is reasonable if $np$ and $nq$ are at least 5. This is the case in our example: $np = 10(0.5) = 5$ and $nq = 10(0.5) = 5$.

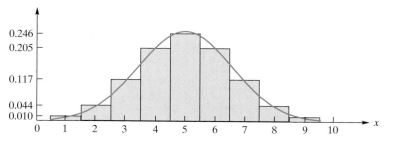

**FIGURE 16.22**   Normal approximation to binomial distribution.

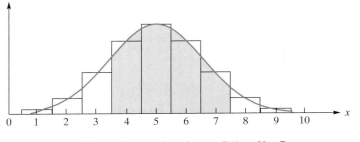

**FIGURE 16.23**   Normal approximation to $P(4 \leq X \leq 7)$.

Let us now use the normal approximation to estimate a binomial probability for $n = 10$ and $p = 0.5$. If $X$ denotes the number of successes, then its mean is

$$np = 10(0.5) = 5$$

and its standard deviation is

$$\sqrt{npq} = \sqrt{10(0.5)(0.5)} = \sqrt{2.5} \approx 1.58$$

The probability function for $X$ is given by

$$f(x) = {}_{10}C_x(0.5)^x(0.5)^{10-x}$$

We approximate this distribution by the normal distribution with $\mu = 5$ and $\sigma = \sqrt{2.5}$.

Suppose we estimate the probability that there are between 4 and 7 successes, inclusive, which is given by

$$P(4 \leq X \leq 7) = P(X = 4) + P(X = 5) + P(X = 6) + P(X = 7)$$

$$= \sum_{x=4}^{7} {}_{10}C_x(0.5)^x(0.5)^{10-x}$$

This probability is the sum of the areas of the *rectangles* for $X = 4, 5, 6,$ and 7 in Figure 16.23. Under the normal curve, we have shaded the corresponding area that we will compute as an approximation to this probability. Note that the shading extends not from 4 to 7, but from $4 - \frac{1}{2}$ to $7 + \frac{1}{2}$, that is, from 3.5 to 7.5. This "continuity correction" of 0.5 on each end of the interval allows most of the area in the appropriate rectangles to be included in the approximation, and *such a correction must always be made*. The phrase *continuity correction* is used because $X$ is treated as though it were a continuous random variable. We now convert the $X$-values 3.5 and 7.5 to $Z$-values:

$$z_1 = \frac{3.5 - 5}{\sqrt{2.5}} \approx -0.95$$

$$z_2 = \frac{7.5 - 5}{\sqrt{2.5}} \approx 1.58$$

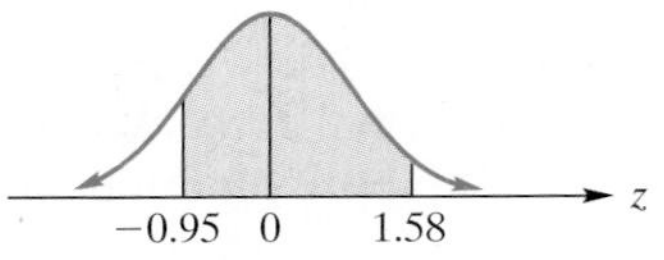

Thus,

$$P(4 \leq X \leq 7) \approx P(-0.95 \leq Z \leq 1.58)$$

which corresponds to the area under a standard normal curve between $z = -0.95$ and $z = 1.58$ (Figure 16.24). This area is the sum of the area between $z = -0.95$ and $z = 0$, which, by symmetry, is $A(0.95)$, and the area between $z = 0$ and $z = 1.58$, which is $A(1.58)$. Hence,

$$P(4 \leq X \leq 7) \approx P(-0.95 \leq Z \leq 1.58)$$

$$= A(0.95) + A(1.58)$$

$$= 0.3289 + 0.4429 = 0.7718$$

This result is close to the true value, 0.7734 (to four decimal places).

**FIGURE 16.24**
$P(-0.95 \leq Z \leq 1.58)$.

**NORMAL APPROXIMATION TO A BINOMIAL DISTRIBUTION**

On a game show, the grand prize is hidden behind one of four doors. Assume that the probability of selecting the grand prize is $p = \frac{1}{4}$. There were 20 winners among the last 60 contestants. Suppose that $X$ is the number of contestants that win the grand prize, and $X$ is binomial with $n = 60$. Approximate $P(X = 20)$ by using the normal approximation.

**CAUTION**

Do not ignore the continuity correction.

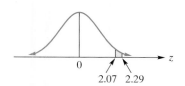

**FIGURE 16.25**
$P(2.07 \leq Z \leq 2.29)$.

● EXAMPLE 1   **Normal Approximation to a Binomial Distribution**

*Suppose $X$ is a binomial random variable with $n = 100$ and $p = 0.3$. Estimate $P(X = 40)$ by using the normal approximation.*

**Solution:** We have

$$P(X = 40) = {}_{100}C_{40}(0.3)^{40}(0.7)^{60}$$

using the formula that was mentioned at the beginning of this section. We use a normal distribution with

$$\mu = np = 100(0.3) = 30$$

and

$$\sigma = \sqrt{npq} = \sqrt{100(0.3)(0.7)} = \sqrt{21} \approx 4.58$$

Converting the corrected $X$-values 39.5 and 40.5 to $Z$-values gives

$$z_1 = \frac{39.5 - 30}{\sqrt{21}} \approx 2.07$$

$$z_2 = \frac{40.5 - 30}{\sqrt{21}} \approx 2.29$$

Therefore,

$$P(X = 40) \approx P(2.07 \leq Z \leq 2.29)$$

This probability is the area under a standard normal curve between $z = 2.07$ and $z = 2.29$ (Figure 16.25). That area is the difference of the area between $z = 0$ and $z = 2.29$, which is $A(2.29)$, and the area between $z = 0$ and $z = 2.07$, which is $A(2.07)$. Thus,

$$P(X = 40) \approx P(2.07 \leq Z \leq 2.29)$$

$$= A(2.29) - A(2.07)$$

$$= 0.4890 - 0.4808 = 0.0082 \qquad \text{(from Appendix C)}$$

NOW WORK PROBLEM 3 ●●●

● EXAMPLE 2   **Quality Control**

*In a quality-control experiment, a sample of 500 items is taken from an assembly line. Customarily, 8% of the items produced are defective. What is the probability that more than 50 defective items appear in the sample?*

**Solution:** If $X$ is the number of defective items in the sample, then we will consider $X$ to be binomial with $n = 500$ and $p = 0.08$. To find $P(X \geq 51)$, we use the normal approximation to the binomial distribution with

$$\mu = np = 500(0.08) = 40$$

and

$$\sigma = \sqrt{npq} = \sqrt{500(0.08)(0.92)} = \sqrt{36.8} \approx 6.07$$

Converting the corrected value 50.5 to a $Z$-value gives

$$z = \frac{50.5 - 40}{\sqrt{36.8}} \approx 1.73$$

Thus,

$$P(X \geq 51) \approx P(Z \geq 1.73)$$

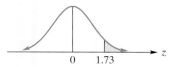

**FIGURE 16.26**   $P(Z \geq 1.73)$.

This probability is the area under a standard normal curve to the right of $z = 1.73$ (Figure 16.26). That area is the difference of the area to the right of $z = 0$, which is 0.5, and the area between $z = 0$ and $z = 1.73$, which is $A(1.73)$. Hence,

$$P(X \geq 51) \approx P(Z \geq 1.73)$$

$$= 0.5 - A(1.73) = 0.5 - 0.4582 = 0.0418$$

NOW WORK PROBLEM 7 ●●●

## Problems 16.3

*In Problems 1–4, X is a binomial random variable with the given values of n and p. Calculate the indicated probabilities by using the normal approximation.*

1. $n = 150$, $p = 0.4$; $P(X \geq 52)$, $P(X \geq 74)$

2. $n = 50$, $p = 0.3$; $P(X = 19)$, $P(X \leq 18)$

*3. $n = 200$, $p = 0.6$; $P(X = 125)$, $P(110 \leq X \leq 135)$

4. $n = 25$, $p = 0.25$; $P(X \geq 7)$

5. **Die Tossing** Suppose a fair die is tossed 300 times. What is the probability that a 5 turns up between 45 and 60 times, inclusive?

6. **Coin Tossing** For a biased coin, $P(H) = 0.4$ and $P(T) = 0.6$. If the coin is tossed 200 times, what is the probability of getting between 90 and 100 heads, inclusive?

*7. **Truck Breakdown** A delivery service has a fleet of 60 trucks. At any given time, the probability of a truck being out of use due to factors such as breakdowns and maintenance is 0.1. What is the probability that 7 or more trucks are out of service at any time?

8. **Quality Control** In a manufacturing plant, a sample of 200 items is taken from the assembly line. For each item in the sample, the probability of being defective is 0.05. What is the probability that there are 7 or more defective items in the sample?

9. **True–False Exam** In a true–false exam with 25 questions, what is the probability of getting at least 13 correct answers by just guessing on all the questions? If there are 100 questions instead of 25, what is the probability of getting at least 60 correct answers by just guessing?

10. **Multiple-Choice Exam** In a multiple-choice test with 50 questions, each question has four answers, only one of which is correct. If a student guesses on the last 20 questions, what is the probability of getting at least half of them correct?

11. **Poker** In a poker game, the probability of being dealt a hand consisting of three cards of one suit and two cards of another suit (in any order) is about 0.1. In 100 dealt hands, what is the probability that 16 or more of them will be as just described?

12. **Taste Test** A major cola company sponsors a national taste test, in which subjects sample its cola as well as the best-selling brand. Neither cola is identified by brand. The subjects are then asked to choose the cola that tastes better. If each of the 35 subjects in a supermarket actually have no preference and arbitrarily choose one of the colas, what is the probability that 25 or more of them choose the cola from the sponsoring company?

## 16.4 Review

### Important Terms and Symbols

**Examples**

| Section 16.1 | **Continuous Random Variables** | |
| --- | --- | --- |
| | continuous random variable    uniform density function | Ex. 1, p. 727 |
| | exponential density function    exponential distribution | Ex. 3, p. 728 |
| | cumulative distribution function | Ex. 4, p. 729 |
| | mean, $\mu$    variance, $\sigma^2$    standard deviation, $\sigma$ | Ex. 5, p. 730 |
| Section 16.2 | **The Normal Distribution** | |
| | normal distribution    normal density function | Ex. 1, p. 733 |
| | standard normal curve    standard normal random variable | Ex. 2, p. 734 |
| | standard normal distribution    standard normal density function | Ex. 4, p. 736 |
| Section 16.3 | **The Normal Approximation to the Binomial Distribution** | |
| | continuity correction | Ex. 1, p. 739 |

## Summary

A continuous random variable $X$ can assume any value in an interval or intervals. A density function for $X$ is a function that has the following properties:

1. $f(x) \geq 0$     2. $\int_{-\infty}^{\infty} f(x)\, dx = 1$

3. $P(a \leq X \leq b) = \int_a^b f(x)\, dx$

Property 3 means that the area under the graph of $f$ and above the $x$-axis from $x = a$ to $x = b$ is $P(a \leq X \leq b)$. The probability that $X$ assumes a particular value is 0.

The continuous random variable $X$ has a uniform distribution over $[a, b]$ if its density function is given by

$$f(x) = \begin{cases} \dfrac{1}{b-a} & \text{if } a \leq x \leq b \\ 0 & \text{otherwise} \end{cases}$$

$X$ has an exponential density function $f$ if

$$f(x) = \begin{cases} ke^{-kx} & \text{if } x \geq 0 \\ 0 & \text{if } x < 0 \end{cases}$$

where $k$ is a positive constant.

The cumulative distribution function $F$ for the continuous random variable $X$ with density function $f$ is given by

$$F(x) = P(X \le x) = \int_{-\infty}^{x} f(t)\, dt$$

Geometrically, $F(x)$ represents the area under the density curve to the left of $x$. By using $F$, we are able to find $P(a \le x \le b)$:

$$P(a \le x \le b) = F(b) - F(a)$$

The mean $\mu$ of $X$ (also called expectation of $X$, $E(X)$) is given by

$$\mu = E(X) = \int_{-\infty}^{\infty} x f(x)\, dx$$

provided that the integral is convergent. The variance is given by

$$\sigma^2 = \mathrm{Var}(X) = \int_{-\infty}^{\infty} (x - \mu)^2 f(x)\, dx$$

$$= \int_{-\infty}^{\infty} x^2 f(x)\, dx - \mu^2$$

provided that the integral is convergent. The standard deviation is given by

$$\sigma = \sqrt{\mathrm{Var}(X)}$$

The graph of the normal density function

$$f(x) = \frac{1}{\sigma \sqrt{2\pi}} e^{-(1/2)((x-\mu)/\sigma)^2}$$

is called a normal curve and is bell shaped. If $X$ has a normal distribution, then the probability that $X$ lies within one standard deviation of the mean $\mu$ is (approximately) 0.68; within two standard deviations, the probability is 0.95; and within three standard deviations, it is 0.997. If $Z$ is a normal random variable with $\mu = 0$ and $\sigma = 1$, then $Z$ is called a standard normal random variable. The probability $P(0 < Z < z_0)$ is the area under the graph of the standard normal curve from $z = 0$ to $z = z_0$ and is denoted $A(z_0)$. Values of $A(z_0)$ appear in Appendix C.

If $X$ is normally distributed with mean $\mu$ and standard deviation $\sigma$, then $X$ can be transformed into a standard normal random variable by the change-of-variable formula

$$Z = \frac{X - \mu}{\sigma}$$

With this formula, probabilities for $X$ can be found by using areas under the standard normal curve.

If $X$ is a binomial random variable and the number $n$ of independent trials is large, then the distribution of $X$ can be approximated by using a normal random variable with mean $np$ and standard deviation $\sqrt{npq}$, where $p$ is the probability of success on any trial and $q = 1 - p$. It is important that continuity corrections be considered when we estimate binomial probabilities by a normal random variable.

## Review Problems

*Problem numbers shown in color indicate problems suggested for use as a practice chapter test.*

1. Suppose $X$ is a continuous random variable with density function given by

$$f(x) = \begin{cases} \frac{1}{3} + kx^2 & \text{if } 0 \le x \le 1 \\ 0 & \text{otherwise} \end{cases}$$

   (a) Find $k$.

   (b) Find $P(\frac{1}{2} < X < \frac{3}{4})$.

   (c) Find $P(X \ge \frac{1}{2})$.

   (d) Find the cumulative distribution function.

2. Suppose $X$ is exponentially distributed with $k = \frac{1}{3}$. Find $P(X > 2)$.

3. Suppose $X$ is a random variable with density function given by

$$f(x) = \begin{cases} \frac{2}{25}x & \text{if } 0 \le x \le 5 \\ 0 & \text{otherwise} \end{cases}$$

   (a) Find $\mu$.

   (b) Find $\sigma$.

4. Let $X$ be uniformly distributed over the interval $[2, 6]$. Find $P(X < 5)$.

*Let $X$ be normally distributed with mean 20 and standard deviation 4. In Problems 5–10, determine the given probabilities.*

5. $P(X > 22)$

6. $P(X < 21)$

7. $P(14 < X < 18)$

8. $P(X > 10)$

9. $P(X < 23)$

10. $P(23 < X < 33)$

*In Problems 11 and 12, $X$ is a binomial random variable with $n = 100$ and $p = 0.35$. Find the given probabilities by using the normal approximation.*

11. $P(25 \le X \le 47)$

12. $P(X = 48)$

13. **Heights of Individuals**   The heights (in inches) of individuals in a certain group are normally distributed with mean 68 and standard deviation 2. Find the probability that an individual from this group is taller than 6 ft.

14. **Coin Tossing**   If a fair coin is tossed 500 times, use the normal approximation to the binomial distribution to estimate the probability that a head comes up at least 215 times.

# Mathematical Snapshot

## Cumulative Distribution from Data

What Section 16.3 said about histograms of discrete random variables is even more directly true for continuous random variables: The probability density curve can be thought of as the limiting case of a probability histogram. Indeed, this fact is often used to explain the idea of a probability density function.

With continuous variables, a histogram divides the range of possible values into a series of intervals, called bins. Above each bin is a bar whose height indicates how much of the data set lies in that bin. Figure 16.27 illustrates this. The rightmost bin is the interval from 8 to 10. Because one-fifth of the data values lie in that bin, the bar covers one-fifth of the area of all the bars put together.

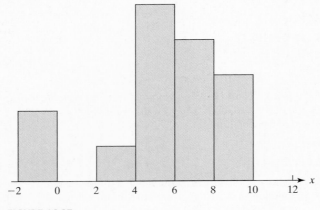

**FIGURE 16.27**

A probability density curve is the limit of a histogram's outline as the data set gets very large and the bin size gets very small. Figure 16.28 illustrates a larger data set and smaller bin size.

Unfortunately, dozens of data values are normally needed before a histogram's contours begin to smooth out. As a practical matter, we might want to "cheat" and get an

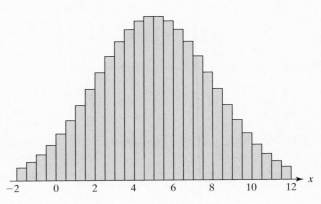

**FIGURE 16.28**

idea of the shape of the probability density function using fewer data values—and without having to draw a histogram.

Here is a way to do that: First use the data values to plot points that reveal the *cumulative distribution* curve, and then use this curve to infer the shape of the probability density curve. The steps are as follows:

**Step 1:** Determine $n$, the sample size.

**Step 2:** Arrange the data values in order, least to greatest. The smallest data value is $v(1)$, the next-smallest is $v(2)$, and so on.

**Step 3:** On a set of coordinate axes, plot $n$ points with coordinates $\left( v(i), \dfrac{i - \frac{1}{2}}{n} \right)$ for $i$ ranging from 1 to $n$.

**Step 4:** Determine what cumulative distribution function the plot suggests.

**Step 5:** Find the probability density function as the derivative of the cumulative distribution function.

In step 3, we are plotting each data value $v(i)$ against the experimental probability, based on the data, that a new value would be less than $v(i)$. This probability is calculated by taking the number of values below $v(i)$, namely $i - 1$; adding a term of $\frac{1}{2}$ to split the $i$th data point in two and count half of it as "below $v(i)$"; and dividing the result by $n$, the total number of values.

Let us see how this works with data values generated using a known probability density function. On a graphing calculator, we use the *rand* command or its equivalent to generate 15 values (step 1) using the uniform density function that equals 1 on the interval from 0 to 1 and equals 0 elsewhere. One such run produces the following values (ordered from lowest to highest and rounded to three decimal places): 0.043, 0.074, 0.093, 0.198, 0.293, 0.311, 0.399, 0.400, 0.409, 0.566, 0.654, 0.665, 0.760, 0.919, 0.967 (step 2).

When the corresponding probabilities are plotted (step 3), the result is as shown in Figure 16.29.

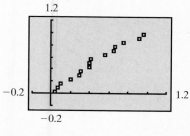

FIGURE 16.29

Even if we did not know how the points had been generated, we could still notice that all data values are between 0 and 1 and that the plotted points lie fairly close to the line $y = x$. This suggests (step 4) the cumulative distribution function

$$F(x) = \begin{cases} 0 & x < 0 \\ x & 0 \le x \le 1 \\ 1 & x > 1 \end{cases}$$

The derivative of this function with respect to $x$ (step 5) is

$$P(x) = \begin{cases} 0 & x < 0 \\ 1 & 0 < x < 1 \\ 0 & x > 1 \end{cases}$$

which is exactly the function that was used to generate the data values.[2] The method works.

A word of caution, however. By nature, cumulative distribution functions are increasing from left to right and therefore all have a broadly similar shape. The plot in Figure 16.29, for example, might instead be interpreted as reflecting the cumulative distribution function

$$F_2(x) = \begin{cases} 0 & x < 0 \\ 1 - e^{-2x} & 0 \le x \end{cases}$$

The fit would not be quite so good as for $F(x)$, but it would not look out of the question either. So the method described here for identifying a possible cumulative distribution function and its derivative, the probability density function, is best supplemented by other information, such as knowledge of the process producing the data.

## Problems

1. Generate your own run of 15 values using a uniform density function, and plot the results to obtain a picture of the cumulative distribution function. How well do your results fit with the known distribution function?

2. Repeat Problem 1 for a normal density function. (On the TI-83 Plus, use the *randNorm(* command.) In step 4, perform a logistic regression. Although the cumulative distribution function for a normal density function is *not* actually a logistic function, it has a very similar shape, so that a logistic function can be used as an approximation. Then, if your calculator has the capability, plot the derivative of the logistic function. Otherwise, note where the logistic function's slope is greatest and what happens to the slope at the ends of the curve. How does the behavior of the derivative compare with the behavior of the normal density function used to generate the data values?

3. Visit a Web site with a table of data values and see if you can determine the nature of the probability density function. You might try the near-real-time earthquake list at the U.S. Geological Survey (wwwneic.cr.usgs.gov) or one of the many data sets published by the U.S. Census (www.census.org). Why do you think the data are distributed as they are?

[2]Notice that $P(i)$ is undefined for $x = 0$ and $x = 1$. This does not matter.

# 17

# MULTIVARIABLE CALCULUS

 **Mathematical Snapshot** Data Analysis to Model Cooling

We know (from Chapter 13) how to maximize a company's profit when both revenue and cost are written as functions of a single quantity, namely the number of units produced. But of course the production level is itself determined by other factors—and, in general, no single variable can represent them.

The amount of oil pumped from an oil field each week, for example, depends on both the number of pumps and the number of hours that the pumps are operated. The number of pumps in the field will depend on the amount of capital originally available to build the pumps as well as the size and shape of the field. The number of hours that the pumps can be operated depends on the labor available to run and maintain the pumps. In addition, the amount of oil that the owner will be willing to have pumped from the oil field will depend on the current demand for oil—which is related to the price of the oil.

Maximizing the weekly profit from an oil field will require a balance between the number of pumps and the amount of time each pump can be operated. The maximum profit will not be achieved by building more pumps than can be operated or by running a few pumps full-time.

This is an example of the general problem of maximizing profit when production depends on several factors. The solution involves an analysis of the production function, which relates production output to resources allocated for production. Because, in general, several variables are needed to describe the resource allocation, the most profitable allocation cannot be found by differentiation with respect to a single variable, as in preceding chapters. The more advanced techniques necessary to do the job will be covered in this chapter.

## 17.1 Functions of Several Variables

Suppose a manufacturer produces two products, X and Y. Then the total cost depends on the levels of production of *both* X and Y. Table 17.1 is a schedule that indicates total cost at various levels. For example, when 5 units of X and 6 units of Y are produced, the total cost $c$ is 17. In this situation, it seems natural to associate the number 17 with the *ordered pair* (5, 6):

$$(5, 6) \mapsto 17$$

The first element of the ordered pair, 5, represents the number of units of X produced, while the second element, 6, represents the number of units of Y produced. Corresponding to the other production situations, we have

$$(5, 7) \mapsto 19$$

$$(6, 6) \mapsto 18$$

and

$$(6, 7) \mapsto 20$$

**TABLE 17.1**

| No. of Units of X Produced, $x$ | No. of Units of Y Produced, $y$ | Total Cost of Production, $c$ |
|---|---|---|
| 5 | 6 | 17 |
| 5 | 7 | 19 |
| 6 | 6 | 18 |
| 6 | 7 | 20 |

This correspondence can be considered an input–output relation where the inputs are ordered pairs. With each input, we associate exactly one output. Thus, the correspondence defines a function $f$ whose domain consists of (5, 6), (5, 7), (6, 6), (6, 7) and whose range consists of 17, 19, 18, 20. In function notation,

$$f(5, 6) = 17 \quad f(5, 7) = 19$$

$$f(6, 6) = 18 \quad f(6, 7) = 20$$

We say that the total-cost schedule can be described by $c = f(x, y)$, a function of the two independent variables $x$ and $y$. The letter $c$ is the dependent variable.

Turning to another function of two variables, we see that the equation

$$z = \frac{2}{x^2 + y^2}$$

defines $z$ as a function of $x$ and $y$:

$$z = f(x, y) = \frac{2}{x^2 + y^2}$$

The domain of $f$ is all ordered pairs of real numbers $(x, y)$ for which the equation has meaning when the first and second elements of $(x, y)$ are substituted for $x$ and $y$, respectively, in the equation. Thus, the domain of $f$ is all ordered pairs except $(0, 0)$. For example, to find $f(2, 3)$, we substitute $x = 2$ and $y = 3$ into the expression $2/(x^2 + y^2)$. We obtain $f(2, 3) = 2/(2^2 + 3^2) = 2/13$.

We do not have to look as far as the previous $f$ for functions of several variables. Ordinary addition of real numbers defines the function

$$z = f(x, y) = x + y$$

which generalizes to the linear functions studied in Chapter 7. We can just as easily consider functions where the inputs are ordered triples of real numbers. In Example 2 of Section 7.4 we had

$$Z = 3x_1 + 4x_2 + \frac{3}{2}x_3$$

and we could certainly write $Z = f(x_1, x_2, x_3)$. There is no reason why a function of two variables must be defined for pairs of arbitrary *real* numbers. In Section 5.4 we studied $a_{\overline{n}|r}$, the present value of $n$ one-dollar payments at the interest rate of $r$ per period. The notation is strange, but if we write

$$A = a(n, r) = a_{\overline{n}|r}$$

we see that for input pairs $(n, r)$, where $n$ is a positive integer and $r$ is a (rational) number in the the interval $(0, 1]$, the function $a$ so defined provides real numbers as given, approximately, by the partial listing of Appendix A. For still another example, this time from Section 8.2, consider

$$C(n, r) = {}_nC_r$$

the number of combinations of $n$ objects taken $r$ at a time.

**PRINCIPLES IN PRACTICE 1**

**FUNCTIONS OF TWO VARIABLES**

The cost per day for manufacturing both 12-ounce and 20-ounce coffee mugs is given by $c = 160 + 2x + 3y$, where $x$ is the number of 12-ounce mugs and $y$ is the number of 20-ounce mugs. What is the cost per day of manufacturing

1. 500 12-ounce and 700 20-ounce mugs?
2. 1000 12-ounce and 750 20-ounce mugs?

### EXAMPLE 1  Functions of Two Variables

**a.** $f(x, y) = \dfrac{x+3}{y-2}$ is a function of two variables. Because the denominator is zero when $y = 2$, the domain of $f$ is all $(x, y)$ such that $y \neq 2$. Some function values are

$$f(0, 3) = \frac{0+3}{3-2} = 3$$

$$f(3, 0) = \frac{3+3}{0-2} = -3$$

Note that $f(0, 3) \neq f(3, 0)$.

**b.** $h(x, y) = 4x$ defines $h$ as a function of $x$ and $y$. The domain is all ordered pairs of real numbers. Some function values are

$$h(2, 5) = 4(2) = 8$$

$$h(2, 6) = 4(2) = 8$$

Note that the function values are independent of the choice of $y$.

**c.** If $z^2 = x^2 + y^2$ and $x = 3$ and $y = 4$, then $z^2 = 3^2 + 4^2 = 25$. Consequently, $z = \pm 5$. Thus, with the ordered pair $(3, 4)$, we *cannot* associate exactly one output number. Hence $z^2 = x^2 + y^2$ does not define $z$ as a function of $x$ and $y$.

NOW WORK PROBLEM 1

### EXAMPLE 2  Temperature–Humidity Index

*On hot and humid days, many people tend to feel uncomfortable. The degree of discomfort is numerically given by the temperature–humidity index, THI, which is a function of two variables, $t_d$ and $t_w$:*

$$\text{THI} = f(t_d, t_w) = 15 + 0.4(t_d + t_w)$$

*where $t_d$ is the dry-bulb temperature (in degrees Fahrenheit) and $t_w$ is the wet-bulb temperature (in degrees Fahrenheit) of the air. Evaluate the THI when $t_d = 90$ and $t_w = 80$.*

**Solution:** We want to find $f(90, 80)$:

$$f(90, 80) = 15 + 0.4(90 + 80) = 15 + 68 = 83$$

When the THI is greater than 75, most people are uncomfortable. In fact, the THI was once called the "discomfort index." Many electric utilities closely follow this index so that they can anticipate the demand that air-conditioning places on their systems.

NOW WORK PROBLEM 3

If $y = f(x)$ is a function of one variable, the domain of $f$ can be geometrically represented by points on the real-number line. The function itself can be represented by its graph in a coordinate plane, sometimes called a two-dimensional coordinate system. However, for a function of two variables, $z = f(x, y)$, the domain (consisting of ordered pairs of real numbers) can be geometrically represented by a *region* in the plane. The function itself can be geometrically represented in a ***three*-dimensional rectangular coordinate system.** Such a system is formed when three mutually perpendicular real-number lines in space intersect at the origin of each line, as in Figure 17.1. The three number lines are called the $x$-, $y$-, and $z$-axes, and their point of intersection is called the origin of the system. The arrows indicate the positive directions of the axes, and the negative portions of the axes are shown as dashed lines.

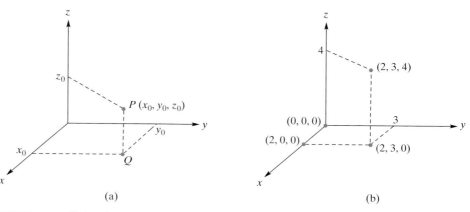

(a)                                         (b)

**FIGURE 17.2**   Points in space.

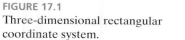

**FIGURE 17.1**
Three-dimensional rectangular
coordinate system.

To each point $P$ in space, we can assign a unique ordered triple of numbers, called the *coordinates* of $P$. To do this [see Figure 17.2(a)], from $P$, we construct a line perpendicular to the $x,y$-plane—that is, the plane determined by the $x$- and $y$-axes. Let $Q$ be the point where the line intersects this plane. From $Q$, we construct perpendiculars to the $x$- and $y$-axes. These lines intersect the $x$- and $y$-axes at $x_0$ and $y_0$, respectively. From $P$, a perpendicular to the $z$-axis is constructed that intersects the axis at $z_0$. Thus, we assign to $P$ the ordered triple $(x_0, y_0, z_0)$. It should also be evident that with each ordered triple of numbers we can assign a unique point in space. Due to this one-to-one correspondence between points in space and ordered triples, an ordered triple can be called a point. In Figure 17.2(b), points $(2, 0, 0)$, $(2, 3, 0)$, and $(2, 3, 4)$ are shown. Note that the origin corresponds to $(0, 0, 0)$. Typically, the negative portions of the axes are not shown unless required.

We can represent a function of two variables, $z = f(x, y)$, geometrically. To each ordered pair $(x, y)$ in the domain of $f$, we assign the point $(x, y, f(x, y))$. The set of all such points is called the *graph* of $f$. Such a graph appears in Figure 17.3. You can consider $z = f(x, y)$ as representing a surface in space.[1]

In Chapter 10, the continuity of a function of one variable was discussed. If $y = f(x)$, then to say that $f$ is continuous at $x = a$ is to say that we can make the values $f(x)$ a close as we like to $f(a)$ by taking $x$ sufficiently close to, but different from, $a$. This concept extends to a function of two variables. We say that the function $z = f(x, y)$ is continuous at $(a, b)$ if we can make the values $f(x, y)$ a close as we like to $f(a, b)$ by taking $(x, y)$ sufficiently close to, but different from, $(a, b)$. Loosely interpreting this concept, and without delving into it in great depth, we can say that a function of two variables is continuous on its domain (that is, continuous at each point in its domain) if its graph is an unbroken surface.

In general, a **function of $n$ variables** is a function whose domain consists of ordered $n$-tuples $(x_1, x_2, \ldots, x_n)$. For example, $f(x, y, z) = 2x + 3y + 4z$ is a function of three variables with a domain consisting of all ordered triples. The function

---

[1] We will freely use the term *surface* in an intuitive sense.

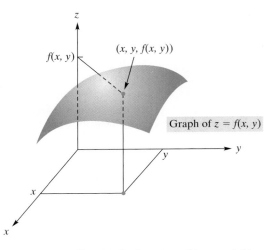

**FIGURE 17.3**    Graph of a function of two variables.

$g(x_1, x_2, x_3, x_4) = x_1 x_2 x_3 x_4$ is a function of four variables with a domain consisting of all ordered 4-tuples. Although functions of several variables are extremely important and useful, we cannot visualize the graphs of functions of more than two variables.

We now give a brief discussion of sketching surfaces in space. We begin with planes that are parallel to a coordinate plane. By a "coordinate plane" we mean a plane containing two coordinate axes. For example, the plane determined by the $x$- and $y$-axes is the $x,y$-**plane.** Similarly, we speak of the $x,z$-**plane** and the $y,z$-**plane.** The coordinate planes divide space into eight parts, called *octants*. In particular, the part containing all points $(x, y, z)$ such that $x$, $y$, and $z$ are positive is called the **first octant.**

Names are not usually assigned to the remaining seven octants.

Suppose $S$ is a plane that is parallel to the $x,y$-plane and passes through the point $(0, 0, 5)$. [See Figure 17.4(a).] Then the point $(x, y, z)$ will lie on $S$ if and only if $z = 5$; that is, $x$ and $y$ can be any real numbers, but $z$ must equal 5. For this reason, we say that $z = 5$ is an equation of $S$. Similarly, an equation of the plane parallel to the $x,z$-plane and passing through the point $(0, 2, 0)$ is $y = 2$ [Figure 17.4(b)]. The equation $x = 3$ is an equation of the plane passing through $(3, 0, 0)$ and parallel to the $y,z$-plane [Figure 17.4(c)]. Now let us look at planes in general.

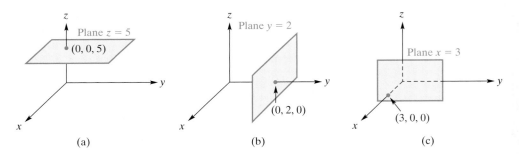

|       |       |       |
|-------|-------|-------|
| (a)   | (b)   | (c)   |

**FIGURE 17.4**    Planes parallel to coordinate planes.

In space, the graph of an equation of the form

$$Ax + By + Cz + D = 0$$

where $D$ is a constant and $A$, $B$, and $C$ are constants that are not all zero, is a plane. Since three distinct points (not lying on the same line) determine a plane, a convenient way to sketch a plane is to first determine the points, if any, where the plane intersects the $x$-, $y$-, and $z$-axes. These points are called *intercepts*.

## ● EXAMPLE 3   Graphing a Plane

*Sketch the plane $2x + 3y + z = 6$.*

**Solution:** The plane intersects the $x$-axis when $y = 0$ and $z = 0$. Thus, $2x = 6$, which gives $x = 3$. Similarly, if $x = z = 0$ then $y = 2$; if $x = y = 0$, then $z = 6$. Therefore, the intercepts are $(3, 0, 0)$, $(0, 2, 0)$ and $(0, 0, 6)$. After these points are plotted, a plane is passed through them. The portion of the plane in the first octant is shown in Figure 17.5(a); however, you should realize that the plane extends indefinitely into space.

NOW WORK PROBLEM 19 ●●●

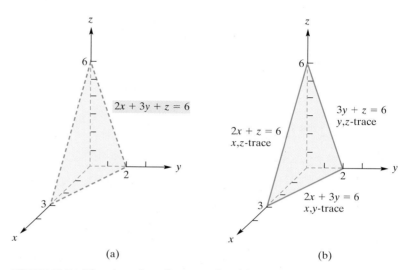

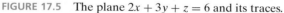

(a)                          (b)

**FIGURE 17.5**   The plane $2x + 3y + z = 6$ and its traces.

A surface can be sketched with the aid of its **traces.** These are the intersections of the surface with the coordinate planes. To illustrate, for the plane $2x + 3y + z = 6$ in Example 3, the trace in the $x,y$-plane is obtained by setting $z = 0$. This gives $2x + 3y = 6$, which is an equation of a *line* in the $x,y$-plane. Similarly, setting $x = 0$ gives the trace in the $y,z$-plane: the line $3y + z = 6$. The $x,z$-trace is the line $2x + z = 6$. [See Figure 17.5(b).]

## ● EXAMPLE 4   Sketching a Surface

*Sketch the surface $2x + z = 4$.*

**Solution:** This equation has the form of a plane. The $x$- and $z$-intercepts are $(2, 0, 0)$ and $(0, 0, 4)$, and there is no $y$-intercept, since $x$ and $z$ cannot both be zero. Setting $y = 0$ gives the $x,z$-trace $2x + z = 4$, which is a line in the $x,z$-plane. In fact, the intersection of the surface with *any* plane $y = k$ is also $2x + z = 4$. Hence, the plane appears as in Figure 17.6.

NOW WORK PROBLEM 21 ●●●

Our final examples deal with surfaces that are not planes but whose graphs can be easily obtained.

## ● EXAMPLE 5   Sketching a Surface

*Sketch the surface $z = x^2$.*

**Solution:** The $x,z$-trace is the curve $z = x^2$, which is parabola. In fact, for *any* fixed value of $y$, we get $z = x^2$. Thus, the graph appears as in Figure 17.7.

NOW WORK PROBLEM 25 ●●●

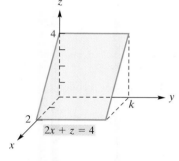

**FIGURE 17.6**   The plane $2x + z = 4$.

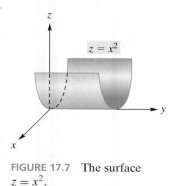

**FIGURE 17.7**   The surface $z = x^2$.

Note that this equation places no restriction on $y$.

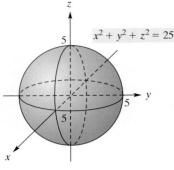

**FIGURE 17.8** The surface $x^2 + y^2 + z^2 = 25$.

● EXAMPLE 6 **Sketching a Surface**

*Sketch the surface $x^2 + y^2 + z^2 = 25$.*

**Solution:** Setting $z = 0$ gives the $x,y$-trace $x^2 + y^2 = 25$, which is a circle of radius 5. Similarly, the $y,z$- and $x,z$-traces are the circles $y^2 + z^2 = 25$ and $x^2 + z^2 = 25$, respectively. Note also that since $x^2 + y^2 = 25 - z^2$, the intersection of the surface with the plane $z = k$, where $-5 \leq k \leq 5$, is a circle. For example, if $z = 3$, the intersection is the circle $x^2 + y^2 = 16$. If $z = 4$, the intersection is $x^2 + y^2 = 9$. That is, cross sections of the surface that are parallel to the $x,y$-plane are circles. The surface appears in Figure 17.8; it is a sphere.

NOW WORK PROBLEM 27 ●●●

## Problems 17.1

*In Problems 1–12, determine the indicated function values for the given functions.*

*1. $f(x, y) = 4x - y^2 + 3$;   $f(1, 2)$

2. $f(x, y) = 3x^2y - 4y$;   $f(2, -1)$

*3. $g(x, y, z) = e^{2x}(3y + z)$;   $g(0, 3, -1)$

4. $g(x, y, z) = x^2yz + xy^2z + xyz^2$;   $g(3, 1, -2)$

5. $h(r, s, t, u) = \dfrac{rs}{t^2 - u^2}$;   $h(-3, 3, 5, 4)$

6. $h(r, s, t, u) = \ln(ru)$;   $h(1, 5, 3, 1)$

7. $g(p_A, p_B) = 2p_A(p_A^2 - 5)$;   $g(4, 8)$

8. $g(p_A, p_B) = p_A\sqrt{p_B} + 10$;   $g(8, 4)$

9. $F(x, y, z) = 3$;   $F(2, 0, -1)$

10. $F(x, y, z) = \dfrac{2x}{(y + 1)z}$;   $F(1, 0, 3)$

11. $f(x, y) = e^{x+y}$;   $f(x_0 + h, y_0)$

12. $f(x, y) = x^2y - 3y^3$;   $f(r + t, r)$

13. **Ecology** A method of ecological sampling to determine animal populations in a given area involves first marking all the animals obtained in a sample of $R$ animals from the area and then releasing them so that they can mix with unmarked animals. At a later date a second sample is taken of $M$ animals and the number of these that are marked, $S$, is noted. Based on $R$, $M$, and $S$, an estimate of the total population of animals in the sample area is given by

$$N = f(R, M, S) = \frac{RM}{S}$$

Find $f(400, 400, 80)$. This method is called the *mark-and-recapture procedure*.[2]

14. **Genetics** Under certain conditions, if two brown-eyed parents have exactly $k$ children, the probability that there will be exactly $r$ blue-eyed children is given by

$$P(r, k) = \frac{k! \left(\frac{1}{4}\right)^r \left(\frac{3}{4}\right)^{k-r}}{r!(k - r)!} \quad r = 0, 1, 2, \ldots, k$$

Find the probability that, out of a total of four children, exactly three will be blue-eyed.

*In Problems 15–18, find equations of the planes that satisfy the given conditions.*

15. Parallel to the $x,z$-plane and also passes through the point $(0, 2, 0)$

16. Parallel to the $y,z$-plane and also passes through the point $(-2, 0, 0)$

17. Parallel to the $x,y$-plane and also passes through the point $(2, 7, 6)$

18. Parallel to the $y,z$-plane and also passes through the point $(-4, -2, 7)$

*In Problems 19–28, sketch the given surfaces.*

*19. $x + y + z = 1$          20. $2x + y + 2z = 6$

*21. $3x + 6y + 2z = 12$      22. $2x + 3y + 5z = 1$

23. $x + 2y = 2$             24. $y = 3z + 2$

*25. $z = 4 - x^2$            26. $y = z^2$

*27. $x^2 + y^2 + z^2 = 9$    28. $3x^2 + 2y^2 = 1$

OBJECTIVE

To compute partial derivatives.

## 17.2 Partial Derivatives

•••

Figure 17.9 shows the surface $z = f(x, y)$ and a plane that is parallel to the $x,z$-plane and that passes through the point $(a, b, f(a, b))$ on the surface. The equation of this plane is $y = b$. Hence, any point on the curve that is the intersection of the surface $z = f(x, y)$ with the plane $y = b$ must have the form $(x, b, f(x, b))$. Thus, the curve can be described by the equation $z = f(x, b)$. Since $b$ is constant, $z = f(x, b)$ can be considered a function of one variable, $x$. When the derivative of this function is evaluated at $a$, it gives the slope of the tangent line to this curve at the point

[2] E. P. Odum, *Ecology* (New York: Holt, Rinehart and Winston, 1966).

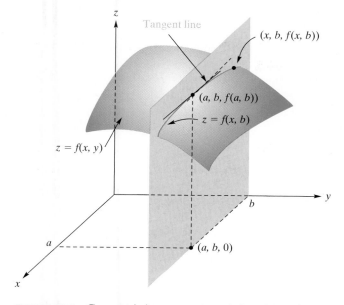

FIGURE 17.9   Geometric interpretation of $f_x(a, b)$.

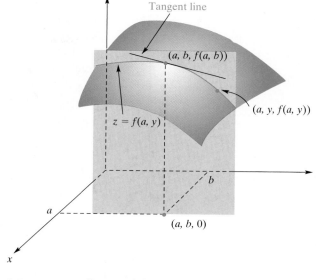

FIGURE 17.10   Geometric interpretation of $f_y(a, b)$.

$(a, b, f(a, b))$. (See Figure 17.9.) This slope is called the *partial derivative of f with respect to x at* $(a, b)$ and is denoted $f_x(a, b)$. In terms of limits,

$$f_x(a, b) = \lim_{h \to 0} \frac{f(a + h, b) - f(a, b)}{h} \tag{1}$$

On the other hand, in Figure 17.10, the plane $x = a$ is parallel to the $y, z$-plane and cuts the surface $z = f(x, y)$ in a curve given by $z = f(a, y)$, a function of $y$. When the derivative of this function is evaluated at $b$, it gives the slope of the tangent line to this curve at the point $(a, b, f(a, b))$. This slope is called the *partial derivative of f with respect to y at* $(a, b)$ and is denoted $f_y(a, b)$. In terms of limits,

$$f_y(a, b) = \lim_{h \to 0} \frac{f(a, b + h) - f(a, b)}{h} \tag{2}$$

We say that $f_x(a, b)$ is the slope of the tangent line to the graph of $f$ at $(a, b, f(a, b))$ *in the x-direction;* similarly, $f_y(a, b)$ is the slope of the tangent line *in the y-direction.*

For generality, by replacing $a$ and $b$ in Equations (1) and (2) by $x$ and $y$, respectively, we get the following definition.

This gives us a geometric interpretation of a partial derivative.

> **DEFINITION**
> If $z = f(x, y)$, the **partial derivative of f with respect to x**, denoted $f_x$, is the function given by
>
> $$f_x(x, y) = \lim_{h \to 0} \frac{f(x + h, y) - f(x, y)}{h}$$
>
> provided that the limit exists.
>     The **partial derivative of f with respect to y**, denoted $f_y$, is the function given by
>
> $$f_y(x, y) = \lim_{h \to 0} \frac{f(x, y + h) - f(x, y)}{h}$$
>
> provided that the limit exists.

By analyzing the foregoing definition, we can state the following procedure to find $f_x$ and $f_y$:

This gives us a mechanical way to find partial derivatives.

**Procedure to Find** $f_x(x, y)$ **and** $f_y(x, y)$

To find $f_x$, treat $y$ as a constant, and differentiate $f$ with respect to $x$ in the usual way.

To find $f_y$, treat $x$ as a constant, and differentiate $f$ with respect to $y$ in the usual way.

●**EXAMPLE 1** **Finding Partial Derivatives**

*If* $f(x, y) = xy^2 + x^2y$, *find* $f_x(x, y)$ *and* $f_y(x, y)$. *Also, find* $f_x(3, 4)$ *and* $f_y(3, 4)$.

**Solution:** To find $f_x(x, y)$, we treat $y$ as a constant and differentiate $f$ with respect to $x$:

$$f_x(x, y) = (1)y^2 + (2x)y = y^2 + 2xy$$

To find $f_y(x, y)$, we treat $x$ as a constant and differentiate with respect to $y$:

$$f_y(x, y) = x(2y) + x^2(1) = 2xy + x^2$$

Note that $f_x(x, y)$ and $f_y(x, y)$ are each functions of the two variables $x$ and $y$. To find $f_x(3, 4)$ we evaluate $f_x(x, y)$ when $x = 3$ and $y = 4$:

$$f_x(3, 4) = 4^2 + 2(3)(4) = 40$$

Similarly,

$$f_y(3, 4) = 2(3)(4) + 3^2 = 33$$

NOW WORK PROBLEM 1 ●●●

Notations for partial derivatives of $z = f(x, y)$ are in Table 17.2. Table 17.3 gives notations for partial derivatives evaluated at $(a, b)$. Note that the symbol $\partial$ (not $d$) is used to denote a partial derivative. The symbol $\partial z/\partial x$ is read "the partial derivative of $z$ with respect to $x$."

**TABLE 17.2**

| Partial Derivative of $f$ (or $z$) with Respect to $x$ | Partial Derivative of $f$ (or $z$) with Respect to $y$ |
|---|---|
| $f_x(x, y)$ | $f_y(x, y)$ |
| $\dfrac{\partial}{\partial x}(f(x, y))$ | $\dfrac{\partial}{\partial y}(f(x, y))$ |
| $\dfrac{\partial z}{\partial x}$ | $\dfrac{\partial z}{\partial y}$ |

**TABLE 17.3**

| Partial Derivative of $f$ (or $z$) with Respect to $x$ Evaluated at $(a, b)$ | Partial Derivative of $f$ (or $z$) with Respect to $y$ Evaluated at $(a, b)$ |
|---|---|
| $f_x(a, b)$ | $f_y(a, b)$ |
| $\left.\dfrac{\partial z}{\partial x}\right|_{(a,b)}$ | $\left.\dfrac{\partial z}{\partial y}\right|_{(a,b)}$ |
| $\left.\dfrac{\partial z}{\partial x}\right|_{\substack{x=a \\ y=b}}$ | $\left.\dfrac{\partial z}{\partial y}\right|_{\substack{x=a \\ y=b}}$ |

●**EXAMPLE 2** **Finding Partial Derivatives**

**a.** *If* $z = 3x^3y^3 - 9x^2y + xy^2 + 4y$, *find* $\dfrac{\partial z}{\partial x}, \dfrac{\partial z}{\partial y}, \left.\dfrac{\partial z}{\partial x}\right|_{(1,0)}$ *and* $\left.\dfrac{\partial z}{\partial y}\right|_{(1,0)}$.

**Solution:** To find $\partial z/\partial x$, we differentiate $z$ with respect to $x$ while treating $y$ as a constant:

$$\frac{\partial z}{\partial x} = 3(3x^2)y^3 - 9(2x)y + (1)y^2 + 0$$

$$= 9x^2y^3 - 18xy + y^2$$

Evaluating the latter equation at $(1, 0)$, we obtain

$$\left.\frac{\partial z}{\partial x}\right|_{(1,0)} = 9(1)^2(0)^3 - 18(1)(0) + 0^2 = 0$$

To find $\partial z/\partial y$, we differentiate $z$ with respect to $y$ while treating $x$ as a constant:

$$\frac{\partial z}{\partial y} = 3x^3(3y^2) - 9x^2(1) + x(2y) + 4(1)$$

$$= 9x^3y^2 - 9x^2 + 2xy + 4$$

Thus,

$$\left.\frac{\partial z}{\partial y}\right|_{(1,0)} = 9(1)^3(0)^2 - 9(1)^2 + 2(1)(0) + 4 = -5$$

**b.** *If $w = x^2 e^{2x+3y}$, find $\partial w/\partial x$ and $\partial w/\partial y$.*

**Solution:** To find $\partial w/\partial x$, we treat $y$ as a constant and differentiate with respect to $x$. Since $x^2 e^{2x+3y}$ is a product of two functions, each involving $x$, we use the product rule:

$$\frac{\partial w}{\partial x} = x^2 \frac{\partial}{\partial x}(e^{2x+3y}) + e^{2x+3y} \frac{\partial}{\partial x}(x^2)$$

$$= x^2(2e^{2x+3y}) + e^{2x+3y}(2x)$$

$$= 2x(x+1)e^{2x+3y}$$

To find $\partial w/\partial y$, we treat $x$ as a constant and differentiate with respect to $y$:

$$\frac{\partial w}{\partial y} = x^2 \frac{\partial}{\partial y}(e^{2x+3y}) = 3x^2 e^{2x+3y}$$

NOW WORK PROBLEM 27 ●●

We have seen that, for a function of two variables, two partial derivatives can be considered. Actually, the concept of partial derivatives can be extended to functions of more than two variables. For example, with $w = f(x, y, z)$ we have three partial derivatives:

the partial with respect to $x$, denoted $f_x(x, y, z)$, $\partial w/\partial x$, and so on;
the partial with respect to $y$, denoted $f_y(x, y, z)$, $\partial w/\partial y$, and so on;
and
the partial with respect to $z$, denoted $f_z(x, y, z)$, $\partial w/\partial z$, and so on

To determine $\partial w/\partial x$, treat $y$ and $z$ as constants, and differentiate $w$ with respect to $x$. For $\partial w/\partial y$, treat $x$ and $z$ as constants, and differentiate with respect to $y$. For $\partial w/\partial z$, treat $x$ and $y$ as constants, and differentiate with respect to $z$. For a function of $n$ variables, we have $n$ partial derivatives, which are determined in an analogous way.

●**EXAMPLE 3** **Partial Derivatives of a Function of Three Variables**

*If $f(x, y, z) = x^2 + y^2 z + z^3$, find $f_x(x, y, z)$, $f_y(x, y, z)$, and $f_z(x, y, z)$.*

**Solution:** To find $f_x(x, y, z)$, we treat $y$ and $z$ as constants and differentiate $f$ with respect to $x$:

$$f_x(x, y, z) = 2x$$

Treating $x$ and $z$ as constants and differentiating with respect to $y$, we have

$$f_y(x, y, z) = 2yz$$

Treating $x$ and $y$ as constants and differentiating with respect to $z$, we have

$$f_z(x, y, z) = y^2 + 3z^2$$

NOW WORK PROBLEM 23 ●●

⬤ **EXAMPLE 4** Partial Derivatives of a Function of Four Variables

If $p = g(r, s, t, u) = \dfrac{rsu}{rt^2 + s^2t}$, find $\dfrac{\partial p}{\partial s}$, $\dfrac{\partial p}{\partial t}$, and $\left. \dfrac{\partial p}{\partial t} \right|_{(0,1,1,1)}$.

**Solution:** To find $\partial p/\partial s$, first note that $p$ is a quotient of two functions, each involving the variable $s$. Thus, we use the quotient rule and treat $r$, $t$, and $u$ as constants:

$$\frac{\partial p}{\partial s} = \frac{(rt^2 + s^2t)\dfrac{\partial}{\partial s}(rsu) - rsu\dfrac{\partial}{\partial s}(rt^2 + s^2t)}{(rt^2 + s^2t)^2}$$

$$= \frac{(rt^2 + s^2t)(ru) - (rsu)(2st)}{(rt^2 + s^2t)^2}$$

Simplification gives

$$\frac{\partial p}{\partial s} = \frac{ru(rt - s^2)}{t(rt + s^2)^2} \qquad \text{(a factor of } t \text{ cancels)}$$

To find $\partial p/\partial t$, we can first write $p$ as

$$p = rsu(rt^2 + s^2t)^{-1}$$

Next, we use the power rule and treat $r$, $s$, and $u$ as constants:

$$\frac{\partial p}{\partial t} = rsu(-1)(rt^2 + s^2t)^{-2}\frac{\partial}{\partial t}(rt^2 + s^2t)$$

$$= -rsu(rt^2 + s^2t)^{-2}(2rt + s^2)$$

so that

$$\frac{\partial p}{\partial s} = -\frac{rsu(2rt + s^2)}{(rt^2 + s^2t)^2}$$

Letting $r = 0$, $s = 1$, $t = 1$, and $u = 1$ gives

$$\left. \frac{\partial p}{\partial t} \right|_{(0,1,1,1)} = -\frac{0(1)(1)(2(0)(1) + (1)^2)}{(0(1)^2 + (1)^2(1))^2} = 0$$

NOW WORK PROBLEM 31 ⬤⬤⬤

# Problems 17.2

*In Problems 1–26, a function of two or more variables is given. Find the partial derivative of the function with respect to each of the variables.*

*1. $f(x, y) = 4x^2 + 3y^2 - 7$   2. $f(x, y) = 2x^2 + 3xy$

3. $f(x, y) = 2y + 1$   4. $f(x, y) = \ln 2$

5. $g(x, y) = 3x^4y + 2xy^2 - 5xy + 8x - 9y$

6. $g(x, y) = (x + 1)^2 + (y - 3)^3 + 5xy^3 - 2$

7. $g(p, q) = \sqrt{pq}$   8. $g(w, z) = \sqrt[3]{w^2 + z^2}$

9. $h(s, t) = \dfrac{s^2 + 4}{t - 3}$   10. $h(u, v) = \dfrac{8uv^2}{u^2 + v^2}$

11. $u(q_1, q_2) = \frac{1}{2}\ln(q_1 + 2) + \frac{1}{3}\ln(q_2 + 5)$

12. $Q(l, k) = 2l^{0.38}k^{1.79} - 3l^{1.03} + 2k^{0.13}$

13. $h(x, y) = \dfrac{x^2 + 3xy + y^2}{\sqrt{x^2 + y^2}}$   14. $h(x, y) = \dfrac{\sqrt{x + 9}}{x^2y + y^2x}$

15. $z = e^{5xy}$   16. $z = (x^2 + y^2)e^{2x+3y+1}$

17. $z = 5x\ln(x^2 + y)$   18. $z = \ln(5x^3y^2 + 2y^4)^4$

19. $f(r, s) = \sqrt{r + 2s}(r^3 - 2rs + s^2)$

20. $f(r, s) = \sqrt{rs}\,e^{2+r}$

21. $f(r, s) = e^{3-r}\ln(7 - s)$

22. $f(r, s) = (5r^2 + 3s^3)(2r - 5s)$

*23. $g(x, y, z) = 2x^3y^2 + 2xy^3z + 4z^2$

24. $g(x, y, z) = 2xy^2z^6 - 4x^2y^3z^2 + 3xyz$

25. $g(r, s, t) = e^{s+t}(r^2 + 7s^3)$

26. $g(r, s, t, u) = rs\ln(2t + 5u)$

*In Problems 27–34, evaluate the given partial derivatives.*

*27. $f(x, y) = x^3y + 7x^2y^2$;   $f_x(1, -2)$

28. $z = \sqrt{2x^3 + 5xy + 2y^2}$;   $\left. \dfrac{\partial z}{\partial x} \right|_{\substack{x=0 \\ y=1}}$

29. $g(x, y, z) = e^x\sqrt{y + 2z}$;   $g_z(0, 6, 4)$

30. $g(x, y, z) = \dfrac{3x^2y^2 + 2xy + x - y}{xy - yz + xz}$,   $g_y(1, 1, 5)$

*31. $h(r, s, t, u) = (s^2 + tu)\ln(2r + 7st)$;   $h_s(1, 0, 0, 1)$

**32.** $h(r, s, t, u) = \dfrac{7r + 3s^2 u^2}{s}$; $\quad h_t(4, 3, 2, 1)$

**33.** $f(r, s, t) = rst(r^2 + s^3 + t^4)$; $\quad f_s(1, -1, 2)$

**34.** $z = \dfrac{x^2 + y^2}{e^{x^2 + y^2}}$; $\quad \dfrac{\partial z}{\partial x}\bigg|_{\substack{x=0 \\ y=0}}$, $\quad \dfrac{\partial z}{\partial y}\bigg|_{\substack{x=1 \\ y=1}}$

**35.** If $z = xe^{x-y} + ye^{y-x}$, show that

$$\frac{\partial z}{\partial x} + \frac{\partial z}{\partial y} = e^{x-y} + e^{y-x}$$

**36. Stock Prices of a Dividend Cycle** In a discussion of stock prices of a dividend cycle, Palmon and Yaari[3] consider the function $f$ given by

$$u = f(t, r, z) = \frac{(1 + r)^{1-z} \ln(1 + r)}{(1 + r)^{1-z} - t}$$

where $u$ is the instantaneous rate of ask-price appreciation, $r$ is an annual opportunity rate of return, $z$ is the fraction of a dividend cycle over which a share of stock is held by a midcycle seller, and $t$ is the effective rate of capital gains tax. They claim that

$$\frac{\partial u}{\partial z} = \frac{t(1 + r)^{1-z} \ln^2(1 + r)}{[(1 + r)^{1-z} - t]^2}$$

Verify this.

**37. Money Demand** In a discussion of inventory theory of money demand, Swanson[4] considers the function

$$F(b, C, T, i) = \frac{bT}{C} + \frac{iC}{2}$$

and determines that $\dfrac{\partial F}{\partial C} = -\dfrac{bT}{C^2} + \dfrac{i}{2}$. Verify this partial derivative.

**38. Interest Rate Deregulation** In an article on interest rate deregulation, Christofi and Agapos[5] arrive at the equation

$$r_L = r + D\frac{\partial r}{\partial D} + \frac{dC}{dD} \qquad (3)$$

where $r$ is the deposit rate paid by commercial banks, $r_L$ is the rate earned by commercial banks, $C$ is the administrative cost of transforming deposits into return-earning assets, and $D$ is the savings deposit level. Christofi and Agapos state that

$$r_L = r\left[\frac{1 + \eta}{\eta}\right] + \frac{dC}{dD} \qquad (4)$$

where $\eta = \dfrac{r/D}{\partial r/\partial D}$ is the deposit elasticity with respect to the deposit rate. Express Equation (3) in terms of $\eta$ to verify Equation (4).

**39. Advertising and Profitability** In an analysis of advertising and profitability, Swales[6] considers a function $f$ given by

$$R = f(r, a, n) = \frac{r}{1 + a\left(\dfrac{n - 1}{2}\right)}$$

where $R$ is the adjusted rate of profit, $r$ is the accounting rate of profit, $a$ is a measure of advertising expenditures, and $n$ is the number of years that advertising fully depreciates. In the analysis, Swales determines $\partial R/\partial n$. Find this partial derivative.

OBJECTIVE

To develop the notions of partial marginal cost, marginal productivity, and competitive and complementary products.

# 17.3 Applications of Partial Derivatives

From Section 17.2, we know that if $z = f(x, y)$, then $\partial z/\partial x$ and $\partial z/\partial y$ can be geometrically interpreted as giving the slopes of the tangent lines to the surface $z = f(x, y)$ in the $x$- and $y$-directions, respectively. There are other interpretations: Because $\partial z/\partial x$ is the derivative of $z$ with respect to $x$ when $y$ is held fixed, and because a derivative is a rate of change, we have

Here we have "rate of change" interpretations of partial derivatives.

$\dfrac{\partial z}{\partial x}$ is the rate of change of $z$ with respect to $x$ when $y$ is held fixed.

Similarly,

$\dfrac{\partial z}{\partial y}$ is the rate of change of $z$ with respect to $y$ when $x$ is held fixed.

We will now look at some applications in which the "rate of change" notion of a partial derivative is very useful.

---

[3]D. Palmon and U. Yaari, "Taxation of Capital Gains and the Behavior of Stock Prices over the Dividend Cycle," *The American Economist*, XXVII, no. 1 (1983), 13–22.

[4]P. E. Swanson, "Integer Constraints on the Inventory Theory of Money Demand," *Quarterly Journal of Business and Economics*, 23, no. 1 (1984), 32–37.

[5]A. Christofi and A. Agapos, "Interest Rate Deregulation: An Empirical Justification," *Review of Business and Economic Research*, XX (1984), 39–49.

[6]J. K. Swales, "Advertising as an Intangible Asset: Profitability and Entry Barriers: A Comment on Reekie and Bhoyrub," *Applied Economics*, 17, no. 4 (1985), 603–17.

Suppose a manufacturer produces $x$ units of product X and $y$ units of product Y. Then the total cost $c$ of these units is a function of $x$ and $y$ and is called a **joint-cost function.** If such a function is $c = f(x, y)$, then $\partial c/\partial x$ is called the **(partial) marginal cost with respect to** $x$ and is the rate of change of $c$ with respect to $x$ when $y$ is held fixed. Similarly, $\partial c/\partial y$ is the **(partial) marginal cost with respect to** $y$ and is the rate of change of $c$ with respect to $y$ when $x$ is held fixed.

For example, if $c$ is expressed in dollars and $\partial c/\partial y = 2$, then the cost of producing an extra unit of Y when the level of production of X is fixed is approximately two dollars.

If a manufacturer produces $n$ products, the joint-cost function is a function of $n$ variables, and there are $n$ (partial) marginal-cost functions.

### ● EXAMPLE 1   Marginal Costs

*A company manufactures two types of skis, the Lightning and the Alpine models. Suppose the joint-cost function for producing x pairs of the Lightning model and y pairs of the Alpine model per week is*

$$c = f(x, y) = 0.07x^2 + 75x + 85y + 6000$$

*where c is expressed in dollars. Determine the marginal costs $\partial c/\partial x$ and $\partial c/\partial y$ when $x = 100$ and $y = 50$, and interpret the results.*

**Solution:** The marginal costs are

$$\frac{\partial c}{\partial x} = 0.14x + 75 \quad \text{and} \quad \frac{\partial c}{\partial y} = 85$$

Thus,

$$\left.\frac{\partial c}{\partial x}\right|_{(100,50)} = 0.14(100) + 75 = 89 \tag{1}$$

and

$$\left.\frac{\partial c}{\partial y}\right|_{(100,50)} = 85 \tag{2}$$

Equation (1) means that increasing the output of the Lightning model from 100 to 101, while maintaining production of the Alpine model at 50, increases costs by approximately \$89. Equation (2) means that increasing the output of the Alpine model from 50 to 51 and holding production of the Lightning model at 100 will increase costs by approximately \$85. In fact, since $\partial c/\partial y$ is a constant function, the marginal cost with respect to $y$ is \$85 at all levels of production.

NOW WORK PROBLEM 1  ◖●●

### ● EXAMPLE 2   Loss of Body Heat

*On a cold day, a person may feel colder when the wind is blowing than when the wind is calm because the rate of heat loss is a function of both temperature and wind speed. The equation*

$$H = (10.45 + 10\sqrt{w} - w)(33 - t)$$

*indicates the rate of heat loss H (in kilocalories per square meter per hour) when the air temperature is t (in degrees Celsius) and the wind speed is w (in meters per second). For $H = 2000$, exposed flesh will freeze in one minute.[7]*

**a.** *Evaluate H when $t = 0$ and $w = 4$.*

**Solution:** When $t = 0$ and $w = 4$,

$$H = (10.45 + 10\sqrt{4} - 4)(33 - 0) = 872.85$$

---

[7]G. E. Folk, Jr., *Textbook of Environmental Physiology*, 2nd ed. (Philadelphia: Lea & Febiger, 1974).

**b.** *Evaluate $\partial H/\partial w$ and $\partial H/\partial t$ when $t = 0$ and $w = 4$, and interpret the results.*

Solution:

$$\frac{\partial H}{\partial w} = \left(\frac{5}{\sqrt{w}} - 1\right)(33 - t), \quad \frac{\partial H}{\partial w}\bigg|_{\substack{t=0 \\ w=4}} = 49.5$$

$$\frac{\partial H}{\partial t} = (10.45 + 10\sqrt{w} - w)(-1), \quad \frac{\partial H}{\partial t}\bigg|_{\substack{t=0 \\ w=4}} = -26.45$$

These equations mean that when $t = 0$ and $w = 4$, increasing $w$ by a small amount while keeping $t$ fixed will make $H$ increase approximately 49.5 times as much as $w$ increases. Increasing $t$ by a small amount while keeping $w$ fixed will make $H$ *decrease* approximately 26.45 times as much as $t$ increases.

**c.** *When $t = 0$ and $w = 4$, which has a greater effect on H: a change in wind speed of 1 m/s or a change in temperature of 1°C?*

Solution: Since the partial derivative of $H$ with respect to $w$ is greater in magnitude than the partial with respect to $t$ when $t = 0$ and $w = 4$, a change in wind speed of 1 m/s has a greater effect on $H$.

NOW WORK PROBLEM 13 ⬤⬤⬤

The output of a product depends on many factors of production. Among these may be labor, capital, land, machinery, and so on. For simplicity, let us suppose that output depends only on labor and capital. If the function $P = f(l, k)$ gives the output $P$ when the producer uses $l$ units of labor and $k$ units of capital, then this function is called a **production function.** We define the **marginal productivity with respect to** $l$ to be $\partial P/\partial l$. This is the rate of change of $P$ with respect to $l$ when $k$ is held fixed. Likewise, the **marginal productivity with respect to** $k$ is $\partial P/\partial k$ and is the rate of change of $P$ with respect to $k$ when $l$ is held fixed.

⬤ **EXAMPLE 3    Marginal Productivity**

*A manufacturer of a popular toy has determined that the production function is $P = \sqrt{lk}$, where $l$ is the number of labor-hours per week and $k$ is the capital (expressed in hundreds of dollars per week) required for a weekly production of $P$ gross of the toy. (One gross is 144 units.) Determine the marginal productivity functions, and evaluate them when $l = 400$ and $k = 16$. Interpret the results.*

Solution:  Since $P = (lk)^{1/2}$,

$$\frac{\partial P}{\partial l} = \frac{1}{2}(lk)^{-1/2}k = \frac{k}{2\sqrt{lk}}$$

and

$$\frac{\partial P}{\partial k} = \frac{1}{2}(lk)^{-1/2}l = \frac{l}{2\sqrt{lk}}$$

Evaluating these equations when $l = 400$ and $k = 16$, we obtain

$$\frac{\partial P}{\partial l}\bigg|_{\substack{l=400 \\ k=16}} = \frac{16}{2\sqrt{400(16)}} = \frac{1}{10}$$

and

$$\frac{\partial P}{\partial k}\bigg|_{\substack{l=400 \\ k=16}} = \frac{400}{2\sqrt{400(16)}} = \frac{5}{2}$$

Thus, if $l = 400$ and $k = 16$, increasing $l$ to 401 and holding $k$ at 16 will increase output by approximately $\frac{1}{10}$ gross. But if $k$ is increased to 17 while $l$ is held at 400, the output increases by approximately $\frac{5}{2}$ gross.

NOW WORK PROBLEM 5 ⬤⬤⬤

## Competitive and Complementary Products

Sometimes two products may be related such that changes in the price of one of them affect the demand for the other. A typical example is that of butter and margarine. If such a relationship exists between products A and B, then the demand for each product is dependent on the prices of both. Suppose $q_A$ and $q_B$ are the quantities demanded for A and B, respectively, and $p_A$ and $p_B$ are their respective prices. Then both $q_A$ and $q_B$ are functions of $p_A$ and $p_B$:

$$q_A = f(p_A, p_B) \qquad \text{demand function for A}$$

$$q_B = g(p_A, p_B) \qquad \text{demand function for B}$$

We can find four partial derivatives:

$$\frac{\partial q_A}{\partial p_A} \quad \textit{the marginal demand for } A \textit{ with respect to } p_A$$

$$\frac{\partial q_A}{\partial p_B} \quad \textit{the marginal demand for } A \textit{ with respect to } p_B$$

$$\frac{\partial q_B}{\partial p_A} \quad \textit{the marginal demand for } B \textit{ with respect to } p_A$$

$$\frac{\partial q_B}{\partial p_B} \quad \textit{the marginal demand for } B \textit{ with respect to } p_B$$

Under typical conditions, if the price of B is fixed and the price of A increases, then the quantity of A demanded will decrease. Thus, $\partial q_A/\partial p_A < 0$. Similarly, $\partial q_B/\partial p_B < 0$. However, $\partial q_A/\partial p_B$ and $\partial q_B/\partial p_A$ may be either positive or negative. If

$$\frac{\partial q_A}{\partial p_B} > 0 \quad \text{and} \quad \frac{\partial q_B}{\partial p_A} > 0$$

then A and B are said to be **competitive products** or **substitutes.** In this situation, an increase in the price of B causes an increase in the demand for A, if it is assumed that the price of A does not change. Similarly, an increase in the price of A causes an increase in the demand for B when the price of B is held fixed. Butter and margarine are examples of substitutes.

Proceeding to a different situation, we say that if

$$\frac{\partial q_A}{\partial p_B} < 0 \quad \text{and} \quad \frac{\partial q_B}{\partial p_A} < 0$$

then A and B are **complementary products.** In this case, an increase in the price of B causes a decrease in the demand for A if the price of A does not change. Similarly, an increase in the price of A causes a decrease in the demand for B when the price of B is held fixed. For example, cars and gasoline are complementary products. An increase in the price of gasoline will make driving more expensive. Hence, the demand for cars will decrease. And an increase in the price of cars will reduce the demand for gasoline.

● EXAMPLE 4   **Determining Whether Products Are Competitive or Complementary**

*The demand functions for products* A *and* B *are each a function of the prices of* A *and* B *and are given by*

$$q_A = \frac{50\sqrt[3]{p_B}}{\sqrt{p_A}} \quad \text{and} \quad q_B = \frac{75 p_A}{\sqrt[3]{p_B^2}}$$

*respectively. Find the four marginal-demand functions, and determine whether* A *and* B *are competitive products, complementary products, or neither.*

**Solution:** Writing $q_A = 50 p_A^{-1/2} p_B^{1/3}$ and $q_B = 75 p_A p_B^{-2/3}$, we have

$$\frac{\partial q_A}{\partial p_A} = 50 \left(-\frac{1}{2}\right) p_A^{-3/2} p_B^{1/3} = -25 p_A^{-3/2} p_B^{1/3}$$

$$\frac{\partial q_A}{\partial p_B} = 50 p_A^{-1/2} \left(\frac{1}{3}\right) p_B^{-2/3} = \frac{50}{3} p_A^{-1/2} p_B^{-2/3}$$

$$\frac{\partial q_B}{\partial p_A} = 75(1) p_B^{-2/3} = 75 p_B^{-2/3}$$

$$\frac{\partial q_B}{\partial p_B} = 75 p_A \left(-\frac{2}{3}\right) p_B^{-5/3} = -50 p_A p_B^{-5/3}$$

Since $p_A$ and $p_B$ represent prices, they are both positive. Hence, $\partial q_A / \partial p_B > 0$ and $\partial q_B / \partial p_A > 0$. We conclude that A and B are competitive products.

NOW WORK PROBLEM 19 ●●●

# Problems 17.3

*For the joint-cost functions in Problems 1–3, find the indicated marginal cost at the given production level.*

*1. $c = 7x + 0.3y^2 + 2y + 900$;   $\dfrac{\partial c}{\partial y}$, $x = 20$, $y = 30$

2. $c = x\sqrt{x + y} + 5000$;   $\dfrac{\partial c}{\partial x}$, $x = 40$, $y = 60$

3. $c = 0.03(x + y)^3 - 0.6(x + y)^2 + 9.5(x + y) + 7700$;   $\dfrac{\partial c}{\partial x}$, $x = 50$, $y = 80$

*For the production functions in Problems 4 and 5, find the marginal productivity functions $\partial P/\partial k$ and $\partial P/\partial l$.*

4. $P = 15lk - 3l^2 + 5k^2 + 500$

*5. $P = 2.314 l^{0.357} k^{0.643}$

6. **Cobb–Douglas Production Function** In economics, a Cobb–Douglas production function is a production function of the form $P = A l^\alpha k^\beta$, where $A$, $\alpha$, and $\beta$ are constants and $\alpha + \beta = 1$. For such a function, show that
   (a) $\partial P/\partial l = \alpha P/l$
   (b) $\partial P/\partial k = \beta P/k$
   (c) $l \dfrac{\partial P}{\partial l} + k \dfrac{\partial P}{\partial k} = P$. This means that summing the products of the marginal productivity of each factor and the amount of that factor results in the total product $P$.

*In Problems 7–9, $q_A$ and $q_B$ are demand functions for products A and B, respectively. In each case, find $\partial q_A/\partial p_A$, $\partial q_A/\partial p_B$, $\partial q_B/\partial p_A$, $\partial q_B/\partial p_B$ and determine whether A and B are competitive, complementary, or neither.*

7. $q_A = 1000 - 50 p_A + 2 p_B$;   $q_B = 500 + 4 p_A - 20 p_B$

8. $q_A = 20 - p_A - 2 p_B$;   $q_B = 50 - 2 p_A - 3 p_B$

9. $q_A = \dfrac{100}{p_A \sqrt{p_B}}$;   $q_B = \dfrac{500}{p_B \sqrt[3]{p_A}}$

10. **Canadian Manufacturing** The production function for the Canadian manufacturing industries for 1927 is estimated by[8]

$P = 33.0 l^{0.46} k^{0.52}$, where $P$ is product, $l$ is labor, and $k$ is capital. Find the marginal productivities for labor and capital, and evaluate when $l = 1$ and $k = 1$.

11. **Dairy Farming** An estimate of the production function for dairy farming in Iowa (1939) is given by[9]

$$P = A^{0.27} B^{0.01} C^{0.01} D^{0.23} E^{0.09} F^{0.27}$$

where $P$ is product, $A$ is land, $B$ is labor, $C$ is improvements, $D$ is liquid assets, $E$ is working assets, and $F$ is cash operating expenses. Find the marginal productivities for labor and improvements.

12. **Production Function** Suppose a production function is given by $P = \dfrac{kl}{2k + 3l}$.
    (a) Determine the marginal productivity functions.
    (b) Show that when $k = l$, the marginal productivities sum to $\dfrac{1}{5}$.

*13. **M.B.A. Compensation** In a study of success among graduates with master's of business administration (M.B.A.) degrees, it was estimated that for staff managers (which include accountants, analysts, etc.), current annual compensation (in dollars) was given by

$$z = 43,960 + 4480x + 3492y$$

where $x$ and $y$ are the number of years of work experience before and after receiving the M.B.A. degree, respectively.[10] Find $\partial z / \partial x$ and interpret your result.

---

[8]P. Daly and P. Douglas, "The Production Function for Canadian Manufactures," *Journal of the American Statistical Association,* 38 (1943), 178–86.

[9]G. Tintner and O. H. Brownlee, "Production Functions Derived from Farm Records," *American Journal of Agricultural Economics,* 26 (1944), 566–71.

[10]Adapted from A. G. Weinstein and V. Srinivasen, "Predicting Managerial Success of Master of Business Administration (M.B.A.) Graduates," *Journal of Applied Psychology,* 59, no. 2 (1974), 207–12.

14. **Status** A person's general status $S_g$ is believed to be a function of status attributable to education, $S_e$, and status attributable to income, $S_i$, where $S_g$, $S_e$, and $S_i$ are represented numerically. If

$$S_g = 7\sqrt[3]{S_e}\sqrt{S_i}$$

determine $\partial S_g/\partial S_e$ and $\partial S_g/\partial S_i$ when $S_e = 125$ and $S_i = 100$, and interpret your results.[11]

15. **Reading Ease** Sometimes we want to evaluate the degree of readability of a piece of writing. Rudolf Flesch[12] developed a function of two variables that will do this, namely,

$$R = f(w, s) = 206.835 - (1.015w + 0.846s)$$

where $R$ is called the *reading ease score*, $w$ is the average number of words per sentence in 100-word samples, and $s$ is the average number of syllables in such samples. Flesch says that an article for which $R = 0$ is "practically unreadable," but one with $R = 100$ is "easy for any literate person." (a) Find $\partial R/\partial w$ and $\partial R/\partial s$. (b) Which is "easier" to read: an article for which $w = w_0$ and $s = s_0$, or one for which $w = w_0 + 1$ and $s = s_0$?

16. **Model for Voice** The study of frequency of vibrations of a taut wire is useful in considering such things as an individual's voice. Suppose

$$\omega = \frac{1}{bL}\sqrt{\frac{\tau}{\pi\rho}}$$

where $\omega$ (a Greek letter read "omega") is frequency, $b$ is diameter, $L$ is length, $\rho$ (a Greek letter read "rho") is density, and $\tau$ (a Greek letter read "tau") is tension.[13] Find $\partial\omega/\partial b$, $\partial\omega/\partial L$, $\partial\omega/\partial\rho$, and $\partial\omega/\partial\tau$.

17. **Traffic Flow** Consider the following traffic-flow situation. On a highway where two lanes of traffic flow in the same direction, there is a maintenance vehicle blocking the left lane. (See Figure 17.11.) Two vehicles (*lead* and *following*) are in the right lane with a gap between them. The *subject* vehicle can choose either to fill or not to fill the gap. That decision may be based not only on the distance $x$ shown in the diagram, but also on other factors (such as the velocity of the *following* vehicle). A *gap index* $g$ has been used in

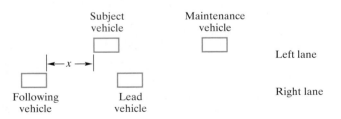

**FIGURE 17.11** Diagram for Problem 17.

analyzing such a decision.[14,15] The greater the $g$-value, the greater is the propensity for the *subject* vehicle to fill the gap. Suppose

$$g = \frac{x}{V_F} - \left(0.75 + \frac{V_F - V_S}{19.2}\right)$$

where $x$ (in feet) is as before, $V_F$ is the velocity of the *following* vehicle (in feet per second), and $V_S$ is the velocity of the *subject* vehicle (in feet per second). From the diagram, it seems reasonable that if both $V_F$ and $V_S$ are fixed and $x$ increases, then $g$ should increase. Show that this is true by applying calculus to the function $g$. Assume that $x$, $V_F$, and $V_S$ are positive.

18. **Demand** Suppose the demand equations for related products A and B are

$$q_A = e^{-(p_A + p_B)} \quad \text{and} \quad q_B = \frac{16}{p_A^2 p_B^2}$$

where $q_A$ and $q_B$ are the number of units of A and B demanded when the unit prices (in thousands of dollars) are $p_A$ and $p_B$, respectively.

(a) Classify A and B as competitive, complementary, or neither.

(b) If the unit prices of A and B are $1000 and $2000, respectively, estimate the change in the demand for A when the price of B is decreased by $20 and the price of A is held constant.

*19. **Demand** The demand equations for related products A and B are given by

$$q_A = 10\sqrt{\frac{p_B}{p_A}} \quad \text{and} \quad q_B = 3\sqrt[3]{\frac{p_A}{p_B}}$$

where $q_A$ and $q_B$ are the quantities of A and B demanded and $p_A$ and $p_B$ are the corresponding prices (in dollars) per unit.

(a) Find the values of the two marginal demands for product A when $p_A = 9$ and $p_B = 16$.

(b) If $p_B$ were reduced to 14 from 16, with $p_A$ fixed at 9, use part (a) to estimate the corresponding change in demand for product A.

20. **Joint-Cost Function** A manufacturer's joint-cost function for producing $q_A$ units of product A and $q_B$ units of product B is given by

$$c = \frac{q_A^2(q_B^3 + q_A)^{1/2}}{17} + q_A q_B^{1/3} + 600$$

where $c$ is in dollars.

(a) Find the marginal-cost functions with respect to $q_A$ and $q_B$.

(b) Evaluate the marginal-cost function with respect to $q_A$ when $q_A = 17$ and $q_B = 8$. Round your answer to two decimal places.

[11]Adapted from R. K. Leik and B. F. Meeker, *Mathematical Sociology* (Englewood Cliffs, NJ: Prentice-Hall, Inc., 1975).

[12]R. Flesch, *The Art of Readable Writing* (New York: Harper & Row Publishers, Inc., 1949).

[13]R. M. Thrall, J. A. Mortimer, K. R. Rebman, and R. F. Baum, eds., *Some Mathematical Models in Biology,* rev. ed., Report No. 40241-R-7. Prepared at University of Michigan, 1967.

[14]P. M. Hurst, K. Perchonok, and E. L. Seguin, "Vehicle Kinematics and Gap Acceptance," *Journal of Applied Psychology,* 52, no. 4 (1968), 321–24.

[15]K. Perchonok and P. M. Hurst, "Effect of Lane-Closure Signals upon Driver Decision Making and Traffic Flow," *Journal of Applied Psychology,* 52, no. 5 (1968), 410–13.

**(c)** Use your answer to part (a) to estimate the change in cost if production of product A is decreased from 17 to 16 units, while production of product B is held constant at 8 units.

**21. Elections** For the congressional elections of 1974, the Republican percentage, $R$, of the Republican–Democratic vote in a district is given (approximately) by[16]

$$R = f(E_r, E_d, I_r, I_d, N)$$

$$= 15.4725 + 2.5945\,E_r - 0.0804\,E_r^2 - 2.3648\,E_d$$

$$+ 0.0687\,E_d^2 + 2.1914\,I_r - 0.0912\,I_r^2$$

$$- 0.8096\,I_d + 0.0081\,I_d^2 - 0.0277\,E_r\,I_r$$

$$+ 0.0493\,E_d\,I_d + 0.8579\,N - 0.0061\,N^2$$

Here $E_r$ and $E_d$ are the campaign expenditures (in units of $10,000) by Republicans and Democrats, respectively; $I_r$ and $I_d$ are the number of terms served in Congress, *plus one*, for the Republican and Democratic candidates, respectively, and $N$ is the percentage of the two-party presidential vote that Richard Nixon received in the district for 1968. The variable $N$ gives a measure of Republican strength in the district.

**(a)** In the Federal Election Campaign Act of 1974, Congress set a limit of $188,000 on campaign expenditures. By analyzing $\partial R/\partial E_r$, would you have advised a Republican candidate who served nine terms in Congress to spend $188,000 on his or her campaign?

**(b)** Find the percentage above which the Nixon vote had a negative effect on $R$; that is, find $N$ when $\partial R/\partial N < 0$. Give your answer to the nearest percent.

**22. Sales** After a new product has been launched onto the market, its sales volume (in thousands of units) is given by

$$S = \frac{AT + 450}{\sqrt{A + T^2}}$$

where $T$ is the time (in months) since the product was first introduced and $A$ is the amount (in hundreds of dollars) spent each month on advertising.

**(a)** Verify that the partial derivative of sales volume with respect to time is given by

$$\frac{\partial S}{\partial T} = \frac{A^2 - 450T}{(A + T^2)^{3/2}}$$

**(b)** Use the result in part (a) to predict the number of months that will elapse before the sales volume begins to decrease if the amount allocated to advertising is held fixed at $9000 per month.

*Let $f$ be a demand function for product* A *and* $q_A = f(p_A, p_B)$, *where* $q_A$ *is the quantity of* A *demanded when the price per unit of* A *is* $p_A$ *and the price per unit of product* B *is* $p_B$. *The partial elasticity of demand for* A *with respect to* $p_A$, *denoted* $\eta_{p_A}$, *is defined as* $\eta_{p_A} = (p_A/q_A)(\partial q_A/\partial p_A)$. *The partial elasticity of demand for* A *with respect to* $p_B$, *denoted* $\eta_{p_B}$, *is defined as* $\eta_{p_B} = (p_B/q_A)(\partial q_A/\partial p_B)$. *Loosely speaking,* $\eta_{p_A}$ *is the ratio of a percentage change in the quantity of* A *demanded to a percentage change in the price of* A *when the price of* B *is fixed. Similarly,* $\eta_{p_B}$ *can be loosely interpreted as the ratio of a percentage change in the quantity of* A *demanded to a percentage change in the price of* B *when the price of* A *is fixed. In Problems 23–25, find* $\eta_{p_A}$ *and* $\eta_{p_B}$ *for the given values of* $p_A$ *and* $p_B$.

**23.** $q_A = 1000 - 50p_A + 2p_B$; $p_A = 2$, $p_B = 10$

**24.** $q_A = 60 - 3p_A - 2p_B$; $p_A = 5$, $p_B = 3$

**25.** $q_A = 100/(p_A\sqrt{p_B})$; $p_A = 1$, $p_B = 4$

OBJECTIVE

To find partial derivatives of a function defined implicitly.

# 17.4 Implicit Partial Differentiation[17]

An equation in $x$, $y$, and $z$ does not necessarily define $z$ as a function of $x$ and $y$. For example, in the equation

$$z^2 - x^2 - y^2 = 0 \tag{1}$$

if $x = 1$ and $y = 1$, then $z^2 - 1 - 1 = 0$, so $z = \pm\sqrt{2}$. Thus, Equation (1) does not define $z$ as a function of $x$ and $y$. However, solving Equation (1) for $z$ gives

$$z = \sqrt{x^2 + y^2} \quad \text{or} \quad z = -\sqrt{x^2 + y^2}$$

each of which defines $z$ as a function of $x$ and $y$. Although Equation (1) does not explicitly express $z$ as a function of $x$ and $y$, it can be thought of as expressing $z$ *implicitly* as one of two different functions of $x$ and $y$. Note that the equation $z^2 - x^2 - y^2 = 0$ has the form $F(x, y, z) = 0$, where $F$ is a function of three variables. Any equation of the form $F(x, y, z) = 0$ can be thought of as expressing $z$ implicitly as one of a set of possible functions of $x$ and $y$. Moreover, we can find $\partial z/\partial x$ and $\partial z/\partial y$ directly from the form $F(x, y, z) = 0$.

To find $\partial z/\partial x$ for

$$z^2 - x^2 - y^2 = 0 \tag{2}$$

---

[16]J. Silberman and G. Yochum, "The Role of Money in Determining Election Outcomes," *Social Science Quarterly*, 58, no. 4 (1978), 671–82.

[17]This section can be omitted without loss of continuity.

we first differentiate both sides of Equation (2) with respect to $x$ while treating $z$ as a function of $x$ and $y$ and treating $y$ as a constant:

$$\frac{\partial}{\partial x}(z^2 - x^2 - y^2) = \frac{\partial}{\partial x}(0)$$

$$\frac{\partial}{\partial x}(z^2) - \frac{\partial}{\partial x}(x^2) - \frac{\partial}{\partial x}(y^2) = 0$$

$$2z\frac{\partial z}{\partial x} - 2x - 0 = 0$$

Because $y$ is treated as a constant, $\frac{\partial y}{\partial x} = 0$.

Solving for $\partial z/\partial x$, we obtain

$$2z\frac{\partial z}{\partial x} = 2x$$

$$\frac{\partial z}{\partial x} = \frac{x}{z}$$

To find $\partial z/\partial y$, we differentiate both sides of Equation (2) with respect to $y$ while treating $z$ as a function of $x$ and $y$ and treating $x$ as a constant:

$$\frac{\partial}{\partial y}(z^2 - x^2 - y^2) = \frac{\partial}{\partial y}(0)$$

$$2z\frac{\partial z}{\partial y} - 0 - 2y = 0 \qquad \left(\frac{\partial x}{\partial y} = 0\right)$$

$$2z\frac{\partial z}{\partial y} = 2y$$

Hence,

$$\frac{\partial z}{\partial y} = \frac{y}{z}$$

The method we used to find $\partial z/\partial x$ and $\partial z/\partial y$ is called *implicit partial differentiation*.

● **EXAMPLE 1  Implicit Partial Differentiation**

*If* $\dfrac{xz^2}{x+y} + y^2 = 0$, *evaluate* $\dfrac{\partial z}{\partial x}$ *when* $x = -1$, $y = 2$, *and* $z = 2$.

**Solution:** We treat $z$ as a function of $x$ and $y$ and differentiate both sides of the equation with respect to $x$:

$$\frac{\partial}{\partial x}\left(\frac{xz^2}{x+y}\right) + \frac{\partial}{\partial x}(y^2) = \frac{\partial}{\partial x}(0)$$

Using the quotient rule for the first term on the left, we have

$$\frac{(x+y)\dfrac{\partial}{\partial x}(xz^2) - xz^2\dfrac{\partial}{\partial x}(x+y)}{(x+y)^2} + 0 = 0$$

Using the product rule for $\dfrac{\partial}{\partial x}(xz^2)$ gives

$$\frac{(x+y)\left[x\left(2z\dfrac{\partial z}{\partial x}\right) + z^2(1)\right] - xz^2(1)}{(x+y)^2} = 0$$

Solving for $\partial z/\partial x$, we obtain

$$2xz(x+y)\frac{\partial z}{\partial x} + z^2(x+y) - xz^2 = 0$$

$$\frac{\partial z}{\partial x} = \frac{xz^2 - z^2(x+y)}{2xz(x+y)} = -\frac{yz}{2x(x+y)} \qquad z \neq 0$$

Thus,

$$\frac{\partial z}{\partial x}\bigg|_{(-1,2,2)} = 2$$

NOW WORK PROBLEM 13

● **EXAMPLE 2** **Implicit Partial Differentiation**

*If $se^{r^2+u^2} = u\ln(t^2+1)$, determine $\partial t/\partial u$.*

**Solution:** We consider $t$ as a function of $r$, $s$, and $u$. By differentiating both sides with respect to $u$ while treating $r$ and $s$ as constants, we get

$$\frac{\partial}{\partial u}(se^{r^2+u^2}) = \frac{\partial}{\partial u}(u\ln(t^2+1))$$

$$2sue^{r^2+u^2} = u\frac{\partial}{\partial u}(\ln(t^2+1)) + \ln(t^2+1)\frac{\partial}{\partial u}(u) \qquad \text{(product rule)}$$

$$2sue^{r^2+u^2} = u\frac{2t}{t^2+1}\frac{\partial t}{\partial u} + \ln(t^2+1)$$

Therefore,

$$\frac{\partial t}{\partial u} = \frac{(t^2+1)(2sue^{r^2+u^2} - \ln(t^2+1))}{2ut}$$

NOW WORK PROBLEM 1

## Problems 17.4

*In Problems 1–11, find the indicated partial derivatives by the method of implicit partial differentiation.*

*1. $2x^2 + 3y^2 + 5z^2 = 900$;  $\partial z/\partial x$

2. $z^2 - 5x^2 + y^2 = 0$;  $\partial z/\partial x$

3. $2z^3 - x^2 - 4y^2 = 0$;  $\partial z/\partial y$

4. $3x^2 + y^2 + 2z^3 = 9$;  $\partial z/\partial y$

5. $x^2 - 2y - z^2 + x^2yz^2 = 20$;  $\partial z/\partial x$

6. $z^3 + 2x^2z^2 - xy = 0$;  $\partial z/\partial x$

7. $e^x + e^y + e^z = 10$;  $\partial z/\partial y$

8. $xyz + 3y^3x^2 - \ln z^3 = 0$;  $\partial z/\partial y$

9. $\ln(z) + 9z - xy = 1$;  $\partial z/\partial x$

10. $\ln x + \ln y - \ln z = e^y$;  $\partial z/\partial x$

11. $(z^2 + 6xy)\sqrt{x^3 + 5} = 2$;  $\partial z/\partial y$

*In Problems 12–20, evaluate the indicated partial derivatives for the given values of the variables.*

12. $xz + xyz - 5 = 0$;  $\partial z/\partial x$, $x = 1$, $y = 4$, $z = 1$

*13. $3xz^2 + 2yz^2 - 7x^4y = 3$;  $\partial z/\partial x$, $x = 1$, $y = 0$, $z = 1$

14. $e^{zx} = xyz$;  $\partial z/\partial y$, $x = 1$, $y = -e^{-1}$, $z = -1$

15. $e^{yz} = -xyz$;  $\partial z/\partial x$, $x = -e^2/2$, $y = 1$, $z = 2$

16. $\sqrt{xz + y^2} - xy = 0$;  $\partial z/\partial y$, $x = 2$, $y = 2$, $z = 6$

17. $\ln z = 4x + y$;  $\partial z/\partial x$, $x = 5$, $y = -20$, $z = 1$

18. $\dfrac{2r^2s^2}{s^2 + t^2} = t$;  $\partial r/\partial t$, $r = 1$, $s = 1$, $t = 1$

19. $\dfrac{s^2 + t^2}{rs} = 10$;  $\partial t/\partial r$, $r = 1$, $s = 2$, $t = 4$

20. $\ln(x + y + z) + xyz = ze^{x+y+z}$;  $\partial z/\partial x$, $x = 0$, $y = 1$, $z = 0$

21. **Joint-Cost Function**  A joint-cost function is defined implicitly by the equation

$$c + \sqrt{c} = 12 + q_A\sqrt{9 + q_B^2}$$

where $c$ denotes the total cost (in dollars) for producing $q_A$ units of product A and $q_B$ units of product B.

(a) If $q_A = 6$ and $q_B = 4$, find the corresponding value of $c$.

(b) Determine the marginal costs with respect to $q_A$ and $q_B$ when $q_A = 6$ and $q_B = 4$.

---

OBJECTIVE

To compute higher-order partial derivatives.

## 17.5 Higher-Order Partial Derivatives

If $z = f(x, y)$, then not only is $z$ a function of $x$ and $y$, but also $f_x$ and $f_y$ are each functions of $x$ and $y$, which may themselves have partial derivatives. If we can differentiate $f_x$ and $f_y$, we obtain **second-order partial derivatives** of $f$. Symbolically,

$$f_{xx} \text{ means } (f_x)_x \qquad f_{xy} \text{ means } (f_x)_y$$

$$f_{yx} \text{ means } (f_y)_x \qquad f_{yy} \text{ means } (f_y)_y$$

In terms of $\partial$-notation,

$$\frac{\partial^2 z}{\partial x^2} \text{ means } \frac{\partial}{\partial x}\left(\frac{\partial z}{\partial x}\right) \qquad \frac{\partial^2 z}{\partial y \, \partial x} \text{ means } \frac{\partial}{\partial y}\left(\frac{\partial z}{\partial x}\right)$$

$$\frac{\partial^2 z}{\partial x \, \partial y} \text{ means } \frac{\partial}{\partial x}\left(\frac{\partial z}{\partial y}\right) \qquad \frac{\partial^2 z}{\partial y^2} \text{ means } \frac{\partial}{\partial y}\left(\frac{\partial z}{\partial y}\right)$$

Note that to find $f_{xy}$, we first differentiate $f$ with respect to $x$. For $\partial^2 z/\partial x \, \partial y$, we first differentiate with respect to $y$.

**CAUTION**

For $z = f(x, y)$, $f_{xy} = \partial^2 z/\partial y \, \partial x$.

We can extend our notation beyond second-order partial derivatives. For example, $f_{xxy}$ ($= \partial^3 z/\partial y \, \partial x^2$) is a third-order partial derivative of $f$, namely, the partial derivative of $f_{xx}$ ($= \partial^2 z/\partial x^2$) with respect to $y$. The generalization of higher-order partial derivatives to functions of more than two variables should be obvious.

● **EXAMPLE 1  Second-Order Partial Derivatives**

*Find the four second-order partial derivatives of* $f(x, y) = x^2 y + x^2 y^2$.

**Solution:** Since

$$f_x(x, y) = 2xy + 2xy^2$$

we have

$$f_{xx}(x, y) = \frac{\partial}{\partial x}(2xy + 2xy^2) = 2y + 2y^2$$

and

$$f_{xy}(x, y) = \frac{\partial}{\partial y}(2xy + 2xy^2) = 2x + 4xy$$

Also, since

$$f_y(x, y) = x^2 + 2x^2 y$$

we have

$$f_{yy}(x, y) = \frac{\partial}{\partial y}(x^2 + 2x^2 y) = 2x^2$$

and

$$f_{yx}(x, y) = \frac{\partial}{\partial x}(x^2 + 2x^2 y) = 2x + 4xy$$

**NOW WORK PROBLEM 1** ●●●

The derivatives $f_{xy}$ and $f_{yx}$ are called **mixed partial derivatives.** Observe in Example 1 that $f_{xy}(x, y) = f_{yx}(x, y)$. Under suitable conditions, mixed partial derivatives of a function are equal; that is, the order of differentiation is of no concern. You may assume that this is the case for all the functions that we consider.

● **EXAMPLE 2  Mixed Partial Derivative**

*Find the value of* $\left.\dfrac{\partial^3 w}{\partial z \, \partial y \, \partial x}\right|_{(1,2,3)}$ *if* $w = (2x + 3y + 4z)^3$.

**Solution:**

$$\frac{\partial w}{\partial x} = 3(2x + 3y + 4z)^2 \frac{\partial}{\partial x}(2x + 3y + 4z)$$

$$= 6(2x + 3y + 4z)^2$$

$$\frac{\partial^2 w}{\partial y \, \partial x} = 6 \cdot 2(2x + 3y + 4z)\frac{\partial}{\partial y}(2x + 3y + 4z)$$

$$= 36(2x + 3y + 4z)$$

$$\frac{\partial^3 w}{\partial z \, \partial y \, \partial x} = 36 \cdot 4 = 144$$

Thus,

$$\frac{\partial^3 w}{\partial z\, \partial y\, \partial x}\bigg|_{(1,2,3)} = 144$$

NOW WORK PROBLEM 3

### ● EXAMPLE 3   Second-Order Partial Derivative of an Implicit Function[18]

*Determine* $\dfrac{\partial^2 z}{\partial x^2}$ *if* $z^2 = xy$.

**Solution:** By implicit differentiation, we first determine $\partial z/\partial x$:

$$\frac{\partial}{\partial x}(z^2) = \frac{\partial}{\partial x}(xy)$$

$$2z\frac{\partial z}{\partial x} = y$$

$$\frac{\partial z}{\partial x} = \frac{y}{2z} \qquad z \ne 0$$

Differentiating both sides with respect to $x$, we obtain

$$\frac{\partial}{\partial x}\left(\frac{\partial z}{\partial x}\right) = \frac{\partial}{\partial x}\left(\frac{1}{2}yz^{-1}\right)$$

$$\frac{\partial^2 z}{\partial x^2} = -\frac{1}{2}yz^{-2}\frac{\partial z}{\partial x}$$

Substituting $y/(2z)$ for $\partial z/\partial x$, we have

$$\frac{\partial^2 z}{\partial x^2} = -\frac{1}{2}yz^{-2}\left(\frac{y}{2z}\right) = -\frac{y^2}{4z^3} \qquad z \ne 0$$

NOW WORK PROBLEM 23

## Problems 17.5

*In Problems 1–10, find the indicated partial derivatives.*

*1. $f(x, y) = 6xy^2$;   $f_x(x, y)$, $f_{xy}(x, y)$, $f_{yx}(x, y)$

2. $f(x, y) = 2x^3y^2 + 6x^2y^3 - 3xy$;   $f_x(x, y)$, $f_{xx}(x, y)$

*3. $f(x, y) = 7x^2 + 3y$;   $f_y(x, y)$, $f_{yy}(x, y)$, $f_{yyx}(x, y)$

4. $f(x, y) = (x^2 + xy + y^2)(x^2 + xy + 1)$;   $f_x(x, y)$, $f_{xy}(x, y)$

5. $f(x, y) = 9e^{2xy}$;   $f_y(x, y)$, $f_{yx}(x, y)$, $f_{yxy}(x, y)$

6. $f(x, y) = \ln(x^2 + y^2) + 2$;   $f_x(x, y)$, $f_{xx}(x, y)$, $f_{xy}(x, y)$

7. $f(x, y) = (x + y)^2(xy)$;   $f_x(x, y)$, $f_y(x, y)$, $f_{xx}(x, y)$, $f_{yy}(x, y)$

8. $f(x, y, z) = x^2y^3z^4$;   $f_x(x, y, z)$, $f_{xz}(x, y, z)$, $f_{zx}(x, y, z)$

9. $z = e^{\sqrt{x^2 + y^2}}$;   $\dfrac{\partial z}{\partial y}$, $\dfrac{\partial^2 z}{\partial y^2}$

10. $z = \dfrac{\ln(x^2 + 5)}{y}$;   $\dfrac{\partial z}{\partial x}$, $\dfrac{\partial^2 z}{\partial y\, \partial x}$

*In Problems 11–16, find the indicated value.*

11. If $f(x, y, z) = 7$, find $f_{yxx}(4, 3, -2)$.

12. If $f(x, y, z) = z^2(3x^2 - 4xy^3)$, find $f_{xyz}(1, 2, 3)$.

13. If $f(l, k) = 3l^3k^6 - 2l^2k^7$, find $f_{klk}(2, 1)$.

14. If $f(x, y) = 3x^3y^2 + xy - x^2y^2$, find $f_{xxy}(5, 1)$ and $f_{xyx}(5, 1)$.

15. If $f(x, y) = y^2e^x + \ln(xy)$, find $f_{xyy}(1, 1)$.

16. If $f(x, y) = x^3 - 6xy^2 + x^2 - y^3$, find $f_{xy}(1, -1)$.

17. **Cost Function**   Suppose the cost $c$ of producing $q_A$ units of product A and $q_B$ units of product B is given by

$$c = (3q_A^2 + q_B^3 + 4)^{1/3}$$

and the coupled demand functions for the products are given by

$$q_A = 10 - p_A + p_B^2$$

and

$$q_B = 20 + p_A - 11p_B$$

Find the value of

$$\frac{\partial^2 c}{\partial q_A\, \partial q_B}$$

when $p_A = 25$ and $p_B = 4$.

18. For $f(x, y) = x^4y^4 + 3x^3y^2 - 7x + 4$, show that

$$f_{xyx}(x, y) = f_{xxy}(x, y)$$

19. For $f(x, y) = 8x^3 + 2x^2y^2 + 5y^4$, show that

$$f_{xy}(x, y) = f_{yx}(x, y)$$

---

[18]Omit if Section 17.4 was not covered.

**20.** For $f(x, y) = e^{xy}$, show that

$$f_{xx}(x, y) + f_{xy}(x, y) + f_{yx}(x, y) + f_{yy}(x, y)$$
$$= f(x, y)((x + y)^2 + 2)$$

**21.** For $z = \ln(x^2 + y^2)$, show that $\dfrac{\partial^2 z}{\partial x^2} + \dfrac{\partial^2 z}{\partial y^2} = 0$.

[19]**22.** If $3z^2 - 2x^3 - 4y^4 = 0$, find $\dfrac{\partial^2 z}{\partial x^2}$.

*[19]**23.** If $z^2 - 3x^2 + y^2 = 0$, find $\dfrac{\partial^2 z}{\partial y^2}$.

[19]**24.** If $2z^2 = x^2 + 2xy + xz$, find $\dfrac{\partial^2 z}{\partial x \, \partial y}$.

---

OBJECTIVE

To show how to find the partial derivative of a function of functions by using the chain rule.

## 17.6  Chain Rule[20]

Suppose a manufacturer of two related products A and B has a joint-cost function given by

$$c = f(q_A, q_B)$$

where $c$ is the total cost of producing quantities $q_A$ and $q_B$ of A and B, respectively. Furthermore, suppose the demand functions for the products are

$$q_A = g(p_A, p_B) \quad \text{and} \quad q_B = h(p_A, p_B)$$

where $p_A$ and $p_B$ are the prices per unit of A and B, respectively. Since $c$ is a function of $q_A$ and $q_B$, and since both $q_A$ and $q_B$ are themselves functions of $p_A$ and $p_B$, $c$ can be viewed as a function of $p_A$ and $p_B$. (Appropriately, the variables $q_A$ and $q_B$ are called *intermediate variables* of $c$.) Consequently, we should be able to determine $\partial c/\partial p_A$, the rate of change of total cost with respect to the price of A. One way to do this is to substitute the expressions $g(p_A, p_B)$ and $h(p_A, p_B)$ for $q_A$ and $q_B$, respectively, into $c = f(q_A, q_B)$. Then $c$ is a function of $p_A$ and $p_B$, and we can differentiate $c$ with respect to $p_A$ directly. This approach has some drawbacks—especially when $f, g$, or $h$ is given by a complicated expression. Another way to approach the problem would be to use the chain rule (actually *a* chain rule), which we now state without proof.

> **Chain Rule**
>
> Let $z = f(x, y)$, where both $x$ and $y$ are functions of $r$ and $s$ given by $x = x(r, s)$ and $y = y(r, s)$. If $f, x$, and $y$ have continuous partial derivatives, then $z$ is a function of $r$ and $s$, and
>
> $$\frac{\partial z}{\partial r} = \frac{\partial z}{\partial x}\frac{\partial x}{\partial r} + \frac{\partial z}{\partial y}\frac{\partial y}{\partial r}$$
>
> and
>
> $$\frac{\partial z}{\partial s} = \frac{\partial z}{\partial x}\frac{\partial x}{\partial s} + \frac{\partial z}{\partial y}\frac{\partial y}{\partial s}$$

Note that in the chain rule, the number of intermediate variables of $z$ (two) is the same as the number of terms that compose each of $\partial z/\partial r$ and $\partial z/\partial s$.

Returning to the original situation concerning the manufacturer, we see that if $f, q_A$, and $q_B$ have continuous partial derivatives, then, by the chain rule,

$$\frac{\partial c}{\partial p_A} = \frac{\partial c}{\partial q_A}\frac{\partial q_A}{\partial p_A} + \frac{\partial c}{\partial q_B}\frac{\partial q_B}{\partial p_A}$$

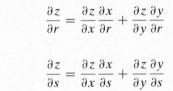EXAMPLE 1    **Rate of Change of Cost**

*For a manufacturer of cameras and film, the total cost $c$ of producing $q_C$ cameras and $q_F$ units of film is given by*

$$c = 30q_C + 0.015q_C q_F + q_F + 900$$

---

[19]Omit if Section 17.4 was not covered.

[20]This section can be omitted without loss of continuity.

*The demand functions for the cameras and film are given by*

$$q_C = \frac{9000}{p_C\sqrt{p_F}} \quad \text{and} \quad q_F = 2000 - p_C - 400p_F$$

*where $p_C$ is the price per camera and $p_F$ is the price per unit of film. Find the rate of change of total cost with respect to the price of the camera when $p_C = 50$ and $p_F = 2$.*

**Solution:** We must first determine $\partial c/\partial p_C$. By the chain rule,

$$\frac{\partial c}{\partial p_C} = \frac{\partial c}{\partial q_C}\frac{\partial q_C}{\partial p_C} + \frac{\partial c}{\partial q_F}\frac{\partial q_F}{\partial p_C}$$

$$= (30 + 0.015q_F)\left[\frac{-9000}{p_C^2\sqrt{p_F}}\right] + (0.015q_C + 1)(-1)$$

When $p_C = 50$ and $p_F = 2$, then $q_C = 90\sqrt{2}$ and $q_F = 1150$. Substituting these values into $\partial c/\partial p_C$ and simplifying, we have

$$\left.\frac{\partial c}{\partial p_C}\right|_{\substack{p_C=50 \\ p_F=2}} \approx -123.2$$

NOW WORK PROBLEM 1

The chain rule can be extended. For example, suppose $z = f(v, w, x, y)$ and $v$, $w$, $x$, and $y$ are all functions of $r$, $s$, and $t$. Then, if certain conditions of continuity are assumed, $z$ is a function of $r$, $s$, and $t$, and we have

$$\frac{\partial z}{\partial r} = \frac{\partial z}{\partial v}\frac{\partial v}{\partial r} + \frac{\partial z}{\partial w}\frac{\partial w}{\partial r} + \frac{\partial z}{\partial x}\frac{\partial x}{\partial r} + \frac{\partial z}{\partial y}\frac{\partial y}{\partial r}$$

$$\frac{\partial z}{\partial s} = \frac{\partial z}{\partial v}\frac{\partial v}{\partial s} + \frac{\partial z}{\partial w}\frac{\partial w}{\partial s} + \frac{\partial z}{\partial x}\frac{\partial x}{\partial s} + \frac{\partial z}{\partial y}\frac{\partial y}{\partial s}$$

and

$$\frac{\partial z}{\partial t} = \frac{\partial z}{\partial v}\frac{\partial v}{\partial t} + \frac{\partial z}{\partial w}\frac{\partial w}{\partial t} + \frac{\partial z}{\partial x}\frac{\partial x}{\partial t} + \frac{\partial z}{\partial y}\frac{\partial y}{\partial t}$$

Observe that the number of intermediate variables of $z$ (four) is the same as the number of terms that form each of $\partial z/\partial r$, $\partial z/\partial s$, and $\partial z/\partial t$.

Now consider the situation where $z = f(x, y)$ such that $x = x(t)$ and $y = y(t)$. Then

$$\frac{dz}{dt} = \frac{\partial z}{\partial x}\frac{dx}{dt} + \frac{\partial z}{\partial y}\frac{dy}{dt}$$

Here we use the symbol $dz/dt$ rather than $\partial z/\partial t$, since $z$ can be considered a function of *one* variable $t$. Likewise, the symbols $dx/dt$ and $dy/dt$ are used rather than $\partial x/\partial t$ and $\partial y/\partial t$. As is typical, the number of terms that compose $dz/dt$ equals the number of intermediate variables of $z$. Other situations would be treated in a similar way.

Use the partial derivative symbols and the ordinary derivative symbols appropriately.

**EXAMPLE 2    Chain Rule**

**a.** *If $w = f(x, y, z) = 3x^2y + xyz - 4y^2z^3$, where*

$$x = 2r - 3s \quad y = 6r + s \quad z = r - s$$

*determine $\partial w/\partial r$ and $\partial w/\partial s$.*

**Solution:** Since $x$, $y$, and $z$ are functions of $r$ and $s$, then, by the chain rule,

$$\frac{\partial w}{\partial r} = \frac{\partial w}{\partial x}\frac{\partial x}{\partial r} + \frac{\partial w}{\partial y}\frac{\partial y}{\partial r} + \frac{\partial w}{\partial z}\frac{\partial z}{\partial r}$$

$$= (6xy + yz)(2) + (3x^2 + xz - 8yz^3)(6) + (xy - 12y^2z^2)(1)$$

$$= x(18x + 13y + 6z) + 2yz(1 - 24z^2 - 6yz)$$

Also,

$$\frac{\partial w}{\partial s} = \frac{\partial w}{\partial x}\frac{\partial x}{\partial s} + \frac{\partial w}{\partial y}\frac{\partial y}{\partial s} + \frac{\partial w}{\partial z}\frac{\partial z}{\partial s}$$

$$= (6xy + yz)(-3) + (3x^2 + xz - 8yz^3)(1) + (xy - 12y^2z^2)(-1)$$

$$= x(3x - 19y + z) - yz(3 + 8z^2 - 12yz)$$

**b.** If $z = \dfrac{x + e^y}{y}$, where $x = rs + se^{rt}$ and $y = 9 + rt$, evaluate $\partial z/\partial s$ when $r = -2, s = 5,$ and $t = 4$.

**Solution:** Since $x$ and $y$ are functions of $r$, $s$, and $t$ (note that we can write $y = 9 + rt + 0 \cdot s$), by the chain rule,

$$\frac{\partial z}{\partial s} = \frac{\partial z}{\partial x}\frac{\partial x}{\partial s} + \frac{\partial z}{\partial y}\frac{\partial y}{\partial s}$$

$$= \left(\frac{1}{y}\right)(r + e^{rt}) + \frac{\partial z}{\partial y} \cdot (0) = \frac{r + e^{rt}}{y}$$

If $r = -2, s = 5,$ and $t = 4$, then $y = 1$. Thus,

$$\left.\frac{\partial z}{\partial s}\right|_{\substack{r=-2\\s=5\\t=4}} = \frac{-2 + e^{-8}}{1} = -2 + e^{-8}$$

NOW WORK PROBLEM 13

**EXAMPLE 3   Chain Rule**

**a.** Determine $\partial y/\partial r$ if $y = x^2 \ln(x^4 + 6)$ and $x = (r + 3s)^6$.

**Solution:** By the chain rule,

$$\frac{\partial y}{\partial r} = \frac{dy}{dx}\frac{\partial x}{\partial r}$$

$$= \left[x^2 \cdot \frac{4x^3}{x^4 + 6} + 2x \cdot \ln(x^4 + 6)\right][6(r + 3s)^5]$$

$$= 12x(r + 3s)^5\left[\frac{2x^4}{x^4 + 6} + \ln(x^4 + 6)\right]$$

**b.** Given that $z = e^{xy}, x = r - 4s,$ and $y = r - s,$ find $\partial z/\partial r$ in terms of $r$ and $s$.

**Solution:**

$$\frac{\partial z}{\partial r} = \frac{\partial z}{\partial x}\frac{\partial x}{\partial r} + \frac{\partial z}{\partial y}\frac{\partial y}{\partial r}$$

$$= (ye^{xy})(1) + (xe^{xy})(1)$$

$$= (x + y)e^{xy}$$

Since $x = r - 4s$ and $y = r - s$,

$$\frac{\partial z}{\partial r} = [(r - 4s) + (r - s)]e^{(r-4s)(r-s)}$$

$$= (2r - 5s)e^{r^2 - 5rs + 4s^2}$$

NOW WORK PROBLEM 15

## Problems 17.6

*In Problems 1–12, find the indicated derivatives by using the chain rule.*

*1. $z = 5x + 3y, x = 2r + 3s, y = r - 2s$;   $\partial z/\partial r, \partial z/\partial s$

2. $z = 2x^2 + 3xy + 2y^2, x = r^2 - s^2, y = r^2 + s^2$;   $\partial z/\partial r, \partial z/\partial s$

3. $z = e^{x+y}, x = t^2 + 3, y = \sqrt{t^3}$;   $dz/dt$

4. $z = \sqrt{8x + y}, x = t^2 + 3t + 4, y = t^3 + 4$;   $dz/dt$

5. $w = x^2 z^2 + xyz + yz^2$, $x = 5t$,
   $y = 2t + 3$, $z = 6 - t$;   $dw/dt$

6. $w = \ln(x^2 + y^2 + z^2)$,
   $x = 2 - 3t$, $y = t^2 + 3$, $z = 4 - t$;   $dw/dt$

7. $z = (x^2 + xy^2)^3$, $x = r + s + t$,
   $y = 2r - 3s + 8t$;   $\partial z/\partial t$

8. $z = \sqrt{x^2 + y^2}$, $x = r^2 + s - t$,
   $y = r - s + t$;   $\partial z/\partial r$

9. $w = x^2 + xyz + z^2$, $x = r^2 - s^2$,
   $y = rs$, $z = r^2 + s^2$;   $\partial w/\partial s$

10. $w = e^{xyz}$, $x = r^2 s^3$, $y = \ln(r - s)$, $z = \sqrt{rs^2}$;   $\partial w/\partial r$

11. $y = x^2 - 7x + 5$, $x = 19rs + 2s^2 t^2$;   $\partial y/\partial r$

12. $y = 4 - x^2$, $x = 2r + 3s - 4t$;   $\partial y/\partial t$

*13. If $z = (4x + 3y)^3$, where $x = r^2 s$ and $y = r - 2s$, evaluate $\partial z/\partial r$ when $r = 0$ and $s = 1$.

14. If $z = \sqrt{2x + 3y}$, where $x = 3t + 5$ and $y = t^2 + 2t + 1$, evaluate $dz/dt$ when $t = 1$.

*15. If $w = e^{2x+3y}(x^2 + 4z^2)$, where $x = rs$, $y = 2s - 3r$, and $z = r + s$, evaluate $\partial w/\partial s$ when $r = 1$ and $s = 0$.

16. If $y = x/(x - 5)$, where $x = 2t^2 - 3rs - r^2 t$, evaluate $\partial y/\partial t$ when $r = 0$, $s = 2$, and $t = -1$.

17. **Cost Function**   Suppose the cost $c$ of producing $q_A$ units of product A and $q_B$ units of product B is given by

$$c = (3q_A^2 + q_B^3 + 4)^{1/3}$$

and the coupled demand functions for the products are

given by

$$q_A = 10 - p_A + p_B^2$$

and

$$q_B = 20 + p_A - 11p_B$$

Use a chain rule to evaluate $\dfrac{\partial c}{\partial p_A}$ and $\dfrac{\partial c}{\partial p_B}$ when $p_A = 25$ and $p_B = 4$.

18. Suppose $w = f(x, y)$, where $x = g(t)$ and $y = h(t)$.
    (a) State a chain rule that gives $dw/dt$.
    (b) Suppose $h(t) = t$, so that $w = f(x, t)$ where $x = g(t)$. Use part (a) to find $dw/dt$ and simplify your answer.

19. (a) Suppose $w$ is a function of $x$ and $y$, where both $x$ and $y$ are functions of $s$ and $t$. State a chain rule that expresses $\partial w/\partial t$ in terms of derivatives of these functions.
    (b) Let $w = 2x^2 \ln|3x - 5y|$, where $x = s\sqrt{t^2 + 2}$ and $y = t - 3e^{2-s}$. Use part (a) to evaluate $\partial w/\partial t$ when $s = 1$ and $t = 0$.

20. **Production Function**   In considering a production function $P = f(l, k)$, where $l$ is labor input and $k$ is capital input, Fon, Boulier, and Goldfarb[21] assume that $l = Lg(h)$, where $L$ is the number of workers, $h$ is the number of hours per day per worker, and $g(h)$ is a labor effectiveness function. In maximizing profit $p$ given by

$$p = aP - whL$$

where $a$ is the price per unit of output and $w$ is the hourly wage per worker, Fon, Boulier, and Goldfarb determine $\partial p/\partial L$ and $\partial p/\partial h$. Assume that $k$ is independent of $L$ and $h$, and determine these partial derivatives.

# 17.7 Maxima and Minima for Functions of Two Variables

OBJECTIVE

To discuss relative maxima and relative minima, to find critical points, and to apply the second-derivative test for a function of two variables.

We now extend the notion of relative maxima and minima (or relative extrema) to functions of two variables.

**DEFINITION**

A function $z = f(x, y)$ is said to have a ***relative maximum*** at the point $(a, b)$—that is, when $x = a$ and $y = b$—if, for all points $(x, y)$ in the plane that are sufficiently close to $(a, b)$, we have

$$f(a, b) \geq f(x, y) \qquad (1)$$

For a ***relative minimum,*** we replace $\geq$ by $\leq$ in Equation (1).

To say that $z = f(x, y)$ has a relative maximum at $(a, b)$ means, geometrically, that the point $(a, b, f(a, b))$ on the graph of $f$ is higher than (or is as high as) all other points on the surface that are "near" $(a, b, f(a, b))$. In Figure 17.12(a), $f$ has a relative maximum at $(a, b)$. Similarly, the function $f$ in Figure 17.12(b) has a relative minimum when $x = y = 0$, which corresponds to a *low* point on the surface.

Recall that in locating extrema for a function $y = f(x)$ of one variable, we examine those values of $x$ in the domain of $f$ for which $f'(x) = 0$ or $f'(x)$ does not exist. For functions of two (or more) variables, a similar procedure is followed.

---

[21] V. Fon, B. L. Boulier, and R. S. Goldfarb, "The Firm's Demand for Daily Hours of Work: Some Implications," *Atlantic Economic Journal*, XIII, no. 1 (1985), 36–42.

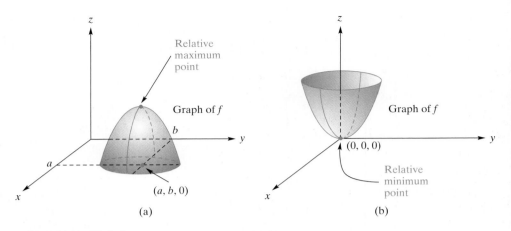

FIGURE 17.12    Relative extrema.

However, for the functions that concern us, extrema will not occur where a derivative does not exist, and such situations will be excluded from consideration.

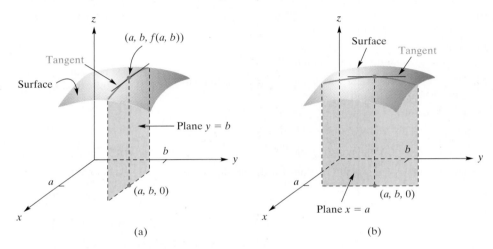

FIGURE 17.13    At relative extremum, $f_x(x, y) = 0$ and $f_y(x, y) = 0$.

Suppose $z = f(x, y)$ has a relative maximum at $(a, b)$, as indicated in Figure 17.13(a). Then the curve where the plane $y = b$ intersects the surface must have a relative maximum when $x = a$. Hence, the slope of the tangent line to the surface in the $x$-direction must be 0 at $(a, b)$. Equivalently, $f_x(x, y) = 0$ at $(a, b)$. Similarly, on the curve where the plane $x = a$ intersects the surface [Figure 17.13(b)], there must be a relative maximum when $y = b$. Thus, in the $y$-direction, the slope of the tangent to the surface must be 0 at $(a, b)$. Equivalently, $f_y(x, y) = 0$ at $(a, b)$. Since a similar discussion applies to a relative minimum, we can combine these results as follows:

**CAUTION**

Rule 1 does not imply that there must be an extremum at a critical point. Just as in the case of functions of one variable, a critical point can give rise to a relative maximum, a relative minimum, or neither. A critical point is only a *candidate* for a relative extremum.

**RULE 1**

If $z = f(x, y)$ has a relative maximum or minimum at $(a, b)$, and if both $f_x$ and $f_y$ are defined for all points close to $(a, b)$, it is necessary that $(a, b)$ be a solution of the system

$$\begin{cases} f_x(x, y) = 0 \\ f_y(x, y) = 0 \end{cases}$$

A point $(a, b)$ for which $f_x(a, b) = f_y(a, b) = 0$ is called a **critical point** of $f$. Thus, from Rule 1, we infer that, to locate relative extrema for a function, we should examine its critical points.

Two additional comments are in order: First, Rule 1, as well as the notion of a critical point, can be extended to functions of more than two variables. For example, to locate possible extrema for $w = f(x, y, z)$, we would examine those points for which $w_x = w_y = w_z = 0$. Second, for a function whose domain is restricted, a thorough examination for absolute extrema would include a consideration of boundary points.

● EXAMPLE 1   **Finding Critical Points**

*Find the critical points of the following functions.*

**a.** $f(x, y) = 2x^2 + y^2 - 2xy + 5x - 3y + 1$.

   **Solution:** Since $f_x(x, y) = 4x - 2y + 5$ and $f_y(x, y) = 2y - 2x - 3$, we solve the system

$$\begin{cases} 4x - 2y + 5 = 0 \\ -2x + 2y - 3 = 0 \end{cases}$$

   This gives $x = -1$ and $y = \frac{1}{2}$. Thus, $\left(-1, \frac{1}{2}\right)$ is the only critical point.

**b.** $f(l, k) = l^3 + k^3 - lk$.

   **Solution:**

$$\begin{cases} f_l(l, k) = 3l^2 - k = 0 & \text{(2)} \\ f_k(l, k) = 3k^2 - l = 0 & \text{(3)} \end{cases}$$

   From Equation (2), $k = 3l^2$. Substituting for $k$ in Equation (3) gives

$$0 = 27l^4 - l = l(27l^3 - 1)$$

   Hence, either $l = 0$ or $l = \frac{1}{3}$. If $l = 0$, then $k = 0$; if $l = \frac{1}{3}$, then $k = \frac{1}{3}$. The critical points are therefore $(0, 0)$ and $\left(\frac{1}{3}, \frac{1}{3}\right)$.

**c.** $f(x, y, z) = 2x^2 + xy + y^2 + 100 - z(x + y - 100)$.

   **Solution:** Solving the system

$$\begin{cases} f_x(x, y, z) = 4x + y - z = 0 \\ f_y(x, y, z) = x + 2y - z = 0 \\ f_z(x, y, z) = -x - y + 100 = 0 \end{cases}$$

   gives the critical point $(25, 75, 175)$, as you should verify.

NOW WORK PROBLEM 1   ●●●

● EXAMPLE 2   **Finding Critical Points**

*Find the critical points of*

$$f(x, y) = x^2 - 4x + 2y^2 + 4y + 7$$

**Solution:** We have $f_x(x, y) = 2x - 4$ and $f_y(x, y) = 4y + 4$. The system

$$\begin{cases} 2x - 4 = 0 \\ 4y + 4 = 0 \end{cases}$$

gives the critical point $(2, -1)$. Observe that we can write the given function as

$$f(x, y) = x^2 - 4x + 4 + 2(y^2 + 2y + 1) + 1$$
$$= (x - 2)^2 + 2(y + 1)^2 + 1$$

and $f(2, -1) = 1$. Clearly, if $(x, y) \neq (2, -1)$, then $f(x, y) > 1$. Hence, a relative minimum occurs at $(2, -1)$. Moreover, there is an *absolute minimum* at $(2, -1)$, since $f(x, y) > f(2, -1)$ for *all* $(x, y) \neq (2, -1)$.

NOW WORK PROBLEM 3   ●●●

Although in Example 2 we were able to show that the critical point gave rise to a relative extremum, in many cases this is not so easy to do. There is, however, a second-derivative test that gives conditions under which a critical point will be a relative maximum or minimum. We state it now, omitting the proof.

**RULE 2    Second-Derivative Test for Functions of Two Variables**

Suppose $z = f(x, y)$ has continuous partial derivatives $f_{xx}$, $f_{yy}$, and $f_{xy}$ at all points $(x, y)$ near a critical point $(a, b)$. Let $D$ be the function defined by

$$D(x, y) = f_{xx}(x, y) f_{yy}(x, y) - (f_{xy}(x, y))^2$$

Then

1. if $D(a, b) > 0$ and $f_{xx}(a, b) < 0$, then $f$ has a relative maximum at $(a, b)$;
2. if $D(a, b) > 0$ and $f_{xx}(a, b) > 0$, then $f$ has a relative minimum at $(a, b)$;
3. if $D(a, b) < 0$, then $f$ has a *saddle point* at $(a, b)$ (see Example 4);
4. if $D(a, b) = 0$, then no conclusion about an extremum at $(a, b)$ can be drawn, and further analysis is required.

● **EXAMPLE 3    Applying the Second-Derivative Test**

*Examine $f(x, y) = x^3 + y^3 - xy$ for relative maxima or minima by using the second-derivative test.*

**Solution:**  First we find critical points:

$$f_x(x, y) = 3x^2 - y \quad f_y(x, y) = 3y^2 - x$$

In the same manner as in Example 1(b), solving $f_x(x, y) = f_y(x, y) = 0$ gives the critical points $(0, 0)$ and $\left(\frac{1}{3}, \frac{1}{3}\right)$.
Now,

$$f_{xx}(x, y) = 6x \qquad f_{yy}(x, y) = 6y \qquad f_{xy}(x, y) = -1$$

Thus,

$$D(x, y) = (6x)(6y) - (-1)^2 = 36xy - 1$$

Since $D(0, 0) = 36(0)(0) - 1 = -1 < 0$, there is no relative extremum at $(0, 0)$. Also, since $D\left(\frac{1}{3}, \frac{1}{3}\right) = 36\left(\frac{1}{3}\right)\left(\frac{1}{3}\right) - 1 = 3 > 0$ and $f_{xx}\left(\frac{1}{3}, \frac{1}{3}\right) = 6\left(\frac{1}{3}\right) = 2 > 0$, there is a relative minimum at $\left(\frac{1}{3}, \frac{1}{3}\right)$. At this point, the value of the function is

$$f\left(\tfrac{1}{3}, \tfrac{1}{3}\right) = \left(\tfrac{1}{3}\right)^3 + \left(\tfrac{1}{3}\right)^3 - \left(\tfrac{1}{3}\right)\left(\tfrac{1}{3}\right) = -\tfrac{1}{27}$$

NOW WORK PROBLEM 7 ●●

● **EXAMPLE 4    A Saddle Point**

*Examine $f(x, y) = y^2 - x^2$ for relative extrema.*

**Solution:**  Solving

$$f_x(x, y) = -2x = 0 \quad \text{and} \quad f_y(x, y) = 2y = 0$$

we get the critical point $(0, 0)$. Now we apply the second-derivative test. At $(0, 0)$, and indeed at any point,

$$f_{xx}(x, y) = -2 \quad f_{yy}(x, y) = 2 \quad f_{xy}(x, y) = 0$$

Because $D(0, 0) = (-2)(2) - (0)^2 = -4 < 0$, no relative extremum exists at $(0, 0)$. A sketch of $z = f(x, y) = y^2 - x^2$ appears in Figure 17.14. Note that, for the surface

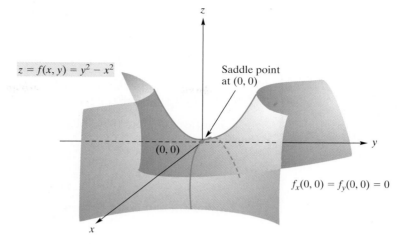

The surface in Figure 17.14 is called a hyperbolic paraboloid.

**FIGURE 17.14**  Saddle point.

curve cut by the plane $y = 0$, there is a *maximum* at $(0, 0)$; but for the surface curve cut by the plane $x = 0$, there is a *minimum* at $(0, 0)$. Thus, on the *surface*, no relative extremum can exist at the origin, although $(0, 0)$ is a critical point. Around the origin the curve is saddle shaped, and $(0, 0)$ is called a *saddle point* of $f$.

NOW WORK PROBLEM 11

● EXAMPLE 5   **Finding Relative Extrema**

*Examine* $f(x, y) = x^4 + (x - y)^4$ *for relative extrema.*

**Solution:**  If we set

$$f_x(x, y) = 4x^3 + 4(x - y)^3 = 0 \qquad (4)$$

and

$$f_y(x, y) = -4(x - y)^3 = 0 \qquad (5)$$

then, from Equation (5), we have $x - y = 0$, or $x = y$. Substituting into Equation (4) gives $4x^3 = 0$, or $x = 0$. Thus, $x = y = 0$, and $(0, 0)$ is the only critical point. At $(0, 0)$,

$$f_{xx}(x, y) = 12x^2 + 12(x - y)^2 = 0$$
$$f_{yy}(x, y) = 12(x - y)^2 = 0$$

and

$$f_{xy}(x, y) = -12(x - y)^2 = 0$$

Hence, $D(0, 0) = 0$, and the second-derivative test gives no information. However, for all $(x, y) \neq (0, 0)$, we have $f(x, y) > 0$, whereas $f(0, 0) = 0$. Therefore, at $(0, 0)$ the graph of $f$ has a low point, and we conclude that $f$ has a relative (and absolute) minimum at $(0, 0)$.

NOW WORK PROBLEM 13

## Applications

In many situations involving functions of two variables, and especially in their applications, the nature of the given problem is an indicator of whether a critical point is in fact a relative (or absolute) maximum or a relative (or absolute) minimum. In such cases, the second-derivative test is not needed. Often, in mathematical studies of applied problems, the appropriate second-order conditions are assumed to hold.

● EXAMPLE 6    **Maximizing Output**

*Let P be a production function given by*

$$P = f(l, k) = 0.54l^2 - 0.02l^3 + 1.89k^2 - 0.09k^3$$

*where l and k are the amounts of labor and capital, respectively, and P is the quantity of output produced. Find the values of l and k that maximize P.*

**Solution:** To find the critical points, we solve the system $P_l = 0$ and $P_k = 0$;

$$P_l = 1.08l - 0.06l^2 \qquad P_k = 3.78k - 0.27k^2$$
$$= 0.06l(18 - l) = 0 \qquad = 0.27k(14 - k) = 0$$
$$l = 0, l = 18 \qquad\qquad k = 0, k = 14$$

There are four critical points: $(0, 0)$, $(0, 14)$, $(18, 0)$, and $(18, 14)$.

Now we apply the second-derivative test to each critical point. We have

$$P_{ll} = 1.08 - 0.12l \quad P_{kk} = 3.78 - 0.54k \quad P_{lk} = 0$$

Thus,

$$D(l, k) = P_{ll} P_{kk} - [P_{lk}]^2$$
$$= (1.08 - 0.12l)(3.78 - 0.54k)$$

At $(0, 0)$,

$$D(0, 0) = 1.08(3.78) > 0$$

Since $D(0, 0) > 0$ and $P_{ll} = 1.08 > 0$, there is a relative minimum at $(0, 0)$. At $(0, 14)$,

$$D(0, 14) = 1.08(-3.78) < 0$$

Because $D(0, 14) < 0$, there is no relative extremum at $(0, 14)$. At $(18, 0)$,

$$D(18, 0) = (-1.08)(3.78) < 0$$

Since $D(18, 0) < 0$, there is no relative extremum at $(18, 0)$. At $(18, 14)$,

$$D(18, 14) = (-1.08)(-3.78) > 0$$

Because $D(18, 14) > 0$ and $P_{ll} = -1.08 < 0$, there is a relative maximum at $(18, 14)$. Hence, the maximum output is obtained when $l = 18$ and $k = 14$.

NOW WORK PROBLEM 21

● EXAMPLE 7    **Profit Maximization**

*A candy company produces two types of candy, A and B, for which the average costs of production are constant at $2 and $3 per pound, respectively. The quantities $q_A$, $q_B$ (in pounds) of A and B that can be sold each week are given by the joint-demand functions*

$$q_A = 400(p_B - p_A)$$

*and*

$$q_B = 400(9 + p_A - 2p_B)$$

*where $p_A$ and $p_B$ are the selling prices (in dollars per pound) of A and B, respectively. Determine the selling prices that will maximize the company's profit P.*

**Solution:** The total profit is given by

$$P = \begin{pmatrix} \text{profit} \\ \text{per pound} \\ \text{of A} \end{pmatrix} \begin{pmatrix} \text{pounds} \\ \text{of A} \\ \text{sold} \end{pmatrix} + \begin{pmatrix} \text{profit} \\ \text{per pound} \\ \text{of B} \end{pmatrix} \begin{pmatrix} \text{pounds} \\ \text{of B} \\ \text{sold} \end{pmatrix}$$

For A and B, the profits per pound are $p_A - 2$ and $p_B - 3$, respectively. Thus,

$$P = (p_A - 2)q_A + (p_B - 3)q_B$$
$$= (p_A - 2)[400(p_B - p_A)] + (p_B - 3)[400(9 + p_A - 2p_B)]$$

Notice that $P$ is expressed as a function of two variables, $p_A$ and $p_B$. To maximize $P$, we set its partial derivatives equal to 0:

$$\frac{\partial P}{\partial p_A} = (p_A - 2)[400(-1)] + [400(p_B - p_A)](1) + (p_B - 3)[400(1)]$$
$$= 0$$
$$\frac{\partial P}{\partial p_B} = (p_A - 2)[400(1)] + (p_B - 3)[400(-2)] + 400(9 + p_A - 2p_B)](1)$$
$$= 0$$

Simplifying the preceding two equations gives

$$\begin{cases} -2p_A + 2p_B - 1 = 0 \\ 2p_A - 4p_B + 13 = 0 \end{cases}$$

whose solution is $p_A = 5.5$ and $p_B = 6$. Moreover, we find that

$$\frac{\partial^2 P}{\partial p_A^2} = -800 \quad \frac{\partial^2 P}{\partial p_B^2} = -1600 \quad \frac{\partial^2 P}{\partial p_B \partial p_A} = 800$$

Therefore,

$$D(5.5, 6) = (-800)(-1600) - (800)^2 > 0$$

Since $\partial^2 P/\partial p_A^2 < 0$, we indeed have a maximum, and the company should sell candy A at \$5.50 per pound and B at \$6.00 per pound.

NOW WORK PROBLEM 23

## EXAMPLE 8   Profit Maximization for a Monopolist[22]

Suppose a monopolist is practicing price discrimination by selling the same product in two separate markets at different prices. Let $q_A$ be the number of units sold in market A, where the demand function is $p_A = f(q_A)$, and let $q_B$ be the number of units sold in market B, where the demand function is $p_B = g(q_B)$. Then the revenue functions for the two markets are

$$r_A = q_A f(q_A) \quad \text{and} \quad r_B = q_B g(q_B)$$

Assume that all units are produced at one plant, and let the cost function for producing $q = q_A + q_B$ units be $c = c(q)$. Keep in mind that $r_A$ is a function of $q_A$ and $r_B$ is a function of $q_B$. The monopolist's profit $P$ is

$$P = r_A + r_B - c$$

To maximize $P$ with respect to outputs $q_A$ and $q_B$, we set its partial derivatives equal to zero. To begin with,

$$\frac{\partial P}{\partial q_A} = \frac{dr_A}{dq_A} + 0 - \frac{\partial c}{\partial q_A}$$
$$= \frac{dr_A}{dq_A} - \frac{dc}{dq}\frac{\partial q}{\partial q_A} = 0 \quad \text{(chain rule)}$$

[22]Omit if Section 17.6 was not covered.

Because

$$\frac{\partial q}{\partial q_A} = \frac{\partial}{\partial q_A}(q_A + q_B) = 1$$

we have

$$\frac{\partial P}{\partial q_A} = \frac{dr_A}{dq_A} - \frac{dc}{dq} = 0 \qquad (6)$$

Similarly,

$$\frac{\partial P}{\partial q_B} = \frac{dr_B}{dq_B} - \frac{dc}{dq} = 0 \qquad (7)$$

From Equations (6) and (7), we get

$$\frac{dr_A}{dq_A} = \frac{dc}{dq} = \frac{dr_B}{dq_B}$$

But $dr_A/dq_A$ and $dr_B/dq_B$ are marginal revenues, and $dc/dq$ is marginal cost. Hence, to maximize profit, it is necessary to charge prices (and distribute output) so that the marginal revenues in both markets will be the same and, loosely speaking, will also be equal to the cost of the last unit produced in the plant.

NOW WORK PROBLEM 25

## Problems 17.7

*In Problems 1–6, find the critical points of the functions.*

*1. $f(x, y) = x^2 + y^2 - 5x + 4y + xy$

2. $f(x, y) = x^2 + 4y^2 - 6x + 16y$

*3. $f(x, y) = \frac{5}{3}x^3 + \frac{2}{3}y^3 - \frac{15}{2}x^2 + y^2 - 4y + 7$

4. $f(x, y) = xy - x + y$

5. $f(x, y, z) = 2x^2 + xy + y^2 + 100 - z(x + y - 200)$

6. $f(x, y, z, w) = x^2 + y^2 + z^2 - w(x - y + 2z - 6)$

*In Problems 7–20, find the critical points of the functions. For each critical point, determine, by the second-derivative test, whether it corresponds to a relative maximum, to a relative minimum, or to neither, or whether the test gives no information.*

*7. $f(x, y) = x^2 + 3y^2 + 4x - 9y + 3$

8. $f(x, y) = -2x^2 + 8x - 3y^2 + 24y + 7$

9. $f(x, y) = y - y^2 - 3x - 6x^2$

10. $f(x, y) = 2x^2 + \frac{3}{2}y^2 + 3xy - 10x - 9y + 2$

*11. $f(x, y) = x^2 + 3xy + y^2 + x + 3$

12. $f(x, y) = \frac{x^3}{3} + y^2 - 2x + 2y - 2xy$

*13. $f(x, y) = \frac{1}{3}(x^3 + 8y^3) - 2(x^2 + y^2) + 1$

14. $f(x, y) = x^2 + y^2 - xy + x^3$

15. $f(l, k) = \frac{l^2}{2} + 2lk + 3k^2 - 69l - 164k + 17$

16. $f(l, k) = l^2 + k^2 - 2lk$

17. $f(p, q) = pq - \frac{1}{p} - \frac{1}{q}$

18. $f(x, y) = (x - 3)(y - 3)(x + y - 3)$.

19. $f(x, y) = (y^2 - 4)(e^x - 1)$

20. $f(x, y) = \ln(xy) + 2x^2 - xy - 6x$

*21. **Maximizing Output** Suppose

$$P = f(l, k) = 1.08l^2 - 0.03l^3 + 1.68k^2 - 0.08k^3$$

is a production function for a firm. Find the quantities of inputs $l$ and $k$ that maximize output $P$.

22. **Maximizing Output** In a certain office, computers C and D are utilized for $c$ and $d$ hours, respectively. If daily output $Q$ is a function of $c$ and $d$, namely,

$$Q = 18c + 20d - 2c^2 - 4d^2 - cd$$

find the values of $c$ and $d$ that maximize $Q$.

*In Problems 23–35, unless otherwise indicated, the variables $p_A$ and $p_B$ denote selling prices of products A and B, respectively. Similarly, $q_A$ and $q_B$ denote quantities of A and B that are produced and sold during some time period. In all cases, the variables employed will be assumed to be units of output, input, money, and so on.*

*23. **Profit** A candy company produces two varieties of candy, A and B, for which the constant average costs of production are 60 and 70 (cents per lb), respectively. The demand functions for A and B are given by

$$q_A = 5(p_B - p_A) \quad \text{and} \quad q_B = 500 + 5(p_A - 2p_B)$$

Find the selling prices $p_A$ and $p_B$ that maximize the company's profit.

24. **Profit** Repeat Problem 23 if the constant costs of production of A and B are $a$ and $b$ (cents per lb), respectively.

*25. **Price Discrimination** Suppose a monopolist is practicing price discrimination in the sale of a product by charging different prices in two separate markets. In market A the demand function is

$$p_A = 100 - q_A$$

and in B it is

$$p_B = 84 - q_B$$

where $q_A$ and $q_B$ are the quantities sold per week in A and B, and $p_A$ and $p_B$ are the respective prices per unit. If the monopolist's cost function is

$$c = 600 + 4(q_A + q_B)$$

how much should be sold in each market to maximize profit? What selling prices give this maximum profit? Find the maximum profit.

**26. Profit**   A monopolist sells two competitive products, A and B, for which the demand functions are

$$q_A = 3 - p_A + 2p_B \quad \text{and} \quad q_B = 5 + 5p_A - 2p_B$$

If the constant average cost of producing a unit of A is 3 and a unit of B is 2, how many units of A and B should be sold to maximize the monopolist's profit?

**27. Profit**   For products A and B, the joint-cost function for a manufacturer is

$$c = \frac{3}{2}q_A^2 + 3q_B^2$$

and the demand functions are $p_A = 60 - q_A^2$ and $p_B = 72 - 2q_B^2$. Find the level of production that maximizes profit.

**28. Profit**   For a monopolist's products A and B, the joint-cost function is $c = 2(q_A + q_B + q_A q_B)$, and the demand functions are $q_A = 20 - 2p_A$ and $q_B = 10 - p_B$. Find the values of $p_A$ and $p_B$ that maximize profit. What are the quantities of A and B that correspond to these prices? What is the total profit?

**29. Cost**   An open-top rectangular box is to have a volume of $6\ \text{ft}^3$. The cost per square foot of materials is \$3 for the bottom, \$1 for the front and back, and \$0.50 for the other two sides. Find the dimensions of the box so that the cost of materials is minimized. (See Figure 17.15.)

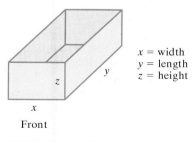

$x$ = width
$y$ = length
$z$ = height

Front

**FIGURE 17.15**   Diagram for Problem 29.

**30. Collusion**   Suppose A and B are the only two firms in the market selling the same product. (We say that they are *duopolists*.) The industry demand function for the product is

$$p = 92 - q_A - q_B$$

where $q_A$ and $q_B$ denote the output produced and sold by A and B, respectively. For A, the cost function is $c_A = 10q_A$; for B, it is $c_B = 0.5q_B^2$. Suppose the firms decide to enter into an agreement on output and price control by jointly acting as a monopoly. In this case, we say they enter into *collusion*.

Show that the profit function for the monopoly is given by

$$P = pq_A - c_A + pq_B - c_B$$

Express $P$ as a function of $q_A$ and $q_B$, and determine how output should be allocated so as to maximize the profit of the monopoly.

**31.** Suppose $f(x, y) = -2x^2 + 5y^2 + 7$, where $x$ and $y$ must satisfy the equation $3x - 2y = 7$. Find the relative extrema of $f$, subject to the given condition on $x$ and $y$, by first solving the second equation for $y$. Substitute the result for $y$ in the given equation. Thus, $f$ is expressed as a function of one variable, for which extrema may be found in the usual way.

**32.** Repeat Problem 31 if $f(x, y) = x^2 + 4y^2 + 6$, subject to the condition that $2x - 8y = 20$.

**33.** Suppose the joint-cost function

$$c = q_A^2 + 3q_B^2 + 2q_A q_B + aq_A + bq_B + d$$

has a relative minimum value of 15 when $q_A = 3$ and $q_B = 1$. Determine the values of the constants $a$, $b$, and $d$.

**34.** Suppose that the function $f(x, y)$ has continuous partial derivatives $f_{xx}$, $f_{yy}$, and $f_{xy}$ at all points $(x, y)$ near a critical point $(a, b)$. Let $D(x, y) = f_{xx}(x, y)f_{yy}(x, y) - (f_{xy}(x, y))^2$ and suppose that $D(a, b) > 0$.

(a) Show that $f_{xx}(a, b) < 0$ if and only if $f_{yy}(a, b) < 0$.
(b) Show that $f_{xx}(a, b) > 0$ if and only if $f_{yy}(a, b) > 0$.

**35. Profit from Competitive Products**   A monopolist sells two competitive products, A and B, for which the demand equations are

$$p_A = 35 - 2q_A^2 + q_B$$

and

$$p_B = 20 - q_B + q_A$$

The joint-cost function is

$$c = -8 - 2q_A^3 + 3q_A q_B + 30q_A + 12q_B + \frac{1}{2}q_A^2$$

(a) How many units of A and B should be sold to obtain a relative maximum profit for the monopolist? Use the second-derivative test to justify your answer.
(b) Determine the selling prices required to realize the relative maximum profit. Also, find this relative maximum profit.

**36. Profit and Advertising**   A retailer has determined that the number of TV sets he can sell per week is

$$\frac{5x}{2 + x} + \frac{2y}{5 + y}$$

where $x$ and $y$ represent his weekly expenditures (in dollars) on newspaper and radio advertising, respectively. The profit is \$250 per sale, less the cost of advertising, so the weekly profit is given by the formula

$$P = 250\left[\frac{5x}{2 + x} + \frac{2y}{5 + y}\right] - x - y$$

Find the values of $x$ and $y$ for which the profit is a relative maximum. Use the second-derivative test to verify that your answer corresponds to a relative maximum profit.

37. **Profit from Tomato Crop**   The revenue (in dollars per square meter of ground) obtained from the sale of a crop of tomatoes grown in an artificially heated greenhouse is given by

$$r = 5T(1 - e^{-x})$$

where $T$ is the temperature (in °C) maintained in the greenhouse and $x$ is the amount of fertilizer applied per square meter. The cost of fertilizer is $20x$ dollars per square meter, and the cost of heating is given by $0.1T^2$ dollars per square meter.

(a) Find an expression, in terms of $T$ and $x$, for the profit per square meter obtained from the sale of the crop of tomatoes.

(b) Verify that the pairs

$$(T, x) = (20, \ln 5) \quad \text{and} \quad (T, x) = (5, \ln \tfrac{5}{4})$$

are critical points of the profit function in part (a). (*Note:* You need not derive the pairs.)

(c) The points in part (b) are the only critical points of the profit function in part (a). Use the second-derivative test to determine whether either of these points corresponds to a relative maximum profit per square meter.

OBJECTIVE

To find critical points for a function, subject to constraints, by applying the method of Lagrange multipliers.

# 17.8 Lagrange Multipliers

We will now find relative maxima and minima for a function on which certain *constraints* are imposed. Such a situation could arise if a manufacturer wished to minimize a joint-cost function and yet obtain a particular production level.

Suppose we want to find the relative extrema of

$$w = x^2 + y^2 + z^2 \tag{1}$$

subject to the constraint that $x$, $y$, and $z$ must satisfy

$$x - y + 2z = 6 \tag{2}$$

We can transform $w$, which is a function of three variables, into a function of two variables such that the new function reflects constraint (2). Solving Equation (2) for $x$, we get

$$x = y - 2z + 6 \tag{3}$$

which, when substituted for $x$ in Equation (1), gives

$$w = (y - 2z + 6)^2 + y^2 + z^2 \tag{4}$$

Since $w$ is now expressed as a function of two variables, to find relative extrema we follow the usual procedure of setting the partial derivatives of $w$ equal to 0:

$$\frac{\partial w}{\partial y} = 2(y - 2z + 6) + 2y = 4y - 4z + 12 = 0 \tag{5}$$

$$\frac{\partial w}{\partial z} = -4(y - 2z + 6) + 2z = -4y + 10z - 24 = 0 \tag{6}$$

Solving Equations (5) and (6) simultaneously gives $y = -1$ and $z = 2$. Substituting into Equation (3), we get $x = 1$. Hence, the only critical point of Equation (1) subject to the constraint represented by Equation (2) is $(1, -1, 2)$. By using the second-derivative test on Equation (4) when $y = -1$ and $z = 2$, we have

$$\frac{\partial^2 w}{\partial y^2} = 4 \quad \frac{\partial^2 w}{\partial z^2} = 10 \quad \frac{\partial^2 w}{\partial z \, \partial y} = -4$$

$$D(-1, 2) = 4(10) - (-4)^2 = 24 > 0$$

Thus $w$, subject to the constraint, has a relative minimum at $(1, -1, 2)$.

This solution was found by using the constraint to express one of the variables in the original function in terms of the other variables. Often this is not practical, but there is another technique, called the method of **Lagrange multipliers**,[23] that avoids this step and yet allows us to obtain critical points.

The method is as follows. Suppose we have a function $f(x, y, z)$ subject to the constraint $g(x, y, z) = 0$. We construct a new function $F$ of *four* variables defined by

---

[23]After the French mathematician Joseph-Louis Lagrange (1736–1813).

the following (where $\lambda$ is a Greek letter read "lambda"):

$$F(x, y, z, \lambda) = f(x, y, z) - \lambda g(x, y, z)$$

It can be shown that if $(a, b, c)$ is a critical point of $f$, subject to the constraint $g(x, y, z) = 0$, there exists a value of $\lambda$, say, $\lambda_0$, such that $(a, b, c, \lambda_0)$ is a critical point of $F$. The number $\lambda_0$ is called a **Lagrange multiplier.** Also, if $(a, b, c, \lambda_0)$ is a critical point of $F$, then $(a, b, c)$ is a critical point of $f$, subject to the constraint. Thus, to find critical points of $f$, subject to $g(x, y, z) = 0$, we instead find critical points of $F$. These are obtained by solving the simultaneous equations

$$\begin{cases} F_x(x, y, z, \lambda) = 0 \\ F_y(x, y, z, \lambda) = 0 \\ F_z(x, y, z, \lambda) = 0 \\ F_\lambda(x, y, z, \lambda) = 0 \end{cases}$$

At times, ingenuity must be used to solve the equations. Once we obtain a critical point $(a, b, c, \lambda_0)$ of $F$, we can conclude that $(a, b, c)$ is a critical point of $f$, subject to the constraint $g(x, y, z) = 0$. Although $f$ and $g$ are functions of three variables, the method of Lagrange multipliers can be extended to $n$ variables.

Let us illustrate the method of Lagrange multipliers for the original situation, namely,

$$f(x, y, z) = x^2 + y^2 + z^2 \quad \text{subject to} \quad x - y + 2z = 6$$

First, we write the constraint as $g(x, y, z) = x - y + 2z - 6 = 0$. Second, we form the function

$$\begin{aligned} F(x, y, z, \lambda) &= f(x, y, z) - \lambda g(x, y, z) \\ &= x^2 + y^2 + z^2 - \lambda(x - y + 2z - 6) \end{aligned}$$

Next, we set each partial derivative of $F$ equal to 0. For convenience, we will write $F_x(x, y, z, \lambda)$ as $F_x$, and so on:

$$\begin{cases} F_x = 2x - \lambda = 0 & \text{(7)} \\ F_y = 2y + \lambda = 0 & \text{(8)} \\ F_z = 2z - 2\lambda = 0 & \text{(9)} \\ F_\lambda = -x + y - 2z + 6 = 0 & \text{(10)} \end{cases}$$

From Equations (7)–(9), we see immediately that

$$x = \frac{\lambda}{2} \qquad y = -\frac{\lambda}{2} \qquad z = \lambda \qquad \text{(11)}$$

Substituting these values into Equation (10), we obtain

$$-\frac{\lambda}{2} - \frac{\lambda}{2} - 2\lambda + 6 = 0$$

$$-3\lambda + 6 = 0$$

$$\lambda = 2$$

Thus, from Equation (11),

$$x = 1 \quad y = -1 \quad z = 2$$

Hence, the only critical point of $f$, subject to the constraint, is $(1, -1, 2)$, at which there may exist a relative maximum, a relative minimum, or neither of these. The method of Lagrange multipliers does not directly indicate which of these possibilities occur, although from our previous work, we saw that it is indeed a relative minimum. In applied problems, the nature of the problem itself may give a clue as to how a critical point is to be regarded. Often the existence of either a relative minimum or a relative maximum is assumed, and a critical point is treated accordingly. Actually, sufficient second-order conditions for relative extrema are available, but we will not consider them.

### ● EXAMPLE 1    Method of Lagrange Multipliers

*Find the critical points for* $z = f(x, y) = 3x - y + 6$*, subject to the constraint* $x^2 + y^2 = 4$.

**Solution:** We write the constraint as $g(x, y) = x^2 + y^2 - 4 = 0$ and construct the function

$$F(x, y, \lambda) = f(x, y) - \lambda g(x, y) = 3x - y + 6 - \lambda(x^2 + y^2 - 4)$$

Setting $F_x = F_y = F_\lambda = 0$, we have

$$\begin{cases} 3 - 2x\lambda = 0 & \text{(12)} \\ -1 - 2y\lambda = 0 & \text{(13)} \\ -x^2 - y^2 + 4 = 0 & \text{(14)} \end{cases}$$

From Equations (12) and (13), we can express $x$ and $y$ in terms of $\lambda$. Then we will substitute for $x$ and $y$ in Equation (14) and solve for $\lambda$. Knowing $\lambda$, we can find $x$ and $y$. To begin, from Equations (12) and (13), we have

$$x = \frac{3}{2\lambda} \quad \text{and} \quad y = -\frac{1}{2\lambda}$$

Substituting into Equation (14), we obtain

$$-\frac{9}{4\lambda^2} - \frac{1}{4\lambda^2} + 4 = 0$$

$$-\frac{10}{4\lambda^2} + 4 = 0$$

$$\lambda = \pm\frac{\sqrt{10}}{4}$$

With these $\lambda$-values, we can find $x$ and $y$. If $\lambda = \sqrt{10}/4$, then

$$x = \frac{3}{2\left(\frac{\sqrt{10}}{4}\right)} = \frac{3\sqrt{10}}{5} \quad y = -\frac{1}{2\left(\frac{\sqrt{10}}{4}\right)} = -\frac{\sqrt{10}}{5}$$

Similarly, if $\lambda = -\sqrt{10}/4$,

$$x = -\frac{3\sqrt{10}}{5} \qquad y = \frac{\sqrt{10}}{5}$$

Thus, the critical points of $f$, subject to the constraint, are $(3\sqrt{10}/5, -\sqrt{10}/5)$ and $(-3\sqrt{10}/5, \sqrt{10}/5)$. Note that the values of $\lambda$ do not appear in the answer; they are simply a means to obtain the solution.

NOW WORK PROBLEM 1 ●●●

### ● EXAMPLE 2    Method of Lagrange Multipliers

*Find critical points for* $f(x, y, z) = xyz$*, where* $xyz \neq 0$*, subject to the constraint* $x + 2y + 3z = 36$.

**Solution:** We have

$$F(x, y, z, \lambda) = xyz - \lambda(x + 2y + 3z - 36)$$

Setting $F_x = F_y = F_z = F_\lambda = 0$ gives, respectively,

$$\begin{cases} yz - \lambda = 0 \\ xz - 2\lambda = 0 \\ xy - 3\lambda = 0 \\ -x - 2y - 3z + 36 = 0 \end{cases}$$

Because we cannot directly express $x$, $y$, and $z$ in terms of $\lambda$ only, we cannot follow the procedure in Example 1. However, observe that we can express the products $yz$, $xz$, and $xy$ as multiples of $\lambda$. This suggests that, by looking at quotients of equations, we can obtain a relation between two variables that does not involve $\lambda$. (The $\lambda$'s will cancel.) Proceeding to do this, we write the foregoing system as

$$\begin{cases} yz = \lambda & \text{(15)} \\ xz = 2\lambda & \text{(16)} \\ xy = 3\lambda & \text{(17)} \\ x + 2y + 3z - 36 = 0 & \text{(18)} \end{cases}$$

Dividing each side of Equation (15) by the corresponding side of Equation (16), we get

$$\frac{yz}{xz} = \frac{\lambda}{2\lambda} \quad \text{so} \quad y = \frac{x}{2}$$

This division is valid, since $xyz \neq 0$. Similarly, from Equations (15) and (17), we get

$$\frac{yz}{xy} = \frac{\lambda}{3\lambda} \quad \text{so} \quad z = \frac{x}{3}$$

Now that we have $y$ and $z$ expressed in terms of $x$ only, we can substitute into Equation (18) and solve for $x$:

$$x + 2\left(\frac{x}{2}\right) + 3\left(\frac{x}{3}\right) - 36 = 0$$

$$x = 12$$

Thus, $y = 6$ and $z = 4$. Hence, $(12, 6, 4)$ is the only critical point satisfying the given conditions. Note that in this situation, we found the critical point without having to find the value for $\lambda$.

NOW WORK PROBLEM 7 ●●●

● EXAMPLE 3   **Minimizing Costs**

*Suppose a firm has an order for 200 units of its product and wishes to distribute its manufacture between two of its plants, plant 1 and plant 2. Let $q_1$ and $q_2$ denote the outputs of plants 1 and 2, respectively, and suppose the total-cost function is given by $c = f(q_1, q_2) = 2q_1^2 + q_1 q_2 + q_2^2 + 200$. How should the output be distributed in order to minimize costs?*

**Solution:** We minimize $c = f(q_1, q_2)$, given the constraint $q_1 + q_2 = 200$. We have

$$F(q_1, q_2, \lambda) = 2q_1^2 + q_1 q_2 + q_2^2 + 200 - \lambda(q_1 + q_2 - 200)$$

$$\begin{cases} \dfrac{\partial F}{\partial q_1} = 4q_1 + q_2 - \lambda = 0 & \text{(19)} \\[2mm] \dfrac{\partial F}{\partial q_2} = q_1 + 2q_2 - \lambda = 0 & \text{(20)} \\[2mm] \dfrac{\partial F}{\partial \lambda} = -q_1 - q_2 + 200 = 0 & \text{(21)} \end{cases}$$

We can eliminate $\lambda$ from Equations (19) and (20) and obtain a relation between $q_1$ and $q_2$. Then, solving this equation for $q_2$ in terms of $q_1$ and substituting into Equation (21), we can find $q_1$. We begin by subtracting Equation (20) from Equation (19), which gives

$$3q_1 - q_2 = 0 \quad \text{so} \quad q_2 = 3q_1$$

Substituting into Equation (21), we have

$$-q_1 - 3q_1 + 200 = 0$$
$$-4q_1 = -200$$
$$q_1 = 50$$

Thus, $q_2 = 150$. Accordingly, plant 1 should produce 50 units and plant 2 should produce 150 units in order to minimize costs.

NOW WORK PROBLEM 13 ⬤⬤

An interesting observation can be made concerning Example 3. From Equation (19), $\lambda = 4q_1 + q_2 = \partial c/\partial q_1$, the marginal cost of plant 1. From Equation (20), $\lambda = q_1 + 2q_2 = \partial c/\partial q_2$, the marginal cost of plant 2. Hence, $\partial c/\partial q_1 = \partial c/\partial q_2$, and we conclude that, to minimize cost, it is necessary that the marginal costs of each plant be equal to each other.

⬤ **EXAMPLE 4**   **Least-Cost Input Combination**

*Suppose a firm must produce a given quantity $P_0$ of output in the cheapest possible manner. If there are two input factors $l$ and $k$, and their prices per unit are fixed at $p_l$ and $p_k$, respectively, discuss the economic significance of combining input to achieve least cost. That is, describe the least-cost input combination.*

**Solution:** Let $P = f(l, k)$ be the production function. Then we must minimize the cost function

$$c = lp_l + kp_k$$

subject to

$$P_0 = f(l, k)$$

We construct

$$F(l, k, \lambda) = lp_l + kp_k - \lambda[f(l, k) - P_0]$$

We have

$$\begin{cases} \dfrac{\partial F}{\partial l} = p_l - \lambda \dfrac{\partial}{\partial l}[f(l, k)] = 0 & \text{(22)} \\[2mm] \dfrac{\partial F}{\partial k} = p_k - \lambda \dfrac{\partial}{\partial k}[f(l, k)] = 0 & \text{(23)} \\[2mm] \dfrac{\partial F}{\partial \lambda} = -f(l, k) + P_0 = 0 \end{cases}$$

From Equations (22) and (23),

$$\lambda = \frac{p_l}{\dfrac{\partial}{\partial l}[f(l, k)]} = \frac{p_k}{\dfrac{\partial}{\partial k}[f(l, k)]} \tag{24}$$

Hence,

$$\frac{p_l}{p_k} = \frac{\dfrac{\partial}{\partial l}[f(l, k)]}{\dfrac{\partial}{\partial k}[f(l, k)]}$$

We conclude that when the least-cost combination of factors is used, the ratio of the marginal productivities of the input factors must be equal to the ratio of their corresponding unit prices.

NOW WORK PROBLEM 15 ◖●●

## Multiple Constraints

The method of Lagrange multipliers is by no means restricted to problems involving a single constraint. For example, suppose $f(x, y, z, w)$ were subject to constraints $g_1(x, y, z, w) = 0$ and $g_2(x, y, z, w) = 0$. Then there would be two lambdas, $\lambda_1$ and $\lambda_2$ (one corresponding to each constraint), and we would construct the function $F = f - \lambda_1 g_1 - \lambda_2 g_2$. We would then solve the system

$$F_x = F_y = F_z = F_w = F_{\lambda_1} = F_{\lambda_2} = 0$$

### ◖● EXAMPLE 5  Method of Lagrange Multipliers with Two Constraints

*Find critical points for* $f(x, y, z) = xy + yz$, *subject to the constraints* $x^2 + y^2 = 8$ *and* $yz = 8$.

**Solution:** Set

$$F(x, y, z, \lambda_1, \lambda_2) = xy + yz - \lambda_1(x^2 + y^2 - 8) - \lambda_2(yz - 8)$$

Then

$$\begin{cases} F_x = y - 2x\lambda_1 = 0 \\ F_y = x + z - 2y\lambda_1 - z\lambda_2 = 0 \\ F_z = y - y\lambda_2 = 0 \\ F_{\lambda_1} = -x^2 - y^2 + 8 = 0 \\ F_{\lambda_2} = -yz + 8 = 0 \end{cases}$$

You would probably agree that this appears to be a challenging system to solve. Thus, ingenuity will come into play. Here is one sequence of operations that will allow us to find the critical points. We can write the system as

$$\begin{cases} \dfrac{y}{2x} = \lambda_1 & \text{(25)} \\[2mm] x + z - 2y\lambda_1 - z\lambda_2 = 0 & \text{(26)} \\[2mm] \lambda_2 = 1 & \text{(27)} \\[2mm] x^2 + y^2 = 8 & \text{(28)} \\[2mm] z = \dfrac{8}{y} & \text{(29)} \end{cases}$$

Substituting $\lambda_2 = 1$ from Equation (27) into Equation (26) and simplifying gives the equation $x - 2y\lambda_1 = 0$, so

$$\lambda_1 = \frac{x}{2y}$$

Substituting into Equation (25) gives

$$\frac{y}{2x} = \frac{x}{2y}$$

$$y^2 = x^2 \qquad \text{(30)}$$

Substituting into Equation (28) gives $x^2 + x^2 = 8$, from which it follows that $x = \pm 2$. If $x = 2$, then, from Equation (30), we have $y = \pm 2$. Similarly, if $x = -2$, then $y = \pm 2$. Thus, if $x = 2$ and $y = 2$, then, from Equation (29), we obtain $z = 4$. Continuing in this manner, we obtain four critical points:

$$(2, 2, 4) \quad (2, -2, -4) \quad (-2, 2, 4) \quad (-2, -2, -4)$$

NOW WORK PROBLEM 9 ◖●●

## Problems 17.8

*In Problems 1–12, find, by the method of Lagrange multipliers, the critical points of the functions, subject to the given constraints.*

*1. $f(x, y) = x^2 + 4y^2 + 6;$   $2x - 8y = 20$

2. $f(x, y) = -2x^2 + 5y^2 + 7;$   $3x - 2y = 7$

3. $f(x, y, z) = x^2 + y^2 + z^2;$   $2x + y - z = 9$

4. $f(x, y, z) = x + y + z;$   $xyz = 8$

5. $f(x, y, z) = 2x^2 + xy + y^2 + z;$   $x + 2y + 4z = 3$

6. $f(x, y, z) = xyz^2;$   $x - y + z = 20 \ (xyz^2 \neq 0)$

*7. $f(x, y, z) = xyz;$   $x + 2y + 3z = 18 \ (xyz \neq 0)$

8. $f(x, y, z) = x^2 + y^2 + z^2;$   $x + y + z = 3$

*9. $f(x, y, z) = x^2 + 2y - z^2;$   $2x - y = 0, \ y + z = 0$

10. $f(x, y, z) = x^2 + y^2 + z^2;$   $x + y + z = 4, \ x - y + z = 4$

11. $f(x, y, z) = xy^2z;$   $x + y + z = 1, \ x - y + z = 0 \ (xyz \neq 0)$

12. $f(x, y, z, w) = 3x^2 + y^2 + 2z^2 - 5w^2;$   $x + 6y + 3z + 2w = 4$

*13. **Production Allocation**   To fill an order for 100 units of its product, a firm wishes to distribute production between its two plants, plant 1 and plant 2. The total-cost function is given by

$$c = f(q_1, q_2) = 0.1q_1^2 + 7q_1 + 15q_2 + 1000$$

where $q_1$ and $q_2$ are the numbers of units produced at plants 1 and 2, respectively. How should the output be distributed in order to minimize costs? (You may assume that the critical point obtained does correspond to the minimum cost.)

14. **Production Allocation**   Repeat Problem 13 if the cost function is

$$c = 3q_1^2 + q_1q_2 + 2q_2^2$$

and a total of 200 units are to be produced.

*15. **Maximizing Output**   The production function for a firm is

$$f(l, k) = 12l + 20k - l^2 - 2k^2$$

The cost to the firm of $l$ and $k$ is 4 and 8 per unit, respectively. If the firm wants the total cost of input to be 88, find the greatest output possible, subject to this budget constraint. (You may assume that the critical point obtained does correspond to the maximum output.)

16. **Maximizing Output**   Repeat Problem 15, given that

$$f(l, k) = 20l + 25k - l^2 - 3k^2$$

and the budget constraint is $2l + 4k = 50$.

17. **Advertising Budget**   A computer company has a monthly advertising budget of $60,000. Its marketing department estimates that if $x$ dollars are spent each month on advertising in newspapers and $y$ dollars per month on television advertising, then the monthly sales will be given by $S = 90x^{1/4}y^{3/4}$ dollars. If the profit is 10% of sales, less the advertising cost, determine how to allocate the advertising budget in order to maximize the monthly profit. (You may assume that the critical point obtained does correspond to the maximum profit.)

18. **Maximizing Production**   When $l$ units of labor and $k$ units of capital are invested, a manufacturer's total production $q$ is given by the Cobb–Douglas production function

$q = 6l^{2/5}k^{3/5}$. Each unit of labor costs \$25 and each unit of capital costs \$69. If exactly \$25,875 is to be spent on production, determine the numbers of units of labor and capital that should be invested to maximize production. (You may assume that the maximum occurs at the critical point obtained.)

19. **Political Advertising**   Newspaper advertisements for political parties always have some negative effects. The recently elected party assumed that the three most important election issues $X$, $Y$, and $Z$, had to be mentioned in each ad, with space $x$, $y$, and $z$ units, respectively, allotted to each. The combined bad effect of this coverage was estimated by the party's backroom boys as

$$B(x, y, z) = x^2 + y^2 + 2z^2$$

Aesthetics dictated that the total space for $X$ and $Y$ together must be 20, and realism suggested that the total space allotted to $Y$ and $Z$ together must also be 20 units. What values of $x$, $y$, and $z$ in each ad would produce the lowest negative effect? (You may assume that any critical point obtained provides the minimum effect.)

20. **Maximizing Profit**   Suppose a manufacturer's production function is given by

$$16q = 65 - 4(l - 4)^2 - 2(k - 5)^2$$

and the cost to the manufacturer is \$8 per unit of labor and \$16 per unit of capital, so that the total cost (in dollars) is $8l + 16k$. The selling price of the product is \$64 per unit.

(a) Express the profit as a function of $l$ and $k$. Give your answer in expanded form.

(b) Find all critical points of the profit function obtained in part (a). Apply the second-derivative test at each critical point. If the profit is a relative maximum at a critical point, compute the corresponding relative maximum profit.

(c) The profit may be considered a function of $l$, $k$, and $q$ (that is, $P = 64q - 8l - 16k$), subject to the constraint

$$16q = 65 - 4(l - 4)^2 - 2(k - 5)^2$$

Use the method of Lagrange multipliers to find all critical points of $P = 64q - 8l - 16k$, subject to the constraint.

*Problems 21–24 refer to the following definition. A utility function is a function that attaches a measure to the satisfaction or utility a consumer gets from the consumption of products per unit of time. Suppose $U = f(x, y)$ is such a function, where $x$ and $y$ are the amounts of two products, $X$ and $Y$. The marginal utility of $X$ is $\partial U/\partial x$ and approximately represents the change in total utility resulting from a one-unit change in consumption of product $X$ per unit of time. We define the marginal utility of $Y$ in similar fashion. If the prices of $X$ and $Y$ are $p_x$ and $p_y$, respectively, and the consumer has an income or budget of $I$ to spend, then the budget constraint is*

$$xp_x + yp_y = I$$

*In Problems 21–23, find the quantities of each product that the consumer should buy, subject to the budget, that will allow maximum satisfaction. That is, in Problems 21 and 22, find values of $x$ and $y$ that maximize $U = f(x, y)$, subject to $xp_x + yp_y = I$.*

*Perform a similar procedure for Problem 23. Assume that such a maximum exists.*

**21.** $U = x^3 y^3$;    $p_x = 2$, $p_y = 3$, $I = 48$ $(x^3 y^3 \neq 0)$

**22.** $U = 40x - 5x^2 + 4y - 2y^2$; $p_x = 2$, $p_y = 3$, $I = 10$

**23.** $U = f(x, y, z) = xyz$;    $p_x = p_y = p_z = 1$, $I = 100$ $(xyz \neq 0)$

**24.** Let $U = f(x, y)$ be a utility function subject to the budget constraint $xp_x + yp_y = I$, where $p_x$, $p_y$, and $I$ are constants. Show that, to maximize satisfaction, it is necessary that

$$\lambda = \frac{f_x(x, y)}{p_x} = \frac{f_y(x, y)}{p_y}$$

where $f_x(x, y)$ and $f_y(x, y)$ are the marginal utilities of $X$ and $Y$, respectively. Show that $f_x(x, y)/p_x$ is the marginal utility of one dollar's worth of $X$. Hence, maximum satisfaction is obtained when the consumer allocates the budget so that the marginal utility of a dollar's worth of $X$ is equal to the marginal utility per dollar's worth of $Y$. Performing the same procedure as that for $U = f(x, y)$, verify that this is true for $U = f(x, y, z, w)$, subject to the corresponding budget equation. In each case, $\lambda$ is called the *marginal utility of income.*

OBJECTIVE

To develop the method of least squares and introduce index numbers.

# 17.9  Lines of Regression[24]

To study the influence of advertising on sales, a firm compiled the data in Table 17.4. The variable $x$ denotes advertising expenditures in hundreds of dollars, and the variable $y$ denotes the resulting sales revenue in thousands of dollars. If each pair $(x, y)$ of data is plotted, the result is called a **scatter diagram** [Figure 17.16(a)].

From an observation of the distribution of the points, it is reasonable to assume that a relationship exists between $x$ and $y$ and that it is approximately linear. On this basis, we may fit "by eye" a straight line that approximates the given data [Figure 17.16(b)] and, from this line, predict a value of $y$ for a given value of $x$. The line seems consistent with the trend of the data, although other lines could be drawn as well. Unfortunately, determining a line "by eye" is not very objective. We want to apply criteria in specifying what we will call a line of "best fit." A frequently used technique is called the **method of least squares.**

**TABLE 17.4**

| Expenditures $x$ | 2 | 3 | 4.5 | 5.5 | 7 |
|---|---|---|---|---|---|
| Revenue $y$ | 3 | 6 | 8 | 10 | 11 |

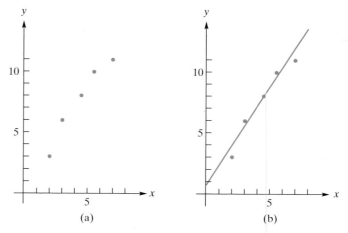

**FIGURE 17.16**   Scatter diagram and straight-line approximation to data points.

To apply the method of least squares to the data in Table 17.4, we first assume that $x$ and $y$ are approximately linearly related and that we can fit a straight line

$$\widehat{y} = a + bx \tag{1}$$

that approximates the given points by a suitable objective choice of the constants $a$ and $b$. For a given value of $x$ in Equation (1), $\widehat{y}$ is the corresponding predicted value of $y$, and $(x, \widehat{y})$ will be on the line. Our aim is that $\widehat{y}$ be near $y$.

When $x = 2$, the observed value of $y$ is 3. Our predicted value of $y$ is obtained by substituting $x = 2$ in Equation (1), which yields $\widehat{y} = a + 2b$. The error of estimation, or vertical deviation of the point $(2, 3)$ from the line, is $\widehat{y} - y$, which is

$$a + 2b - 3$$

---

[24]This section can be omitted without loss of continuity.

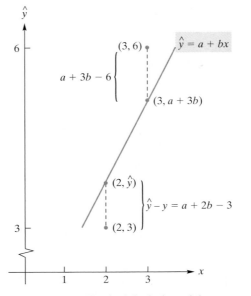

**FIGURE 17.17** Vertical deviation of data points from straight-line approximation.

This vertical deviation is indicated (although exaggerated for clarity) in Figure 17.17. Similarly, the vertical deviation of $(3, 6)$ from the line is $a+3b-6$, as is also illustrated. To avoid possible difficulties associated with positive and negative deviations, we will consider the squares of the deviations and will form the sum $S$ of all such squares for the given data:

$$S = (a + 2b - 3)^2 + (a + 3b - 6)^2 + (a + 4.5b - 8)^2$$
$$+ (a + 5.5b - 10)^2 + (a + 7b - 11)^2$$

The method of least squares requires that we choose as the line of "best fit" the one obtained by selecting $a$ and $b$ so as to minimize $S$. We can minimize $S$ with respect to $a$ and $b$ by solving the system

$$\begin{cases} \dfrac{\partial S}{\partial a} = 0 \\ \dfrac{\partial S}{\partial b} = 0 \end{cases}$$

We have

$$\frac{\partial S}{\partial a} = 2(a + 2b - 3) + 2(a + 3b - 6) + 2(a + 4.5b - 8)$$
$$+ 2(a + 5.5b - 10) + 2(a + 7b - 11) = 0$$
$$\frac{\partial S}{\partial b} = 4(a + 2b - 3) + 6(a + 3b - 6) + 9(a + 4.5b - 8)$$
$$+ 11(a + 5.5b - 10) + 14(a + 7b - 11) = 0$$

which, when simplified, give

$$\begin{cases} 10a + 44b = 76 \\ 44a + 225b = 384 \end{cases}$$

Solving for $a$ and $b$, we obtain

$$a = \frac{102}{157} \approx 0.65 \quad b = \frac{248}{157} \approx 1.58$$

From our calculations of $\partial S/\partial a$ and $\partial S/\partial b$, we see that $S_{aa} = 10 > 0$, $S_{bb} = 225$, and $S_{ab} = 44$. Thus $D = S_{aa}S_{bb} - (S_{ab})^2 = 10 \cdot 225 - 44^2 = 314 > 0$. It follows from the second-derivative test of Section 17.7 that $S$ has a minimum value at the critical point. Hence, in the sense of least squares, the line of best fit $\widehat{y} = a + bx$ is

$$\widehat{y} = 0.65 + 1.58x \qquad (2)$$

This is, in fact, the line shown in Figure 17.16(b). It is called the **least squares line of y on x** or the **linear regression line of y on x**. The constants $a$ and $b$ are called **linear regression coefficients**. With Equation (2), we would predict that when $x = 5$, the corresponding value of $y$ is $\widehat{y} = 0.65 + 1.58(5) = 8.55$.

More generally, suppose we are given the following $n$ pairs of observations:

$$(x_1, y_1), (x_2, y_2), \ldots, (x_n, y_n)$$

If we assume that $x$ and $y$ are approximately linearly related and that we can fit a straight line

$$\widehat{y} = a + bx$$

that approximates the data, the sum of the squares of the errors $\widehat{y} - y$ is

$$S = (a + bx_1 - y_1)^2 + (a + bx_2 - y_2)^2 + \cdots + (a + bx_n - y_n)^2$$

Since $S$ must be minimized with respect to $a$ and $b$,

$$\begin{cases} \dfrac{\partial S}{\partial a} = 2(a + bx_1 - y_1) + 2(a + bx_2 - y_2) + \cdots + 2(a + bx_n - y_n) = 0 \\[2mm] \dfrac{\partial S}{\partial b} = 2x_1(a + bx_1 - y_1) + 2x_2(a + bx_2 - y_2) + \cdots + 2x_n(a + bx_n - y_n) = 0 \end{cases}$$

Dividing both equations by 2 and using summation notation, we have

$$\begin{cases} na + \left( \displaystyle\sum_{i=1}^{n} x_i \right) b - \displaystyle\sum_{i=1}^{n} y_i = 0 \\[4mm] \left( \displaystyle\sum_{i=1}^{n} x_i \right) a + \left( \displaystyle\sum_{i=1}^{n} x_i^2 \right) b - \displaystyle\sum_{i=1}^{n} x_i y_i = 0 \end{cases}$$

which is a system of two linear equations in $a$ and $b$, the so-called *normal equations:*

$$\begin{cases} na + \left( \displaystyle\sum_{i=1}^{n} x_i \right) b = \displaystyle\sum_{i=1}^{n} y_i \\[4mm] \left( \displaystyle\sum_{i=1}^{n} x_i \right) a + \left( \displaystyle\sum_{i=1}^{n} x_i^2 \right) b = \displaystyle\sum_{i=1}^{n} x_i y_i \end{cases}$$

The coefficients are of course no more than simple sums of values obtained from the observed data. The solution is obtained easily using the techniques of Section 3.4.

$$a = \frac{\left( \displaystyle\sum_{i=1}^{n} x_i^2 \right) \left( \displaystyle\sum_{i=1}^{n} y_i \right) - \left( \displaystyle\sum_{i=1}^{n} x_i \right) \left( \displaystyle\sum_{i=1}^{n} x_i y_i \right)}{n \displaystyle\sum_{i=1}^{n} x_i^2 - \left( \displaystyle\sum_{i=1}^{n} x_i \right)^2} \qquad (3)$$

$$b = \frac{n \displaystyle\sum_{i=1}^{n} x_i y_i - \left( \displaystyle\sum_{i=1}^{n} x_i \right) \left( \displaystyle\sum_{i=1}^{n} y_i \right)}{n \displaystyle\sum_{i=1}^{n} x_i^2 - \left( \displaystyle\sum_{i=1}^{n} x_i \right)^2} \qquad (4)$$

Now we have $S_{aa} = 2n > 0$ and $D = S_{aa} S_{bb} - (S_{ab})^2 = (2n)(2 \sum x_i^2) - (2 \sum x_i)^2$, independent of $(a, b)$. It can be shown that for distinct $x_i$ and $n \geq 2$ that $D > 0$ so $a$ and $b$, given by Equations (3) and (4), do indeed minimize $S$. [For example, when

$n = 2$, $D > 0$ is provably equivalent to $(x_1 - x_2)^2 > 0$, which is true for distinct $x_1$ and $x_2$.]

Computing the linear regression coefficients $a$ and $b$ by the formulas of Equations (3) and (4) gives the linear regression line of $y$ on $x$, namely, $\widehat{y} = a + bx$, which can be used to estimate $y$ for any given value of $x$.

In the next example, as well as in the exercises, you will encounter **index numbers.** They are used to relate a variable in one period of time to the same variable in another period, called the *base period*. An index number is a *relative* number that describes data that are changing over time. Such data are referred to as *time series*.

For example, consider the time-series data of total production of widgets in the United States for 2002–2006, given in Table 17.5. If we choose 2003 as the base year and assign the index number 100 to it, then the other index numbers are obtained by dividing each year's production by the 2003 production of 900 and multiplying the result by 100. We can, for example, interpret the index 106 for 2006 as meaning that production for that year was 106% of the production in 2003.

**TABLE 17.5**

| Year | Production (in thousands) | Index (based on 2003) |
|------|---------------------------|-----------------------|
| 2002 | 828 | 92 |
| 2003 | 900 | 100 |
| 2004 | 936 | 104 |
| 2005 | 891 | 99 |
| 2006 | 954 | 106 |

In time-series analysis, index numbers are obviously of great advantage if the data involve numbers of great magnitude. But regardless of the magnitude of the data, index numbers simplify the task of comparing changes in data over periods of time.

● **EXAMPLE 1  Determining a Linear-Regression Line**

*By means of the linear-regression line, use the following table to represent the trend for the index of total U.S. government revenue from 1995 to 2000 (1995 = 100).*

| Year | 1995 | 1996 | 1997 | 1998 | 1999 | 2000 |
|------|------|------|------|------|------|------|
| Index | 100 | 107 | 117 | 127 | 135 | 150 |

*Source: Economic Report of the President*, 2001, U.S. Government Printing Office, Washington, DC, 2001.

**Solution:** We will let $x$ denote time and $y$ denote the index and treat $y$ as a linear function of $x$. Also, we will designate 1995 by $x = 1$, 1996 by $x = 2$, and so on. There are $n = 6$ pairs of measurements. To determine the linear-regression coefficients by using Equations (3) and (4), we first perform the arithmetic:

| Year | $x_i$ | $y_i$ | $x_i y_i$ | $x_i^2$ |
|------|-------|-------|-----------|---------|
| 1995 | 1 | 100 | 100 | 1 |
| 1996 | 2 | 107 | 214 | 4 |
| 1997 | 3 | 117 | 351 | 9 |
| 1998 | 4 | 127 | 508 | 16 |
| 1999 | 5 | 135 | 675 | 25 |
| 2000 | 6 | 150 | 900 | 36 |
| Total | 21 | 736 | 2748 | 91 |
| | $= \displaystyle\sum_{i=1}^{6} x_i$ | $= \displaystyle\sum_{i=1}^{6} y_i$ | $= \displaystyle\sum_{i=1}^{6} x_i y_i$ | $= \displaystyle\sum_{i=1}^{6} x_i^2$ |

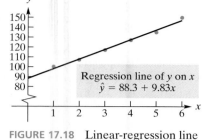

**FIGURE 17.18**   Linear-regression line for government revenue.

Hence, by Equation (3),

$$a = \frac{91(736) - 21(2748)}{6(91) - (21)^2} \approx 88.3$$

and by Equation (4),

$$b = \frac{6(2748) - 21(736)}{6(91) - (21)^2} \approx 9.83$$

Thus, the regression line of $y$ on $x$ is

$$\widehat{y} = 88.3 + 9.83x$$

whose graph, as well as a scatter diagram, appears in Figure 17.18.

NOW WORK PROBLEM 1

---

## TECHNOLOGY

The TI-83 Plus has a utility that computes the equation of the least squares line for a set of data. We will illustrate by giving the procedure for the six data points $(x_i, y_i)$ of Example 1. After pressing STAT and ENTER, we enter all the $x$-values and then the $y$-values. (See Figure 17.19.)

Next, we press STAT and move to CALC. Finally, pressing 8 and ENTER gives the result shown in Figure 17.20. (The number $r \approx 0.99448$ is called the *coefficient of correlation* and is a measure of the degree to which the given data are linearly related.)

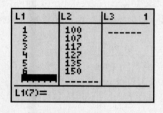

**FIGURE 17.19**   Data of Example 1.

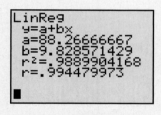

**FIGURE 17.20**   Equation of least squares line.

---

## Problems 17.9

*In this exercise set, use a graphing calculator if your instructor permits you to do so.*

*In Problems 1–4, find an equation of the least squares linear-regression line of y on x for the given data, and sketch both the line and the data. Predict the value of y corresponding to x = 3.5.*

*1.

| $x$ | 1 | 2 | 3 | 4 | 5 | 6 |
|---|---|---|---|---|---|---|
| $y$ | 1.5 | 2.3 | 2.6 | 3.7 | 4.0 | 4.5 |

2.

| $x$ | 1 | 2 | 3 | 4 | 5 | 6 | 7 |
|---|---|---|---|---|---|---|---|
| $y$ | 1 | 1.8 | 2 | 4 | 4.5 | 7 | 9 |

3.

| $x$ | 2 | 3 | 4.5 | 5.5 | 7 |
|---|---|---|---|---|---|
| $y$ | 3 | 5 | 8 | 10 | 11 |

4.

| $x$ | 2 | 3 | 4 | 5 | 6 | 7 |
|---|---|---|---|---|---|---|
| $y$ | 2.4 | 2.9 | 3.3 | 3.8 | 4.3 | 4.9 |

5. **Demand**   A firm finds that when the price of its product is $p$ dollars per unit, the number of units sold is $q$, as indicated in the following table:

| Price, $p$ | 10 | 20 | 40 | 50 | 60 | 70 |
|---|---|---|---|---|---|---|
| Demand, $q$ | 75 | 65 | 56 | 50 | 42 | 34 |

Find an equation of the regression line of $q$ on $p$.

6. **Water and Crop Yield**   On a farm, an agronomist finds that the amount of water applied (in inches) and the corresponding yield of a certain crop (in tons per acre) are as given in the following table:

| Water, $x$ | 8 | 16 | 24 | 32 |
|---|---|---|---|---|
| Yield, $y$ | 5.2 | 5.7 | 6.3 | 6.7 |

Find an equation of the regression line of $y$ on $x$. Predict $y$ when $x = 20$.

7. **Virus**   A rabbit was injected with a virus, and $x$ hours after the injection the temperature $y$ (in degrees Fahrenheit) of the rabbit was measured.[25] The data are given in the following table:

| Elapsed Time, $x$ | 24 | 32 | 48 | 56 |
|---|---|---|---|---|
| Temperature, $y$ | 102.8 | 104.5 | 106.5 | 107.0 |

Find an equation of the regression line of $y$ on $x$, and estimate the rabbit's temperature 40 hours after the injection.

---

[25]R. R. Sokal and F. J. Rohlf, *Introduction to Biostatistics* (San Francisco: W. H. Freeman & Company, Publishers, 1973).

**8. Psychology**   In a psychological experiment, four persons were subjected to a stimulus. Both before and after the stimulus, the systolic blood pressure (in millimeters of mercury) of each subject was measured. The data are given in the following table:

| **Blood Pressure** | | | | |
|---|---|---|---|---|
| **Before Stimulus**, $x$ | 131 | 132 | 135 | 141 |
| **After Stimulus**, $y$ | 139 | 139 | 142 | 149 |

Find an equation of the regression line of $y$ on $x$, where $x$ and $y$ are as defined in the table.

*For the time series in Problems 9 and 10, fit a linear-regression line by least squares; that is, find an equation of the linear-regression line of $y$ on $x$. In each case, let the first year in the table correspond to $x = 1$.*

**9.**

**Production of Product A, 2002–2006 (in thousands of units)**

| Year | Production |
|---|---|
| 2002 | 10 |
| 2003 | 15 |
| 2004 | 16 |
| 2005 | 18 |
| 2006 | 21 |

**10. Industrial Production**   In the following table, let 1975 correspond to $x = 1$, 1977 correspond to $x = 3$, and so on:

**Index of Industrial Production—Electrical Machinery (based on 1977)**

| Year | Index |
|---|---|
| 1975 | 77 |
| 1977 | 100 |
| 1979 | 126 |
| 1981 | 134 |

*Source: Economic Report of the President*, 1988, U.S. Government Printing Office, Washington, DC, 1988.

**11. Computer Shipments**

(a) Find an equation of the least squares line of $y$ on $x$ for the following data (refer to 2002 as year $x = 1$, and so on):

**Overseas Shipments of Computers by Acme Computer Co. (in thousands)**

| Year | Quantity |
|---|---|
| 2002 | 35 |
| 2003 | 31 |
| 2004 | 26 |
| 2005 | 24 |
| 2006 | 26 |

(b) For the data in part (a), refer to 2002 as year $x = -2$, 2003 as year $x = -1$, 2004 as year $x = 0$ and so on. Then $\sum_{i=1}^{5} x_i = 0$. Fit a least squares line and observe how the calculation is simplified.

**12. Medical Care**   For the following time series, find an equation of the linear-regression line that best fits the data (refer to 1983 as year $x = -2$, 1984 as year $x = -1$, and so on):

**Consumer Price Index—Medical Care, 1983–1987 (based on 1967)**

| Year | Index |
|---|---|
| 1983 | 357 |
| 1984 | 380 |
| 1985 | 403 |
| 1986 | 434 |
| 1987 | 462 |

*Source: Economic Report of the President*, 1988, U.S. Government Printing Office, Washington, DC, 1988.

OBJECTIVE

To compute double and triple integrals.

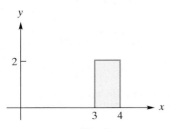

**FIGURE 17.21**   Region over which $\int_0^2 \int_3^4 xy\,dx\,dy$ is evaluated.

## 17.10  Multiple Integrals

Recall that the definite integral of a function of one variable is concerned with integration over an *interval*. There are also definite integrals of functions of two variables, called (definite) **double integrals.** These involve integration over a *region* in the plane. For example, the symbol

$$\int_0^2 \int_3^4 xy\,dx\,dy = \int_0^2 \left( \int_3^4 xy\,dx \right) dy$$

is the double integral of $f(x, y) = xy$ over a region determined by the limits of integration. That region consists of all points $(x, y)$ in the $x,y$-plane such that $3 \le x \le 4$ and $0 \le y \le 2$. (See Figure 17.21.)

A double integral is a limit of a sum of the form $\sum f(x, y)\,\Delta x\,\Delta y$, where, in this example, the points $(x, y)$ are in the shaded region. A geometric interpretation of a double integral will be given later.

To evaluate

$$\int_0^2 \int_3^4 xy\, dx\, dy = \int_0^2 \left( \int_3^4 xy\, dx \right) dy$$

we use successive integrations starting with the innermost integral. First, we evaluate

$$\int_3^4 xy\, dx$$

by treating $y$ as a constant and integrating with respect to $x$ between the limits 3 and 4:

$$\int_3^4 xy\, dx = \left. \frac{x^2 y}{2} \right|_3^4$$

Substituting the limits for the variable $x$, we have

$$\frac{4^2 \cdot y}{2} - \frac{3^2 \cdot y}{2} = \frac{16y}{2} - \frac{9y}{2} = \frac{7}{2}y$$

Now we integrate this result with respect to $y$ between the limits 0 and 2:

$$\int_0^2 \frac{7}{2}y\, dy = \left. \frac{7y^2}{4} \right|_0^2 = \frac{7 \cdot 2^2}{4} - 0 = 7$$

Thus,

$$\int_0^2 \int_3^4 xy\, dx\, dy = 7$$

Now consider the double integral

$$\int_0^1 \int_{x^3}^{x^2} (x^3 - xy)\, dy\, dx = \int_0^1 \left( \int_{x^3}^{x^2} (x^3 - xy)\, dy \right) dx$$

Here we integrate first with respect to $y$ and then with respect to $x$. The region over which the integration takes places is all points $(x, y)$ such that $x^3 \le y \le x^2$ and $0 \le x \le 1$. (See Figure 17.22.) This double integral is evaluated by first treating $x$ as a constant and integrating $x^3 - xy$ with respect to $y$ between $x^3$ and $x^2$, and then integrating the result with respect to $x$ between 0 and 1:

$$\int_0^1 \int_{x^3}^{x^2} (x^3 - xy)\, dy\, dx$$

$$= \int_0^1 \left( \int_{x^3}^{x^2} (x^3 - xy)\, dy \right) dx = \int_0^1 \left. \left( x^3 y - \frac{xy^2}{2} \right) \right|_{x^3}^{x^2} dx$$

$$= \int_0^1 \left[ \left( x^3 (x^2) - \frac{x(x^2)^2}{2} \right) - \left( x^3 (x^3) - \frac{x(x^3)^2}{2} \right) \right] dx$$

$$= \int_0^1 \left( x^5 - \frac{x^5}{2} - x^6 + \frac{x^7}{2} \right) dx = \int_0^1 \left( \frac{x^5}{2} - x^6 + \frac{x^7}{2} \right) dx$$

$$= \left. \left( \frac{x^6}{12} - \frac{x^7}{7} + \frac{x^8}{16} \right) \right|_0^1 = \left( \frac{1}{12} - \frac{1}{7} + \frac{1}{16} \right) - 0 = \frac{1}{336}$$

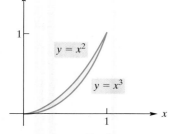

**FIGURE 17.22**   Region over which $\int_0^1 \int_{x^3}^{x^2} (x^3 - xy)\, dy\, dx$ is evaluated.

### ● EXAMPLE 1    Evaluating a Double Integral

*Find* $\displaystyle\int_{-1}^{1}\int_{0}^{1-x}(2x+1)\,dy\,dx.$

**Solution:**  Here we first integrate with respect to $y$ and then integrate the result with respect to $x$:

$$\int_{-1}^{1}\int_{0}^{1-x}(2x+1)\,dy\,dx = \int_{-1}^{1}\left(\int_{0}^{1-x}(2x+1)\,dy\right)dx$$

$$= \int_{-1}^{1}(2xy+y)\Big|_{0}^{1-x}\,dx = \int_{-1}^{1}((2x(1-x)+(1-x))-0)\,dx$$

$$= \int_{-1}^{1}(-2x^{2}+x+1)\,dx = \left(-\frac{2x^{3}}{3}+\frac{x^{2}}{2}+x\right)\Big|_{-1}^{1}$$

$$= \left(-\frac{2}{3}+\frac{1}{2}+1\right)-\left(\frac{2}{3}+\frac{1}{2}-1\right)=\frac{2}{3}$$

NOW WORK PROBLEM 9  ◖●●

### ● EXAMPLE 2    Evaluating a Double Integral

*Find* $\displaystyle\int_{1}^{\ln 2}\int_{e^{y}}^{2}dx\,dy.$

**Solution:**  Here we first integrate with respect to $x$ and then integrate the result with respect to $y$:

$$\int_{1}^{\ln 2}\int_{e^{y}}^{2}dx\,dy = \int_{1}^{\ln 2}\left(\int_{e^{y}}^{2}dx\right)dy = \int_{1}^{\ln 2}x\Big|_{e^{y}}^{2}\,dy$$

$$= \int_{1}^{\ln 2}(2-e^{y})\,dy = (2y-e^{y})\Big|_{1}^{\ln 2}$$

$$= (2\ln 2 - 2) - (2-e) = 2\ln 2 - 4 + e$$

$$= \ln 4 - 4 + e$$

NOW WORK PROBLEM 13  ◖●●

A double integral can be interpreted in terms of the volume of a region between the $x,y$-plane and a surface $z = f(x, y)$ if $z \geq 0$. In Figure 17.23 is a region whose volume we will consider. The element of volume for this region is a vertical column

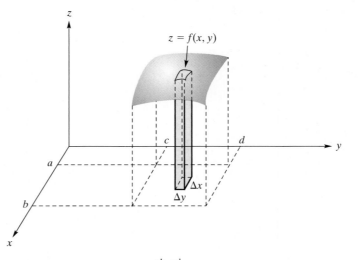

FIGURE 17.23   Interpreting $\int_{a}^{b}\int_{c}^{d}f(x, y)\,dy\,dx$ in terms of volume, where $f(x, y) \geq 0$.

with height approximately $z = f(x, y)$ and base area $\Delta y \, \Delta x$. Thus, its volume is approximately $f(x, y) \Delta y \, \Delta x$. The volume of the entire region can be found by summing the volumes of all such elements for $a \leq x \leq b$ and $c \leq y \leq d$ via a double integral:

$$\text{volume} = \int_a^b \int_c^d f(x, y) \, dy \, dx$$

**Triple integrals** are handled by successively evaluating three integrals, as the next example shows.

● EXAMPLE 3   **Evaluating a Triple Integral**

*Find* $\displaystyle\int_0^1 \int_0^x \int_0^{x-y} x \, dz \, dy \, dx$.

**Solution:**

$$\int_0^1 \int_0^x \int_0^{x-y} x \, dz \, dy \, dx = \int_0^1 \int_0^x \left( \int_0^{x-y} x \, dz \right) dy \, dx$$

$$= \int_0^1 \int_0^x (xz) \Big|_0^{x-y} dy \, dx = \int_0^1 \int_0^x (x(x-y) - 0) \, dy \, dx$$

$$= \int_0^1 \int_0^x (x^2 - xy) \, dy \, dx = \int_0^1 \left( \int_0^x (x^2 - xy) \, dy \right) dx$$

$$= \int_0^1 \left( x^2 y - \frac{xy^2}{2} \right) \Big|_0^x dx = \int_0^1 \left[ \left( x^3 - \frac{x^3}{2} \right) - 0 \right] dx$$

$$= \int_0^1 \frac{x^3}{2} \, dx = \frac{x^4}{8} \Big|_0^1 = \frac{1}{8}$$

NOW WORK PROBLEM 21   ●●●

# Problems 17.10

*In Problems 1–22, evaluate the multiple integrals.*

**1.** $\displaystyle\int_0^3 \int_0^4 x \, dy \, dx$

**2.** $\displaystyle\int_1^4 \int_0^3 y \, dy \, dx$

**3.** $\displaystyle\int_0^1 \int_0^1 xy \, dx \, dy$

**4.** $\displaystyle\int_0^2 \int_0^3 x^2 \, dy \, dx$

**5.** $\displaystyle\int_1^3 \int_1^2 (x^2 - y) \, dx \, dy$

**6.** $\displaystyle\int_{-2}^3 \int_0^2 (y^2 - 2xy) \, dy \, dx$

**7.** $\displaystyle\int_0^1 \int_0^2 (x + y) \, dy \, dx$

**8.** $\displaystyle\int_0^3 \int_0^x (x^2 + y^2) \, dy \, dx$

**\*9.** $\displaystyle\int_1^4 \int_0^{5x} y \, dy \, dx$

**10.** $\displaystyle\int_1^2 \int_0^{x-1} 2y \, dy \, dx$

**11.** $\displaystyle\int_0^1 \int_{3x}^{x^2} 14x^2 y \, dy \, dx$

**12.** $\displaystyle\int_0^2 \int_0^{x^2} xy \, dy \, dx$

**\*13.** $\displaystyle\int_0^3 \int_0^{\sqrt{9-x^2}} y \, dy \, dx$

**14.** $\displaystyle\int_0^1 \int_{y^2}^y y \, dx \, dy$

**15.** $\displaystyle\int_{-1}^1 \int_x^{1-x} 3(x + y) \, dy \, dx$

**16.** $\displaystyle\int_0^3 \int_{y^2}^{3y} 5x \, dx \, dy$

**17.** $\displaystyle\int_0^1 \int_0^y e^{x+y} \, dx \, dy$

**18.** $\displaystyle\int_0^1 \int_0^1 e^{y-x} \, dx \, dy$

**19.** $\displaystyle\int_{-1}^0 \int_{-1}^2 \int_1^2 6xy^2 z^3 \, dx \, dy \, dz$

**20.** $\displaystyle\int_0^1 \int_0^x \int_0^{x+y} x^2 \, dz \, dy \, dx$

**\*21.** $\displaystyle\int_0^1 \int_{x^2}^x \int_0^{xy} dz \, dy \, dx$

**22.** $\displaystyle\int_1^e \int_{\ln x}^x \int_0^y dz \, dy \, dx$

**23. Statistics**   In the study of statistics, a joint density function $z = f(x, y)$ defined on a region in the $x,y$-plane is represented by a surface in space. The probability that

$$a \leq x \leq b \quad \text{and} \quad c \leq y \leq d$$

is given by

$$P(a \leq x \leq b, c \leq y \leq d) = \int_c^d \int_a^b f(x, y) \, dx \, dy$$

and is represented by the volume between the graph of $f$ and the rectangular region given by

$$a \leq x \leq b \quad \text{and} \quad c \leq y \leq d$$

If $f(x, y) = e^{-(x+y)}$ is a joint density function, where $x \geq 0$ and $y \geq 0$, find

$$P(0 \leq x \leq 2, 1 \leq y \leq 2)$$

and give your answer in terms of $e$.

**24. Statistics**    In Problem 23, let $f(x, y) = 12e^{-4x-3y}$ for $x, y \geq 0$. Find

$$P(3 \leq x \leq 4, 2 \leq y \leq 6)$$

and give your answer in terms of $e$.

**25. Statistics**    In Problem 23, let $f(x, y) = 1$, where $0 \leq x \leq 1$ and $0 \leq y \leq 1$. Find $P(x \geq 1/2, y \geq 1/3)$.

**26. Statistics**    In Problem 23, let $f$ be the uniform density function $f(x, y) = 1/8$ defined over the rectangle $0 \leq x \leq 4, 0 \leq y \leq 2$. Determine the probability that $0 \leq x \leq 1$ and $0 \leq y \leq 1$.

# 17.11 Review

## Important Terms and Symbols                                            Examples

| | | |
|---|---|---|
| **Section 17.1** | **Functions of Several Variables** | |
| | $f(x_1, x_2, \ldots, x_n)$    function of $n$ variables | Ex. 1, p. 746 |
| | three-dimensional coordinates    $x,y$-plane    $x,z$-plane    $y,z$-plane | Ex. 3, p. 749 |
| | octant    traces | Ex. 5, p. 749 |
| **Section 17.2** | **Partial Derivatives** | |
| | partial derivative    $\dfrac{\partial z}{\partial x} = f_x(x, y)$    $\dfrac{\partial z}{\partial x}\Big|_{(a,b)} = f_x(a, b)$ | Ex. 2, p. 752 |
| **Section 17.3** | **Applications of Partial Derivatives** | |
| | joint-cost function    production function    marginal productivity | Ex. 3, p. 757 |
| | competitive products    complementary products | Ex. 4, p. 758 |
| **Section 17.4** | **Implicit Partial Differentiation** | |
| | implicit partial differentiation | Ex. 1, p. 762 |
| **Section 17.5** | **Higher-Order Partial Derivatives** | |
| | $\dfrac{\partial^2 z}{\partial y \partial x} = f_{xy}$    $\dfrac{\partial^2 z}{\partial x \partial y} = f_{yx}$    $\dfrac{\partial^2 z}{\partial x^2} = f_{xx}$    $\dfrac{\partial^2 z}{\partial y^2} = f_{yy}$ | Ex. 1, p. 764 |
| **Section 17.6** | **Chain Rule** | |
| | chain rule    intermediate variable | Ex. 1, p. 766 |
| **Section 17.7** | **Maxima and Minima for Functions of Two Variables** | |
| | relative maxima and minima    critical point | Ex. 1, p. 771 |
| | second-derivative test for functions of two variables | Ex. 3, p. 772 |
| **Section 17.8** | **Lagrange Multipliers** | |
| | Lagrange multipliers | Ex. 1, p. 780 |
| **Section 17.9** | **Lines of Regression** | |
| | method of least squares    linear regression of $y$ on $x$    index numbers | Ex. 1, p. 788 |
| **Section 17.10** | **Multiple Integrals** | |
| | double integral    triple integral | Ex. 3, p. 793 |

## Summary

We can extend the concept of a function of one variable to functions of several variables. The inputs for functions of $n$ variables are $n$-tuples. Generally, the graph of a function of two variables is a surface in a three-dimensional coordinate system.

For a function of $n$ variables, we can consider $n$ partial derivatives. For example, if $w = f(x, y, z)$, we have the partial derivatives of $f$ with respect to $x$, with respect to $y$, and with respect to $z$, denoted $f_x$, $f_y$, and $f_z$, or $\partial f/\partial x$, $\partial f/\partial y$, and $\partial f/\partial z$, respectively. To find $f_x(x, y, z)$, we treat $y$ and $z$ as constants and differentiate $f$ with respect to $x$ in the usual way. The other partial derivatives are found in a similar fashion. We can interpret $f_x(x, y, z)$ as the approximate change in $w$ that results from a one-unit change in $x$ when $y$ and $z$ are held fixed. There are similar interpretations for the other partial derivatives. A function of several variables may be defined implicitly. In this case, its partial derivatives are found by implicit partial differentiation.

Functions of several variables occur frequently in business and economic analysis, as well as in other areas of study. If a manufacturer produces $x$ units of product X and $y$ units of product Y, then the total cost $c$ of these units is a function of $x$ and $y$ and is called a joint-cost function. The partial derivatives $\partial c/\partial x$ and $\partial c/\partial y$ are called the marginal costs with respect to $x$ and $y$, respectively. We can interpret, for example, $\partial c/\partial x$ as the approximate cost of producing an extra unit of X while the level of production of Y is held fixed.

If $l$ units of labor and $k$ units of capital are used to produce $P$ units of a product, then the function $P = f(l, k)$ is called a production function. The partial derivatives of $P$ are called marginal productivity functions.

Suppose two products, A and B, are such that the quantity demanded of each is dependent on the prices of both. If $q_A$ and $q_B$ are the quantities of A and B demanded when the prices of

A and B are $p_A$ and $p_B$, respectively, then $q_A$ and $q_B$ are each functions of $p_A$ and $p_B$. When $\partial q_A/\partial p_B > 0$ and $\partial q_B/\partial p_A > 0$, then A and B are called competitive products (or substitutes). When $\partial q_A/\partial p_B < 0$ and $\partial q_B/\partial p_A < 0$, then A and B are called complementary products.

If $z = f(x, y)$, where $x = x(r, s)$ and $y = y(r, s)$, then $z$ can be considered as a function of $r$ and $s$. To find, for example, $\partial z/\partial r$, a chain rule can be used:

$$\frac{\partial z}{\partial r} = \frac{\partial z}{\partial x}\frac{\partial x}{\partial r} + \frac{\partial z}{\partial y}\frac{\partial y}{\partial r}$$

A partial derivative of a function of $n$ variables is itself a function of $n$ variables. By successively taking partial derivatives of partial derivatives, we obtain higher-order partial derivatives. For example, if $f$ is a function of $x$ and $y$, then $f_{xy}$ denotes the partial derivative of $f_x$ with respect to $y$; $f_{xy}$ is called the second-partial derivative of $f$, first with respect to $x$ and then with respect to $y$.

If the function $f(x, y)$ has a relative extremum at $(a, b)$, then $(a, b)$ must be a solution of the system

$$\begin{cases} f_x(x, y) = 0 \\ f_y(x, y) = 0 \end{cases}$$

Any solution of this system is called a critical point of $f$. Thus, critical points are the candidates at which a relative extremum may occur. The second-derivative test for functions of two variables gives conditions under which a critical point corresponds to a relative maximum or a relative minimum. The test states that if $(a, b)$ is a critical point of $f$ and

$$D(x, y) = f_{xx}(x, y)f_{yy}(x, y) - [f_{xy}(x, y)]^2$$

then

1. if $D(a, b) > 0$ and $f_{xx}(a, b) < 0$, then $f$ has a relative maximum at $(a, b)$;

2. if $D(a, b) > 0$ and $f_{xx}(a, b) > 0$, then $f$ has a relative minimum at $(a, b)$;

3. if $D(a, b) < 0$, then $f$ has a saddle point at $(a, b)$;

4. if $D(a, b) = 0$, no conclusion about an extremum at $(a, b)$ can yet be drawn, and further analysis is required.

To find critical points of a function of several variables, subject to a constraint, we can sometimes use the method of Lagrange multipliers. For example, to find the critical points of $f(x, y, z)$, subject to the constraint $g(x, y, z) = 0$, we first form the function

$$F(x, y, z, \lambda) = f(x, y, z) - \lambda g(x, y, z)$$

By solving the system

$$\begin{cases} F_x = 0 \\ F_y = 0 \\ F_z = 0 \\ F_\lambda = 0 \end{cases}$$

we obtain the critical points of $F$. If $(a, b, c, \lambda_0)$ is such a critical point, then $(a, b, c)$ is a critical point of $f$, subject to the constraint. It is important to write the constraint in the form $g(x, y, z) = 0$. For example, if the constraint is $2x + 3y - z = 4$, then $g(x, y, z) = 2x + 3y - z - 4$. If $f(x, y, z)$ is subject to two constraints, $g_1(x, y, z) = 0$ and $g_2(x, y, z) = 0$, then we would form the function $F = f - \lambda_1 g_1 - \lambda_2 g_2$ and solve the system

$$\begin{cases} F_x = 0 \\ F_y = 0 \\ F_z = 0 \\ F_{\lambda_1} = 0 \\ F_{\lambda_2} = 0 \end{cases}$$

Sometimes sample data for two variables, say, $x$ and $y$, may be related in such a way that the relationship is approximately linear. When such data points $(x_i, y_i)$, where $i = 1, 2, 3, \ldots, n$, are given to us, we can fit a straight line that approximates them. Such a line is the linear-regression line of $y$ on $x$ and is given by

$$\widehat{y} = a + bx$$

where

$$a = \frac{\left(\sum_{i=1}^{n} x_i^2\right)\left(\sum_{i=1}^{n} y_i\right) - \left(\sum_{i=1}^{n} x_i\right)\left(\sum_{i=1}^{n} x_i y_i\right)}{n\sum_{i=1}^{n} x_i^2 - \left(\sum_{i=1}^{n} x_i\right)^2}$$

and

$$b = \frac{n\sum_{i=1}^{n} x_i y_i - \left(\sum_{i=1}^{n} x_i\right)\left(\sum_{i=1}^{n} y_i\right)}{n\sum_{i=1}^{n} x_i^2 - \left(\sum_{i=1}^{n} x_i\right)^2}$$

The $\widehat{y}$-values can be used to predict $y$-values for given values of $x$.

When working with functions of several variables, we can consider their multiple integrals. These are determined by successive integration. For example, the double integral

$$\int_1^2 \int_0^y (x + y)\, dx\, dy$$

is determined by first treating $y$ as a constant and integrating $x + y$ with respect to $x$. After evaluating between the limits $0$ and $y$, we integrate that result with respect to $y$ from $y = 1$ to $y = 2$. Thus,

$$\int_1^2 \int_0^y (x + y)\, dx\, dy = \int_1^2 \left(\int_0^y (x + y)\, dx\right) dy$$

Triple integrals involve functions of three variables and are also evaluated by successive integration.

# Review Problems

*Problem numbers shown in color indicate problems suggested for use as a practice chapter test.*

*In Problems 1–4, sketch the given surfaces.*

1. $x + y + z = 1$
2. $z = x$
3. $z = y^2$
4. $x^2 + z^2 = 1$

*In Problems 5–16, find the indicated partial derivatives.*

5. $f(x, y) = 4x^2 + 6xy + y^2 - 1$;  $f_x(x, y), f_y(x, y)$
6. $P = l^3 + k^3 - lk$;  $\partial P/\partial l, \partial P/\partial k$
7. $z = \dfrac{x}{x + y}$;  $\dfrac{\partial z}{\partial x}, \dfrac{\partial z}{\partial y}$
8. $f(p_A, p_B) = 4(p_A - 10) + 5(p_B - 15)$;  $f_{p_B}(p_A, p_B)$
9. $f(x, y) = \ln\sqrt{x^2 + y^2}$;  $\dfrac{\partial}{\partial y}[f(x, y)]$
10. $w = \dfrac{x}{\sqrt{x^2 + y^2}}$;  $\dfrac{\partial w}{\partial y}$
11. $w = e^{x^2 yz}$;  $w_{xy}(x, y, z)$
12. $f(x, y) = xy\ln(xy)$;  $f_{xy}(x, y)$
13. $f(x, y, z) = (x + y + z)(x^2 + y^2 + z^2)$;  $\dfrac{\partial^2}{\partial z^2}(f(x, y, z))$
14. $z = (x^2 - y)(y^2 - 2xy)$;  $\partial^2 z/\partial y^2$
15. $w = e^{x+y+z}\ln xyz$;  $\partial w/\partial y, \partial^2 w/\partial z\,\partial x$
16. $P = 100l^{0.11}k^{0.89}$;  $\partial^2 P/\partial k\partial l$
17. If $f(x, y, z) = \dfrac{x + y}{xz}$, find $f_{xyz}(2, 7, 4)$
18. If $f(x, y, z) = (6x + 1)e^{y^2 \ln(z+1)}$, find $f_{xyz}(0, 1, 0)$
19. [26] If $w = x^2 + 2xy + 3y^2$, $x = e^r$, and $y = \ln(r + s)$, find $\partial w/\partial r$ and $\partial w/\partial s$.
20. [26] If $z = \ln(x/y) + e^{xy} - xy$, $x = r^2 + s^2$, and $y = (r + s)^2$, find $\partial z/\partial s$.
21. [26] If $x^2 + 2xy - 2z^2 + xz + 2 = 0$, find $\partial z/\partial x$.
22. [26] If $z^2 + \ln(yz) + \ln z + x + z = 0$, find $\partial z/\partial y$.

23. **Production Function** If a manufacturer's production function is defined by $P = 20l^{0.7}k^{0.3}$, determine the marginal productivity functions.

24. **Joint-Cost Function** A manufacturer's cost for producing $x$ units of product X and $y$ units of product Y is given by

$$c = 3x + 0.05xy + 9y + 500$$

Determine the (partial) marginal cost with respect to $x$ when $x = 50$ and $y = 100$.

25. **Competitive/Complementary Products**
If $q_A = 100 - p_A + 2p_B$ and $q_B = 150 + 3p_A - 2p_B$, where $q_A$ and $q_B$ are the number of units demanded of products A and B, respectively, and $p_A$ and $p_B$ are their respective prices per unit, determine whether A and B are competitive products or complementary products or neither.

26. **Innovation** For industry, the following model describes the rate $\alpha$ (a Greek letter read "alpha") at which an innovation substitutes for an established process:[27]

$$\alpha = Z + 0.530P - 0.027S$$

Here, $Z$ is a constant that depends on the particular industry, $P$ is an index of profitability of the innovation, and $S$ is an index of the extent of the investment necessary to make use of the innovation. Find $\partial\alpha/\partial P$ and $\partial\alpha/\partial S$.

27. Examine $f(x, y) = x^2 + 2y^2 - 2xy - 4y + 3$ for relative extrema.

28. Examine $f(w, z) = 2w^3 + 2z^3 - 6wz + 7$ for relative extrema.

29. **Minimizing Material** An open-top rectangular cardboard box is to have a volume of 32 cubic feet. Find the dimensions of the box so that the amount of cardboard used is minimized.

30. The function

$$f(x, y) = ax^2 + by^2 + cxy - 10x - 20y$$

has a critical point at $(x, y) = (1, 2)$, and the second-derivative test is inconclusive at this point. Determine the values of the constants $a$, $b$, and $c$.

31. **Maximizing Profit** A dairy produces two types of cheese, A and B, at constant average costs of 50 cents and 60 cents per pound, respectively. When the selling price per pound of A is $p_A$ cents and of B is $p_B$ cents, the demands (in pounds) for A and B, are, respectively,

$$q_A = 250(p_B - p_A)$$

and

$$q_B = 32{,}000 + 250(p_A - 2p_B)$$

Find the selling prices that yield a relative maximum profit. Verify that the profit has a relative maximum at these prices.

32. Find all critical points of $f(x, y, z) = xy^2z$, subject to the condition that

$$x + y + z - 1 = 0 \ (xyz \neq 0)$$

33. Find all critical points of $f(x, y, z) = x^2 + y^2 + z^2$, subject to the constraint $3x + 2y + z = 14$.

34. **Surviving Infection** In an experiment,[28] a group of fish was injected with living bacteria. Of those fish maintained at $28°C$, the percentage $p$ that survived the infection $t$ hours after the injection is given in the following table:

| $t$ | 8 | 10 | 18 | 20 | 48 |
|---|---|---|---|---|---|
| $p$ | 82 | 79 | 78 | 78 | 64 |

Find the linear-regression line of $p$ on $t$.

[27] A. P. Hurter, Jr., A. H. Rubenstein, et al., "Market Penetration by New Innovations: The Technological Literature," *Technological Forecasting and Social Change*, 11 (1978), 197–221.

[28] J. B. Covert and W. W. Reynolds, "Survival Value of Fever in Fish," *Nature*, 267, no. 5606 (1977), 43–45.

[26] Problem 19–22 refer to Section 17.4 or Section 17.6.

**35. Equipment Expenditures**   Find the least squares linear-regression line of $y$ on $x$ for the data given in the following table (refer to year 1993 as year $x = 1$, etc.):

Equipment Expenditures of Allied Computer Company, 1993–1998 (in millions of dollars)

| Year | Expenditures |
|------|--------------|
| 1993 | 15 |
| 1994 | 22 |
| 1995 | 21 |
| 1996 | 26 |
| 1997 | 27 |
| 1998 | 34 |

*In Problems 36–39, evaluate the double integrals.*

**36.** $\displaystyle\int_{1}^{2}\int_{0}^{y} x^2 y^2 \, dx \, dy$

**37.** $\displaystyle\int_{0}^{1}\int_{0}^{y^2} xy \, dx \, dy$

**38.** $\displaystyle\int_{1}^{4}\int_{x^2}^{2x} y \, dy \, dx$

**39.** $\displaystyle\int_{0}^{1}\int_{\sqrt{x}}^{x^2} 7(x^2 + 2xy - 3y^2) \, dy \, dx$

# Mathematical Snapshot

Mathematical Snapshot

## Data Analysis to Model Cooling[29]

In Chapter 15 you worked with Newton's law of cooling, which can be used to describe the temperature of a cooling body with respect to time. Here you will determine that relationship in an empirical way via data analysis. This will illustrate how mathematical models are designed in many real-world situations.

Suppose that you want to create a mathematical model of the cooling of hot tea after it is placed in a refrigerator. To do this you place a pitcher containing hot tea and a thermometer in the refrigerator and periodically read and record the temperature of the tea. Table 17.6 gives the collected data, where $T$ is the Fahrenheit temperature $t$ minutes after the tea is placed in the refrigerator. Initially, that is, at $t = 0$, the temperature is $124°F$; when $t = 391$, then $T = 47°F$. After being in the refrigerator overnight, the temperature is $45°F$. Figure 17.24 gives a graph of the data points $(t, T)$ for $t = 0$ to $t = 391$.

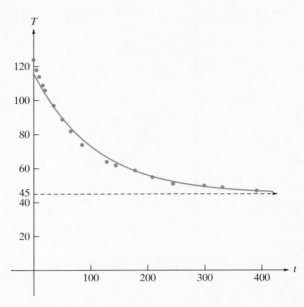

FIGURE 17.24   Data points and exponential approximation.

**TABLE 17.6**

| Time | Temperature | Time | Temperature |
|------|-------------|------|-------------|
| $t$ | $T$ | $t$ | $T$ |
| 0 min | 124°F | 128 min | 64°F |
| 5 | 118 | 144 | 62 |
| 10 | 114 | 178 | 59 |
| 16 | 109 | 208 | 55 |
| 20 | 106 | 244 | 51 |
| 35 | 97 | 299 | 50 |
| 50 | 89 | 331 | 49 |
| 65 | 82 | 391 | 47 |
| 85 | 74 | Overnight | 45 |

The pattern of these points strongly suggests that they nearly lie on the graph of a decreasing exponential function, such as the one shown in Figure 17.24. In particular, because the overnight temperature is $45°F$, this exponential function should have $T = 45$ as a horizontal asymptote. Such a function has the form

$$\widehat{T} = Ce^{at} + 45 \qquad (1)$$

where $\widehat{T}$ gives the predicted temperature at time $t$, and $C$ and $a$ are constants with $a < 0$. (Note that since $a < 0$, then as $t \to \infty$, you have $Ce^{at} \to 0$, so $Ce^{at} + 45 \to 45$.)

Now the problem is to find the values of $C$ and $a$ so that the curve given by Equation (1) best fits the data. By writing Equation (1) as

$$\widehat{T} - 45 = Ce^{at}$$

and then taking the natural logarithm of each side, we obtain a linear form:

$$\ln(\widehat{T} - 45) = \ln(Ce^{at})$$
$$\ln(\widehat{T} - 45) = \ln C + \ln e^{at}$$
$$\ln(\widehat{T} - 45) = \ln C + at \qquad (2)$$

Letting $\widehat{T}_l = \ln(\widehat{T} - 45)$, Equation (2) becomes

$$\widehat{T}_l = at + \ln C \qquad (3)$$

Because $a$ and $\ln C$ are constants, Equation (3) is a linear equation in $\widehat{T}_l$ and $t$. This means that for the original data, if you plot the points $(t, \ln(T - 45))$, they should nearly lie on a straight line. These points are shown in Figure 17.25, where $T_l$ represents $\ln(T - 45)$. Thus for the line given by Equation (3) that predicts $T_l = \ln(T - 45)$, you can assume that it is the linear regression line of $T_l$ on $t$. That is, $a$ and $\ln C$ are linear regression coefficients. By using the formulas

[29]Adapted from Gloria Barrett, Dot Doyle, and Dan Teague, "Using Data Analysis in Precalculus to Model Cooling," *The Mathematics Teacher*, 81, no. 8 (November 1988), 680–84. By permission of the National Council of Teachers of Mathematics.

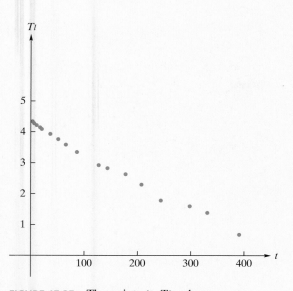

FIGURE 17.25  The points $(t, T_l)$, where $T_l = \ln(T - 45)$, nearly lie on a straight line.

for these coefficients and a calculator, you can determine that

$$a = \frac{17\left(\sum_{i=1}^{17} t_i\, T_{l_i}\right) - \left(\sum_{i=1}^{17} t_i\right)\left(\sum_{i=1}^{17} T_{l_i}\right)}{17\left(\sum_{i=1}^{17} t_i^2\right) - \left(\sum_{i=1}^{17} t_i\right)^2} \approx -0.00921$$

and

$$\ln C = \frac{\left(\sum_{i=1}^{17} t_i^2\right)\left(\sum_{i=1}^{17} T_{l_i}\right) - \left(\sum_{i=1}^{17} t_i\right)\left(\sum_{i=1}^{17} t_i\, T_{l_i}\right)}{17\left(\sum_{i=1}^{17} t_i^2\right) - \left(\sum_{i=1}^{17} t_i\right)^2}$$

$$\approx 4.260074$$

Since $\ln C \approx 4.260074$, then $C \approx e^{4.260074} \approx 70.82$. Thus from Equation (1),

$$\widehat{T} = 70.82 e^{-0.00921t} + 45$$

which is a model that predicts the temperature of the cooling tea. The graph of this function is the curve shown in Figure 17.24.

## Problems

**1.** Plot the following data points on an $x,y$-coordinate plane:

| $x$ | 0 | 1 | 4 | 7 | 10 |
|---|---|---|---|---|---|
| $y$ | 15 | 12 | 9 | 7 | 6 |

Suppose that these points nearly lie on the graph of a decreasing exponential function with horizontal asymptote $y = 5$. Use the technique discussed in this mathematical snapshot to determine the function.

**2.** Suppose that observed data follow a relation given by $y = C/x^r$, where $x, y, C > 0$. By taking the natural logarithm of each side, show that $\ln x$ and $\ln y$ are linearly related. Thus, the points $(\ln x, \ln y)$ lie on a straight line.

**3.** Use Newton's law of cooling (see Section 15.6) and the data points $(0, 124)$ and $(128, 64)$ to determine the temperature $T$ of the tea discussed in the snapshot at time $t$. Assume that the ambient temperature is $45°F$.

**4.** Try obtaining the final regression equation in the snapshot using the regression capability of a graphing calculator. First use linear regression. How does your result compare with the one in the snapshot? Then try skipping the linear-form transformation and perform an exponential regression. What difficulty do you encounter, if any? How could it be overcome?

# APPENDIX B

## Table of Selected Integrals

*Rational Forms Containing* $(a + bu)$

**1.** $\displaystyle\int u^n \, du = \frac{u^{n+1}}{n+1} + C, \; n \neq -1$

**2.** $\displaystyle\int \frac{du}{a + bu} = \frac{1}{b} \ln |a + bu| + C$

**3.** $\displaystyle\int \frac{u \, du}{a + bu} = \frac{u}{b} - \frac{a}{b^2} \ln |a + bu| + C$

**4.** $\displaystyle\int \frac{u^2 \, du}{a + bu} = \frac{u^2}{2b} - \frac{au}{b^2} + \frac{a^2}{b^3} \ln |a + bu| + C$

**5.** $\displaystyle\int \frac{du}{u(a + bu)} = \frac{1}{a} \ln \left| \frac{u}{a + bu} \right| + C$

**6.** $\displaystyle\int \frac{du}{u^2(a + bu)} = -\frac{1}{au} + \frac{b}{a^2} \ln \left| \frac{a + bu}{u} \right| + C$

**7.** $\displaystyle\int \frac{u \, du}{(a + bu)^2} = \frac{1}{b^2} \left( \ln |a + bu| + \frac{a}{a + bu} \right) + C$

**8.** $\displaystyle\int \frac{u^2 \, du}{(a + bu)^2} = \frac{u}{b^2} - \frac{a^2}{b^3(a + bu)} - \frac{2a}{b^3} \ln |a + bu| + C$

**9.** $\displaystyle\int \frac{du}{u(a + bu)^2} = \frac{1}{a(a + bu)} + \frac{1}{a^2} \ln \left| \frac{u}{a + bu} \right| + C$

**10.** $\displaystyle\int \frac{du}{u^2(a + bu)^2} = -\frac{a + 2bu}{a^2 u(a + bu)} + \frac{2b}{a^3} \ln \left| \frac{a + bu}{u} \right| + C$

**11.** $\displaystyle\int \frac{du}{(a + bu)(c + ku)} = \frac{1}{bc - ak} \ln \left| \frac{a + bu}{c + ku} \right| + C$

**12.** $\displaystyle\int \frac{u \, du}{(a + bu)(c + ku)} = \frac{1}{bc - ak} \left[ \frac{c}{k} \ln |c + ku| - \frac{a}{b} \ln |a + bu| \right] + C$

*Forms Containing* $\sqrt{a + bu}$

**13.** $\displaystyle\int u\sqrt{a + bu} \, du = \frac{2(3bu - 2a)(a + bu)^{3/2}}{15b^2} + C$

**14.** $\displaystyle\int u^2 \sqrt{a + bu} \, du = \frac{2(8a^2 - 12abu + 15b^2 u^2)(a + bu)^{3/2}}{105b^3} + C$

**15.** $\displaystyle\int \frac{u \, du}{\sqrt{a + bu}} = \frac{2(bu - 2a)\sqrt{a + bu}}{3b^2} + C$

**16.** $\displaystyle\int \frac{u^2 \, du}{\sqrt{a + bu}} = \frac{2(3b^2 u^2 - 4abu + 8a^2)\sqrt{a + bu}}{15b^3} + C$

**17.** $\int \frac{du}{u\sqrt{a+bu}} = \frac{1}{\sqrt{a}} \ln\left|\frac{\sqrt{a+bu}-\sqrt{a}}{\sqrt{a+bu}+\sqrt{a}}\right| + C,\ a > 0$

**18.** $\int \frac{\sqrt{a+bu}\,du}{u} = 2\sqrt{a+bu} + a\int \frac{du}{u\sqrt{a+bu}}$

## Forms Containing $\sqrt{a^2 - u^2}$

**19.** $\int \frac{du}{(a^2-u^2)^{3/2}} = \frac{u}{a^2\sqrt{a^2-u^2}} + C$

**20.** $\int \frac{du}{u\sqrt{a^2-u^2}} = -\frac{1}{a}\ln\left|\frac{a+\sqrt{a^2-u^2}}{u}\right| + C$

**21.** $\int \frac{du}{u^2\sqrt{a^2-u^2}} = -\frac{\sqrt{a^2-u^2}}{a^2u} + C$

**22.** $\int \frac{\sqrt{a^2-u^2}\,du}{u} = \sqrt{a^2-u^2} - a\ln\left|\frac{a+\sqrt{a^2-u^2}}{u}\right| + C,\ a > 0$

## Forms Containing $\sqrt{u^2 \pm a^2}$

**23.** $\int \sqrt{u^2\pm a^2}\,du = \frac{1}{2}\left(u\sqrt{u^2\pm a^2} \pm a^2\ln\left|u+\sqrt{u^2\pm a^2}\right|\right) + C$

**24.** $\int u^2\sqrt{u^2\pm a^2}\,du = \frac{u}{8}(2u^2\pm a^2)\sqrt{u^2\pm a^2} - \frac{a^4}{8}\ln\left|u+\sqrt{u^2\pm a^2}\right| + C$

**25.** $\int \frac{\sqrt{u^2+a^2}\,du}{u} = \sqrt{u^2+a^2} - a\ln\left|\frac{a+\sqrt{u^2+a^2}}{u}\right| + C$

**26.** $\int \frac{\sqrt{u^2\pm a^2}\,du}{u^2} = -\frac{\sqrt{u^2\pm a^2}}{u} + \ln\left|u+\sqrt{u^2\pm a^2}\right| + C$

**27.** $\int \frac{du}{\sqrt{u^2\pm a^2}} = \ln\left|u+\sqrt{u^2\pm a^2}\right| + C$

**28.** $\int \frac{du}{u\sqrt{u^2+a^2}} = \frac{1}{a}\ln\left|\frac{\sqrt{u^2+a^2}-a}{u}\right| + C$

**29.** $\int \frac{u^2du}{\sqrt{u^2\pm a^2}} = \frac{1}{2}\left(u\sqrt{u^2\pm a^2} \mp a^2\ln\left|u+\sqrt{u^2\pm a^2}\right|\right) + C$

**30.** $\int \frac{du}{u^2\sqrt{u^2\pm a^2}} = -\frac{\pm\sqrt{u^2\pm a^2}}{a^2u} + C$

**31.** $\int (u^2\pm a^2)^{3/2}du = \frac{u}{8}(2u^2\pm 5a^2)\sqrt{u^2\pm a^2} + \frac{3a^4}{8}\ln\left|u+\sqrt{u^2\pm a^2}\right| + C$

**32.** $\int \frac{du}{(u^2\pm a^2)^{3/2}} = \frac{\pm u}{a^2\sqrt{u^2\pm a^2}} + C$

**33.** $\int \frac{u^2du}{(u^2\pm a^2)^{3/2}} = \frac{-u}{\sqrt{u^2\pm a^2}} + \ln\left|u+\sqrt{u^2\pm a^2}\right| + C$

## Rational Forms Containing $a^2 - u^2$ and $u^2 - a^2$

**34.** $\int \frac{du}{a^2-u^2} = \frac{1}{2a}\ln\left|\frac{a+u}{a-u}\right| + C$

**35.** $\int \frac{du}{u^2-a^2} = \frac{1}{2a}\ln\left|\frac{u-a}{u+a}\right| + C$

## Exponential and Logarithmic Forms

**36.** $\displaystyle\int e^u\,du = e^u + C$

**37.** $\displaystyle\int a^u\,du = \frac{a^u}{\ln a} + C, a > 0, a \neq 1$

**38.** $\displaystyle\int u e^{au}\,du = \frac{e^{au}}{a^2}(au - 1) + C$

**39.** $\displaystyle\int u^n e^{au}\,du = \frac{u^n e^{au}}{a} - \frac{n}{a}\int u^{n-1} e^{au}\,du$

**40.** $\displaystyle\int \frac{e^{au}\,du}{u^n} = -\frac{e^{au}}{(n-1)u^{n-1}} + \frac{a}{n-1}\int \frac{e^{au}\,du}{u^{n-1}}, n \neq 1$

**41.** $\displaystyle\int \ln u\,du = u \ln u - u + C$

**42.** $\displaystyle\int u^n \ln u\,du = \frac{u^{n+1}\ln u}{n+1} - \frac{u^{n+1}}{(n+1)^2} + C,\ n \neq -1$

**43.** $\displaystyle\int u^n \ln^m u\,du = \frac{u^{n+1}}{n+1}\ln^m u - \frac{m}{n+1}\int u^n \ln^{m-1} u\,du, m,\ n \neq -1$

**44.** $\displaystyle\int \frac{du}{u \ln u} = \ln\left|\ln u\right| + C$

**45.** $\displaystyle\int \frac{du}{a + be^{cu}} = \frac{1}{ac}\left(cu - \ln\left|a + be^{cu}\right|\right) + C$

## Miscellaneous Forms

**46.** $\displaystyle\int \sqrt{\frac{a+u}{b+u}}\,du = \sqrt{(a+u)(b+u)} + (a-b)\ln(\sqrt{a+u} + \sqrt{b+u}) + C$

**47.** $\displaystyle\int \frac{du}{\sqrt{(a+u)(b+u)}} = \ln\left|\frac{a+b}{2} + u + \sqrt{(a+u)(b+u)}\right| + C$

**48.** $\displaystyle\int \sqrt{a + bu + cu^2}\,du = \frac{2cu + b}{4c}\sqrt{a + bu + cu^2}$

$$- \frac{b^2 - 4ac}{8c^{3/2}}\ln\left|2cu + b + 2\sqrt{c}\sqrt{a + bu + cu^2}\right| + C, c > 0$$

# APPENDIX D
## Section1.5

## 1.5  Summation Notation

There was a time when school teachers made their students add up all the positive integers from 1 to 105 (say), perhaps as punishment for unruly behaviour while the teacher was out of the classroom. In other words, the students were to find

$$1 + 2 + 3 + 4 + 5 + 6 + 7 + \cdots + 104 + 105 \qquad (1)$$

A related exercise was to find

$$1 + 4 + 9 + 16 + \cdots + 81 + 100 + 121 \qquad (2)$$

The three dots notation is supposed to convey the idea of continuing the task, using the same pattern, until the last explicitly given terms have been added too. With this notation there are no hard and fast rules about how many terms at the beginning and end are to be given explicitly. The custom is to provide as many as are needed to ensure that the intended reader will find the expression unambiguous. This is too imprecise for many mathematical applications.

Suppose that for any positive integer $i$ we define $a_i = i^2$. Then, for example, $a_6 = 36$ and $a_8 = 64$. The instruction, "Add together the numbers $a_i$, for $i$ taking on the integer values 1 through 11 inclusive" is a precise statement of Equation (2). It would be precise regardless of the formula defining the values $a_i$, and this leads to the following:

**DEFINITION**
If, for each positive integer $i$, there is given a unique number $a_i$, and $m$ and $n$ are positive integers with $m \leq n$, then *the sum of the numbers $a_i$, **with i successively taking on the values m through n is denoted***

$$\sum_{i=m}^{n} a_i$$

Thus

$$\sum_{i=m}^{n} a_i = a_m + a_{m+1} + a_{m+2} + \cdots + a_n \qquad (3)$$

The $\sum$ is the Greek capital letter sigma, from which we get the letter S. It stands for "sum," and the expression $\sum_{i=m}^{n} a_i$, can be read as the the sum of all numbers $a_i$, where $i$ ranges from $m$ to $n$ (through positive integers being understood). The description of $a_i$ may be very simple. For example, in Equation (1) we have $a_i = i$ and

$$\sum_{i=1}^{105} i = 1 + 2 + 3 + \cdots + 105 \qquad (4)$$

while Equation (2) is

$$\sum_{i=1}^{11} i^2 = 1 + 4 + 9 + \cdots + 121 \qquad (5)$$

We have merely defined a notation, which is called **summation notation.** In Equation (3), $i$ is the *index of summation* and $m$ and $n$ are called the *bounds of summation*. It is important to understand from the outset that the name of the index of summation can be replaced by any other so that we have

$$\sum_{i=m}^{n} a_i = \sum_{j=m}^{n} a_j = \sum_{\alpha=m}^{n} a_\alpha = \sum_{N=m}^{n} a_N$$

for example. In each case, replacing the index of summation by the positive integers $m$ through $n$ successively and adding results in

$$a_m + a_{m+1} + a_{m+2} + \cdots + a_n$$

We now illustrate with some concrete examples.

### ● EXAMPLE 1   Evaluating Sums

*Evaluate the given sums.*

**a.** $\displaystyle\sum_{n=3}^{7}(5n - 2)$

Solution:

$$\sum_{n=3}^{7}(5n - 2) = [5(3) - 2] + [5(4) - 2] + [5(5) - 2] + [5(6) - 2] + [5(7) - 2]$$
$$= 13 + 18 + 23 + 28 + 33$$
$$= 115$$

**b.** $\displaystyle\sum_{j=1}^{6}(j^2 + 1)$

Solution:

$$\sum_{j=1}^{6}(j^2 + 1) = (1^2 + 1) + (2^2 + 1) + (3^2 + 1) + (4^2 + 1) + (5^2 + 1) + (6^2 + 1)$$
$$= 2 + 5 + 10 + 17 + 26 + 37$$
$$= 97$$

NOW WORK PROBLEM 5 ●●●

## ●EXAMPLE 2   Writing a Sum Using Summation Notation

*Write the sum* $14 + 16 + 18 + 20 + 22 + \cdots + 100$ *in summation notation.*

Solution: There are many ways to express this sum in sigma notation. One method is to notice that the values being added are $2n$, for $n = 7$ to 50. The sum can thus be written as

$$\sum_{n=7}^{50} 2n$$

Another method is to notice that the values being added are $2k + 12$, for $k = 1$ to 44. The sum can thus be represented as

$$\sum_{k=1}^{44} (2k + 12)$$

NOW WORK PROBLEM 9 ●●●

Since summation notation is used to express the addition of terms, we can use the properties of addition when performing operations on sums written in summation notation. By applying these properties, we can create a list of properties, and formulas for summation notation.

By the distributive property of addition,

$$ca_1 + ca_2 + \cdots + ca_n = c(a_1 + a_2 + \cdots + a_n)$$

So, in summation notation,

$$\sum_{i=m}^{n} ca_i = c \sum_{i=m}^{n} a_i \tag{6}$$

Note that $c$ must be constant with respect to $i$ for Equation (6) to be used.

By the commutative property of addition,

$$a_1 + b_1 + a_2 + b_2 + \cdots + a_n + b_n = a_1 + a_2 + \cdots + a_n + b_1 + b_2 + \cdots + b_n$$

So we have

$$\sum_{i=m}^{n} (a_i + b_i) = \sum_{i=m}^{n} a_i + \sum_{i=m}^{n} b_i \tag{7}$$

Sometimes we want to change the bounds of summation.

$$\sum_{i=m}^{n} a_i = \sum_{i=p}^{p+n-m} a_{i+m-p}. \tag{8}$$

A sum of 37 terms can be regarded as the sum of the first 17 terms plus the sum of the next 20 terms. The next rule generalzes this observation.

$$\sum_{i=m}^{p-1} a_i + \sum_{i=p}^{n} a_i = \sum_{i=m}^{n} a_i \tag{9}$$

In addition to these four basic rules, there are some other rules worth noting. The first two follow, respectively, from Equations (6) and (7):

$$\sum_{i=1}^{n} c = cn \tag{10}$$

$$\sum_{i=m}^{n} (a_i - b_i) = \sum_{i=m}^{n} a_i - \sum_{i=m}^{n} b_i$$

Establishing the next three formulas is best done by a proof method called mathematical induction, which we will not demonstrate here.

$$\sum_{i=1}^{n} i = \frac{n(n+1)}{2} \tag{12}$$

$$\sum_{i=1}^{n} i^2 = \frac{n(n+1)(2n+1)}{6} \tag{13}$$

$$\sum_{i=1}^{n} i^3 = \frac{n^2(n+1)^2}{4} \tag{14}$$

However, we can deduce Equation (12). If we add the following equations, "vertically," term by term,

$$\sum_{i=1}^{n} i = 1 + 2 + 3 + \cdots + n$$

$$\sum_{i=1}^{n} i = n + (n-1) + (n-2) + \cdots + 1$$

we get

$$2\sum_{i=1}^{n} i = (n+1) + (n+1) + (n+1) + \cdots + (n+1)$$

and since there are $n$ terms on the right, we conclude

$$\sum_{i=1}^{n} i = \frac{n(n+1)}{2}$$

Observe that if a teacher assigns the task of finding

$$1 + 2 + 3 + 4 + 5 + 6 + 7 + \cdots + 104 + 105$$

as a *punishment* and if he or she knows the formula given by Equation (12), then a student's work can be checked quickly by

$$\sum_{i=1}^{105} i = \frac{105(106)}{2} = 105 \cdot 53 = 5300 + 265 = 5565$$

● EXAMPLE 3   **Applying the Properties of Summation Notation**

*Evaluate the given sums.*

**a.** $\displaystyle\sum_{j=30}^{100} 4$      **b.** $\displaystyle\sum_{k=1}^{100} (5k+3)$      **c.** $\displaystyle\sum_{k=1}^{200} 9k^2$

**Solutions:**

**a.**
$$\sum_{j=30}^{100} 4 = \sum_{j=1}^{71} 4 \qquad \text{[by Equation (8)]}$$

$$= 4 \cdot 71 \qquad \text{[by Equation (10)]}$$

$$= 284$$

**b.**
$$\sum_{k=1}^{100} (5k+3) = \sum_{k=1}^{100} 5k + \sum_{k=1}^{100} 3 \qquad \text{[by Equation (7)]}$$

$$= 5\left(\sum_{k=1}^{100} k\right) + 3\left(\sum_{k=1}^{100} 1\right) \qquad \text{[by Equation (6)]}$$

$$= 5\left(\frac{100 \cdot 101}{2}\right) + 3(100) \qquad \text{[by Equations (12) and (10)]}$$

$$= 25{,}250 + 300$$

$$= 25{,}550$$

**c.**
$$\sum_{k=1}^{200} 9k^2 = 9\sum_{k=1}^{200} k^2 \qquad \text{[by Equation (6)]}$$

$$= 9\left(\frac{200 \cdot 201 \cdot 401}{6}\right) \qquad \text{[by Equation (13)]}$$

$$= 24{,}180{,}300$$

NOW WORK PROBLEM 19

## Problems 1.5

*In Problems 1 and 2, give the bounds of summation and the index of summation for each expression.*

**1.** $\displaystyle\sum_{t=12}^{17}(8t^2 - 5t + 3)$ 　　 **2.** $\displaystyle\sum_{m=3}^{450}(8m - 4)$

*In Problems 3–6, evaluate the given sums.*

**3.** $\displaystyle\sum_{i=1}^{7} 6i$ 　　 **4.** $\displaystyle\sum_{p=0}^{4} 10p$

*5.** $\displaystyle\sum_{k=3}^{9}(10k + 16)$ 　　 **6.** $\displaystyle\sum_{n=7}^{11}(2n - 3)$

*In Problems 7–12, express the given sums in summation notation.*

**7.** $36 + 37 + 38 + 39 + \cdots + 60$

**8.** $1 + 4 + 9 + 16 + 25$

*9.** $5^3 + 5^4 + 5^5 + 5^6 + 5^7 + 5^8$

**10.** $11 + 15 + 19 + 23 + \cdots + 71$

**11.** $2 + 4 + 8 + 16 + 32 + 64 + 128 + 256$

**12.** $10 + 100 + 1000 + \cdots + 100{,}000{,}000$

*In Problems 13–26, evaluate the given sums.*

**13.** $\displaystyle\sum_{k=1}^{43} 100$ 　　 **14.** $\displaystyle\sum_{k=35}^{135} 2$

**15.** $\displaystyle\sum_{k=1}^{n}\left(5 \cdot \frac{1}{n}\right)$ 　　 **16.** $\displaystyle\sum_{k=1}^{200}(k - 100)$

**17.** $\displaystyle\sum_{k=51}^{100} 10k$ 　　 **18.** $\displaystyle\sum_{k=1}^{n}\frac{n}{n+1}k^2$

*19.** $\displaystyle\sum_{k=1}^{20}(5k^2 + 3k)$ 　　 **20.** $\displaystyle\sum_{k=1}^{100}\frac{3k^2 - 200k}{101}$

**21.** $\displaystyle\sum_{k=51}^{100} k^2$ 　　 **22.** $\displaystyle\sum_{k=1}^{50}(k + 50)^2$

**23.** $\displaystyle\sum_{k=1}^{10}\left\{\left[4 - \left(\frac{2k}{10}\right)^2\right]\left(\frac{2}{10}\right)\right\}$

**24.** $\displaystyle\sum_{k=1}^{100}\left\{\left[4 - \left(\frac{2}{100}k\right)^2\right]\left(\frac{2}{100}\right)\right\}$

**25.** $\displaystyle\sum_{k=1}^{n}\left\{\left[5 - \left(\frac{3}{n} \cdot k\right)^2\right]\frac{3}{n}\right\}$

**26.** $\displaystyle\sum_{k=1}^{n}\frac{k^2}{(n+1)(2n+1)}$

# Answers to Odd-Numbered Problems

**25.** (a) 76%; (b) 74.4% Japanese, 25.6% non-Japanese;
(c) 75% Japanese, 25% non-Japanese

## MATHEMATICAL SNAPSHOT—CHAPTER 9 (page 446)

**1.** 7

**3.** Against Always Defect:
$\begin{bmatrix} 0 & 0 & 0 & 0 \\ 1 & 0.1 & 1 & 0.1 \\ 0 & 0 & 0 & 0 \\ 0 & 0.9 & 0 & 0.9 \end{bmatrix};$

Against Always Cooperate:
$\begin{bmatrix} 1 & 0.1 & 1 & 0.1 \\ 0 & 0 & 0 & 0 \\ 0 & 0.9 & 0 & 0.9 \\ 0 & 0 & 0 & 0 \end{bmatrix}$

Against regular Tit-for-tat:
$\begin{bmatrix} 1 & 0.1 & 0 & 0 \\ 0 & 0 & 1 & 0.1 \\ 0 & 0.9 & 0 & 0 \\ 0 & 0 & 0 & 0.9 \end{bmatrix}$

## PRINCIPLES IN PRACTICE 10.1

**1.** The limit as $x \to a$ does not exist if $a$ is an integer, but it exists if $a$ is any other value.

**2.** $\frac{4}{3}\pi$ cc    **3.** 3616    **4.** 20    **5.** 2

## PROBLEMS 10.1 (page 457)

**1.** (a) 1; (b) 0; (c) 1

**3.** (a) 1; (b) does not exist; (c) 3

**5.** $f(-0.9) = -3.7$, $f(-0.99) = -3.97$, $f(-0.999) = -3.997$, $f(-1.001) = -4.003$, $f(-1.01) = -4.03$, $f(-1.1) = -4.3$; $-4$

**7.** $f(-0.1) \approx 0.9516$, $f(-0.01) \approx 0.9950$, $f(-0.001) \approx 0.9995$, $f(0.001) \approx 1.0005$, $f(0.01) \approx 1.0050$, $f(0.1) \approx 1.0517$; 1

**9.** 16    **11.** 20    **13.** $-47$    **15.** $-\frac{5}{2}$    **17.** 0

**19.** 5    **21.** $-2$    **23.** 3    **25.** 5    **27.** $\frac{1}{6}$

**29.** $-\frac{1}{5}$    **31.** $\frac{11}{9}$    **33.** 4    **35.** $2x$    **37.** $-3$

**39.** $2x$    **41.** $3x^2 - 8x$    **43.** $\frac{1}{4}$

**45.** (a) 1; (b) 0    **47.** 11.00    **49.** 4.00

**51.** Does not exist

## PRINCIPLES IN PRACTICE 10.2

**1.** $\lim_{x \to \infty} p(x) = 0$. The graph starts out high and quickly goes down toward zero. Accordingly, consumers are willing to purchase large quantities of the product at prices close to 0.

**2.** $\lim_{x \to \infty} y(x) = 500$. The greatest yearly sales they can expect with unlimited advertising is $500,000.

**3.** $\lim_{x \to \infty} C(x) = \infty$. This means that the cost continues to increase without bound as more units are made.

**4.** The limit does not exist; $250.

## PROBLEMS 10.2 (page 465)

**1.** (a) 2; (b) 3; (c) does not exist; (d) $-\infty$; (e) $\infty$; (f) $\infty$; (g) $\infty$; (h) 0; (i) 1; (j) 1; (k) 1

**3.** 1    **5.** $-\infty$    **7.** $-\infty$    **9.** $\infty$    **11.** 0

**13.** $\infty$    **15.** 0    **17.** $\infty$    **19.** 0    **21.** 1

**23.** 0    **25.** $\infty$    **27.** 0    **29.** $-\frac{2}{5}$    **31.** $-\infty$

**33.** $\frac{2}{5}$    **35.** $-\infty$    **37.** $\frac{16}{3}$    **39.** $-\frac{1}{2}$    **41.** $\infty$

**43.** $\infty$    **45.** $\infty$    **47.** Does not exist

**49.** $\infty$    **51.** 0    **53.** 1

**55.** (a) 1; (b) 2; (c) does not exist; (d) 1; (e) 2

**57.** (a) 0; (b) 0; (c) 0; (d) $-\infty$; (e) $-\infty$

**59.**
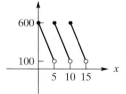
$\lim_{q \to \infty} \bar{c} = 6$

**61.** 50,000    **63.** 20

**65.** 1, 0.5, 0.525, 0.631, 0.912, 0.986, 0.998; conclude limit is 1

**67.** 0    **69.** (a) 11; (b) 9; (c) does not exist

## PROBLEMS 10.3 (page 471)

**7.** Continuous at $-2$ and 0    **9.** Discontinuous at $\pm 3$

**11.** Continuous at 2 and 0    **13.** $f$ is a polynomial function

**15.** $f$ is a rational function and the denominator is never zero.

**17.** None    **19.** $x = -4$    **21.** None    **23.** $x = -5, 3$

**25.** $x = 0$, $\pm 1$    **27.** None    **29.** $x = 0$    **31.** None

**33.** $x = 2$

**35.** Discontinuities at $t = 1, 2, 3, 4$

**37.** Yes, no, no

## PRINCIPLES IN PRACTICE 10.4

**1.** $0 < x < 4$

## PROBLEMS 10.4 (page 475)

**1.** $(-\infty, -1), (4, \infty)$    **3.** $[-2, 5]$

**5.** $\left(-\frac{7}{2}, -2\right)$    **7.** No solution

**9.** $(-\infty, -6], [-2, 3]$    **11.** $(-\infty, -4), (0, 5)$

**13.** $[0, \infty)$      **15.** $(-\infty, -5], [-3, 0]$

**17.** $(-\infty, -3), (0, 3)$      **19.** $(1, \infty)$

**21.** $(-\infty, -5), [-2, 1), [3, \infty)$   **23.** $(-5, -1)$

**25.** $(-\infty, -1 - \sqrt{3}], [-1 + \sqrt{3}, \infty)$

**27.** Between 37 and 103, inclusive

**29.** 17 in. by 17 in.      **31.** $(-\infty, -7.72]$

**33.** $(-\infty, -0.5), (0.667, \infty)$

## REVIEW PROBLEMS—CHAPTER 10 (page 477)

**1.** $-5$    **3.** $2$    **5.** $x$    **7.** $-\dfrac{8}{3}$    **9.** $0$

**11.** $\dfrac{2}{7}$    **13.** Does not exist   **15.** $-1$

**17.** $\dfrac{1}{9}$    **19.** $-\infty$    **21.** $\infty$

**23.** $-\infty$    **25.** $1$    **27.** $-\infty$    **29.** $8$    **31.** $23$

**35.** Continuous everywhere; $f$ is a polynomial function.

**37.** $x = -3$    **39.** None    **41.** $x = -4, 1$   **43.** $x = -2$

**45.** $(-\infty, -6), (2, \infty)$      **47.** $(-\infty, 7]$

**49.** $(-\infty, -5), (-1, 1)$      **51.** $(-\infty, -4), [-3, 0], (2, \infty)$

**53.** $1.00$    **55.** $0$      **57.** $[2.00, \infty)$

## MATHEMATICAL SNAPSHOT—CHAPTER 10 (page 478)

**1.** $5.3\%$

**3.** An exponential model assumes a fixed repayment rate.

## PRINCIPLES IN PRACTICE 11.1

**1.** $\dfrac{dH}{dt} = 40 - 32t$

## PROBLEMS 11.1 (page 488)

**1. (a)**

| $x$-value of $Q$ | $-3$ | $-2.5$ | $-2.2$ | $-2.1$ | $-2.01$ | $-2.001$ |
|---|---|---|---|---|---|---|
| $m_{PQ}$ | $19$ | $15.25$ | $13.24$ | $12.61$ | $12.0601$ | $12.0060$ |

     **(b)** We estimate that $m_{\text{tan}} = 12$.

**3.** $1$    **5.** $3$    **7.** $-4$    **9.** $0$    **11.** $2x + 4$

**13.** $6q + 2$    **15.** $-\dfrac{6}{x^2}$    **17.** $\dfrac{1}{2\sqrt{x+2}}$   **19.** $-4$

**21.** $0$      **23.** $y = x + 4$      **25.** $y = 4x + 2$

**27.** $y = -3x + 9$      **29.** $\dfrac{r}{r_L - r - \dfrac{dC}{dD}}$      **31.** $-3.000, 13.445$

**33.** $-5.120, 0.038$

**35.** For the $x$-values of the points where the tangent to the graph of $f$ is horizontal, the corresponding values of $f'(x)$ are 0. This is expected because the slope of a horizontal line is zero and the derivative gives the slope of the tangent line.

**37.** $20x^4 - 9x^2$

## PRINCIPLES IN PRACTICE 11.2

**1.** $50 - 0.6q$

## PROBLEMS 11.2 (page 496)

**1.** $0$    **3.** $6x^5$    **5.** $80x^{79}$    **7.** $18x$    **9.** $56w^6$

**11.** $\dfrac{8}{3}x^3$    **13.** $\dfrac{7}{25}t^6$    **15.** $1$      **17.** $8x - 2$

**19.** $4p^3 - 9p^2$      **21.** $3x^2 - \dfrac{1}{2\sqrt{x}}$

**23.** $-39x^2 + 28x - 2$   **25.** $-8x^3$      **27.** $-\dfrac{4}{3}x^3$

**29.** $16x^3 + 3x^2 - 9x + 8$   **31.** $\dfrac{6}{5}x^3 + 7x^2$   **33.** $\dfrac{3}{5}x^{-2/5}$

**35.** $\dfrac{3}{4}x^{-1/4} + \dfrac{10}{3}x^{2/3}$   **37.** $\dfrac{11}{2}x^{-1/2}$ or $\dfrac{11}{2\sqrt{x}}$   **39.** $2r^{-2/3}$

**41.** $-4x^{-5}$      **43.** $-3x^{-4} - 5x^{-6} + 12x^{-7}$

**45.** $-x^{-2}$ or $-\dfrac{1}{x^2}$   **47.** $-40x^{-6}$      **49.** $-4x^{-4}$

**51.** $-\dfrac{1}{2}t^{-2}$      **53.** $\dfrac{1}{7} - 7x^{-2}$

**55.** $-3x^{-2/3} - 2x^{-7/5}$      **57.** $-\dfrac{1}{3}x^{-5/3}$

**59.** $-x^{-3/2}$      **61.** $\dfrac{5}{2}x^{3/2}$

**63.** $9x^2 - 20x + 7$      **65.** $45x^4$

**67.** $\dfrac{1}{3}x^{-2/3} - \dfrac{10}{3}x^{-5/3} = \dfrac{1}{3}x^{-5/3}(x - 10)$

**69.** $3 + \dfrac{2}{q^2}$      **71.** $2x + 4$      **73.** $1$

**75.** $4, 16, -14$    **77.** $0, 0, 0$      **79.** $y = 13x + 2$

**81.** $y = -\dfrac{3}{16}x + \dfrac{1}{2}$      **83.** $y = x + 3$

**85.** $(0, 0), \left(\dfrac{5}{3}, \dfrac{125}{54}\right)$      **87.** $(3, -3)$

**89.** $0$      **91.** The tangent line is $y = 9x - 16$.

## PRINCIPLES IN PRACTICE 11.3

**1.** $2.5$ units

**2.** $\dfrac{dy}{dt} = 16 - 32t$;   $\left.\dfrac{dy}{dt}\right|_{t=0.5} = 0$ feet/s

     When $t = 0.5$ the object reaches its maximum height.

**3.** $1.2$ and $120\%$

## PROBLEMS 11.3 (page 504)

**1.**

| $\Delta t$ | $1$ | $0.5$ | $0.2$ | $0.1$ | $0.01$ | $0.001$ |
|---|---|---|---|---|---|---|
| $\Delta s/\Delta t$ | $9$ | $8$ | $7.4$ | $7.2$ | $7.02$ | $7.002$ |

We estimate the velocity when $t = 1$ to be $7.0000$ m/s. Using differentiation the velocity is 7 m/s.

**3. (a)** 70 m;   **(b)** 25 m/s;   **(c)** 24 m/s

**5. (a)** 8 m;   **(b)** 6.1208 m/s;   **(c)** 6 m/s

**7. (a)** 2 m;   **(b)** 10.261 m/s;   **(c)** 9 m/s

**9.** $\dfrac{dy}{dx} = \dfrac{25}{2}x^{3/2}$; $337.50$      **11.** $0.27$

**13.** $dc/dq = 10$; $10$

**15.** $dc/dq = 0.2q + 3$; $4$

**17.** $dc/dq = 2q + 50$; $80, 82, 84$

**19.** $dc/dq = 0.02q + 5$; $6, 7$

**21.** $dc/dq = 0.00006q^2 - 0.02q + 6$; $4.6, 11$

**23.** $dr/dq = 0.8$; $0.8, 0.8, 0.8$

**25.** $dr/dq = 250 + 90q - 3q^2$; $625, 850, 625$

**27.** $dc/dq = 6.750 - 0.000656q$; 5.438;

$\bar{c} = \dfrac{-10,484.69}{q} + 6.750 - 0.000328q$; 0.851655

**29.** $P = 5,000,000R^{-0.93}$; $dP/dR = -4,650,000R^{-1.93}$

**31.** **(a)** $-7.5$; **(b)** $4.5$

**33.** **(a)** 1; **(b)** $\dfrac{1}{x+4}$; **(c)** 1; **(d)** $\dfrac{1}{9} \approx 0.111$; **(e)** 11.1%

**35.** **(a)** $6x$; **(b)** $\dfrac{6x}{3x^2+7}$; **(c)** 12; **(d)** $\dfrac{12}{19} \approx 0.632$; **(e)** 63.2%

**37.** **(a)** $-3x^2$; **(b)** $-\dfrac{3x^2}{8-x^3}$; **(c)** $-3$; **(d)** $-\dfrac{3}{7} \approx -0.429$; **(e)** $-42.9\%$

**39.** 9.5; 12.8%

**41.** **(a)** $dr/dq = 30 - 0.6q$; **(b)** $\dfrac{4}{45} \approx 0.089$; **(c)** 9%

**43.** $\dfrac{0.432}{t}$      **45.** $3125      **47.** $5.07/unit

## PRINCIPLES IN PRACTICE 11.4

**1.** $\dfrac{dR}{dx} = 6.25 - 6x$

**2.** $T'(x) = 2x - x^2$; $T'(1) = 1$

## PROBLEMS 11.4 (page 513)

**1.** $(4x+1)(6) + (6x+3)(4) = 48x + 18 = 6(8x+3)$

**3.** $(5-3t)(3t^2-4t) + (t^3-2t^2)(-3) = -12t^3 + 33t^2 - 20t$

**5.** $(3r^2-4)(2r-5) + (r^2-5r+1)(6r) = 12r^3 - 45r^2 - 2r + 20$

**7.** $8x^3 - 10x$

**9.** $(x^2+3x-2)(4x-1) + (2x^2-x-3)(2x+3)$
$= 8x^3 + 15x^2 - 20x - 7$

**11.** $(w^2+3w-7)(6w^2) + (2w^3-4)(2w+3)$
$= 10w^4 + 24w^3 - 42w^2 - 8w - 12$

**13.** $(x^2-1)(9x^2-6) + (3x^3-6x+5)(2x) - 4(8x+2)$
$= 15x^4 - 27x^2 - 22x - 2$

**15.** $\dfrac{3}{2}\left[\left(5p^{\frac{1}{2}}-2\right)(3) + (3p-1)\left(5 \cdot \dfrac{1}{2}p^{-\frac{1}{2}}\right)\right]$
$= \dfrac{3}{4}\left(45p^{\frac{1}{2}} - 12 - 5p^{-\frac{1}{2}}\right)$

**17.** 0                **19.** $18x^2 + 94x + 31$

**21.** $\dfrac{(x-1)(5) - (5x)(1)}{(x-1)^2} = -\dfrac{5}{(x-1)^2}$

**23.** $\dfrac{65}{3x^6}$      **25.** $\dfrac{(x-1)(1) - (x+2)(1)}{(x-1)^2} = -\dfrac{3}{(x-1)^2}$

**27.** $\dfrac{(z^2-4)(-2) - (6-2z)(2z)}{(z^2-4)^2} = \dfrac{2(z^2-6z+4)}{(z^2-4)^2}$

**29.** $\dfrac{(x^2-5x)(16x-2) - (8x^2-2x+1)(2x-5)}{(x^2-5x)^2}$
$= \dfrac{-38x^2 - 2x + 5}{(x^2-5x)^2}$

**31.** $\dfrac{(2x^2-3x+2)(2x-4) - (x^2-4x+3)(4x-3)}{(2x^2-3x+2)^2}$
$= \dfrac{5x^2 - 8x + 1}{(2x^2-3x+2)^2}$

**33.** $-\dfrac{100x^{99}}{(x^{100}+7)^2}$      **35.** $2v + \dfrac{8}{v^2}$

**37.** $\dfrac{15x^2 - 2x + 1}{3x^{4/3}}$      **39.** $\dfrac{4}{(x-8)^2} + \dfrac{2}{(3x+1)^2}$

**41.** $\dfrac{[(x+2)(x-4)](1) - (x-5)(2x-2)}{[(x+2)(x-4)]^2} = \dfrac{-(x^2-10x+18)}{[(x+2)(x-4)]^2}$

**43.** $\dfrac{[(t^2-1)(t^3+7)](2t+3) - (t^2+3t)(5t^4-3t^2+14t)}{[(t^2-1)(t^3+7)]^2}$
$= \dfrac{-3t^6 - 12t^5 + t^4 + 6t^3 - 21t^2 - 14t - 21}{[(t^2-1)(t^3+7)]^2}$

**45.** $3 - \dfrac{2x^3 + 3x^2 - 12x + 4}{[x(x-1)(x-2)]^2}$      **47.** $\dfrac{2a}{(a-x)^2}$

**49.** $-6$

**51.** $y = -\dfrac{3}{2}x + \dfrac{15}{2}$

**53.** $y = 16x + 24$      **55.** 1.5

**57.** 1 m, $-1.5$ m/s      **59.** $\dfrac{dr}{dq} = 50 - 0.02q$

**61.** $\dfrac{dr}{dq} = \dfrac{216}{(q+2)^2} - 3$      **63.** $\dfrac{dC}{dI} = 0.672$

**65.** $\dfrac{7}{6}$; $-\dfrac{1}{6}$      **67.** 0.615; 0.385

**69.** **(a)** 0.32; **(b)** 0.026      **71.** $\dfrac{dc}{dq} = \dfrac{6q(q+4)}{(q+2)^2}$

**73.** $\dfrac{9}{10}$      **75.** $\dfrac{0.7355}{(1+0.02744x)^2}$      **77.** $-\dfrac{1}{120}$

## PRINCIPLES IN PRACTICE 11.5

**1.** $288t$

## PROBLEMS 11.5 (page 521)

**1.** $(2u-2)(2x-1) = 4x^3 - 6x^2 - 2x + 2$

**3.** $\left(-\dfrac{2}{w^3}\right)(-1) = \dfrac{2}{(2-x)^3}$

**5.** 0                **7.** 0                **9.** $18(3x+2)^5$

**11.** $30x^2(3+2x^3)^4$

**13.** $200(3x^2-16x+1)(x^3-8x^2+x)^{99}$

**15.** $-6x(x^2-2)^{-4}$

**17.** $-\dfrac{10}{7}(2x+5)(x^2+5x-2)^{-12/7}$

**19.** $\dfrac{1}{2}(10x-1)(5x^2-x)^{-1/2}$

**21.** $\dfrac{1}{2}(2x-1)^{-3/4}$      **23.** $\dfrac{12}{5}x^2(x^3+1)^{-3/5}$

**25.** $-6(4x-1)(2x^2-x+1)^{-2}$  **27.** $-2(2x-3)(x^2-3x)^{-3}$

**29.** $-36x(9x^2+1)^{-3/2}$      **31.** $\dfrac{7}{3}(7x)^{-2/3} + \sqrt[3]{7}$

**33.** $(x^2)[5(x-4)^4(1)] + (x-4)^5(2x) = x(x-4)^4(7x-8)$

**35.** $4x^2\left[\dfrac{1}{2}(5x+1)^{-\frac{1}{2}}(5)\right] + (\sqrt{5x+1})(8x)$
$= 10x^2(5x+1)^{-\frac{1}{2}} + 8x\sqrt{5x+1}$

**37.** $(x^2+2x-1)^3(5) + (5x)[3(x^2+2x-1)^2(2x+2)]$
$= 5(x^2+2x-1)^2(7x^2+8x-1)$

**39.** $(8x-1)^3[4(2x+1)^3(2)] + (2x+1)^4[3(8x-1)^2(8)]$
$= 16(8x-1)^2(2x+1)^3(7x+1)$

**41.** $12\left(\dfrac{x-3}{x+2}\right)^{11}\left[\dfrac{(x+2)(1) - (x-3)(1)}{(x+2)^2}\right] = \dfrac{60(x-3)^{11}}{(x+2)^{13}}$

**43.** $\dfrac{1}{2}\left(\dfrac{x-2}{x+3}\right)^{-1/2}\left[\dfrac{(x+3)(1) - (x-2)(1)}{(x+3)^2}\right]$
$= \dfrac{5}{2(x+3)^2}\left(\dfrac{x-2}{x+3}\right)^{-1/2}$

**45.** $\dfrac{(x^2+4)^3(2)-(2x-5)[3(x^2+4)^2(2x)]}{(x^2+4)^6}$

$=\dfrac{-2(5x^2-15x-4)}{(x^2+4)^4}$

**47.** $\dfrac{(3x-1)^3[40(8x-1)^4]-(8x-1)^5[9(3x-1)^2]}{(3x-1)^6}$

$=\dfrac{(8x-1)^4(48x-31)}{(3x-1)^4}$

**49.** $6\{(5x^2+2)[2x^3(x^4+5)^{-1/2}]+(x^4+5)^{1/2}(10x)\}$
$=12x(x^4+5)^{-1/2}(10x^4+2x^2+25)$

**51.** $8+\dfrac{5}{(t+4)^2}-(8t-7)=15-8t+\dfrac{5}{(t+4)^2}$

**53.** $(x^3-5)^5[(2x+1)^3(2)(x+3)(1)+(x+3)^2(3)(2x+1)^2(2)]$
$\dfrac{-(2x+1)^3(x+3)^2[5(x^3-5)^4(3x^2)]}{(x^3-5)^{10}}$

**55.** 0          **57.** 0          **59.** $y=4x-11$

**61.** $y=-\dfrac{1}{6}x+\dfrac{5}{3}$   **63.** 96%       **65.** 130

**67.** $\approx 13.99$

**69.** (a) $-\dfrac{q}{\sqrt{q^2+20}}$; (b) $-\dfrac{q}{100\sqrt{q^2+20}-q^2-20}$;

   (c) $100-\dfrac{q^2}{\sqrt{q^2+20}}-\sqrt{q^2+20}$

**71.** $-481.5$    **73.** $\dfrac{dc}{dq}=\dfrac{5q(q^2+6)}{(q^2+3)^{3/2}}$   **75.** $48\pi(10)^{-19}$

**77.** (a) $-0.001416x^3+0.01356x^2+1.696x-34.9,\ -256.238$
   (b) $-0.016;\ -1.578\%$

**79.** $-4$          **81.** 40          **83.** 86,111.37

## REVIEW PROBLEMS—CHAPTER 11 (page 524)

**1.** $-2x$          **3.** $\dfrac{\sqrt{3}}{2\sqrt{x}}$          **5.** 0

**7.** $28x^3-18x^2+10x=2x(14x^2-9x+5)$

**9.** $4s^3+4s=4s(s^2+1)$          **11.** $\dfrac{2x}{5}$

**13.** $(x^3+7x^2)(3x^2-2x)+(x^3-x^2+5)(3x^2+14x)$
$=6x^5+30x^4-28x^3+15x^2+70x$

**15.** $100(2x^2+4x)^{99}(4x+4)=400(x+1)(2x^2+4x)^{99}$

**17.** $-\dfrac{6}{(2x+1)^2}$

**19.** $(8+2x)(4)(x^2+1)^3(2x)+(x^2+1)^4(2)$
$=2(x^2+1)^3(9x^2+32x+1)$

**21.** $\dfrac{(z^2+4)(2z)-(z^2-1)(2z)}{(z^2+4)^2}=\dfrac{10z}{(z^2+4)^2}$

**23.** $\dfrac{4}{3}(4x-1)^{-2/3}$

**25.** $-\dfrac{1}{2}(1-x^2)^{-3/2}(-2x)=x(1-x^2)^{-3/2}$

**27.** $(x-6)^4[3(x+5)^2]+(x+5)^3[4(x-6)^3]=$
$(x-6)^3(x+5)^2(7x+2)$

**29.** $\dfrac{(x+6)(5)-(5x-4)(1)}{(x+6)^2}=\dfrac{34}{(x+6)^2}$

**31.** $2\left(-\dfrac{3}{8}\right)x^{-11/8}+\left(-\dfrac{3}{8}\right)(2x)^{-11/8}(2)$
$=-\dfrac{3}{4}(1+2^{-11/8})x^{-11/8}$

**33.** $\dfrac{\sqrt{x^2+5}(2x)-(x^2+6)(1/2)(x^2+5)^{-1/2}(2x)}{x^2+5}=\dfrac{x(x^2+4)}{(x^2+5)^{3/2}}$

**35.** $\left(\dfrac{3}{5}\right)(x^3+6x^2+9)^{-2/5}(3x^2+12x)$

$=\dfrac{9}{5}x(x+4)(x^3+6x^2+9)^{-2/5}$

**37.** $-3z^2+4z-1$          **39.** $y=-4x+3$

**41.** $y=\dfrac{1}{12}x+\dfrac{4}{3}$          **43.** $\dfrac{5}{7}\approx 0.714;\ 71.4\%$

**45.** $dr/dq=20-0.2q$       **47.** $0.569,\ 0.431$

**49.** $dr/dq=500-0.2q$

**51.** $dc/dq=0.125+0.00878q;\ 0.7396$

**53.** 84 eggs/mm          **55.** (a) $\dfrac{4}{3}$; (b) $\dfrac{1}{24}$

**57.** $8\pi$ ft$^3$/ft          **59.** $4q-\dfrac{10{,}000}{q^2}$

**61.** (a) $-315.456$; (b) $-0.00025$; (c) no, since $dr/dm<0$ when
   $m=240$

**63.** 0.305          **65.** $-0.32$

## MATHEMATICAL SNAPSHOT—CHAPTER 11 (page 526)

**1.** The slope is greater—above 0.9. More is spent; less is saved.
**3.** Spend \$705, save \$295      **5.** Answers may vary.

## PRINCIPLES IN PRACTICE 12.1

**1.** $\dfrac{dq}{dp}=\dfrac{12p}{3p^2+4}$          **2.** $\dfrac{dR}{dI}=\dfrac{1}{I\ln 10}$

## PROBLEMS 12.1 (page 533)

**1.** $\dfrac{4}{x}$     **3.** $\dfrac{3}{3x-7}$     **5.** $\dfrac{2}{x}$     **7.** $-\dfrac{2x}{1-x^2}$

**9.** $\dfrac{24X^5+6X^2}{4X^6+2X^3}=\dfrac{3(4X^3+1)}{X(2X^3+1)}$

**11.** $t\left(\dfrac{1}{t}\right)+(\ln t)(1)=1+\ln t$

**13.** $\dfrac{2x^3}{2x+5}+3x^2\ln(2x+5)$     **15.** $\dfrac{8}{(\ln 3)(8x-1)}$

**17.** $2x\left[1+\dfrac{1}{(\ln 2)(x^2+4)}\right]$

**19.** $\dfrac{z\left(\frac{1}{z}\right)-(\ln z)(1)}{z^2}=\dfrac{1-\ln z}{z^2}$

**21.** $\dfrac{(\ln x)^2(2x)-(x^2+3)2(\ln x)\frac{1}{x}}{(\ln x)^4}=\dfrac{2x^2\ln x-2(x^2+3)}{x(\ln x)^3}$

**23.** $\dfrac{3(2x+4)}{x^2+4x+5}=\dfrac{6(x+2)}{x^2+4x+5}$

**25.** $\dfrac{9x}{1+x^2}$     **27.** $\dfrac{2}{1-l^2}$     **29.** $\dfrac{x}{1-x^4}$

**31.** $\dfrac{4x}{x^2+2}+\dfrac{3x^2+1}{x^3+x-1}$

**33.** $\dfrac{26}{x}+\dfrac{65}{3(5x+2)}$     **35.** $\dfrac{2(x^2+1)}{2x+1}+2x\ln(2x+1)$

**37.** $\dfrac{3(1+\ln^2 x)}{x}$          **39.** $\dfrac{4\ln^3(ax)}{x}$

**41.** $\dfrac{x}{2(x-1)}+\ln\sqrt{x-1}$     **43.** $\dfrac{3}{2x\sqrt{4+3\ln x}}$

**45.** $y=5x-20$     **47.** $\dfrac{\ln(3)-1}{\ln^2 3}$     **49.** $\dfrac{25}{7}$

**51.** $\dfrac{dq}{dp} = \dfrac{20}{2p+1}$

**53.** $\dfrac{6a}{(T-a^2+aT)(a-T)}$

**57.** $-1.65, 1.65$

## PRINCIPLES IN PRACTICE 12.2

**1.** $\dfrac{dT}{dt} = Cke^{kt}$

## PROBLEMS 12.2 (page 537)

**1.** $5e^x$  **3.** $4xe^{2x^2+3}$  **5.** $-5e^{9-5x}$

**7.** $(6r+4)e^{3r^2+4r+4} = 2(3r+2)e^{3r^2+4r+4}$

**9.** $x(e^x) + e^x(1) = e^x(x+1)$  **11.** $2xe^{-x^2}(1-x^2)$

**13.** $\dfrac{e^x - e^{-x}}{3}$  **15.** $(6x^2)5^{2x^3}\ln 5$  **17.** $\dfrac{2e^{2w}(w-1)}{w^3}$

**19.** $\dfrac{e^{1+\sqrt{x}}}{2\sqrt{x}}$  **21.** $5x^4 - 5^x\ln 5$  **23.** $\dfrac{2e^x}{(e^x+1)^2}$

**25.** $1$  **27.** $2xe^{x^2\ln x}(1+\ln x^2)$  **29.** $-e$

**31.** $y - e^{-2} = e^{-2}(x+2)$ or $y = e^{-2}x + 3e^{-2}$

**33.** $dp/dq = -0.015e^{-0.001q}, -0.015e^{-0.5}$

**35.** $dc/dq = 10e^{q/700}; 10e^{0.5}; 10e$  **37.** $-5$

**39.** $e$  **41.** $100e^{-2}$  **47.** $-b(10^{A-bM})\ln 10$

**51.** $0.0036$  **53.** $-0.89, 0.56$

## PROBLEMS 12.3 (page 543)

**1.** $-3$, elastic  **3.** $-1$, unit elasticity

**5.** $-\dfrac{53}{52}$, elastic  **7.** $-\left(\dfrac{150}{e}-1\right)$, elastic

**9.** $-1$, unit elasticity  **11.** $-2$, elastic

**13.** $-\dfrac{1}{2}$, inelastic

**15.** $|\eta| = \dfrac{10}{3}$ when $p=10$, $|\eta| = \dfrac{3}{10}$ when $p=3$, $|\eta|=1$ when $p=6.50$

**17.** $-1.2, 0.6\%$ decrease  **23.** (c) $b=0$

**25.** (a) $\eta = -\dfrac{207}{15} = -13.8$, elastic; (b) $27.6\%$; (c) increase, since demand is elastic

**27.** $\eta = -1.6$; $\dfrac{dr}{dq} = 30$

**29.** Maximum at $q=5$; minimum at $q=95$

## PRINCIPLES IN PRACTICE 12.4

**1.** $\dfrac{dP}{dt} = 0.5(P-P^2)$

**2.** $\dfrac{dV}{dt} = 4\pi r^2\dfrac{dr}{dt}$ and $\dfrac{dV}{dt}\Big|_{r=12} = 2880\pi$ in$^3$/minute

**3.** The top of the ladder is sliding down at a rate of $\dfrac{9}{4}$ feet/second.

## PROBLEMS 12.4 (page 548)

**1.** $-\dfrac{x}{4y}$  **3.** $\dfrac{7}{3y^2}$  **5.** $-\dfrac{\sqrt[3]{y^2}}{\sqrt[3]{x^2}}$  **7.** $-\dfrac{y^{1/4}}{x^{1/4}}$

**9.** $-\dfrac{y}{x}$  **11.** $\dfrac{11-y}{x-1}$  **13.** $\dfrac{4y-2x^2}{y^2-4x}$

**15.** $\dfrac{4y^{3/4}}{2y^{1/4}+1}$  **17.** $\dfrac{1-15x^2y^4}{20x^5y^3+2y}$  **19.** $\dfrac{xe^y-y}{x(\ln x - xe^y)}$

**21.** $-\dfrac{e^y}{xe^y+1}$  **23.** $6e^{3x}(1+e^{3x})(x+y)-1$

**25.** $-\dfrac{3}{5}$  **27.** $0; -\dfrac{4x_0}{9y_0}$  **29.** $y=-4x-3$

**31.** $\dfrac{dq}{dp} = -\dfrac{1}{2q}$  **33.** $\dfrac{dq}{dp} = -\dfrac{(q+5)^3}{40}$

**35.** $-\lambda I$  **37.** $-\dfrac{f}{\lambda}$  **39.** $\dfrac{3}{8}$

## PROBLEMS 12.5 (page 552)

**1.** $(x+1)^2(x-2)(x^2+3)\left[\dfrac{2}{x+1}+\dfrac{1}{x-2}+\dfrac{2x}{x^2+3}\right]$

**3.** $(3x^3-1)^2(2x+5)^3\left[\dfrac{18x^2}{3x^3-1}+\dfrac{6}{2x+5}\right]$

**5.** $\dfrac{\sqrt{x+1}\sqrt{x^2-2}\sqrt{x+4}}{2}\left[\dfrac{1}{x+1}+\dfrac{2x}{x^2-2}+\dfrac{1}{x+4}\right]$

**7.** $\dfrac{\sqrt{1-x^2}}{1-2x}\left[\dfrac{x}{x^2-1}+\dfrac{2}{1-2x}\right]$

**9.** $\dfrac{(2x^2+2)^2}{(x+1)^2(3x+2)}\left[\dfrac{4x}{x^2+1}-\dfrac{2}{x+1}-\dfrac{3}{3x+2}\right]$

**11.** $\dfrac{1}{2}\sqrt{\dfrac{(x+3)(x-2)}{2x-1}}\left[\dfrac{1}{x+3}+\dfrac{1}{x-2}-\dfrac{2}{2x-1}\right]$

**13.** $x^{x^2+1}\left(\dfrac{x^2+1}{x}+2x\ln x\right)$  **15.** $\dfrac{x^{1/x}(1-\ln x)}{x^2}$

**17.** $2(3x+1)^{2x}\left[\dfrac{3x}{3x+1}+\ln(3x+1)\right]$

**19.** $4e^x x^{3x}(4+3\ln x)$  **21.** $12$  **23.** $y=96x+36$

**25.** $y=(4e+2e\ln 2)x - 2e - 2e\ln 2$

**27.** $\dfrac{1}{3e^{1.3}}$  **29.** $0.1\%$ decrease

## PRINCIPLES IN PRACTICE 12.6

**1.** 43 and 1958

## PROBLEMS 12.6 (page 556)

**1.** $0.25410$  **3.** $1.32472$  **5.** $-0.68233$  **7.** $0.33767$

**9.** $1.90785$  **11.** $4.141$  **13.** $-4.99$ and $1.94$

**15.** $13.33$  **17.** $2.880$  **19.** $3.45$

## PRINCIPLES IN PRACTICE 12.7

**1.** $\dfrac{d^2h}{dt^2} = -32$ feet/sec$^2$ (*Note:* Negative values indicate the downward direction.)

**2.** $c''(3) = 14$ dollars/unit$^2$

## PROBLEMS 12.7 (page 560)

**1.** $24$  **3.** $0$  **5.** $e^x$  **7.** $3+2\ln x$

**9.** $-\dfrac{60}{q^7}$  **11.** $-\dfrac{1}{4(9-r)^{3/2}}$  **13.** $\dfrac{8}{(2x+3)^3}$

**15.** $\dfrac{4}{(x-1)^3}$  **17.** $-\left[\dfrac{1}{x^2}+\dfrac{1}{(x+6)^2}\right]$

**19.** $e^z(z^2+4z+2)$  **21.** $275$  **23.** $-\dfrac{1}{y^3}$

**25.** $-\dfrac{4}{y^3}$  **27.** $\dfrac{1}{8x^{3/2}}$  **29.** $\dfrac{2(y-1)}{(1+x)^2}$

**31.** $\dfrac{y}{(1-y)^3}$  **33.** $\dfrac{25}{32}$  **35.** $300(5x-3)^2$

**37.** $0.6$  **39.** $\pm 1$  **41.** $-4.99$ and $1.94$

# REVIEW PROBLEMS—CHAPTER 12 (page 561)

**1.** $3e^x + 0 + e^{x^2}(2x) + (e^2)x^{e^2-1} = 3e^x + 2xe^{x^2} + e^2x^{e^2-1}$

**3.** $\dfrac{1}{3r^2 + 7r + 1}(6r + 7) = \dfrac{6r + 7}{3r^2 + 7r + 1}$

**5.** $e^{x^2+4x+5}(2x + 4) = 2(x + 2)e^{x^2+4x+5}$

**7.** $e^x(2x) + (x^2 + 2)e^x = e^x(x^2 + 2x + 2)$

**9.** $\dfrac{\sqrt{(x-6)(x+5)(9-x)}}{2}\left[\dfrac{1}{x-6} + \dfrac{1}{x+5} + \dfrac{1}{x-9}\right]$

**11.** $\dfrac{e^x\left(\dfrac{1}{x}\right) - (\ln x)(e^x)}{e^{2x}} = \dfrac{1 - x\ln x}{xe^x}$

**13.** $\dfrac{2}{q+1} + \dfrac{3}{q+2}$

**15.** $(4x + 2)(\ln 2)2^{2x^2+2x-5}$

**17.** $\dfrac{4e^{2x+1}(2x - 1)}{x^2}$

**19.** $\dfrac{16}{(8x + 5)\ln 2}$

**21.** $\dfrac{1 + 2l + 3l^2}{1 + l + l^2 + l^3}$

**23.** $(x + 1)^{x+1}[1 + \ln(x + 1)]$

**25.** $\dfrac{1}{t} + \dfrac{1}{2} \cdot \dfrac{1}{4 - t^2} \cdot (-2t) = \dfrac{1}{t} - \dfrac{t}{4 - t^2}$

**27.** $y\left[\dfrac{1}{2}\left(\dfrac{1}{x^2 + 1}\right)(2x) + \dfrac{1}{3}\left(\dfrac{1}{x^2 + 2}\right)(2x)\right.$

$\left. - \dfrac{2}{5}\left(\dfrac{1}{2x^3 + 6x}\right)(6x^2 + 6)\right]$

$= y\left[\dfrac{x}{x^2 + 1} + \dfrac{2x}{3(x^2 + 2)} - \dfrac{6(x^2 + 1)}{5(x^3 + 3x)}\right]$,

where $y$ is as given in the problem

**29.** $(x^x)^x(x + 2x \ln x)$    **31.** $4$      **33.** $-2$

**35.** $y = 6x + 6(1 - \ln 2)$ or $y = 6x + 6 - \ln 64$

**37.** $(0, 4\ln 2)$    **39.** $2$    **41.** $2$    **43.** $-\dfrac{y}{x + y}$

**45.** $\dfrac{xy^2 - y}{2x - x^2y}$   **47.** $\dfrac{4}{9}$    **49.** $\dfrac{dy}{dx} = \dfrac{y+1}{y}$; $\dfrac{d^2y}{dx^2} = -\dfrac{y+1}{y^3}$

**51.** $f'(t) = 0.008e^{-0.01t} + 0.00004e^{-0.0002t}$

**53.** $1.13$      **55.** $\eta = -1$, unit elasticity

**57.** $\eta = -0.5$, demand is inelastic

**59.** $-\dfrac{9}{16}, \approx \dfrac{3}{8}\%$ increase    **61.** $1.7693$

# MATHEMATICAL SNAPSHOT—CHAPTER 12 (page 566)

**1.** 305 units

**3.** Answers may vary.

# PRINCIPLES IN PRACTICE 13.1

**1.** There is a relative maximum when $q = 2$, and a relative minimum when $q = 5$.

**2.** The drug is at its greatest concentration 2 hours after injection.

# PROBLEMS 13.1 (page 576)

**1.** Dec. on $(-\infty, -1)$ and $(3, \infty)$; inc. on $(-1, 3)$; rel. min. $(-1, -1)$; rel. max. $(3, 4)$

**3.** Dec. on $(-\infty, -2)$ and $(0, 2)$; inc. on $(-2, 0)$ and $(2, \infty)$; rel. min. $(-2, 1)$ and $(2, 1)$; no rel. max

**5.** Inc. on $(-3, 1)$ and $(2, \infty)$; dec. on $(-\infty, -3)$ and $(1, 2)$; rel. max. when $x = 1$; rel. min. when $x = -3, 2$

**7.** Dec. on $(-\infty, -1)$; inc. on $(-1, 3)$ and $(3, \infty)$; rel. min. when $x = -1$

**9.** Inc. on $(-\infty, 0)$ and $(0, \infty)$; no rel. min. or max

**11.** Inc. on $\left(-\infty, \dfrac{1}{2}\right)$; dec. on $\left(\dfrac{1}{2}, \infty\right)$; rel. max. when $x = \dfrac{1}{2}$

**13.** Dec. on $(-\infty, -5)$ and $(1, \infty)$; inc. on $(-5, 1)$; rel. min. when $x = -5$; rel. max. when $x = 1$

**15.** Dec. on $(-\infty, -1)$ and $(0, 1)$; inc. on $(-1, 0)$ and $(1, \infty)$; rel. max. when $x = 0$; rel. min. when $x = \pm 1$

**17.** Inc. on $\left(-\infty, \dfrac{1}{3}\right)$ and $(2, \infty)$; dec. on $\left(\dfrac{1}{3}, 2\right)$; rel. max. when $x = \dfrac{1}{3}$; rel. min. when $x = 2$

**19.** Inc. on $\left(-\infty, -\dfrac{2}{3}\right)$ and $\left(\dfrac{5}{2}, \infty\right)$; dec. on $\left(-\dfrac{2}{3}, \dfrac{5}{2}\right)$; rel. max. when $x = -\dfrac{2}{3}$; rel. min. when $x = \dfrac{5}{2}$

**21.** Inc. on $(-\infty, 5 - \sqrt{3})$ and $(5 + \sqrt{3}, \infty)$; dec. on $(5 - \sqrt{3}, 5 + \sqrt{3})$; rel. max. when $x = 5 - \sqrt{3}$; rel. min. when $x = 5 + \sqrt{3}$

**23.** Inc. on $(-\infty, -1)$ and $(1, \infty)$; dec. on $(-1, 0)$ and $(0, 1)$; rel. max. when $x = -1$; rel. min. when $x = 1$

**25.** Dec. on $(-\infty, -4)$ and $(0, \infty)$; inc. on $(-4, 0)$; rel. min. when $x = -4$; rel. max. when $x = 0$

**27.** Inc. on $(-\infty, -\sqrt{2})$ and $(0, \sqrt{2})$; dec. on $(-\sqrt{2}, 0)$ and $(\sqrt{2}, \infty)$; rel. max. when $x = \pm\sqrt{2}$; rel. min. when $x = 0$

**29.** Inc. on $(-1, 0)$ and $(1, \infty)$; dec. on $(-\infty, -1)$ and $(0, 1)$; rel. max. when $x = 0$; rel. min. when $x = \pm 1$

**31.** Dec. on $(-\infty, 1)$ and $(1, \infty)$; no rel. extremum

**33.** Dec. on $(0, \infty)$; no rel. extremum

**35.** Dec. on $(-\infty, 0)$ and $(4, \infty)$; inc. on $(0, 2)$ and $(2, 4)$; rel. min. when $x = 0$; rel. max. when $x = 4$

**37.** Inc. on $(-\infty, -3)$ and $(-1, \infty)$; dec. on $(-3, -2)$ and $(-2, -1)$; rel. max. when $x = -3$; rel. min. when $x = -1$

**39.** Dec. on $\left(-\infty, \dfrac{-2 - \sqrt{29}}{5}\right)$ and $\left(\dfrac{-2 + \sqrt{29}}{5}, \infty\right)$; inc. on $\left(\dfrac{-2 - \sqrt{29}}{5}, \dfrac{-2 + \sqrt{29}}{5}\right)$; rel. min. when $x = \dfrac{-2 - \sqrt{29}}{5}$; rel. max. when $x = \dfrac{-2 + \sqrt{29}}{5}$

**41.** Inc. on $(1, \infty)$; dec. on $(-\infty, 1)$; rel. min. when $x = 1$

**43.** Inc. on $(-\infty, 0)$, $\left(0, \dfrac{18}{7}\right)$, and $(6, \infty)$; dec. on $\left(\dfrac{18}{7}, 6\right)$; rel. max. when $x = \dfrac{18}{7}$; rel. min. when $x = 6$

**45.** Dec. on $(-\infty, \infty)$; no rel. extremum.

**47.** Dec. on $\left(0, \dfrac{3\sqrt{2}}{2}\right)$; inc. on $\left(\dfrac{3\sqrt{2}}{2}, \infty\right)$; rel. min. when $x = \dfrac{3\sqrt{2}}{2}$

**49.** Dec. on $(-\infty, 0)$; inc. on $(0, \infty)$; rel. min. when $x = 0$

**51.** Dec. on $(0, 1)$; inc. on $(1, \infty)$; rel. min. when $x = 1$

**53.** Dec. on $\left(-\infty, \dfrac{3}{2}\right)$; inc. on $\left(\dfrac{3}{2}, \infty\right)$; rel. min. when $x = \dfrac{3}{2}$; intercepts: $(-2, 0)$, $(5, 0)$, $(0, -10)$

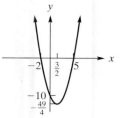

**55.** Dec. on $(-\infty, -1)$ and $(1, \infty)$; inc. on $(-1, 1)$; rel. min. when $x = -1$; rel. max. when $x = 1$; sym. about origin; intercepts: $(\pm\sqrt{3}, 0)$. $(0, 0)$

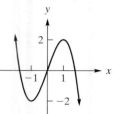

**57.** Inc. on $(-\infty, 1)$ and $(2, \infty)$; dec. on $(1, 2)$; rel. max. when $x = 1$; rel. min. when $x = 2$; intercept: $(0, 0)$

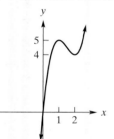

**59.** Inc. on $(-2, -1)$ and $(0, \infty)$; dec. on $(-\infty, -2)$ and $(-1, 0)$; rel. max. when $x = -1$; rel. min. when $x = -2, 0$; intercepts: $(0, 0)$, $(-2, 0)$

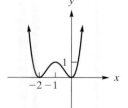

**61.** Dec. on $(-\infty, -2)$ and $\left(-\dfrac{1}{2}, 1\right)$; inc. on $\left(-2, -\dfrac{1}{2}\right)$ and $(1, \infty)$; rel. min. when $x = -2, 1$; rel. max. when $x = -\dfrac{1}{2}$; intercepts: $(1, 0)$, $(-2, 0)$, $(0, 4)$

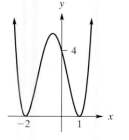

**63.** Dec. on $(1, \infty)$; inc. on $(0, 1)$; rel. max. when $x = 1$; intercepts: $(0, 0)$, $(4, 0)$

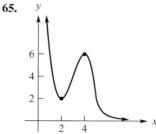

**65.**

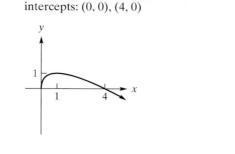

**69.** Never

**71.** 40

**75.** **(a)** 25,300; **(b)** 4; **(c)** 17,200

**77.** Rel. min.: $(-3.83, 0.69)$

**79.** Rel. max.: $(2.74, 3.74)$; rel. min.: $(-2.74, -3.74)$

**81.** Rel. min.: $0, 1.50, 2.00$; rel. max.: $0.57, 1.77$

**83.** **(a)** $f'(x) = 4 - 6x - 3x^2$; **(c)** Dec.: $(-\infty, -2.53)$, $(0.53, \infty)$; inc.: $(-2.53, 0.53)$

## PROBLEMS 13.2 (page 580)

**1.** Maximum: $f(3) = 6$; minimum: $f(1) = 2$

**3.** Maximum: $f(-1) = \dfrac{19}{6}$; minimum: $f(0) = 1$

**5.** Maximum: $f(3) = 84$; minimum: $f(1) = -8$

**7.** Maximum: $f(-2) = 56$; minimum: $f(-1) = -2$

**9.** Maximum: $f(\sqrt{2}) = 4$; minimum: $f(2) = -16$

**11.** Maximum: $f(0) = f(3) = 2$; minimum: $f\left(\dfrac{3\sqrt{2}}{2}\right) = -\dfrac{73}{4}$

**13.** Maximum: $f(-26) = f(28) = 9$; minimum: $f(1) = 0$

**15.** **(a)** $-3.22, -0.78$; **(b)** 2.75; **(c)** 9; **(d)** 14,283

## PROBLEMS 13.3 (page 586)

**1.** Conc. up $\left(-\infty, -\dfrac{3}{4}\right)$, $(0, \infty)$; conc. down $\left(-\dfrac{3}{4}, 0\right)$; inf. pt. when $x = -\dfrac{3}{4}, 0$

**3.** Conc. up $(-\infty, 1)$, $(1, 7)$; conc. down $(7, \infty)$; inf. pt. when $x = 7$

**5.** Conc. up $(-\infty, -\sqrt{2})$, $(\sqrt{2}, \infty)$; conc. down $(-\sqrt{2}, \sqrt{2})$; no inf. pt.

**7.** Conc. down $(-\infty, \infty)$

**9.** Conc. down $(-\infty, -1)$; conc. up $(-1, \infty)$; inf. pt. when $x = -1$

**11.** Conc. down $\left(-\infty, \frac{5}{6}\right)$; conc. up $\left(\frac{5}{6}, \infty\right)$; inf. pt. when

$x = \dfrac{5}{6}$

**13.** Conc. up $(-\infty, -2), (2, \infty)$; conc. down $(-2, 2)$; inf. pt. when $x = \pm 2$

**15.** Conc. up $(-\infty, 0)$; conc. down $(0, \infty)$; inf. pt. when $x = 0$

**17.** Conc. up $\left(-\infty, -\frac{7}{2}\right), \left(\frac{1}{3}, \infty\right)$; conc. down $\left(-\frac{7}{2}, \frac{1}{3}\right)$;

inf. pt. when $x = -\dfrac{7}{2}, \dfrac{1}{3}$

**19.** Conc. down $(-\infty, 0), \left(\dfrac{3 - \sqrt{5}}{2}, \dfrac{3 + \sqrt{5}}{2}\right)$;

conc. up $\left(0, \dfrac{3 - \sqrt{5}}{2}\right), \left(\dfrac{3 + \sqrt{5}}{2}, \infty\right)$; inf. pt. when $x = 0$,

$\dfrac{3 \pm \sqrt{5}}{2}$

**21.** Conc. up $(-\infty, -\sqrt{5}), (-\sqrt{2}, \sqrt{2}), (\sqrt{5}, \infty)$; conc. down $(-\sqrt{5}, -\sqrt{2}), (\sqrt{2}, \sqrt{5})$; inf. pt. when $x = \pm\sqrt{5}, \pm\sqrt{2}$

**23.** Conc. down $(-\infty, 1)$; conc. up $(1, \infty)$

**25.** Conc. down $(-\infty, -1/\sqrt{3}), (1/\sqrt{3}, \infty)$; conc. up $(-1/\sqrt{3}, 1/\sqrt{3})$; inf. pt. when $x = \pm 1/\sqrt{3}$

**27.** Conc. down. $(-\infty, -3), \left(-3, \dfrac{2}{7}\right)$; conc. up $\left(\dfrac{2}{7}, \infty\right)$;

inf. pt. when $x = \dfrac{2}{7}$

**29.** Conc. up $(-\infty, \infty)$

**31.** Conc. down $(-\infty, -2)$; conc. up $(-2, \infty)$; inf. pt. when $x = -2$

**33.** Conc. down $(0, e^{3/2})$; conc. up $(e^{3/2}, \infty)$; inf. pt. when $x = e^{3/2}$

**35.** Int. $(-2, 0), (3, 0), (0, -6)$; dec. $\left(-\infty, \dfrac{1}{2}\right)$; inc. $\left(\dfrac{1}{2}, \infty\right)$;

rel. min. when $x = \dfrac{1}{2}$; conc. up $(-\infty, \infty)$

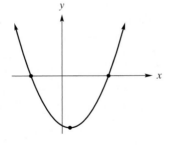

**37.** Int. $(0, 0), \left(\dfrac{5}{2}, 0\right)$; inc. $\left(-\infty, \dfrac{5}{4}\right)$; dec. $\left(\dfrac{5}{4}, \infty\right)$; rel. max.

when $x = \dfrac{5}{4}$; conc. down $(-\infty, \infty)$

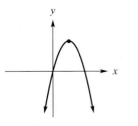

**39.** Int. $(0, -19)$; inc. $(-\infty, 2), (4, \infty)$; dec. $(2, 4)$; rel. max. when $x = 2$; rel. min. when $x = 4$; conc. down $(-\infty, 3)$; conc. up $(3, \infty)$; inf. pt. when $x = 3$

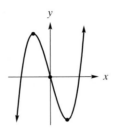

**41.** Int. $(0, 0), (\pm 2\sqrt{3}, 0)$; inc. $(-\infty, -2), (2, \infty)$; dec. $(-2, 2)$; rel. max. when $x = -2$; rel. min. when $x = 2$; conc. down $(-\infty, 0)$; conc. up $(0, \infty)$; inf. pt. when $x = 0$; sym. about origin

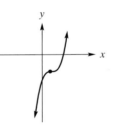

**43.** Int. $(0, -3)$; inc. $(-\infty, 1), (1, \infty)$; no rel. max. or min.; conc. down $(-\infty, 1)$; conc. up $(1, \infty)$; inf. pt. when $x = 1$

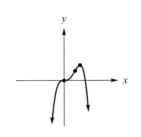

**45.** Int. $(0, 0), (4/3, 0)$; inc. $(-\infty, 0), (0, 1)$; dec. $(1, \infty)$; rel. max. when $x = 1$; conc. up $(0, 2/3)$; conc. down $(-\infty, 0), (2/3, \infty)$; inf. pt. when $x = 0, x = 2/3$

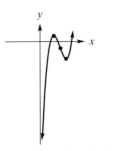

**47.** Int. $(0, -2)$; dec. $(-\infty, -2)$, $(2, \infty)$; inc. $(-2, 2)$; rel. min. when $x = -2$; rel. max. when $x = 2$; conc. up $(-\infty, 0)$; conc. down $(0, \infty)$; inf. pt. when $x = 0$

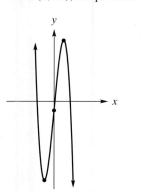

**49.** Int. $(0, -2)$, $(1, 0)$; inc. $(-\infty, 1)$, $(1, \infty)$; conc. down $(-\infty, 1)$; conc. up $(1, \infty)$; inf. pt. when $x = 1$

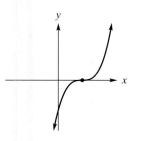

**51.** Int. $(0, 0)$, $(\pm\sqrt[4]{5}, 0)$; dec. $(-\infty, -1)$, $(1, \infty)$; inc. $(-1, 1)$; rel. min. when $x = -1$; rel. max. when $x = 1$; conc. up $(-\infty, 0)$; conc. down $(0, \infty)$; inf. pt. when $x = 0$; sym. about origin.

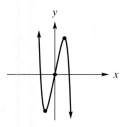

**53.** Int. $(0, 1)$, $(1, 0)$; dec. $(-\infty, 0)$, $(0, 1)$; inc. $(1, \infty)$; rel. min. when $x = 1$; conc. up $(-\infty, 0)$, $(2/3, \infty)$; conc. down $(0, 2/3)$; inf. pt. when $x = 0$, $x = 2/3$

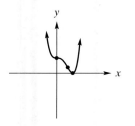

**55.** Int. $(0, 0)$, $(\pm 2, 0)$; inc. $(-\infty, -\sqrt{2})$, $(0, \sqrt{2})$; dec. $(-\sqrt{2}, 0)$, $(\sqrt{2}, \infty)$; rel. max. when $x = \pm\sqrt{2}$; rel. min. when $x = 0$;

conc. down $(-\infty, -\sqrt{2/3})$, $(\sqrt{2/3}, \infty)$; conc. up $(-\sqrt{2/3}, \sqrt{2/3})$; inf. pt. when $x = \pm\sqrt{2/3}$; sym. about $y$-axis

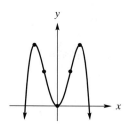

**57.** Int. $(0, 0)$, $(8, 0)$; dec. $(-\infty, 0)$, $(0, 2)$; inc. $(2, \infty)$; rel. min. when $x = 2$; conc. up $(-\infty, -4)$, $(0, \infty)$; conc. down $(-4, 0)$; inf. pt. when $x = -4$, $x = 0$

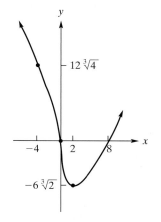

**59.** Int. $(0, 0)$, $(-4, 0)$; dec. $(-\infty, -1)$; inc. $(-1, 0)$, $(0, \infty)$; rel. min. when $x = -1$; conc. up $(-\infty, 0)$, $(2, \infty)$; conc. down $(0, 2)$; inf. pt. when $x = 0$, $x = 2$

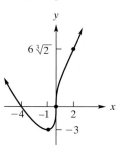

**61.** Int. $(0, 0)$, $(1728, 0)$; inc. $(0, 512)$; dec. $(-\infty, 0)$, $(512, \infty)$; rel. min. when $x = 0$; rel. max. when $x = 512$; conc. down $(-\infty, 0)$, $(0, \infty)$

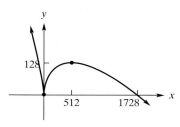

**63.**

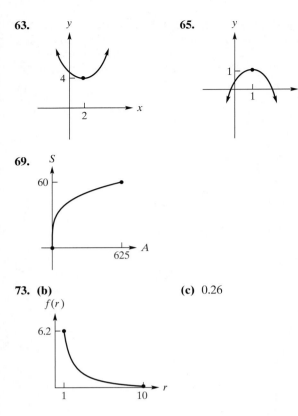

**65.**

**69.**

**73. (b)** **(c)** 0.26

**75.** Two **77.** Above tangent line; concave up

**79.** −2.61, −0.26

## PROBLEMS 13.4 (page 589)

**1.** Rel. min. when $x = \dfrac{5}{2}$; abs. min.

**3.** Rel. max. when $x = \dfrac{1}{4}$; abs. max.

**5.** Rel. max. when $x = -5$; rel. min. when $x = 1$

**7.** Rel. min. when $x = 0$; rel. max. when $x = 2$

**9.** Test fails, when $x = 0$ there is a rel. max. by first-deriv. test

**11.** Rel. max. when $x = -\dfrac{1}{3}$; rel. min. when $x = \dfrac{1}{3}$

**13.** Rel. min. when $x = -5, -2$; rel. max. when $x = -\dfrac{7}{2}$

## PROBLEMS 13.5 (page 598)

**1.** $y = 1, x = 1$ **3.** $y = \dfrac{1}{3}, x = \dfrac{5}{3}$

**5.** $y = 0, x = 0$ **7.** $y = 0, x = 1, x = -1$

**9.** None **11.** $y = 2, x = 2, x = -3$

**13.** $y = 2, x = -\sqrt{5}, x = \sqrt{5}$ **15.** $y = 5, x = 3$

**17.** $y = -x + 1, x = 0, x = -1$ **19.** $y = \dfrac{1}{4}, x = -\dfrac{1}{2}$

**21.** $y = \dfrac{1}{2}, x = -\dfrac{4}{3}$ **23.** $y = 4$

**25.** Dec. $(-\infty, 0), (0, \infty)$; conc. down $(-\infty, 0)$; conc. up $(0, \infty)$; sym. about origin; asymptotes $x = 0, y = 0$

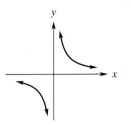

**27.** Int. $(0, 0)$; dec. $(-\infty, 1), (1, \infty)$; conc. up $(1, \infty)$; conc. down $(-\infty, 1)$; asymptotes $x = 1, y = 1$

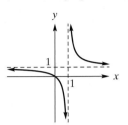

**29.** Dec. $(-\infty, -1), (0, 1)$; inc. $(-1, 0), (1, \infty)$; rel. min. when $x = \pm 1$; conc. up $(-\infty, 0), (0, \infty)$; sym. about $y$-axis; asymptote $x = 0$

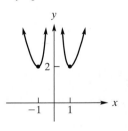

**31.** Int. $(0, -1)$; inc. $(-\infty, -1), (-1, 0)$; dec. $(0, 1), (1, \infty)$; rel. max. when $x = 0$; conc. up $(-\infty, -1), (1, \infty)$; conc. down $(-1, 1)$; asymptotes $x = 1, x = -1, y = 0$; sym. about $y$-axis

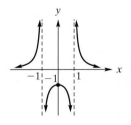

**33.** Int. $(-1, 0), (0, 1)$; inc. $(-\infty, 1), (1, \infty)$; conc. up $(-\infty, 1)$; conc. down $(1, \infty)$; asymptotes $x = 1, y = -1$

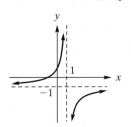

**35.** Int. $(0, 0)$; inc. $\left(-\infty, -\frac{8}{7}\right)$, $(0, \infty)$; dec. $\left(-\frac{8}{7}, -\frac{4}{7}\right)$, $\left(-\frac{4}{7}, 0\right)$; rel. max. when $x = -\frac{8}{7}$; rel. min. when $x = 0$; conc. down $\left(-\infty, -\frac{4}{7}\right)$; conc. up $\left(-\frac{4}{7}, \infty\right)$; asymptotes $x = -\frac{4}{7}$; $y = \frac{1}{7}x - \frac{4}{49}$

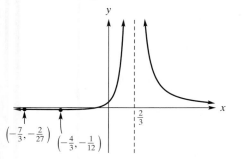

**37.** Int. $\left(0, -\frac{9}{8}\right)$; inc. $\left(-\infty, -\frac{2}{3}\right)$, $\left(-\frac{2}{3}, \frac{1}{3}\right)$; dec. $\left(\frac{1}{3}, \frac{4}{3}\right)$, $\left(\frac{4}{3}, \infty\right)$; rel. max. when $x = \frac{1}{3}$; conc. up $\left(-\infty, -\frac{2}{3}\right)$, $\left(\frac{4}{3}, \infty\right)$; conc. down $\left(-\frac{2}{3}, \frac{4}{3}\right)$; asymptotes $y = 0$, $x = -\frac{2}{3}$, $x = \frac{4}{3}$

**39.** Int. $\left(-\frac{1}{3}, 0\right)$, $\left(0, \frac{1}{4}\right)$; dec. $\left(-\infty, -\frac{4}{3}\right)$, $\left(\frac{2}{3}, \infty\right)$; inc. $\left(-\frac{4}{3}, \frac{2}{3}\right)$; rel. min. when $x = -\frac{4}{3}$; conc. down $\left(-\infty, -\frac{7}{3}\right)$; conc. up $\left(-\frac{7}{3}, \frac{2}{3}\right)$, $\left(\frac{2}{3}, \infty\right)$; inf. pt. when $x = -\frac{7}{3}$ asymptotes $x = \frac{2}{3}$, $y = 0$

**41.** Int. $(-1, 0)$, $(1, 0)$; inc. $(-\sqrt{3}, 0)$, $(0, \sqrt{3})$; dec. $(-\infty, -\sqrt{3})$, $(\sqrt{3}, \infty)$; rel. max. when $x = \sqrt{3}$; rel. min. when $x = -\sqrt{3}$; conc. down $(-\infty, -\sqrt{6})$, $(0, \sqrt{6})$; conc. up $(-\sqrt{6}, 0)$, $(\sqrt{6}, \infty)$; inf. pt. when $x = \pm\sqrt{6}$; asymptotes $x = 0$, $y = 0$; sym. about origin

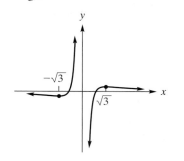

**43.** Int. $(0, 1)$; inc. $(-\infty, -2)$, $(0, \infty)$; dec. $(-2, -1)$, $(-1, 0)$; rel. max. when $x = -2$; rel. min when $x = 0$; conc. down $(-\infty, -1)$; conc. up $(-1, \infty)$; asymptotes $x = -1$; $y = x$

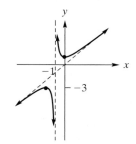

**45.** Int. $(0, 5)$; dec. $\left(-\infty, -\frac{1}{3}\right)$, $\left(-\frac{1}{3}, \frac{1}{3}\right)$; inc. $\left(\frac{1}{3}, 1\right)$, $(1, \infty)$; rel. min. when $x = \frac{1}{3}$; conc. down $\left(-\infty, -\frac{1}{3}\right)$, $(1, \infty)$; conc. up $\left(-\frac{1}{3}, 1\right)$; asymptotes $x = -\frac{1}{3}$, $x = 1$, $y = -1$

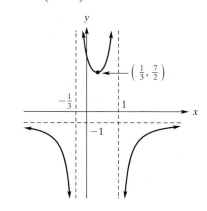

**47.**

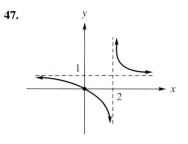

**49.**

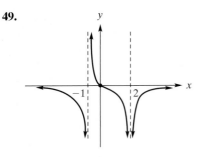

**51.** $x = -\dfrac{a}{b}; y = \dfrac{1}{b}$

**55.** $x \approx \pm 2.45, x \approx 0.67, y = 2$     **57.** $y \approx 0.48$

## PROBLEMS 13.6 (page 607)

**1.** 41 and 41      **3.** 300 ft by 250 ft     **5.** 100 units

**7.** $15     **9. (a)** 110 grams; **(b)** $51\dfrac{9}{11}$ grams

**11.** 500 units; price $= \$60$; profit $= \$11,900$

**13.** $22      **15.** 120 units; $86,000      **17.** 625 units; $4

**19.** $17; $86,700      **21.** 4 ft by 4 ft by 2 ft

**23.** $\dfrac{L}{6}$ in.; $\dfrac{2L^3}{27}$ in.$^3$

**27.** 130 units, $p = \$340$, $P = \$36,980$; 125 units, $p = \$350$, $P = \$34,175$

**29.** 250 per lot (4 lots)      **31.** 35

**33.** 60 mi/h      **35.** 8; $3400

**37.** $5 - \sqrt{3}$ tons; $5 - \sqrt{3}$ tons      **41.** 10 cases; $50.55

## REVIEW PROBLEMS—CHAPTER 13 (page 612)

**1.** $y = 3, x = 4, x = -4$

**3.** $y = \dfrac{5}{9}, x = -\dfrac{2}{3}$

**5.** $x = 0$

**7.** $x = -\dfrac{15}{8}, -1$

**9.** Inc. $(-1, 7)$; dec. on $(-\infty, -1)$ and $(7, \infty)$

**11.** Dec. on $(-\infty, -\sqrt{6}), (0, \sqrt{3}), (\sqrt{3}, \sqrt{6})$; inc. on $(-\sqrt{6}, -\sqrt{3}), (-\sqrt{3}, 0), (\sqrt{6}, \infty)$

**13.** Conc. up on $(-\infty, 0)$ and $\left(\dfrac{1}{2}, \infty\right)$; conc. down on $\left(0, \dfrac{1}{2}\right)$

**15.** Conc. down on $\left(-\infty, \dfrac{1}{2}\right)$; conc. up on $\left(\dfrac{1}{2}, \infty\right)$

**17.** Conc. up on $\left(-\infty, -\dfrac{7}{12}\right), \left(-\dfrac{1}{2}, \infty\right)$; conc. down on $\left(-\dfrac{7}{12}, -\dfrac{1}{2}\right)$

**19.** Rel. max. at $x = 1$; rel. min. at $x = 2$

**21.** Rel. min. at $x = -1$

**23.** Rel. max. at $x = -\dfrac{2}{5}$; rel. min. at $x = 0$

**25.** At $x = 3$

**27.** At $x = 1$

**29.** At $x = 0, 3 \pm \sqrt{3}$

**31.** Maximum: $f(2) = 16$; minimum: $f(1) = -1$

**33.** Maximum: $f(0) = 0$; minimum: $f\left(-\dfrac{6}{5}\right) = -\dfrac{1}{120}$

**35. (a)** $f$ has no relative extrema; **(b)** $f$ is conc. down on $(1, 3)$; inf. pts.: $(1, 2e^{-1}), (3, 10e^{-3})$

**37.** Int. $(-4, 0), (6, 0), (0, -24)$; inc. $(1, \infty)$; dec. $(-\infty, 1)$; rel. min. when $x = 1$; conc. up $(-\infty, \infty)$

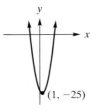

$(1, -25)$

**39.** Int. $(0, 20)$, inc. $(-\infty, -2), (2, \infty)$; dec. $(-2, 2)$; rel. max. when $x = -2$; rel. min. when $x = 2$; conc. up $(0, \infty)$; conc. down $(-\infty, 0)$; inf. pt. when $x = 0$

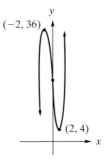

$(-2, 36)$
$(2, 4)$

**41.** Int. $(0, 0), (-1, 0), (1, 0)$; inc. $\left(-\infty, -\dfrac{\sqrt{3}}{3}\right), \left(\dfrac{\sqrt{3}}{3}, \infty\right)$; dec. $\left(-\dfrac{\sqrt{3}}{3}, \dfrac{\sqrt{3}}{3}\right)$; conc. down $(-\infty, 0)$; conc. up $(0, \infty)$; inf. pt. when $x = 0$; sym. about origin

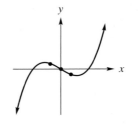

**43.** Int. $(-5, 0)$; inc. $(-10, 0)$; dec. $(-\infty, -10), (0, \infty)$; rel. min. when $x = -10$; conc. up $(-15, 0), (0, \infty)$; conc. down $(-\infty, -15)$; inf. pt. when $x = -15$; horiz. asym. $y = 0$; vert. asym. $x = 0$

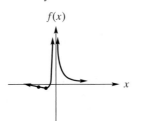

$f(x)$

**45.** Int. $(0, 0)$, inc. $\left(-\infty, -\dfrac{1}{6}\right)$; dec. $\left(-\dfrac{1}{6}, \dfrac{1}{3}\right), \left(\dfrac{1}{3}, \infty\right)$; rel. max. when $x = -\dfrac{1}{6}$; conc. up $\left(-\infty, \dfrac{1}{3}\right), \left(\dfrac{1}{3}, \infty\right)$;

conc. down $\left(-\dfrac{1}{3}, \dfrac{1}{3}\right)$; inf. pt. when $x = -\dfrac{1}{3}$; horiz. asym. $y = 0$; vert. asym. $x = \dfrac{1}{3}$

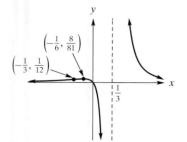

**47.** Int. $(0, 1)$; inc. $(0, \infty)$; dec. $(-\infty, 0)$; rel. min. when $x = 0$; conc. up $(-\infty, \infty)$; sym. about $y$-axis

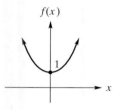

**49.** (a) False; (b) false; (c) true; (d) false; (e) false
**51.** $q > 2$
**57.** Rel. max. $(-1.32, 12.28)$; rel. min. $(0.44, 1.29)$
**59.** $x \approx -0.60$    **61.** 20            **63.** 200
**65.** \$4624                        **67.** 100 ft by 200 ft
**69.** (a) 200 stands at \$120 per stand; (b) 300 stands

## MATHEMATICAL SNAPSHOT—CHAPTER 13 (page 616)

**1.** Figure 13.75 shows that the population reaches its final size in about 45 days.
**3.** The tangent line will not coincide exactly with the curve in the first place. Smaller time steps could reduce the error.

## PROBLEMS 14.1 (page 622)

**1.** $5\,dx$      **3.** $\dfrac{2x^3}{\sqrt{x^4-9}}\,dx$   **5.** $-\dfrac{2}{x^3}\,dx$
**7.** $\dfrac{2x}{x^2+7}\,dx$      **9.** $3e^{2x^2+3}(12x^2+4x+3)\,dx$
**11.** $\Delta y = -0.14, dy = -0.14$
**13.** $\Delta y = -0.28, dy = -0.3$
**15.** $\Delta y \approx 0.049, dy = 0.050$    **17.** (a) $-1$; (b) $2.9$
**19.** $\dfrac{577}{34} \approx 16.97$   **21.** $4\dfrac{1}{32}$    **23.** $-0.03$    **25.** $1.001$
**27.** $\dfrac{1}{2}$       **29.** $\dfrac{1}{6p(p^2+5)^2}$    **31.** $-p^2$
**33.** $\dfrac{1}{36}$      **35.** $-\dfrac{4}{5}$       **37.** $-17; -19.3$
**39.** $2.04$               **41.** $0.7$
**43.** $(1.69 \times 10^{-11})\pi$ cm$^3$   **45.** (c) 42 units

**1.** $\displaystyle\int 28.3\,dq = 28.3q + C$
**2.** $\displaystyle\int 0.12t^2\,dt = 0.04t^3 + C$
**3.** $\displaystyle\int -\dfrac{480}{t^3}\,dt = \dfrac{240}{t^2} + C$
**4.** $\displaystyle\int (500 + 300\sqrt{t})\,dt = 500t + 200t^{3/2} + C$
**5.** $S(t) = 0.7t^3 - 32.7t^2 + 491.6t + C$

## PROBLEMS 14.2 (page 628)

**1.** $7x + C$      **3.** $\dfrac{x^9}{9} + C$      **5.** $-\dfrac{5}{6x^6} + C$
**7.** $-\dfrac{2}{9x^9} + C$   **9.** $-\dfrac{4}{3t^{3/4}} + C$   **11.** $4t + \dfrac{t^2}{2} + C$
**13.** $\dfrac{y^6}{6} - \dfrac{5y^2}{2} + C$      **15.** $t^3 - 2t^2 + 5t + C$
**17.** $(7+e)x + C$      **19.** $\dfrac{x^2}{14} - \dfrac{3x^5}{20} + C$
**21.** $\pi e^x + C$      **23.** $\dfrac{x^{9.3}}{9.3} - \dfrac{9x^7}{7} - \dfrac{1}{x^3} - \dfrac{1}{2x^2} + C$
**25.** $-\dfrac{4x^{3/2}}{9} + C$      **27.** $\dfrac{x^{3/4}}{3} + C$
**29.** $\dfrac{x^4}{12} + \dfrac{3}{2x^2} + C$   **31.** $\dfrac{w^3}{2} + \dfrac{2}{3w} + C$
**33.** $\dfrac{3}{10}u^2 - \dfrac{4}{5}u + C$   **35.** $\dfrac{u^{e+1}}{e+1} + e^u + C$
**37.** $\dfrac{4x^{3/2}}{3} - \dfrac{12x^{5/4}}{5} + C$
**39.** $-\dfrac{3x^{5/3}}{25} - 7x^{1/2} + 3x^2 + C$
**41.** $\dfrac{x^4}{4} - x^3 + \dfrac{5x^2}{2} - 15x + C$  **43.** $\dfrac{2x^{5/2}}{5} + 2x^{3/2} + C$
**45.** $\dfrac{27}{4}u^4 + 18u^3 + 18u^2 + 8u + C$
**47.** $\dfrac{2v^3}{3} + 3v + \dfrac{1}{2v^4} + C$
**49.** $\dfrac{z^3}{6} + \dfrac{5z^2}{2} + C$        **51.** $x + e^x + C$
**53.** No, $F(x) - G(x)$ might be a nonzero constant
**55.** $\dfrac{1}{\sqrt{x^2+1}} + C$

**1.** $N(t) = 800t + 200e^t + 6317.37$
**2.** $y(t) = 14t^3 + 12t^2 + 11t + 3$

## PROBLEMS 14.3 (page 633)

**1.** $y = \dfrac{3x^2}{2} - 4x + 1$        **3.** 60
**5.** $y = -\dfrac{x^4}{4} + \dfrac{2x^3}{3} + x + \dfrac{19}{12}$
**7.** $y = \dfrac{x^4}{12} + x^2 - 5x + 13$    **9.** $p = 0.7$
**11.** $p = 275 - 0.5q - 0.1q^2$   **13.** $c = 1.35q + 200$

**15.** $8079.17

**17.** $G = -\dfrac{P^2}{50} + 2P + 20$

**21.** $80 ($dc/dq = 27.50$ when $q = 50$ is not relevant to problem)

## PRINCIPLES IN PRACTICE 14.4

**1.** $T(t) = 10e^{-0.5t} + C$      **2.** $35 \ln|t + 1| + C$

## PROBLEMS 14.4 (page 639)

**1.** $\dfrac{(x+5)^8}{8} + C$      **3.** $\dfrac{(x^2+3)^6}{6} + C$

**5.** $\dfrac{3}{5}(y^3 + 3y^2 + 1)^{5/3} + C$      **7.** $-\dfrac{5(3x-1)^{-2}}{6} + C$

**9.** $\dfrac{1}{3}(2x - 1)^{3/2} + C$      **11.** $\dfrac{(7x-6)^5}{35} + C$

**13.** $\dfrac{(5u^2 - 9)^{15}}{150} + C$      **15.** $\dfrac{3}{5}(27 + x^5)^{4/3} + C$

**17.** $e^{3x} + C$    **19.** $e^{t^2+t} + C$    **21.** $\dfrac{1}{14}e^{7x^2} + C$

**23.** $-\dfrac{4}{3}e^{-3x} + C$      **25.** $\ln|x + 5| + C$

**27.** $\ln|x^3 + x^4| + C$      **29.** $-\dfrac{3}{4}(z^2 - 6)^{-4} + C$

**31.** $4 \ln|x| + C$      **33.** $\dfrac{1}{3}\ln|s^3 + 5| + C$

**35.** $-\dfrac{5}{2}\ln|4 - 2x| + C$

**37.** $\dfrac{2}{15}(5x)^{3/2} + C = \dfrac{2\sqrt{5}}{3}x^{3/2} + C$

**39.** $\sqrt{x^2 - 4} + C$      **41.** $\dfrac{1}{2}e^{y^4+1} + C$

**43.** $-\dfrac{1}{6}e^{-2v^3+1} + C$      **45.** $-\dfrac{1}{5}e^{-5x} + 2e^x + C$

**47.** $-\dfrac{1}{2}(7 - 2x^2 - 5x)^4 + C$      **49.** $\dfrac{1}{3}\ln|x^3 + 6x| + C$

**51.** $2\ln|3 - 2s + 4s^2| + C$      **53.** $\dfrac{1}{4}\ln(2x^2 + 1) + C$

**55.** $\dfrac{1}{27}(x^3 - x^6)^{-9} + C$      **57.** $\dfrac{1}{4}(x^4 + x^2)^2 + C$

**59.** $\dfrac{7}{4}(4 - x - x^2)^{-4} + C$      **61.** $\dfrac{1}{6}e^{4x^3+3x^2-4} + C$

**63.** $-\dfrac{1}{25}(8 - 5x^2)^{5/2} + C$

**65.** $\dfrac{(2x)^{3/2}}{3} - \sqrt{2x} + C = \dfrac{2\sqrt{2}}{3}x^{3/2} - \sqrt{2}x^{1/2} + C$

**67.** $\dfrac{x^5}{5} + \dfrac{2x^3}{3} + x + C$

**69.** $\dfrac{1}{2}\ln(x^2 + 1) - \dfrac{1}{6(x^6 + 1)} + C$

**71.** $\dfrac{1}{2}\ln|4x + 1| + \dfrac{4}{21}(x^3 - x^6)^{-7} + C$

**73.** $\dfrac{2}{9}(3x + 1)^{3/2} - \dfrac{1}{2}\ln(x^2 + 3) + C$    **75.** $2e^{\sqrt{x}} + C$

**77.** $-\dfrac{1}{4}e^{-x} + \dfrac{1}{4}e^x + C$      **79.** $\dfrac{1}{4}\ln^2(x^2 + 2x) + C$

**81.** $y = -\dfrac{1}{6}(3 - 2x)^3 + \dfrac{11}{2}$

**83.** $y = -\ln|x| + \dfrac{5}{2}x - \dfrac{1}{2} = \ln|1/x| + \dfrac{5}{2}x - \dfrac{1}{2}$

**85.** $160e^{0.05t} + 190$      **87.** $\dfrac{Rr^2}{4K} + B_1\ln|r| + B_2$

## PROBLEMS 14.5 (page 643)

**1.** $\dfrac{x^5}{5} + \dfrac{4}{3}x^3 - 2\ln|x| + C$

**3.** $\dfrac{1}{3}(2x^3 + 4x + 1)^{3/2} + C$

**5.** $-6\sqrt{2 - 3x} + C$      **7.** $\dfrac{4^{7x}}{7\ln 4} + C$

**9.** $7x^2 - 4e^{(1/4)x^2} + C$

**11.** $x^2 - 3x + \dfrac{2}{3}\ln|3x - 1| + C$

**13.** $\dfrac{5}{14}\ln(7e^{2x} + 4) + C$      **15.** $-\dfrac{1}{7}e^{7/x} + C$

**17.** $\dfrac{5}{2}x^2 - \dfrac{45}{2}\ln|x^2 + 9| + C$    **19.** $\dfrac{2}{9}(\sqrt{x} + 2)^3 + C$

**21.** $3(x^{1/3} + 2)^5 + C$      **23.** $\dfrac{1}{2}(\ln^2 x) + C$

**25.** $\dfrac{1}{3}\ln^3(r + 1) + C$      **27.** $\dfrac{3^{\ln x}}{\ln 3} + C$

**29.** $\dfrac{2}{3}e^{(x^3+1)/2} + C$      **31.** $8\ln|\ln(x + 3)| + C$

**33.** $\dfrac{x^2}{2} + x + \ln|x^2 - 3| + C$

**35.** $\dfrac{2}{3}\ln^{3/2}[(x^3 + 1)^2] + C$    **37.** $\dfrac{\sqrt{x^4 - 4x}}{2} - (\ln 7)x + C$

**39.** $x^2 - 8x - 6\ln|x| - \dfrac{2}{x^2} + C$

**41.** $x - \ln|x + 1| + C$      **43.** $\sqrt{e^{x^2} + 2} + C$

**45.** $-\dfrac{(e^{-x} + 6)^3}{3} + C$      **47.** $\dfrac{1}{5}(x^2 + e)^{5/2} + C$

**49.** $\dfrac{1}{36\sqrt{2}}[(8x)^{3/2} + 3]^{3/2} + C$

**51.** $-\dfrac{2}{3}e^{-\sqrt{s^3}} + C$      **53.** $\dfrac{x^3}{3} + x + C$

**55.** $\dfrac{\ln^2 x}{2} + x + C$      **57.** $p = -\dfrac{200}{q(q + 2)}$

**59.** $c = 20\ln|(q + 5)/5| + 2000$

**61.** $C = 2(\sqrt{I} + 1)$      **63.** $C = \dfrac{3}{4}I - \dfrac{1}{3}\sqrt{I} + \dfrac{71}{12}$

**65.** (a) 140 per unit; (b) $14,000; (c) $14,280

**67.** $2500 - 800\sqrt{5} \approx $711$ per acre      **69.** $I = 3$

## PRINCIPLES IN PRACTICE 14.6

**1.** $5975

## PROBLEMS 14.6 (page 651)

**1.** $\dfrac{2}{3}$ square unit      **3.** $\dfrac{15}{32}$ square unit

**5.** $S_n = \dfrac{1}{n}\left[4\left(\dfrac{1}{n}\right) + 4\left(\dfrac{2}{n}\right) + \cdots + 4\left(\dfrac{n}{n}\right)\right] = \dfrac{2(n + 1)}{n}$

**7.** (a) $S_n = \dfrac{n + 1}{2n} + 1$; (b) $\dfrac{3}{2}$

**9.** $\dfrac{1}{2}$ square unit

**11.** $\dfrac{1}{3}$ square unit    **13.** 1 square unit    **15.** 20

**17.** $-18$      **19.** $\dfrac{5}{6}$      **21.** 0      **23.** $\dfrac{11}{4}$

**25.** 14.7 square units    **27.** 2.4      **29.** $-25.5$

## PRINCIPLES IN PRACTICE 14.7

**1.** $32,830　　　　**2.** $28,750

## PROBLEMS 14.7 (page 657)

**1.** 15　　**3.** $\dfrac{15}{2}$　　**5.** $-20$　　**7.** $\dfrac{7}{3}$

**9.** $\dfrac{15}{2}$　　**11.** $\dfrac{4}{3}$　　**13.** $\dfrac{768}{7}$　　**15.** $\dfrac{5}{3}$

**17.** $\dfrac{32}{3}$　　**19.** $-\dfrac{1}{6}$　　**21.** $4\ln 8$　　**23.** $e^5$

**25.** $\dfrac{5}{3}(e-1)$　　**27.** $\dfrac{3}{4}$　　**29.** $\dfrac{38}{9}$　　**31.** $\dfrac{15}{28}$

**33.** $\dfrac{1}{2}\ln 3$　　　　　　**35.** $\dfrac{1}{2}\left(e+\dfrac{1}{e}-2\right)$

**37.** $\dfrac{1}{e^3}-\dfrac{3}{e}-\dfrac{3}{2e^2}+\dfrac{3}{\pi}+\dfrac{3}{2\pi^2}-\dfrac{1}{\pi^3}$　**39.** $\dfrac{e^3}{2}(e^{12}-1)$

**41.** $6+\ln 19$　**43.** $\dfrac{47}{12}$　　**45.** $6-3e$　　**47.** 7

**49.** 0　　　　**51.** $\alpha^{5/2}T$　　**53.** $\displaystyle\int_a^b(-Ax^{-B})\,dx$

**55.** $8639　　**57.** 1,973,333　**59.** $220　　**61.** $1367.99
**63.** 696;492　**65.** $2\,Ri$　　**69.** 0.05　　**71.** 3.52　　**73.** 14.34

## PRINCIPLES IN PRACTICE 14.8

**1.** 76.90 feet　　　　　　**2.** 5.77 grams

## PROBLEMS 14.8 (page 663)

**1.** 413　　　　**3.** $0.340; \dfrac{1}{3}\approx 0.333$　**5.** $\approx 0.767; 0.750$

**7.** $0.883; 2-\ln 3\approx 0.901$　**9.** 2,115,215　**11.** 3.0 square units

**13.** $\dfrac{8}{3}$　　　　**15.** 0.771　　　**17.** $\dfrac{35}{6}\,\text{km}^2$

## PROBLEMS 14.9 (page 667)

*In Problems 1–33, answers are assumed to be expressed in square units.*

**1.** 8　　**3.** $\dfrac{87}{2}$　　**5.** 8　　**7.** $\dfrac{19}{3}$　　**9.** 9

**11.** $\dfrac{50}{3}$　**13.** $\dfrac{9}{2}$　**15.** $\dfrac{123}{4}$　**17.** $\dfrac{32}{3}$　**19.** 1

**21.** 18　　**23.** $\dfrac{26}{3}$　　**25.** $\dfrac{3}{2}\sqrt[3]{2}$　　**27.** $e$

**29.** $\dfrac{3}{2}+2\ln 2=\dfrac{3}{2}+\ln 4$　　**31.** 68

**33.** 2　　　　　　　　**35.** 19 square units

**37.** (a) $\dfrac{1}{16}$;　(b) $\dfrac{3}{4}$;　(c) $\dfrac{7}{16}$

**39.** (a) $\ln\dfrac{7}{3}$　(b) $\ln 5-1$;　(c) $2-\ln 4$

**41.** 1.89 square units　　　**43.** 11.41 square units

## PROBLEMS 14.10 (page 675)

**1.** Area $=\displaystyle\int_{-2}^{3}[(x+6)-x^2]\,dx$

**3.** Area $=\displaystyle\int_{0}^{3}[2x-(x^2-x)]\,dx+\int_{3}^{4}[(x^2-x)-2x]\,dx$

**5.** Area $=\displaystyle\int_{0}^{1}[(y+1)-\sqrt{1-y}\,]\,dy$

**7.** Area $=\displaystyle\int_{1}^{2}[(7-2x^2)-(x^2-5)]\,dx$

*In Problems 9–33, answers are assumed to be expressed in square units.*

**9.** $\dfrac{4}{3}$　**11.** $\dfrac{4\sqrt{2}}{3}$　**13.** $8\sqrt{6}$　**15.** 40　**17.** $\dfrac{125}{6}$

**19.** 9　　**21.** $\dfrac{125}{12}$　　**23.** $\dfrac{256}{9}$　　**25.** $\dfrac{44}{3}$

**27.** $\dfrac{4}{3}(5\sqrt{5}-2\sqrt{2})$　**29.** $\dfrac{1}{2}$　　**31.** $\dfrac{255}{32}-4\ln 2$

**33.** 12　　　　　**35.** $\dfrac{14}{45}$　　　**37.** $\dfrac{3}{2m^3}$ square units

**39.** $2^{4/3}$　　**41.** 4.76 square units　　**43.** 6.17 square units

## PROBLEMS 14.11 (page 677)

**1.** CS = 25.6, PS = 38.4

**3.** CS $= 50\ln 2-25$, PS $= 1.25$

**5.** CS $= 225$, PS $= 450$　　　**7.** $426.67

**9.** $254,000　　　　　**11.** CS $\approx 1197$, PS $\approx 477$

## REVIEW PROBLEMS—CHAPTER 14 (page 680)

**1.** $\dfrac{x^4}{4}+x^2-7x+C$　　**3.** $\dfrac{256}{3}$

**5.** $-3(x+5)^{-2}+C$　　**7.** $2\ln|x^3-6x+1|+C$

**9.** $\dfrac{11\sqrt[3]{11}}{4}-4$　　**11.** $\dfrac{y^4}{4}+\dfrac{2y^3}{3}+\dfrac{y^2}{2}+C$

**13.** $\dfrac{10}{7}t^{7/10}-\dfrac{6}{5}t^{5/6}+C$　**15.** $\dfrac{1}{3}\ln\dfrac{57}{5}$

**17.** $\dfrac{2}{27}(3x^3+2)^{3/2}+C$　**19.** $\dfrac{1}{2}(e^{2y}+e^{-2y})+C$

**21.** $\ln|x|-\dfrac{2}{x}+C$　**23.** 111　　**25.** $\dfrac{35}{3}$

**27.** $4-3\sqrt[3]{2}$　　**29.** $\dfrac{3}{t}-\dfrac{2}{\sqrt{t}}+C$　**31.** $\dfrac{3}{2}-5\ln 2$

**33.** $4(x^{3/2}+1)^{3/2}+C$　**35.** 1　　**37.** $\dfrac{(1+e^{2x})^4}{8}+C$

**39.** $\dfrac{2\sqrt{10^{3x}}}{\ln 10}+C$　　**41.** $y=\dfrac{1}{2}e^{2x}+3x-1$

*In Problems 43–57, answers are assumed to be expressed in square units.*

**43.** $\dfrac{4}{3}$　**45.** $\dfrac{16}{3}$　**47.** $\dfrac{125}{6}$　**49.** $6+\ln 4$

**51.** $\dfrac{2}{3}$　**53.** 36　**55.** $\dfrac{243}{8}$　**57.** $e-1$

**59.** $p=100-\sqrt{2q}$　**61.** $1483.33　　**63.** 0.5507

**65.** 15 square units　　**67.** CS $= 166\dfrac{2}{3}$, PS $= 53\dfrac{1}{3}$

**73.** 15.08 square units　　**75.** CS $\approx 1148$, PS $\approx 251$

## MATHEMATICAL SNAPSHOT—CHAPTER 14 (page 682)

**1.** (a) 475;　(b) 275

**3.** (a) $2,002,500;　(b) 18,000;　(c) $111.25

## PRINCIPLES IN PRACTICE 15.1

**1.** $S(t)=-40te^{0.1t}+400e^{0.1t}+4600$

**2.** $P(t)=0.025t^2-0.05t^2\ln t+0.05t^2(\ln t)^2+C$

## PROBLEMS 15.1 (page 688)

**1.** $\dfrac{2}{3}x(x+5)^{3/2}-\dfrac{4}{15}(x+5)^{5/2}+C$

**3.** $-e^{-x}(x+1)+C$　　**5.** $\dfrac{y^4}{4}\left[\ln(y)-\dfrac{1}{4}\right]+C$

**7.** $x[\ln(4x) - 1] + C$

**9.** $x(2x + 3)^{3/2} - \frac{1}{5}(2x + 3)^{5/2} + C = \frac{3}{5}(2x + 3)^{3/2}(x - 1) + C$

**11.** $-\frac{x}{10(5x + 2)^2} - \frac{1}{50(5x + 2)} + C$

**13.** $-\frac{1}{x}(1 + \ln x) + C$    **15.** $e^2(3e^2 - 1)$

**17.** $\frac{1}{2}(1 - e^{-1})$, parts not needed

**19.** $2(9\sqrt{3} - 10\sqrt{2})$

**21.** $3x(x - 2) \ln(x - 2) - \frac{3}{2}x^2 + C$

**23.** $e^x(x^2 - 2x + 2) + C$

**25.** $\frac{x^3}{3} + 2e^{-x}(x + 1) - \frac{e^{-2x}}{2} + C$

**27.** $\frac{e^{x^2}}{2}(x^2 - 1) + C$

**29.** $\frac{2^{2x-1}}{\ln 2} + \frac{2^{x+1}x}{\ln 2} - \frac{2^{x+1}}{\ln^2 2} + \frac{x^3}{3} + C$

**31.** $2e^3 + 1$ square units    **33.** $\left[\frac{8}{3}\ln(2) - \frac{7}{9}\right]$ square units

**37.** $\int f^{-1}(x)dx = xf^{-1}(x) - F(f^{-1}(x)) + C$

## PRINCIPLES IN PRACTICE 15.2

**1.** $r(q) = \frac{5}{2}\ln\left|\frac{3(q + 1)^3}{q + 3}\right|$

**2.** $V(t) = 150t^2 - 900\ln(t^2 + 6) + C$

## PROBLEMS 15.2 (page 694)

**1.** $\frac{12}{x + 6} - \frac{2}{x + 1}$    **3.** $2 + \frac{8}{x + 2} - \frac{18}{x + 3}$

**5.** $\frac{1}{x + 2} + \frac{2}{(x + 2)^2}$    **7.** $\frac{3}{x} - \frac{2x}{x^2 + 1}$

**9.** $2\ln|x| + 3\ln|x - 1| + C = \ln|x^2(x - 1)^3| + C$

**11.** $-3\ln|x + 1| + 4\ln|x - 2| + C = \ln\left|\frac{(x - 2)^4}{(x + 1)^3}\right| + C$

**13.** $\frac{1}{4}\left[\frac{3x^2}{2} + 2\ln|x - 1| - 2\ln|x + 1|\right] + C$

$= \frac{1}{4}\left(\frac{3x^2}{2} + \ln\left[\frac{x - 1}{x + 1}\right]^2\right) + C$

**15.** $2\ln|x| - \frac{7}{3}\ln|x + 1| + \frac{1}{3}\ln|x - 2| + C = \ln\left|\frac{x^2\sqrt[3]{x - 2}}{\sqrt[3]{(x + 1)^7}}\right| + C$

**17.** $\ln|x^6 + 2x^4 - x^2 - 2| + C$, partial fractions not required.

**19.** $\frac{4}{x - 2} - 5\ln|x - 1| + 7\ln|x - 2| + C = \frac{4}{x - 2} + \ln\left|\frac{(x - 2)^7}{(x - 1)^5}\right| + C$

**21.** $4\ln|x| - \ln(x^2 + 4) + C = \ln\left[\frac{x^4}{x^2 + 4}\right] + C$

**23.** $-\frac{1}{2}\ln(x^2 + 1) - \frac{2}{x - 3} + C$

**25.** $5\ln(x^2 + 1) + 2\ln(x^2 + 2) + C = \ln[(x^2 + 1)^5(x^2 + 2)^2] + C$

**27.** $\frac{3}{2}\ln(x^2 + 2) - \frac{1}{x^2 + 2} + C$

**29.** $18\ln(4) - 10\ln(5) - 8\ln(3)$

**31.** $11 + 24\ln\frac{2}{3}$ square units

## PROBLEMS 15.3 (page 699)

**1.** $\frac{x}{9\sqrt{9 - x^2}} + C$    **3.** $-\frac{\sqrt{16x^2 + 3}}{3x} + C$

**5.** $\frac{1}{6}\ln\left|\frac{x}{6 + 7x}\right| + C$    **7.** $\frac{1}{3}\ln\left|\frac{\sqrt{x^2 + 9} - 3}{x}\right| + C$

**9.** $\frac{1}{2}\left[\frac{4}{5}\ln|4 + 5x| - \frac{2}{3}\ln|2 + 3x|\right] + C$

**11.** $\frac{1}{15}(3x - \ln[5 + 2e^{3x}]) + C$

**13.** $7\left[\frac{1}{5(5 + 2x)} + \frac{1}{25}\ln\left|\frac{x}{5 + 2x}\right|\right] + C$

**15.** $1 + \ln\frac{4}{9}$

**17.** $\frac{1}{2}(x\sqrt{x^2 - 3} - 3\ln|x + \sqrt{x^2 - 3}|) + C$

**19.** $\frac{1}{144}$    **21.** $e^x(x^2 - 2x + 2) + C$

**23.** $\frac{\sqrt{5}}{2}\left(-\frac{\sqrt{5x^2 + 1}}{\sqrt{5}x} + \ln|\sqrt{5}x + \sqrt{5x^2 + 1}|\right) + C$

**25.** $\frac{1}{9}\left(\ln|1 + 3x| + \frac{1}{1 + 3x}\right) + C$

**27.** $\frac{1}{\sqrt{5}}\left(\frac{1}{2\sqrt{7}}\ln\left|\frac{\sqrt{7} + \sqrt{5}x}{\sqrt{7} - \sqrt{5}x}\right|\right) + C$

**29.** $\frac{4}{81}\left[\frac{(3x)^6\ln(3x)}{6} - \frac{(3x)^6}{36}\right] + C = x^6[6\ln(3x) - 1] + C$

**31.** $4(9x - 2)(1 + 3x)^{3/2} + C$    **33.** $\frac{1}{2}\ln|2x + \sqrt{4x^2 - 13}| + C$

**35.** $-\frac{\sqrt{16 - 9x^2}}{8x} + C$

**37.** $\frac{1}{2\pi}(4\sqrt{x} - \ln|\pi + 7e^{4\sqrt{x}}|) + C$

**39.** $\frac{1}{2}\ln(x^2 + 1) + C$    **41.** $(2x^2 + 1)^{3/2} + C$

**43.** $\ln\left|\frac{x - 3}{x - 2}\right| + C$    **45.** $\frac{x^4}{4}\left[\ln(x) - \frac{1}{4}\right] + C$

**47.** $\frac{2}{9}e^{3x^2}(3x^2 - 1) + C$    **49.** $x(\ln x)^2 - 2x\ln(x) + 2x + C$

**51.** $\frac{2}{3}(9\sqrt{3} - 10\sqrt{2})$    **53.** $2(2\sqrt{2} - \sqrt{7})$

**55.** $\frac{7}{2}\ln(2) - \frac{3}{4}$    **57.** $\ln\left|\frac{q_n(1 - q_0)}{q_0(1 - q_n)}\right|$

**59.** (a) $7558.09$; (b) $16,930.75$

**61.** (a) $5481; (b)$535

## PROBLEMS 15.4 (page 702)

**1.** $\frac{7}{3}$    **3.** $-1$    **5.** $0$

**7.** $13$    **9.** $11,050$    **11.** $3155.13$

## PRINCIPLES IN PRACTICE 15.5

**1.** $I = I_o e^{-0.0085x}$

## PROBLEMS 15.5 (page 708)

**1.** $y = -\frac{1}{x^2 + C}$    **3.** $y = (x^2 + 1)^{3/2} + C$

**5.** $y = Ce^x, C > 0$    **7.** $y = Cx, C > 0$

**9.** $y = \sqrt[3]{3x - 2}$  **11.** $y = \ln \dfrac{x^3 + 3}{3}$

**13.** $y = \dfrac{48(3x^2 + 2)^2}{4 + 31(3x^2 + 2)^2}$  **15.** $y = \sqrt{\left(\dfrac{3x^2}{2} + \dfrac{3}{2}\right)^2 - 1}$

**17.** $y = \ln\left(\dfrac{1}{2}\sqrt{x^2 + 3}\right)$  **19.** $c = (q + 1)e^{1/(q+1)}$

**21.** 120 weeks

**23.** $N = 40{,}000e^{0.018t}$; $N = 40{,}000(1.2)^{t/10}$; 57,600

**25.** $2e^{1.14882}$ billion  **27.** 0.01204; 57.57 sec

**29.** 2900 years  **31.** $N = N_0 e^{k(t - t_0)}$, $t \geq t_0$

**33.** 12.6 units  **35.** $A = 400(1 - e^{-t/2})$, 157 g/m²

**37.** **(a)** $V = 60{,}000e^{\frac{t}{9.5}\ln(389/600)}$ **(b)** June 2028

## PROBLEMS 15.6 (page 714)

**1.** 69,200  **3.** 500  **5.** 1990  **7.** **(b)** 375
**9.** 3:21 A.M  **11.** $155,555.56
**13.** $N = M - (M - N_0)e^{-kt}$

## PRINCIPLES IN PRACTICE 15.7

**1.** 20 ml

## PROBLEMS 15.7 (page 718)

**1.** $\dfrac{1}{18}$  **3.** Div  **5.** $\dfrac{1}{e}$  **7.** Div  **9.** $\dfrac{1}{2}$

**11.** 0  **13.** **(a)** 800; **(b)** $\dfrac{2}{3}$  **15.** 4,000,000

**17.** $\dfrac{1}{3}$ square unit  **19.** 20,000 increase

## REVIEW PROBLEMS—CHAPTER 15 (page 720)

**1.** $\dfrac{x^2}{4}[2\ln(x) - 1] + C$  **3.** $2\sqrt{13} + \dfrac{8}{3}\ln\left(\dfrac{3 + \sqrt{13}}{2}\right)$

**5.** $\ln|3x + 1| + 4\ln|x - 2| + C$

**7.** $\dfrac{1}{2(x + 2)} + \dfrac{1}{4}\ln\left|\dfrac{x}{x + 2}\right| + C$

**9.** $-\dfrac{\sqrt{9 - 16x^2}}{9x} + C$  **11.** $\dfrac{3}{2}\ln\left|\dfrac{x - 3}{x + 3}\right| + C$

**13.** $e^{7x}(7x - 1) + C$  **15.** $\dfrac{1}{4}\ln|\ln x^2| + C$

**17.** $x - \dfrac{3}{2}\ln|3 + 2x| + C$  **19.** $2\ln|x| + \dfrac{3}{2}\ln(x^2 + 1) + C$

**21.** $2\sqrt{x + 1}[\ln(x + 1) - 2] + C$  **23.** 34

**25.** $y = Ce^{x^3 + x^2}$, $C > 0$  **27.** $\dfrac{2}{3}$  **29.** Div

**31.** 144,000  **33.** 0.0005; 90%

**35.** $N = \dfrac{450}{1 + 224e^{-1.02t}}$  **37.** 4:16 P.M.

**39.** 0.95

**41.** **(a)** 207, 208; **(b)** 157, 165; **(c)** 41, 41

## MATHEMATICAL SNAPSHOT—CHAPTER 15 (page 722)

**1.** 114; 69  **5.** Answers may vary

## PRINCIPLES IN PRACTICE 16.1

**1.** $\dfrac{1}{3}$  **2.** 0.607

**3.** Mean 5 years, standard deviation 5 years

## PROBLEMS 16.1 (page 731)

**1.** **(a)** $\dfrac{5}{12}$; **(b)** $\dfrac{11}{16} = 0.6875$; **(c)** $\dfrac{13}{16} = 0.8125$; **(d)** $-1 + \sqrt{10}$

**3.** **(a)** $f(x) = \begin{cases} \dfrac{1}{3}, & \text{if } 1 \leq x \leq 4 \\ 0, & \text{otherwise} \end{cases}$

**(b)** $\dfrac{2}{3}$; **(c)** 0; **(d)** $\dfrac{5}{6}$; **(e)** $\dfrac{1}{3}$; **(f)** 0; **(g)** 1; **(h)** $\dfrac{5}{2}$;

**(i)** $\dfrac{\sqrt{3}}{2}$; **(j)** $F(x) = \begin{cases} 0, & \text{if } x < 1 \\ \dfrac{x - 1}{3}, & \text{if } 1 \leq x \leq 4 \\ 1, & \text{if } x > 4 \end{cases}$

$P(X < 2) = \dfrac{1}{3}$, $P(1 < X < 3) = \dfrac{2}{3}$

**5.** **(a)** $f(x) = \begin{cases} \dfrac{1}{b - a}, & \text{if } a \leq x \leq b \\ 0, & \text{otherwise} \end{cases}$

**(b)** $\dfrac{a + b}{2}$; **(c)** $\sigma^2 = \dfrac{(b - a)^2}{12}$, $\sigma = \dfrac{b - a}{\sqrt{12}}$

**7.** **(a)** $-e^{-12} + e^{-3} \approx 0.04978$; **(b)** $-e^{-12} + 1 \approx 0.99999$;
**(c)** $e^{-18} \approx 0.00000$; **(d)** $-e^{-3} + 1 \approx 0.95021$;

**(f)** $F(x) = \begin{cases} 0, & \text{if } x < 0 \\ 1 - e^{-3x}, & \text{if } x \geq 0 \end{cases}$

**9.** **(a)** $\dfrac{1}{8}$; **(b)** $\dfrac{5}{16}$; **(c)** $\dfrac{39}{64} \approx 0.609$; **(d)** 1; **(e)** $\dfrac{8}{3}$;

**(f)** $\dfrac{2\sqrt{2}}{3}$; **(g)** $2\sqrt{2}$; **(h)** $\dfrac{7}{16}$

**11.** $\dfrac{7}{10}$; 5 min  **13.** $e^{-3} \approx 0.050$

## PROBLEMS 16.2 (page 736)

**1.** **(a)** 0.4554; **(b)** 0.3317; **(c)** 0.8907; **(d)** 0.9982;
**(e)** 0.8972; **(f)** 0.4880

**3.** 0.13  **5.** $-1.08$  **7.** 0.34

**9.** **(a)** 0.9970; **(b)** 0.0668; **(c)** 0.0873

**11.** 0.3085  **13.** 0.997  **15.** 8  **17.** 95%  **19.** 90.82%

**21.** **(a)** 1.7%; **(b)** 85.6

## PRINCIPLES IN PRACTICE 16.3

**1.** 0.0396

## PROBLEMS 16.3 (page 740)

**1.** 0.9207; 0.0122    **3.** 0.0430; 0.9232    **5.** 0.7507

**7.** 0.4129          **9.** 0.5; 0.0287    **11.** 0.0336

## REVIEW PROBLEMS—CHAPTER 16 (page 741)

**1. (a)** 2;    **(b)** $\dfrac{9}{32}$;    **(c)** $\dfrac{3}{4}$,

**(d)** $F(x) = \begin{cases} 0, & \text{if } x < 0 \\ \dfrac{x}{3} + \dfrac{2x^3}{3}, & \text{if } 0 \le x \le 1 \\ 1, & \text{if } x > 1 \end{cases}$

**3. (a)** $\dfrac{10}{3}$;    **(b)** $\sqrt{\dfrac{25}{18}} \approx 1.18$    **5.** 0.3085

**7.** 0.2417    **9.** 0.7734    **11.** 0.9817    **13.** 0.0228

## MATHEMATICAL SNAPSHOT—CHAPTER 16 (page 832)

**1.** The result should correspond to the known distribution function.

**3.** Answers may vary

## PRINCIPLES IN PRACTICE 17.1

**1. (a)** $3260;    **(b)** $4410

## PROBLEMS 17.1 (page 750)

**1.** 3       **3.** 8       **5.** −1       **7.** 88       **9.** 3

**11.** $e^{x_0 + h + y_0}$    **13.** 2000    **15.** $y = 2$    **17.** $z = 6$

**19.**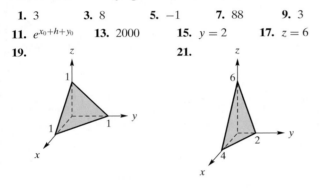

**21.**

**23.**

**25.**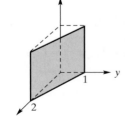
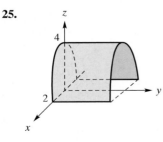

**27.**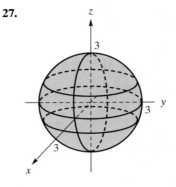

## PROBLEMS 17.2 (page 754)

**1.** $f_x(x, y) = 8x$; $f_y(x, y) = 6y$

**3.** $f_x(x, y) = 0$; $f_y(x, y) = 2$

**5.** $g_x(x, y) = 12x^3 y + 2y^2 - 5y + 8$;
$g_y(x, y) = 3x^4 + 4xy - 5x - 9$

**7.** $g_p(p, q) = \dfrac{q}{2\sqrt{pq}}$; $g_q(p, q) = \dfrac{p}{2\sqrt{pq}}$

**9.** $h_s(s, t) = \dfrac{2s}{t - 3}$; $h_t(s, t) = -\dfrac{s^2 + 4}{(t - 3)^2}$

**11.** $u_{q_1}(q_1, q_2) = \dfrac{1}{2(q_1 + 2)}$; $u_{q_2}(q_1, q_2) = \dfrac{1}{3(q_2 + 5)}$

**13.** $h_x(x, y) = (x^3 + xy^2 + 3y^3)(x^2 + y^2)^{-3/2}$;
$h_y(x, y) = (3x^3 + x^2 y + y^3)(x^2 + y^2)^{-3/2}$

**15.** $\dfrac{\partial z}{\partial x} = 5ye^{5xy}$; $\dfrac{\partial z}{\partial y} = 5xe^{5xy}$

**17.** $\dfrac{\partial z}{\partial x} = 5\left[\dfrac{2x^2}{x^2 + y} + \ln(x^2 + y)\right]$; $\dfrac{\partial z}{\partial y} = \dfrac{5x}{x^2 + y}$

**19.** $f_r(r, s) = \sqrt{r + 2s}\,(3r^2 - 2s) + \dfrac{r^3 - 2rs + s^2}{2\sqrt{r + 2s}}$;

$f_s(r, s) = 2(s - r)\sqrt{r + 2s} + \dfrac{r^3 - 2rs + s^2}{\sqrt{r + 2s}}$

**21.** $f_r(r, s) = -e^{3-r}\ln(7 - s)$; $f_s(r, s) = \dfrac{e^{3-r}}{s - 7}$

**23.** $g_x(x, y, z) = 6x^2 y^2 + 2y^3 z$;
$g_y(x, y, z) = 4x^3 y + 6xy^2 z$;
$g_z(x, y, z) = 2xy^3 + 8z$

**25.** $g_r(r, s, t) = 2re^{s+t}$;
$g_s(r, s, t) = (7s^3 + 21s^2 + r^2)e^{s+t}$;
$g_t(r, s, t) = e^{s+t}(r^2 + 7s^3)$

**27.** 50       **29.** $\dfrac{1}{\sqrt{14}}$       **31.** 0       **33.** 26

**39.** $-\dfrac{ra}{2\left[1 + a\dfrac{n-1}{2}\right]^2}$

## PROBLEMS 17.3 (page 759)

**1.** 20                                    **3.** 1374.5

**5.** $\dfrac{\partial P}{\partial k} = 1.487902\left(\dfrac{l}{k}\right)^{0.357}$; $\dfrac{\partial P}{\partial l} = 0.826098\left(\dfrac{k}{l}\right)^{0.643}$

**7.** $\dfrac{\partial q_A}{\partial p_A} = -50; \dfrac{\partial q_A}{\partial p_B} = 2; \dfrac{\partial q_B}{\partial p_A} = 4; \dfrac{\partial q_B}{\partial p_B} = -20;$ competitive

**9.** $\dfrac{\partial q_A}{\partial p_A} = -\dfrac{100}{p_A^2 p_B^{1/2}}; \dfrac{\partial q_A}{\partial p_B} = -\dfrac{50}{p_A p_B^{3/2}}; \dfrac{\partial q_B}{\partial p_A} = -\dfrac{500}{3 p_B p_A^{4/3}};$

$\dfrac{\partial q_B}{\partial p_B} = -\dfrac{500}{p_B^2 p_A^{1/3}};$ complementary

**11.** $\dfrac{\partial P}{\partial B} = 0.01 A^{0.27} B^{-0.99} C^{0.01} D^{0.23} E^{0.09} F^{0.27};$

$\dfrac{\partial P}{\partial C} = 0.01 A^{0.27} B^{0.01} C^{-0.99} D^{0.23} E^{0.09} F^{0.27}$

**13.** 4480; if a staff manager with an M.B.A. degree had an extra year of work experience before the degree, the manager would receive $4480 per year in extra compensation.

**15. (a)** $-1.015; -0.846;$
**(b)** One for which $w = w_0$ and $s = s_0$.

**17.** $\dfrac{\partial g}{\partial x} = \dfrac{1}{V_F} > 0$ for $V_F > 0$. Thus if $x$ increases and $V_F$ and $V_s$ are fixed, then $g$ increases.

**19. (a)** When $p_A = 9$ and $p_B = 16$, $\dfrac{\partial q_A}{\partial p_A} = -\dfrac{20}{27}$ and $\dfrac{\partial q_A}{\partial p_B} = \dfrac{5}{12}$
**(b)** Demand for A decreases by approximately $\dfrac{5}{6}$ unit.

**21. (a)** No;  **(b)** 70%

**23.** $\eta_{p_A} = -\dfrac{5}{46}, \eta_{p_B} = \dfrac{1}{46}$   **25.** $\eta_{p_A} = -1, \eta_{p_B} = -\dfrac{1}{2}$

## PROBLEMS 17.4 (page 763)

**1.** $-\dfrac{2x}{5z}$   **3.** $\dfrac{4y}{3z^2}$   **5.** $\dfrac{x(yz^2+1)}{z(1-x^2 y)}$

**7.** $-e^{y-z}$   **9.** $\dfrac{yz}{1+9z}$   **11.** $-\dfrac{3x}{z}$

**13.** $-\dfrac{1}{2}$   **15.** $-\dfrac{4}{e^2}$   **17.** 4   **19.** $\dfrac{5}{2}$

**21. (a)** 36;  **(b)** With respect to $q_A$, $\dfrac{60}{13}$; with respect to $q_B$, $\dfrac{288}{65}$

## PROBLEMS 17.5 (page 765)

**1.** $6y^2; 12y; 12y$   **3.** $3; 0; 0$

**5.** $18xe^{2xy}; 18e^{2xy}(2xy+1); 72x(1+xy)e^{2xy}$

**7.** $3x^2 y + 4xy^2 + y^3; 3xy^2 + 4x^2 y + x^3; 6xy + 4y^2; 6xy + 4x^2$

**9.** $\dfrac{zy}{\sqrt{x^2+y^2}}; \dfrac{z}{(x^2+y^2)^{\frac{3}{2}}}\left[x^2 + y^2\sqrt{x^2+y^2}\right]$

**11.** 0   **13.** 744   **15.** $2e$   **17.** $-\dfrac{1}{8}$

**23.** $-\dfrac{y^2+z^2}{z^3} = -\dfrac{3x^2}{z^3}$

## PROBLEMS 17.6 (page 768)

**1.** $\dfrac{\partial z}{\partial r} = 13; \dfrac{\partial z}{\partial s} = 9$   **3.** $\left[2t + \dfrac{3\sqrt{t}}{2}\right] e^{x+y}$

**5.** $5(2xz^2 + yz) + 2(xz + z^2) - (2x^2 z + xy + 2yz)$

**7.** $3(x^2 + xy^2)^2(2x + y^2 + 16xy)$

**9.** $-2s(2x + yz) + r(xz) + 2s(xy + 2z)$

**11.** $19s(2x-7)$   **13.** 324   **15.** $\dfrac{40}{e^9}$

**17.** When $p_A = 25$ and $p_B = 4$, $\dfrac{\partial c}{\partial p_A} = -\dfrac{1}{4}$ and $\dfrac{\partial c}{\partial p_B} = \dfrac{5}{4}$

**19. (a)** $\dfrac{\partial w}{\partial t} = \dfrac{\partial w}{\partial x}\dfrac{\partial x}{\partial t} + \dfrac{\partial w}{\partial y}\dfrac{\partial y}{\partial t};$  **(b)** $-\dfrac{20}{3\sqrt{2}+15e}$

## PROBLEMS 17.7 (page 776)

**1.** $\left(\dfrac{14}{3}, -\dfrac{13}{3}\right)$

**3.** $(0, -2), (0, 1), (3, -2), (3, 1)$

**5.** $(50, 150, 350)$

**7.** $\left(-2, \dfrac{3}{2}\right)$, rel. min.   **9.** $\left(-\dfrac{1}{4}, \dfrac{1}{2}\right)$, rel. max.

**11.** $\left(\dfrac{2}{5}, -\dfrac{3}{5}\right); D = -5 < 0$ no relative extremum

**13.** $(0, 0)$, rel. max.; $\left(4, \dfrac{1}{2}\right)$, rel. min.; $\left(0, \dfrac{1}{2}\right), (4, 0)$, neither

**15.** $(43, 13)$, rel. min.   **17.** $(-1, -1)$, rel. min.

**19.** $(0, -2), (0, 2)$, neither   **21.** $l = 24, k = 14$

**23.** $p_A = 80, p_B = 85$

**25.** $q_A = 48, q_B = 40, p_A = 52, p_B = 44$, profit $= 3304$

**27.** $q_A = 4, q_B = 3$   **29.** 1 ft by 2 ft by 3 ft

**31.** $\left(\dfrac{105}{37}, \dfrac{28}{37}\right)$, rel. min.   **33.** $a = -8, b = -12, d = 33$

**35. (a)** 2 units of A and 3 units B;
**(b)** Selling price for A is 30 and selling price for B is 19. Relative maximum profit is 25.

**37. (a)** $P = 5T(1 - e^{-x}) - 20x - 0.1T^2;$
**(c)** Relative maximum at $(20, \ln 5)$; no relative extremum at $\left(5, \ln \dfrac{5}{4}\right)$

## PROBLEMS 17.8 (page 784)

**1.** $(2, -2)$   **3.** $\left(3, \dfrac{3}{2}, -\dfrac{3}{2}\right)$   **5.** $\left(0, \dfrac{1}{4}, \dfrac{5}{8}\right)$

**7.** $(6, 3, 2)$   **9.** $\left(\dfrac{2}{3}, \dfrac{4}{3}, -\dfrac{4}{3}\right)$   **11.** $\left(\dfrac{1}{4}, \dfrac{1}{2}, \dfrac{1}{4}\right)$

**13.** Plant 1, 40 units; plant 2, 60 units

**15.** 74 units (when $l = 8, k = 7$)

**17.** $15,000 on newspaper advertising and $45,000 on TV advertising

**19.** $x = 5, y = 15, z = 5$   **21.** $x = 12, y = 8$

**23.** $x = \dfrac{100}{3}, y = \dfrac{100}{3}, z = \dfrac{100}{3}$

## PROBLEMS 17.9 (page 789)

**1.** $\hat{y} = 0.98 + 0.61x; 3.12$   **3.** $\hat{y} = 0.057 + 1.67x; 5.90$

**5.** $\hat{q} = 80.5 - 0.643p$   **7.** $\hat{y} = 100 + 0.13x; 105.2$

**9.** $\hat{y} = 8.5 + 2.5x$

**11. (a)** $\hat{y} = 35.9 - 2.5x;$  **(b)** $\hat{y} = 28.4 - 2.5x$

## PROBLEMS 17.10 (page 793)

**1.** 18   **3.** $\dfrac{1}{4}$   **5.** $\dfrac{2}{3}$   **7.** 3

**9.** $\dfrac{525}{2}$   **11.** $-\dfrac{58}{5}$   **13.** 9   **15.** $-1$

**17.** $\dfrac{e^2}{2} - e + \dfrac{1}{2}$  **19.** $-\dfrac{27}{4}$  **21.** $\dfrac{1}{24}$

**23.** $e^{-4} - e^{-2} - e^{-3} + e^{-1}$  **25.** $\dfrac{1}{3}$

## REVIEW PROBLEMS—CHAPTER 17 (page 796)

**1.**

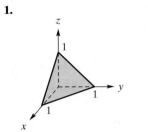

**3.**

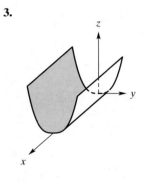

**5.** $8x + 6y$; $6x + 2y$

**7.** $\dfrac{y}{(x+y)^2}$; $-\dfrac{x}{(x+y)^2}$

**9.** $\dfrac{y}{x^2 + y^2}$

**11.** $2xze^{x^2yz}(1 + x^2yz)$

**13.** $2x + 2y + 6z$

**15.** $e^{x+y+z}\left[\ln xyz + \dfrac{1}{y}\right]$; $e^{x+y+z}\left[\ln xyz + \dfrac{1}{x} + \dfrac{1}{z}\right]$

**17.** $\dfrac{1}{64}$

**19.** $2(x+y)e^r + 2\left(\dfrac{x+3y}{r+s}\right)$; $2\left(\dfrac{x+3y}{r+s}\right)$

**21.** $\dfrac{2x + 2y + z}{4z - x}$

**23.** $\dfrac{\partial P}{\partial l} = 14l^{-0.3}k^{0.3}$; $\dfrac{\partial P}{\partial k} = 6l^{0.7}k^{-0.7}$

**25.** Competitive  **27.** $(2, 2)$, rel. min.

**29.** 4 ft by 4 ft by 2 ft

**31.** A, 89 cents per pound; B, 94 cents per pound

**33.** $(3, 2, 1)$  **35.** $\hat{y} = 12.67 + 3.29x$

**37.** $\dfrac{1}{12}$  **39.** $\dfrac{1}{30}$

## MATHEMATICAL SNAPSHOT—CHAPTER 17 (page 798)

**1.** $y = 9.50e^{-0.22399x} + 5$  **3.** $T = 79e^{-0.01113t} + 45$

# Index

evaluating sums, 66
index of summation, 66
writing a sum using, 67–68
Supply curve, 125
Supply equation, 125, 150
Supply functions, 80
Supply schedule, 102
Surface, sketching, 749–750
Symmetry, 596
axis of, 131
defined, 103
graphing with intercepts and, 104–106
and inverse functions, 107
origin, symmetry about, 104, 111
tests for, 104
$x$-axis, symmetry about, 104, 111
$y$-axis, symmetry about, 103–104, 111
System, 433
Systems of equations:
applications of, 150–157
break-even points, 153–156
equilibrium, 150–153
Systems of linear equations, 138–146
three-variable systems, 144–146
general linear equation in the three variables $x$, $y$, and $z$, 144
one-parameter family of solutions, 145–146
solving, 144
two-parameter family of solutions, 146
two-variable systems, 138–144
elimination by addition, 140–141
elimination by substitution, 141
linear system with infinitely many solutions, 142
mixture, 143
Systems of linear inequalities, 283–284

T

Tangent, 481
Tangent line, 481–483
finding an equation of, 485, 495
finding the slope of, 483
slope of, 499
Term, annuities, 208, 211
Theoretical probabilities, 377
Third-order derivative, 557

Three-dimensional rectangular coordinate system, 747
Three-variable systems of linear equations, 144–146
general linear equation in the three variables $x$, $y$, and $z$, 144
one-parameter family of solutions, 145–146
solving, 144
two-parameter family of solutions, 146
Tit-for-Tat, 446–447
Total cost, 48, 154
Total interest paid, formula, 219
Total revenue, 48
Total-cost function, 501
Total-revenue function, 503, 524
Transition matrix, 434, 443
defined, 434
regular, 439
Transitive property of equality, 3
Trapezoidal rule, 659–661
Treasury securities, 224–225
date of maturity, 224
Tree diagram, 345
Trend equations, 112–113
Trials (stages), 369, 386, 413
Triangle inequality, 64
Triangular matrix, 231
Trinomials, 15
factoring, 20
Triple integrals, 793
Trivial solution, homogeneous system, 261
Two-dimensional coordinate system, 747
Two-level tree, 345
Two-point form, 120
Two-state Markov chains, 434
Two-variable systems of linear equations, 138–144
elimination by addition, 140–141
elimination by substitution, 141
linear system with infinitely many solutions, 142
mixture, 143

U

Unbounded feasible region, 287
example, 288–290

Unbounded solutions, 310–311
Unconditional probabilities, 386
Uniform density function, 727
Union, 63, 366
of events, probability of, 373
Union symbol, 63
Unit distance, 2
Upper limit, 648
Upper triangular matrix, 231
U.S. federal income tax, tax brackets, 114–115

V

Variable costs, 48, 154
Variable-quality recording, 72–73
Variables, 27
Variance, 424, 730, 741
example, 425–426
Velocity, 498
finding, 498–499
Venn diagrams, 365
Verhulst–Pearl logistic function, 710
Vertex, 131
Vertical asymptotes, 589–592, 594
finding, 594
Vertical element of area, 665
Vertical lines, equations of, 120
Vertical strip, 665
Vertical-line test, 97, 100, 111

X

$x$-axis, 747
symmetry about, 104, 111
$x$-coordinate, 94
$x,y$-plane, 94, 748
$x,z$-plane, 748

Y

$y$-axis, 747
symmetry about, 104, 111
$y$-coordinate, 94
Yield curve, 225
$y,z$-plane, 748

Z

$z$-axis, 747
Zeno of Elea, 448
Zero matrix, 230, 275
Zero-row, matrices, 252

# Photo Credits